# Astronomy and Astrophysics Olympiad

Volume 1: Topics, Problems and Solutions

# Astronomy and Astrophysics Olympiad

## Volume 1: Topics, Problems and Solutions

**Mihail Sandu**

*Romanian Physics Olympiad Committee, Romania*

World Scientific

NEW JERSEY • LONDON • SINGAPORE • BEIJING • SHANGHAI • HONG KONG • TAIPEI • CHENNAI • TOKYO

*Published by*

World Scientific Publishing Europe Ltd.
57 Shelton Street, Covent Garden, London WC2H 9HE
*Head office:* 5 Toh Tuck Link, Singapore 596224
*USA office:* 27 Warren Street, Suite 401-402, Hackensack, NJ 07601

**British Library Cataloguing-in-Publication Data**
A catalogue record for this book is available from the British Library.

Cover image credit: NASA

Translation from Romanian by Mihaela Iancu, Marilena Mierlă, Ioana, Alexandra Zelko, Andrei Constantin, and Daniel Ciocîrlan

**ASTRONOMY AND ASTROPHYSICS OLYMPIAD**
**Volume 1: Topics, Problems and Solutions**



ISBN 978-1-80061-708-7 (hardcover)
ISBN 978-1-80061-690-5 (paperback)
ISBN 978-1-80061-691-2 (ebook for institutions)
ISBN 978-1-80061-692-9 (ebook for individuals)

For any available supplementary material, please visit
https://www.worldscientific.com/worldscibooks/10.1142/Q0498#t=suppl

Desk Editors: Kannan Krishnan/Gabriel Rawlinson/Shi Ying Koe

Typeset by Stallion Press
Email: enquiries@stallionpress.com

# Foreword

Astronomy and Astrophysics are among the oldest sciences, yet they continue to undergo rapid development. Over time, the focus has shifted from simple observations of celestial motions to detailed investigations of galaxies, black holes and the cosmic microwave background. Today, progress in these fields is shaped by powerful telescopes, large-scale surveys, and theoretical models that push the limits of our current knowledge.

Such progress depends not only on professional research but also on the cultivation of new generations of scientists. Competitions like the Astronomy Olympiad and the Astronomy and Astrophysics Olympiad play an important role in this process. By challenging high school students to engage with advanced concepts and problem-solving techniques, these events help develop the critical skills and curiosity essential for a career in science.

Despite their educational value, there remains a lack of comprehensive resources tailored specifically to these Olympiads. The present collection of three volumes, containing original problems crafted by Professor Mihail Sandu, addresses this need in an outstanding manner, offering students and teachers alike a wide range of tools critically needed for preparing for such competitions.

Professor Sandu is a highly respected educator with decades of experience at both high school and university levels. His contributions to academic competitions are remarkable. Among other achievements, he prepared all theory problems for the 2014 International Olympiad on Astronomy and Astrophysics, as well as all practical test problems for the 2019 International Astronomy Olympiad, both held in Romania. More recently, he played a key role in the first Junior International Olympiad on Astronomy and Astrophysics in 2022. He has published nearly 100 books in Romanian and English, including textbooks and problem collections in Physics and Astronomy that have guided generations of students.

I have had the privilege of knowing Professor Sandu personally. His dedication, clarity of thought, and genuine enthusiasm for teaching are evident both in his presence at competitions and in his writing. Over more than five decades, he has supported and inspired countless students, exemplifying a rare commitment to education and mentorship. I am confident that the present collection will prove to be an invaluable resource for students preparing for Olympiads, and that it will continue to inspire future generations of astronomers and astrophysicists.

Andrei Constantin
Royal Society Dorothy Hodgkin Fellow,
Department of Physics, University of Oxford,
and Physics & Mathematics Tutor
at Mansfield College Oxford

# Contents

# Topic 1

# Elements of Spherical Trigonometry

## 1.1. Definitions and Basic Results

The three concurrent half lines OX, OY, OZ, represented in Figure T1.1, belonging to the concurrent lines XX′, YY′, ZZ′, which indicate the directions of the intersection of any three planes (two by two), define the edges of a trihedral, having as a vertex their intersection point.

The plane angles formed by any two edges of the trihedral (OX, OY; OY, OZ; and OZ, OX) represent the trihedral's faces: $\rho$XOY, $\rho$YOZ, and $\rho$ZOX, respectively.

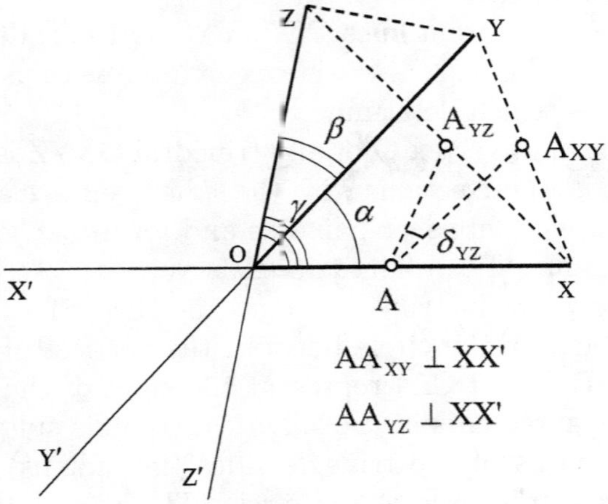


**Fig. T1.1**

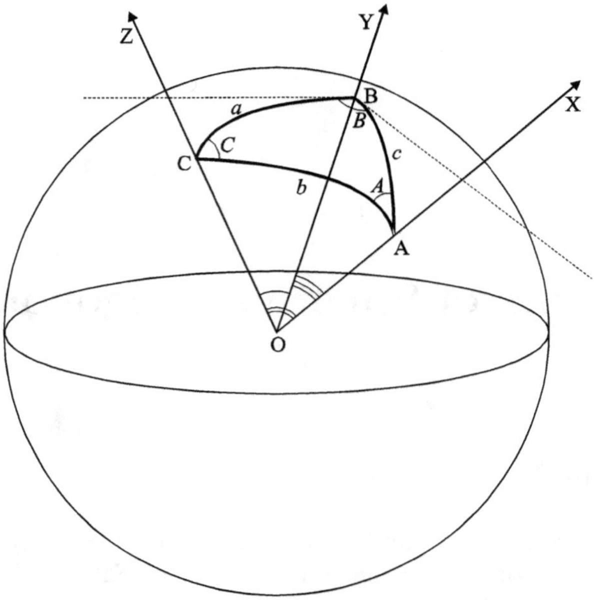


**Fig. T1.2**

The three dihedral angles in the trihedral structure OXYZ are: $\delta_{YZ}$, with the half line OX as its edge; $\delta_{ZX}$, with half line OY as its edge; $\delta_{XY}$, with half line OZ as its edge.

Those three concurrent lines (XX′, YY′, and ZZ′) determine eight trihedra in space. Among these, the one of interest to us is highlighted by the half lines which determine it.

Considering that vertex O of any trihedral OXYZ is the center of a sphere, then its intersections with the sphere surface are three great circular arcs, which intersect pairwise and form a *spherical triangle*, as shown in Figure T1.2. The triangle's vertices (A, B, C) are the intersection between the trihedral edges and the surface of the sphere.

The great arcs of the circle between the vertices of the spherical triangle (AB, BC, and CA) represent the sides of the spherical triangle. The measurements of the spherical triangle sides ($a$, $b$, $c$) are the angular lengths of the triangle sides (in radians), and not the actual lengths of the arcs of the circle. Those are identical to the measurements of the sides corresponding to the trihedral.

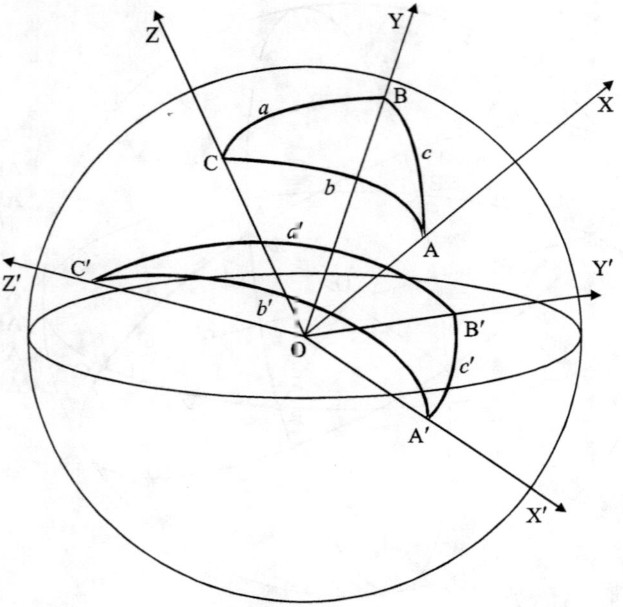


**Fig. T1.3**

Each vertex of the spherical triangle (A, B, C) corresponds to an angle whose measurement ($A$, $B$, $C$) is either the plane angle between the tangents to the great circular arcs that intersect in that vertex, or the dihedral angle between the planes intersecting on the trihedral's edge that passes through that vertex.

The spherical triangle A′B′C′ in Figure T1.3 is named the *polar triangle* of the spherical triangle ABC, because it is determined by the trihedral's edge directions OX′Y′Z′, which intersect the sphere surface. Those directions are constructed so that: the edge OX′ is perpendicular to the plane YOZ; the edge OY′ is perpendicular to the plane ZOX; the edge OZ′ is perpendicular to the plane XOY.

Under these circumstances, vertices $\widehat{\mathrm{A}'}$, $\widehat{\mathrm{B}'}$ and $\widehat{\mathrm{C}'}$ are the spherical poles of the great circle encompassing the arcs BC, CA and AB, respectively.

Definition: the *perimeter of a spherical triangle* is

$$2p = a + b + c.$$

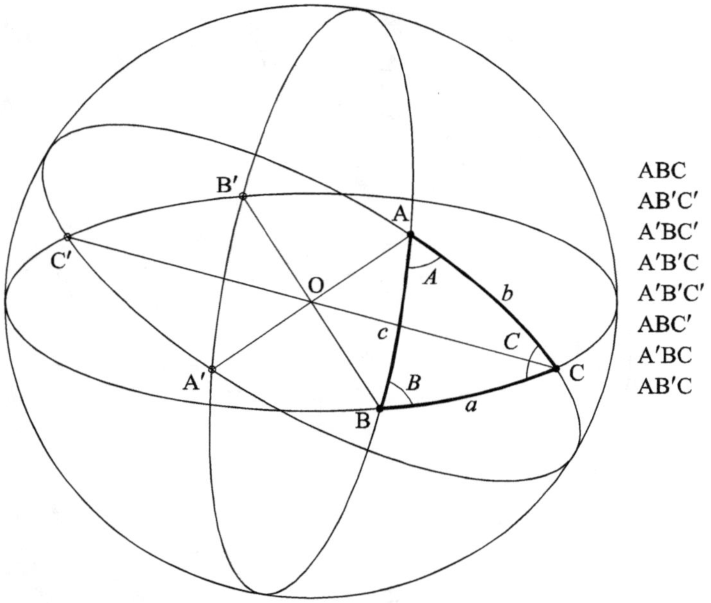


**Fig. T1.4**

The diagram in Figure T1.4 shows that the intersection of any three great circles on the surface of a sphere will form eight spherical triangles, among which we have highlighted the spherical triangle ABC and its elements.

*Because a trihedral corresponds to any spherical triangle, it results that a characteristic of a trihedral is also a characteristic of the defined spherical triangle and vice versa.*

In order to sustain the previous affirmations, we will give a few examples presenting, without demonstration, three theorems and their consequences.

**Theorem 1.** *In any trihedral, any face is smaller than the sum of the other faces*:

$$\angle \mathrm{XOY} < \angle \mathrm{YOZ} + \angle \mathrm{ZOX};$$

$$\angle \mathrm{YOZ} < \angle \mathrm{ZOX} + \angle \mathrm{XOY};$$

$$\angle \mathrm{ZOX} < \angle \mathrm{XOY} + \angle \mathrm{YOZ}.$$

**Corollary 1.** In any spherical triangle, any edge is smaller than the sum of the other two edges:

$$c < a + b;$$

$$a < b + c;$$

$$b < c + a.$$

**Theorem 2.** *In any trihedral, the sum of the faces is smaller than four right angles*:

$$\angle \mathrm{XOY} + \angle \mathrm{YOZ} + \angle \mathrm{ZOX} < 2\pi.$$

**Corollary 2.** In any spherical triangle, the sum of edges is smaller four right angles:

$$a + b + c < 2\pi.$$

**Theorem 3.** *In any trihedral, the sum of dihedral angles is larger than two right angles and smaller than six right angles*:

$$\pi < \angle YZ + \angle ZX + \angle XY < 3\pi.$$

**Corollary 3.** In any spherical triangle, the sum of angles is larger than two right angles and smaller than six right angles:

$$\pi < A + B + C < 3\pi.$$

**Definition 1.** The *excess* of a spherical triangle is

$$2\epsilon = A + B + C - \pi.$$

## 1.2. Fundamental Formulas of Spherical Trigonometry

### a) *Gauss formulas*

The Cartesian coordinates of vertex C, pertaining to the spherical triangle ABC, presented in Figure T1.5, relative to the axis of the tri-orthogonal systems OXYZ and OX′Y′Z′, respectively (whose axes OX and OX′ coincide, being perpendicular to the plane of the diagram), are:

$$\begin{cases} x = r\sin b \sin A; \\ y = -r\mathrm{sinb} \cos A; \\ z = r\cos b; \end{cases}$$

$$\begin{cases} x' = r\sin a\,\sin B; \\ y' = r\sin a\,\cos B; \\ z' = r\cos a. \end{cases}$$

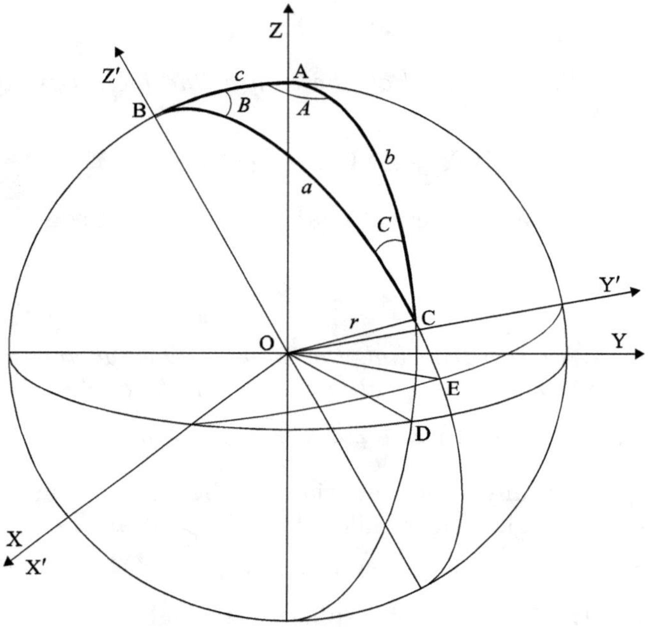


**Fig. T1.5**

If $C_0$ is the projection of C onto the plan of the diagram, as indicated in Figure T1.6, then the relations between the Cartesian coordinates of C relative to both reference systems are:

$$x' = x;$$

$$y' = y\cos c + z\sin c;$$

$$z' = z\cos c - z\sin c.$$

Thus, we obtain:

$$\begin{cases} r\sin a\,\sin B = r\sin b\,\sin A; \\ r\sin a\,\cos B = r\sin b\,\cos c\,\cos A + r\cos b\,\sin c; \\ r\cos a = r\cos b\,\cos c + r\sin b\,\sin c\,\cos A; \end{cases}$$

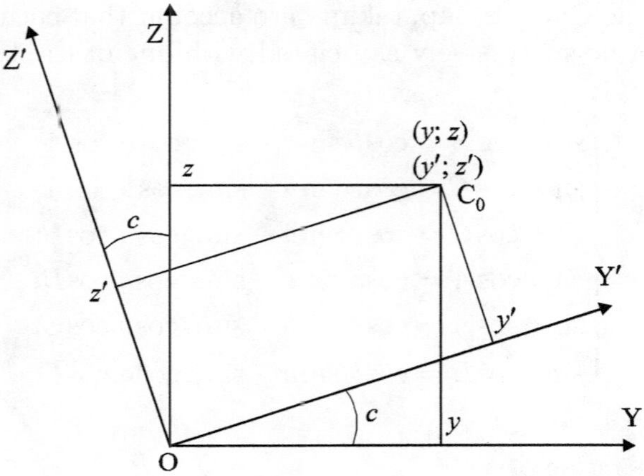


**Fig. T1.6**

$$r \neq 0;$$

$$\begin{cases} \sin a \sin B = \sin b \sin A; \\ \sin a \cos B = \cos b \sin c - \sin b \cos c \cos A; \\ \cos a = \cos b \cos c + \sin b \sin c \cos A. \end{cases}$$

These represent the fundamental formulas of spherical trigonometry, also known as *the Gauss equations,* and they represent the relations between the edges and the angles of the spherical triangle.

### b) *Sine rules*

The *sine rules* for a spherical triangle consist of the first relation in the previous group, to which two more similar relations obtained by circular permutations have been added:

$$\begin{cases} \sin a \sin B = \sin b \sin A; \\ \sin b \sin C = \sin c \sin B; \\ \sin c \sin A = \sin a \sin C. \end{cases}$$

### c) *Five-part rules*

*The five-part rules* for a spherical triangle result if we add five similar relations obtained by permuting the triangle's elements to the second relation in the Gauss group, taking into account that each edge of the triangle can be successively associated with one of the two adjacent angles:

$$\begin{cases} \sin a \cos B = \cos b \sin c - \sin b \cos c \cos A; \\ \sin a \cos C = \cos c \sin b - \sin c \cos b \cos A; \\ \sin b \cos C = \cos c \sin a - \sin c \cos a \cos B; \\ \sin b \cos A = \cos a \sin c - \sin a \cos c \cos B; \\ \sin c \cos A = \cos a \sin b - \sin a \cos b \cos C; \\ \sin c \cos B = \cos b \sin a - \sin b \cos a \cos C. \end{cases}$$

## d) *Cosine rules*

The *cosine rules for the edges of the spherical triangle* consist of the third of the relations in Gauss group, to which two more similar relations obtained by permutations of the triangle's elements have been added:

$$\begin{cases} \cos a = \cos b \cos c + \sin b \sin c \cos A; \\ \cos b = \cos c \cos a + \sin c \sin a \cos B; \\ \cos c = \cos a \cos b + \sin a \sin b \cos C. \end{cases}$$

It is evident that the previous formulas can be written also for the edges of the polar triangle A′B′C′:

$$\begin{cases} \cos a' = \cos b' \cos c' + \sin b' \sin c' \cos A'; \\ \cos b' = \cos c' \cos a' + \sin c' \sin a' \cos B'; \\ \cos c' = \cos a' \cos b' + \sin a' \sin b' \cos C'. \end{cases}$$

Knowing that between the elements of a spherical triangle ABC and the elements of its polar triangle A′B′C′ the relations

$$\begin{cases} A + a' = B + b' = C + c' = \pi; \\ A' + a = B' + b = C' + c = \pi \end{cases}$$

exist, it results that:

$$\begin{cases} \cos A = -\cos B \cos C + \sin B \sin C \cos a; \\ \cos B = -\cos C \cos A + \sin C \sin A \cos b; \\ \cos C = -\cos A \cos B + \sin A \sin B \cos c, \end{cases}$$

representing *the cosine rules for the angles of a spherical triangle.*

### e) *Four-part cotangent formulas*

Dividing the 1st, 3rd and 5th five-part rule equations by the 1st, 2nd and 3rd sine rule equations (right-hand side (RHS) by RHS and left-hand side (LHS) by LHS) and dividing the 2nd, 4th and 6th five-part rule equations by the 3rd, 1st and 2nd sine rule equations, respectively (RHS of first group of equations by LHS of the other group of equations and vice versa), it results that:

$$\begin{cases} \sin c\ \mathrm{ctg}\, b = \cos c\ \cos A + \sin A\ \mathrm{ctg}\, B; \\ \sin a\ \mathrm{ctg}\, c = \cos a\ \cos B + \sin B\ \mathrm{ctg}\, C; \\ \sin b\ \mathrm{ctg}\, a = \cos b\ \cos C + \sin C\ \mathrm{ctg}\, A; \\ \sin b\ \mathrm{ctg}\, c = \cos b\ \cos A + \sin A\ \mathrm{ctg}\, C; \\ \sin c\ \mathrm{ctg}\, a = \cos c\ \cos B + \sin B\ \mathrm{ctg}\, A; \\ \sin a\ \mathrm{ctg}\, b = \cos a\ \cos C + \sin C\ \mathrm{ctg}\, B, \end{cases}$$

representing the four-part cotangent formulas for the edges and the angles of the spherical triangle.

### f) *Expressing angles as functions of edges*

From the first equation of the cotangent formulas group for the edges of the spherical triangle, it results that:

$$\cos A = \frac{\cos a - \cos b \cos c}{\sin b \sin c};$$

$$1 - \cos A = \frac{2 \sin \frac{a+b-c}{2} \sin \frac{a-b+c}{2}}{\sin b \sin c} = 2 \sin^2 \frac{A}{2};$$

$$2p = a + b + c;$$

$$\sin \frac{A}{2} = \sqrt{\frac{\sin (p-b) \sin (p-c)}{\sin b \sin c}};$$

$$1 + \cos A = \frac{2 \sin \frac{a+b-c}{2} \sin \frac{b+c-a}{2}}{\sin b \sin c} = 2 \cos^2 \frac{A}{2};$$

$$\cos\frac{A}{2} = \sqrt{\frac{\sin p \sin(p-a)}{\sin b \sin c}};$$

$$\text{tg}\frac{A}{2} = \sqrt{\frac{\sin(p-b)\sin(p-c)}{\sin p \sin(p-a)}}.$$

Similarly, using the other two equations from the cotangent formulas group for the edges of the spherical triangle, it results that:

$$\begin{cases} \sin\frac{B}{2} = \sqrt{\frac{\sin(p-c)\sin(p-a)}{\sin c \sin a}}; \\ \cos\frac{B}{2} = \sqrt{\frac{\sin p \sin(p-b)}{\sin c \sin a}}; \\ \text{tg}\frac{B}{2} = \sqrt{\frac{\sin(p-a)\sin(p-c)}{\sin p \sin(p-b)}}; \end{cases}$$

$$\begin{cases} \sin\frac{C}{2} = \sqrt{\frac{\sin(p-a)\sin(p-b)}{\sin a \sin b}}; \\ \cos\frac{C}{2} = \sqrt{\frac{\sin p \sin(p-c)}{\sin a \sin b}}; \\ \text{tg}\frac{C}{2} = \sqrt{\frac{\sin(p-a)\sin(p-b)}{\sin p \sin(p-c)}}. \end{cases}$$

**g) *Expressing edges as function of angles***

From the first equation of the cotangent formulas group for the angles of the spherical triangle, it results that:

$$\cos a = \frac{\cos A + \cos B \cos C}{\sin B \sin C};$$

$$1 - \cos a = -\frac{2\cos\frac{A+B+C}{2}\cos\frac{B+C-A}{2}}{\sin B \sin C} = 2\sin^2\frac{a}{2};$$

$$2\epsilon = A + B + C - \pi;$$

$$\sin\frac{a}{2} = \sqrt{\frac{\sin\varepsilon \sin(A-\varepsilon)}{\sin B \sin C}};$$

$$1+\cos a=\frac{2\cos\frac{B-C+A}{2}\cos\frac{B-C-A}{2}}{\sin B\sin C}=2\cos^2\frac{a}{2};$$

$$\cos\frac{a}{2}=\sqrt{\frac{\sin(B-\varepsilon)\sin(C-\varepsilon)}{\sin B\sin C}};$$

$$\text{tg}\frac{a}{2}=\sqrt{\frac{\sin\varepsilon\sin(A-\varepsilon)}{\sin(B-\varepsilon)\sin(C-\varepsilon)}}.$$

Similarly, using the other two equations from the cotangent formulas group for the angles of the spherical triangle, it results that:

$$\begin{cases}\sin\frac{b}{2}=\sqrt{\frac{\sin\varepsilon\sin(B-\varepsilon)}{\sin C\sin A}};\\ \cos\frac{b}{2}=\sqrt{\frac{\sin(C-\varepsilon)\sin(A-\varepsilon)}{\sin C\sin A}};\\ \text{tg}\frac{b}{2}=\sqrt{\frac{\sin\varepsilon\sin(B-\varepsilon)}{\sin(C-\varepsilon)\sin(A-\varepsilon)}};\end{cases}$$

$$\begin{cases}\sin\frac{c}{2}=\sqrt{\frac{\sin\varepsilon\sin(C-\varepsilon)}{\sin A\sin B}};\\ \cos\frac{c}{2}=\sqrt{\frac{\sin(A-\varepsilon)\sin(B-\varepsilon)}{\sin A\sin B}};\\ \text{tg}\frac{c}{2}=\sqrt{\frac{\sin\varepsilon\sin(C-\varepsilon)}{\sin(A-\varepsilon)\sin(B-\varepsilon)}}.\end{cases}$$

### h) *Delambre's analogies*

*Delambre's analogies* allow the calculus of sine and cosine rules for the half-sum and the half-difference, respectively, of two angles of a spherical triangle. For this purpose, using the previous groups of formulas, it results that:

$$\sin\frac{A+B}{2}=\sin\left(\frac{A}{2}+\frac{B}{2}\right)=\sin\frac{A}{2}\cos\frac{B}{2}+\cos\frac{A}{2}\sin\frac{B}{2}$$

$$=\sqrt{\frac{\sin(p-b)\sin(p-c)}{\sin b\sin c}}\sqrt{\frac{\sin p\sin(p-b)}{\sin c\sin a}}$$

$$+\sqrt{\frac{\sin p\sin(p-a)}{\sin b\sin c}}\sqrt{\frac{\sin(p-c)\sin(p-a)}{\sin c\sin a}}$$

$$= \sqrt{\frac{\sin p \sin (p-c)}{\sin a \sin b}} \frac{\sin (p-b) + \sin (p-a)}{\sin c}$$

$$= \cos \frac{C}{2} \frac{2 \sin \frac{c}{2} \cos \frac{a-b}{2}}{2 \sin \frac{c}{2} \cos \frac{c}{2}};$$

$$\sin \frac{A+B}{2} = \frac{\cos \frac{a-b}{2}}{\cos \frac{c}{2}} cos \frac{C}{2}.$$

Similarly, we can deduce:

$$\begin{cases} \sin \frac{B+C}{2} = \frac{\cos \frac{b-c}{2}}{\cos \frac{a}{2}} \cos \frac{A}{2}; \\ \sin \frac{C+A}{2} = \frac{\cos \frac{c-a}{2}}{\cos \frac{b}{2}} \cos \frac{B}{2}; \end{cases}$$

$$\begin{cases} \sin \frac{A-B}{2} = \frac{\sin \frac{a-b}{2}}{\sin \frac{c}{2}} \cos \frac{C}{2}; \\ \sin \frac{B-C}{2} = \frac{\sin \frac{b-c}{2}}{\sin \frac{a}{2}} \cos \frac{A}{2}; \\ \sin \frac{C-A}{2} = \frac{\sin \frac{c-a}{2}}{\sin \frac{b}{2}} \cos \frac{B}{2}; \end{cases}$$

$$\begin{cases} \cos \frac{A+B}{2} = \frac{\cos \frac{a+b}{2}}{\cos \frac{c}{2}} \sin \frac{C}{2}; \\ \cos \frac{B+C}{2} = \frac{\cos \frac{b+c}{2}}{\cos \frac{a}{2}} \sin \frac{A}{2}; \\ \cos \frac{C+A}{2} = \frac{\cos \frac{c+a}{2}}{\cos \frac{b}{2}} \sin \frac{B}{2}; \end{cases}$$

$$\begin{cases} \cos \frac{A-B}{2} = \frac{\sin \frac{a+b}{2}}{\sin \frac{c}{2}} \cos \frac{C}{2}; \\ \cos \frac{B-C}{2} = \frac{\sin \frac{b+c}{2}}{\sin \frac{a}{2}} \sin \frac{A}{2}; \\ \cos \frac{C-A}{2} = \frac{\sin \frac{c+a}{2}}{\sin \frac{b}{2}} \sin \frac{B}{2}. \end{cases}$$

### i) *Napier's analogies*

*Napier's analogies* allow the calculus of the tangent function for the half-sum and the half-difference, respectively, of two angles of a spherical triangle.

These results follow from Delambre's analogies and can be stated as:

$$\begin{cases} \operatorname{tg}\frac{A+B}{2} = \dfrac{\cos\frac{a-b}{2}}{\cos\frac{a+b}{2}}\operatorname{ctg}\dfrac{C}{2}; \\ \operatorname{tg}\frac{B+C}{2} = \dfrac{\cos\frac{b-c}{2}}{\cos\frac{b+c}{2}}\operatorname{ctg}\dfrac{A}{2}; \\ \operatorname{tg}\frac{C+A}{2} = \dfrac{\cos\frac{c-a}{2}}{\cos\frac{c+a}{2}}\operatorname{ctg}\dfrac{B}{2}; \end{cases}$$

$$\begin{cases} \operatorname{tg}\frac{A-B}{2} = \dfrac{\sin\frac{a-b}{2}}{\sin\frac{a+b}{2}}\operatorname{ctg}\dfrac{C}{2}; \\ \operatorname{tg}\frac{B-C}{2} = \dfrac{\sin\frac{b-c}{2}}{\sin\frac{b+c}{2}}\operatorname{ctg}\dfrac{A}{2}; \\ \operatorname{tg}\frac{C-A}{2} = \dfrac{\sin\frac{c-a}{2}}{\sin\frac{c+a}{2}}\operatorname{ctg}\dfrac{B}{2}. \end{cases}$$

## 1.3. Conversion of Celestial Coordinates

### a) *Conversion of horizontal coordinates to hour coordinates*

For a star whose apparent position $\sigma$ on the celestial sphere is represented in Figure T1.7, the relations between the two pairs of celestial coordinates, $(A;\ z)$ and $(H;\ \delta)$ will be established using Gauss formulas for the spherical triangle Z P$\sigma$, named the *parallactic triangle* or the star's *position triangle.*

**Remark:** In the apparent diurnal evolution of star $\sigma$, its parallactic triangle is continuously deformed, and angle $p$ from vertex $\sigma$ (*parallactic angle* of the star; *angle at star*) does not occur in the transformation relations that will be established.

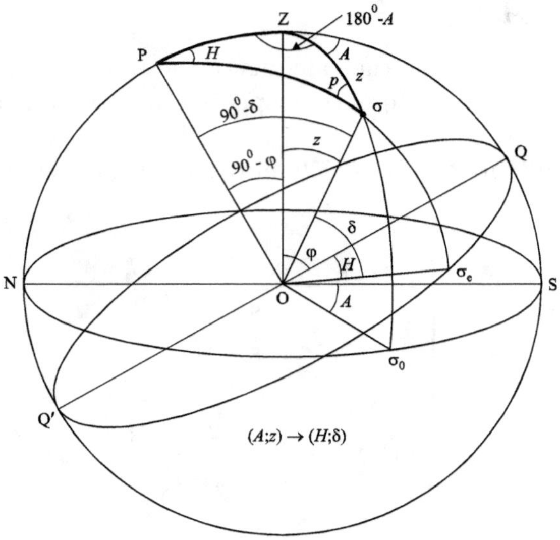


**Fig. T1.7**

Under these circumstances, we have:

$$\begin{cases} \sin \widehat{\mathrm{P}\sigma} \sin H = \sin \widehat{\mathrm{Z}\sigma} \sin(180^\circ - A); \\ \sin \widehat{\mathrm{P}\sigma} \cos H = \cos \widehat{\mathrm{Z}\sigma} \sin \widehat{\mathrm{PZ}} - \sin \widehat{\mathrm{Z}\sigma} \cos \widehat{\mathrm{PZ}} \cos(180^\circ - A); \\ \cos \widehat{\mathrm{P}\sigma} = \cos \widehat{\mathrm{Z}\sigma} \cos \widehat{\mathrm{PZ}} + \sin \widehat{\mathrm{Z}\sigma} \sin \widehat{\mathrm{PZ}} \cos(180^\circ - A); \end{cases}$$

$$\begin{cases} \cos\delta \sin H = \sin z \sin A; \\ \cos\delta \cos H = \cos z \cos\varphi + \sin z \sin\varphi \cos A; \\ \sin\delta = \cos z \sin\varphi - \sin z \cos\varphi \cos A, \end{cases}$$

relations from which the coordinates $(H; \delta)$ can be determined, knowing the coordinates $(A; z)$ and $\varphi$.

For this purpose, we proceed as follows:

$$\begin{cases} \cos\delta \sin H = \sin z \sin A; \\ \cos\delta \cos H = \sin z \cos A \left(\frac{\cos\varphi}{\mathrm{tg}\, z \cos A} + \sin\varphi\right); \\ \sin\delta = \sin z \cos A \left(\frac{\sin\varphi}{\mathrm{tg}\, z \cos A} - \cos\varphi\right); \\ \mathrm{tg} z \cos A = \mathrm{tg}\, \psi, \end{cases}$$

the angular dimension $\psi$ from this substitution being determined by $z$ and $A$;

$$\begin{cases} \cos\delta\,\sin H = \sin z\,\sin A; \\ \cos\delta\,\cos H = \sin z\,\cos A\frac{\cos(\varphi-\psi)}{\sin\psi}; \\ \sin\delta = \sin z\,\cos A\frac{\sin(\varphi-\psi)}{\sin\psi}. \end{cases}$$

From this, the result is:

$$\operatorname{tg} H = \operatorname{tg} A\frac{\sin\psi}{\cos(\varphi-\psi)};$$

$$\operatorname{tg}\delta = \cos H\operatorname{tg}(\varphi-\psi).$$

**b)** ***Transformation of hourly coordinates into equatorial coordinates***

Corresponding to a diurnal moment of sidereal time $t_s$, for a star whose apparent position $\sigma$ on the celestial sphere is represented in Figure T1.8, the relations between the two pairs of celestial coordinates, $(H;\,\delta)$ and $(\alpha;\,\delta)$, will be reduced to the relation

$$\alpha = t_s - H,$$

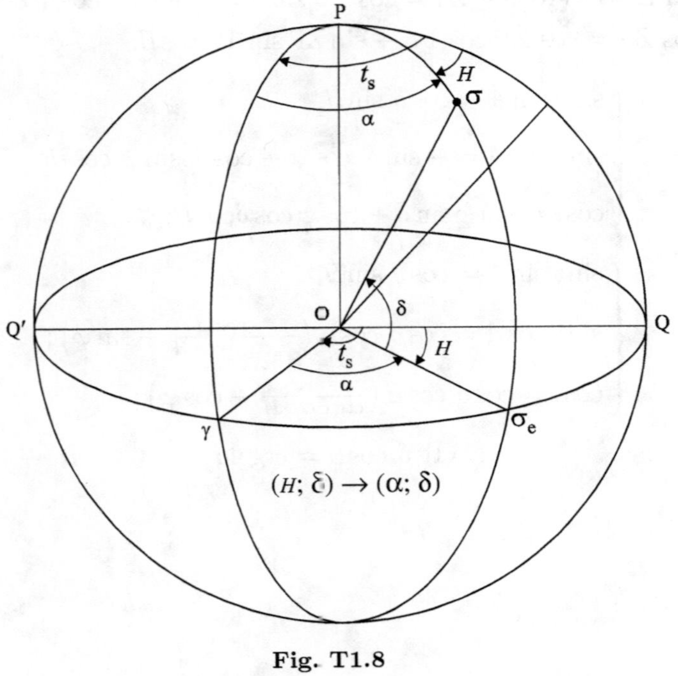


**Fig. T1.8**

taking into account that the declination $\delta$ is the same in both variants.

### c) Transformation of horizontal coordinates into equatorial coordinates

Direct transformation is not possible, and for that reason it will be done based on the previous cases, following the path

$$(A; z) \rightarrow (H; \delta) \rightarrow (\alpha; \delta).$$

### d) Transformation of hourly coordinates into horizontal coordinates

Considering the same parallactic triangle, ZP$\sigma$, presented in Figure T1.7 (analogous to the ABC spherical triangle in Figure T1.5), using the first equation of the sine rules, the fourth equation of the five-part rules and the second equation of the cosine rules for the edges, and taking into account the transformation from ($H$; $\delta$) coordinates to ($A$; $z$) coordinates, we obtain:

$$\begin{cases} \sin \mathrm{Z}\sigma \sin(180^\circ - A) = \sin \mathrm{P}\sigma \sin H; \\ \sin \mathrm{Z}\sigma \cos(180^\circ - A) = \cos \mathrm{P}\sigma \sin \mathrm{ZP} - \sin \mathrm{P}\sigma \cos \mathrm{PZ} \cos H; \\ \cos \mathrm{Z}\sigma = \cos \mathrm{ZP} \cos \mathrm{P}\sigma + \sin \mathrm{ZP} \sin \mathrm{P}\sigma \cos H; \end{cases}$$

$$\begin{cases} \sin z \sin A = \cos\delta \sin H; \\ \sin z \cos A = -\sin\delta \cos\varphi + \cos\delta \sin\varphi \cos H; \\ \cos z = \sin\varphi \sin\delta + \cos\varphi \cos\delta \cos H; \end{cases}$$

$$\begin{cases} \sin z \sin A = \cos\delta \sin H; \\ \sin z \cos A = \cos\delta \cos H \left(-\frac{\cos\varphi}{\operatorname{ctg}\delta \cos H} + \sin\varphi\right); \\ \cos z = \cos\delta \cos H \left(\frac{\sin\varphi}{\operatorname{ctg}\delta \cos H} + \cos\varphi\right); \end{cases}$$

$$\operatorname{ctg}\delta \cos H = \operatorname{ctg}\Phi;$$

$$\begin{cases} \sin z \sin A = \cos\delta \sin H; \\ \sin z \cos A = \cos\delta \cos H \frac{\sin(\varphi-\Phi)}{\cos\Phi}; \\ \cos z = \cos\delta \cos H \frac{\cos(\varphi-\Phi)}{\cos\Phi}. \end{cases}$$

From this, it results that

$$\mathrm{tg} A = \mathrm{tg} H \frac{\cos\Phi}{\sin(\varphi-\Phi)}; \quad \mathrm{tg} z = \frac{\mathrm{tg}(\varphi-\Phi)}{\cos A}.$$

### e) *Transformation of equatorial coordinates into hour coordinates*

As we already know, relative to the diurnal moment of sidereal time $t_s$, indicated in Figure T1.8, passing from equatorial coordinates to hour coordinates, when declination $\delta$ remains the same, implies that

$$H = t_s - \alpha.$$

### f) *Transformation of equatorial coordinates into horizontal coordinates*

Direct transformation is not possible. That is why it is done based on the previous cases, following the path

$$(\alpha; \delta) \rightarrow (H; \delta) \rightarrow (A; z).$$

### g) *Transformation of equatorial coordinates into equatorial coordinates*

On the celestial sphere, if the localization of star $\sigma$ established by the two coordinate systems is the one presented in Figure T1.9, then, using Gauss formulas for the spherical triangle PΠσ (corresponding to the conventional spherical triangle ABC), we obtain:

$$\begin{cases} \sin(90^\circ-\beta)\sin(90^\circ-\lambda)=\sin(90^\circ-\delta)\sin(90^\circ+\alpha); \\ \sin(90^\circ-\beta)\cos(90^\circ-\lambda)=\cos(90^\circ-\delta)\sin\epsilon \\ \qquad\qquad -\sin(90^\circ-\delta)\cos\epsilon\cos(90^\circ+\alpha); \\ \cos(90^\circ-\beta)=\cos(90^\circ-\delta)\cos\epsilon \\ \qquad\qquad +\sin(90^\circ-\delta)\sin\epsilon\cos(90^\circ+\alpha); \end{cases}$$

$$\begin{cases} \cos\beta\ \cos\lambda=\cos\delta\ \cos\alpha; \\ \cos\beta\ \sin\lambda=\sin\delta\ \sin\epsilon+\cos\delta\cos\epsilon\sin\alpha; \\ \sin\beta=\sin\delta\ \cos\epsilon-\cos\delta\ \sin\epsilon\ \sin\alpha; \end{cases}$$

$$\begin{cases} \cos\beta\ \cos\lambda=\cos\delta\ \cos\alpha; \\ \cos\beta\ \sin\lambda=\cos\delta\ \sin\alpha\left(\frac{\sin\varepsilon}{\operatorname{ctg}\delta\sin\alpha}+\cos\varepsilon\right); \\ \sin\beta=\cos\delta\ \sin\alpha\left(\frac{\cos\varepsilon}{\operatorname{ctg}\delta\sin\alpha}-\sin\varepsilon\right); \\ \operatorname{ctg}\delta\sin\alpha=\operatorname{ctg}\Omega; \end{cases}$$

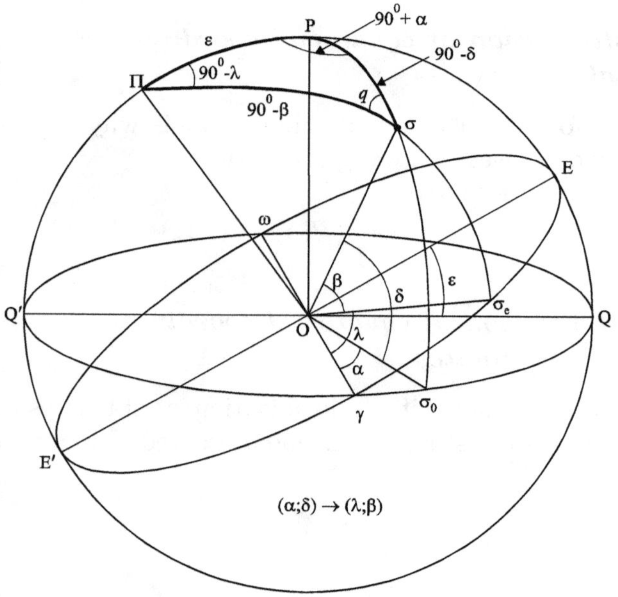


**Fig. T1.9**

$$\begin{cases} \cos\beta\ \cos\lambda = \cos\delta\ \cos\alpha; \\ \cos\beta\ \sin\lambda = \cos\delta\ \sin\alpha\frac{\cos(\varepsilon-\Omega)}{\cos\Omega}; \\ \sin\beta = \cos\delta\ \sin\alpha\frac{\sin(\Omega-\varepsilon)}{\cos\Omega}; \end{cases}$$

$$\operatorname{tg}\lambda = \operatorname{tg}\alpha\frac{\cos(\Omega-\varepsilon)}{\cos\Omega};$$

$$\operatorname{tg}\beta = \sin\lambda\operatorname{tg}(\Omega-\epsilon).$$

## h) *Transformation of elliptical coordinates into equatorial coordinates*

Considering the same parallactic triangle $P\Pi\sigma$, presented in Figure T1.9 (analogous to the conventional spherical triangle ABC), using the first equation of the sine rules, the fourth equation of the five-part rules and the second equation of the cosine rules for edges, and taking into account the transformation from coordinates $(\lambda;\ \beta)$ to coordinates $(\alpha;\ \delta)$, we obtain:

$$\begin{cases} \cos\delta\cos\alpha = \cos\beta\cos\lambda; \\ \sin(90^\circ-\delta)\cos(90^\circ+\alpha) = \cos(90^\circ-\beta)\sin\epsilon \\ \qquad\qquad - \sin(90^\circ-\beta)\cos\epsilon\cos(90^\circ-\lambda); \\ \cos(90^\circ-\delta) = \cos\epsilon\cos(90^\circ-\beta) + \sin\epsilon\sin(90^\circ-\beta)\cos(90^\circ-\lambda); \end{cases}$$

$$\begin{cases} \cos\delta\ \cos\alpha = \cos\beta\ \cos\lambda; \\ \cos\delta\ \sin\alpha = -\sin\beta\ \sin\epsilon + \cos\beta\ \cos\epsilon\ \sin\lambda; \\ \sin\delta = \cos\epsilon\ \sin\beta + \sin\epsilon\cos\beta\ \sin\lambda; \end{cases}$$

$$\begin{cases} \cos\delta\ \cos\alpha = \cos\beta\ \cos\lambda; \\ \cos\delta\ \sin\alpha = \cos\beta\ \sin\lambda\left(-\frac{\sin\varepsilon}{\operatorname{ctg}\beta\ \sin\lambda} + \cos\varepsilon\right); \\ \sin\delta = \cos\beta\ \sin\lambda\left(\frac{\cos\varepsilon}{\operatorname{ctg}\beta\ \sin\lambda} + \sin\varepsilon\right); \end{cases}$$

$$\begin{cases} \operatorname{ctg}\beta\ \sin\lambda = \operatorname{ctg}\Sigma; \\ \cos\delta\ \cos\alpha = \cos\beta\ \cos\lambda; \\ \cos\delta\ \sin\alpha = \cos\beta\ \sin\lambda\frac{\cos(\varepsilon+\Sigma)}{\cos\Sigma}; \end{cases}$$

$$\sin\delta = \cos\beta\ \sin\lambda\frac{\sin(\varepsilon+\Sigma)}{\cos\Sigma};$$

$$\operatorname{tg}\alpha = \operatorname{tg}\lambda\frac{\cos(\varepsilon+\Sigma)}{\cos\Sigma};$$

$$\operatorname{tg}\delta = \sin\alpha\ \operatorname{tg}(\epsilon+\Sigma).$$

In particular, if the considered star is the Sun, for which $\beta = 0$ (as indicated in Figure T1.10), then the spherical triangle $S\gamma S_e$ is a right triangle.

Under these circumstances, the result from the initial group of three relations is:

$$\begin{cases}\cos\delta\cos\alpha = \cos\lambda;\\ \cos\delta\sin\alpha = \cos\epsilon\sin\lambda;\\ \sin\delta = \sin\epsilon\sin\lambda;\end{cases}$$

$$\begin{cases}\operatorname{tg}\alpha = \cos\epsilon\ \operatorname{tg}\lambda;\\ \operatorname{tg}\delta = \operatorname{tg}\epsilon\ \sin\alpha;\\ \sin\delta = \sin\epsilon\ \sin\lambda.\end{cases}$$

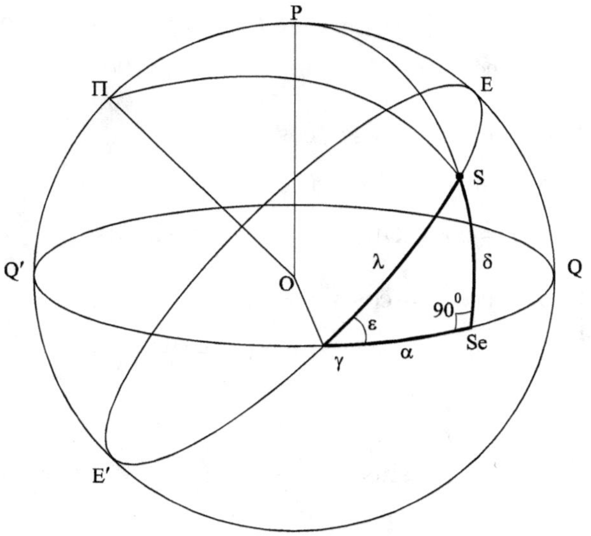


**Fig. T1.10**

# Topic 2

# Determining the Masses of Visual Binary Stars

The ensemble named a *visual binary star* represents a system consisting of two stars gravitationally linked to each other that can be resolved (seen separately) through a telescope if their centers are at an angular distance of at least 1 arcsec.

**1)** According to Kepler's third law and using the image in Figure T2.1, where $p$ is the star s $\Sigma$ parallax and $\beta$ is the angular distance between the two components, the result is:

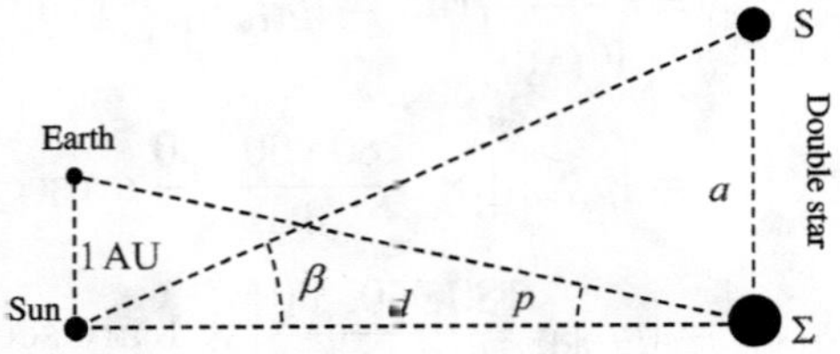


**Fig. T2.1**

$$\tan\beta = \frac{a_{\text{AU}}}{d_{\text{AU}}} \approx \beta_{(\text{rad})} = \frac{\left|a_{(\text{AU})}\right| \times 1\text{AU}}{\left|d_{(\text{AU})}\right| \times 1\text{AU}}\text{rad} = \frac{\left|a_{(\text{AU})}\right|}{\left|d_{(\text{AU})}\right|}\text{rad};$$

$$\beta_{(\text{rad})} = \frac{\left|a_{(\text{AU})}\right|}{\left|d_{(\text{AU})}\right|}\text{rad} = \left|\beta_{(\text{rad})}\right| \times 1\,\text{rad}$$

$$= \left|\beta_{(\text{rad})}\right| \times \frac{180 \cdot 60 \cdot 60}{3.14}\text{ arcsec;}$$

$$\beta_{(\text{rad})} = \left|\beta_{(\text{rad})}\frac{180 \cdot 60 \cdot 60}{3.14}\right| \times 1\text{ arcsec;}$$

$$\beta_{(\text{rad})} = \left|\beta_{(\text{arcsec})}\right| \times \text{ 1arcsec} = |\beta''| \times 1\text{ arcsec;}$$

$$\beta_{(\text{rad})} = \frac{\left|a_{(\text{AU})}\right|}{\left|d_{(\text{AU})}\right|}\text{rad} = |\beta''| \times 1\text{ arcsec;}$$

$$\left|d_{(\text{AU})}\right| = \frac{\left|a_{(\text{AU})}\right|}{|\beta''|}\frac{\text{rad}}{\text{arcsec}};$$

$$\tan p = \frac{1\text{AU}}{d_{(\text{AU})}} = p_{(\text{rad})} = \frac{1}{\left|d_{(\text{AU})}\right|}\text{rad;}$$

$$\tan p = \frac{1\text{AU}}{d_{(\text{AU})}} \approx p_{(\text{rad})} = \frac{1\text{ AU}}{\left|d_{(\text{AU})}\right| \times 1\text{AU}}\text{rad} = \frac{1}{\left|d_{(\text{AU})}\right|}\text{rad;}$$

$$p_{(\text{rad})} = \frac{1}{\left|d_{(\text{AU})}\right|}\text{rad} = \left|p_{(\text{rad})}\right| \times 1\,\text{rad}$$

$$= \left|p_{(\text{rad})}\right| \times \frac{180 \cdot 60 \cdot 60}{3.14}\text{ arcsec;}$$

$$p_{(\text{rad})} = \left|p_{(\text{rad})}\frac{180 \cdot 60 \cdot 60}{3.14}\right| \times 1\text{ arc.sec;}$$

$$p_{(\text{rad})} = \left|p_{(\text{arcsec})}\right| \times \text{ 1arcsec} = |p''| \times \text{1arcsec;}$$

$$p_{(\text{rad})} = \frac{1}{\left|d_{(\text{AU})}\right|}\text{rad} = |p''| \times \text{1arcsec;}$$

$$\left|d_{(\text{AU})}\right| = \frac{1}{|p''|}\frac{\text{rad}}{\text{arcsec}};$$

$$\frac{\left|a_{(\text{AU})}\right|}{|\beta''|}\frac{\text{rad}}{\text{arcsec}} = \frac{1}{|p''|}\frac{\text{rad}}{\text{arcsec}};$$

$$\frac{\left|a_{(\mathrm{AU})}\right|}{|\beta''|}=\frac{1}{|p''|};$$

$$\left|a_{(\mathrm{AU})}\right|=\frac{|\beta''|}{|p''|};$$

$$(m+M)\,T^2=\frac{4\pi^2a^3}{K};$$

$$\frac{T^2\,(m+M)}{a^3}=\frac{4\pi^2}{K},$$

$$T^2=\frac{4\pi^2}{K\,(m+M)}a^3,$$

representing Kepler's third law in the format proposed by Newton, where all involved elements ($T$ – orbital period; $a$ – distance between the two stars; $m$ and $M$ – the two stars' masses; $K$ – the universal attraction constant) are expressed in units of the International System.

Suppose, in particular, that: $\left|T_{(\mathrm{yrs})}\right|$ is the numerical value of a period $T$ expressed in years; $\left|(m+M)_{(M_S)}\right|$ is the numerical value of $(m+M)$, where $m$ and $M$ are expressed in solar mass ($M_S$); $\left|a_{(\mathrm{AU})}\right|$ is the numerical value of the distance $a$ between the two stars expressed in AU. Under these conditions, Kepler's third law becomes:

$$\frac{\left|T_{(\mathrm{yrs})}\right|^2(1\,\mathrm{yr})^2\cdot\left|(m+M)_{(M_S)}\right|M_S}{\left|a_{(\mathrm{AU})}\right|^3(1\mathrm{AU})^3}=\frac{4\pi^2}{K};$$

$$\frac{\left|T_{(\mathrm{yrs})}\right|^2\cdot\left|(m+M)_{(M_S)}\right|}{\left|a_{(\mathrm{AU})}\right|^3}\cdot\frac{(1\,\mathrm{yr})^2\cdot M_S}{(1\mathrm{AU})^3}=\frac{4\pi^2}{K};$$

$$\frac{(1\,\mathrm{yr})^2\cdot M_S}{(1\mathrm{AU})^3}=\frac{(365\cdot 24\cdot 3600)^2\,s^2\cdot 1.989\cdot 10^{30}\,\mathrm{kg}}{(15\cdot 10^{10})^3\,\mathrm{m}^3}$$

$$\approx 5.86\cdot 10^{11}\,\frac{\mathrm{s}^2\mathrm{kg}}{\mathrm{m}^3};$$

$$\frac{4\pi^2}{K} = \frac{4 \cdot 3.14 \cdot 3.14}{6.67 \cdot 10^{-11}\,\mathrm{Nm^2kg^{-2}}} \approx 5.91 \cdot 10^{11}\,\frac{\mathrm{s^2kg}}{\mathrm{m^3}};$$

$$\frac{(1\,\mathrm{yr})^2 \cdot M_S}{(1\mathrm{AU})^3} \approx \frac{4\pi^2}{K};$$

$$\frac{\left|T_{(\mathrm{yrs})}\right|^2 \cdot \left|(m+M)_{(M_S)}\right|}{\left|a_{(\mathrm{AU})}\right|^3} = 1;$$

$$\left[T_{(\mathrm{yrs})}\right]^2 = \frac{1}{\left|(m+M)_{(M_S)}\right|}\left|a_{(\mathrm{AU})}\right|^3,$$

representing Kepler's third law in "solar units";

$$\left|a_{(\mathrm{AU})}\right| = \frac{|\beta''|}{|p''|};$$

$$\frac{\left|T_{(\mathrm{yrs})}\right|^2 \cdot \left|(m+M)_{(M_S)}\right|}{\left(\frac{|\beta''|}{|p''|}\right)^3} = 1;$$

$$|(m+M)_{(M_S)}| = \frac{\left(\frac{|\beta''|}{|p''|}\right)^3}{\left|T_{(\mathrm{yrs})}\right|^2};$$

$$|(m+M)_{(M_S)}| = \left(\frac{|\beta''|}{|p''|}\right)^3 \frac{1}{\left|T_{(\mathrm{yrs})}\right|^2};$$

$$|(m+M)_{(M_S)}| \cdot \left|T_{(\mathrm{yrs})}\right|^2 = \left(\frac{|\beta''|}{|p''|}\right)^3,$$

representing Kepler's third law as a function of the double star parallax;

$$\frac{m+M}{M_S} \cdot \frac{T^2}{(1\,\mathrm{yr})^2} = \left(\frac{|\beta''|}{|p''|}\right)^3 = \left(\frac{\beta_{(\mathrm{rad})}}{p_{(\mathrm{rad})}}\right)^3;$$

$$\left(\frac{|\beta''|}{|p''|}\right)^3 = \left(\frac{\beta_{(\mathrm{rad})}}{p_{(\mathrm{rad})}}\right)^3 = \left(\frac{\frac{a_{(\mathrm{AU})}}{d_{(\mathrm{AU})}}}{\frac{1\mathrm{AU}}{d_{(\mathrm{AU})}}}\right)^3 = \left(\frac{a_{(\mathrm{AU})}}{1\mathrm{AU}}\right)^3$$

$$= \left|a_{(\mathrm{AU})}\right|^3 = \frac{a^3_{(\mathrm{AU})}}{(1\mathrm{AU})^3};$$

$$\frac{m+M}{M_S}\cdot\frac{T^2}{(1\,\text{yr})^2}=\left(\frac{|\beta''|}{|p''|}\right)^3=\left(\frac{\beta_{(\text{rad})}}{p_{(\text{rad})}}\right)^3;$$

$$(m+M)\,T^2=\left(\frac{\beta''}{p''}\right)^3 M_S\times(1\,\text{yr})^2=\frac{a^3}{(1\text{AU})^3}M_S\times(1\,\text{yr})^2$$

$$=\frac{M_S\times(1\,\text{yr})^2}{(1\text{AU})^3}a^3;$$

$$\frac{M_S\times(1\,\text{yr})^2}{(1\text{AU})^3}=5.91\cdot 10^{11}\,\frac{\text{s}^2\text{kg}}{\text{m}^3}=\frac{4\pi^2}{K};$$

$$(m+M)T^2=\frac{4\pi^2}{K}a^3,$$

where $a$, $m$, $M$, $T$ and $K$ are expressed in SI units.

**2)** In Figure T2.2 are represented the movements of the two stars relative to the system's center of mass (CM), on concentric circular trajectories in the sky plane ($\Pi\equiv\Pi_c$; $i=0$). We consider that the

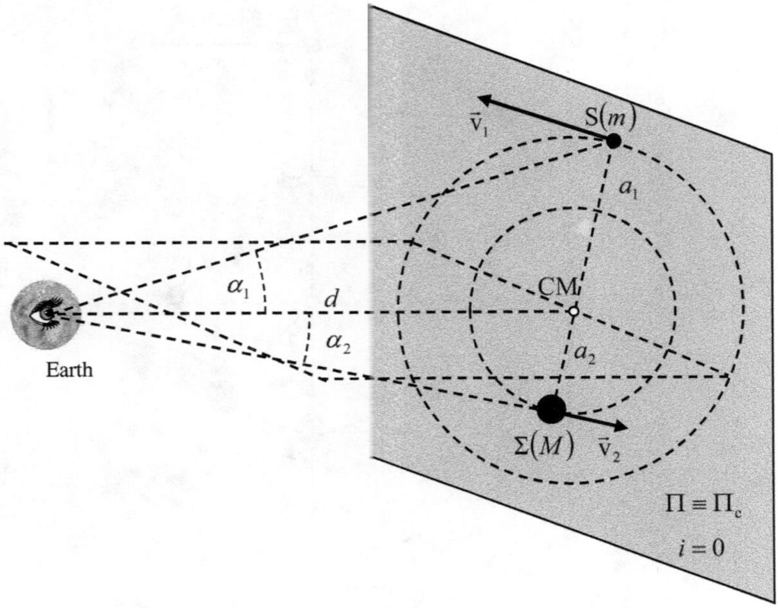


**Fig. T2.2**

system's CM is stationary relative to the observer and the radial components of the two stars' velocities are null.

The result is:

$$\frac{m}{M} = \frac{a_2}{a_1};$$

$$\tan\alpha_1 \approx \alpha_{1(\text{rad})} = \frac{a_{1(\text{AU})}}{d_{(\text{AU})}}; \quad \tan\alpha_2 \approx \alpha_{2(\text{rad})} = \frac{a_{2(\text{AU})}}{d_{(\text{AU})}};$$

$$\frac{a_{2(\text{AU})}}{a_{1(\text{AU})}} = \frac{\alpha_{2(rad)}}{\alpha_{1(\text{rad})}} = \frac{\alpha_2''}{\alpha_1''} = \frac{a_2}{a_1};$$

$$\frac{m}{M} = \frac{\alpha_2''}{\alpha_1''}; \quad m + M = \frac{4\pi^2}{KT^2}\left(\frac{\beta''}{p''}\right)^3.$$

Thus, from the two equations, the masses of the visual binary stellar system components can be determined.

In the image presented in Figure T2.3, the direction of the observation line is included in the $\Pi$ plane of the two stars' circular orbits relative to the CM; thus, the sky plane is $\Pi_c \perp \Pi$ and $i = 90^0$.

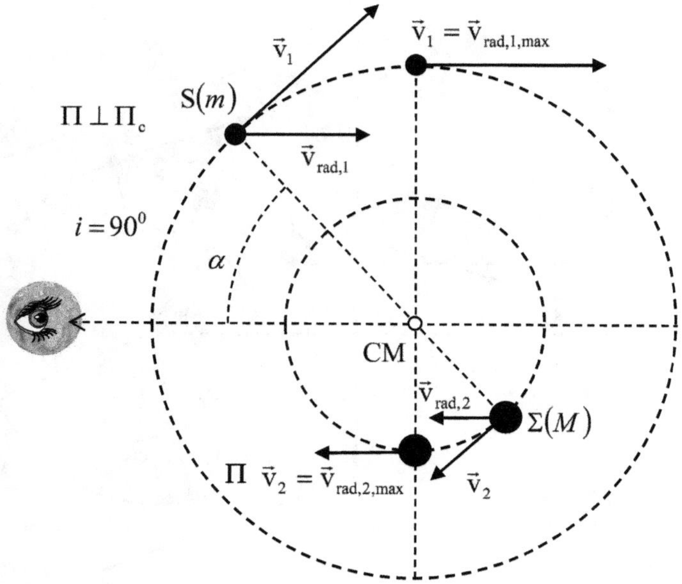


**Fig. T2.3**

We consider that the system's CM is stationary relative to the observer; thus, in any moment the $\vec{v}_1$ and $\vec{v}_2$ velocities are relative both to the CM and to the observer on Earth. As a consequence, the radial components of the two stars' velocities are:

$$v_{rad,1} = v_1 \sin\alpha = v_1 \sin\omega t = v_1 \sin\frac{2\pi}{T}t = v_{rad,1,max}\sin\frac{2\pi}{T}t;$$

$$v_{rad,2} = -v_2 \sin\alpha = -v_2 \sin\omega t = -v_2 \sin\frac{2\pi}{T}t = -v_{rad,2,max}\sin\frac{2\pi}{T}t,$$

(the graphs of these dependencies are represented in Figure T2.4);

$$m\vec{v}_1 + M\vec{v}_2 = 0; \quad mv_1 = Mv_2;$$

$$mv_1 = Mv_2;$$

$$\frac{m}{M} = \frac{v_{rad,2,max}}{v_{rad,2,max}}.$$

In contrast to visual binary stars, spectroscopic binary stars cannot be seen. Only spectral lines can be observed from spectroscopic binary stars.

There are spectroscopic binary stars with only one spectral line, when just the spectrum of a single component is observed, and there

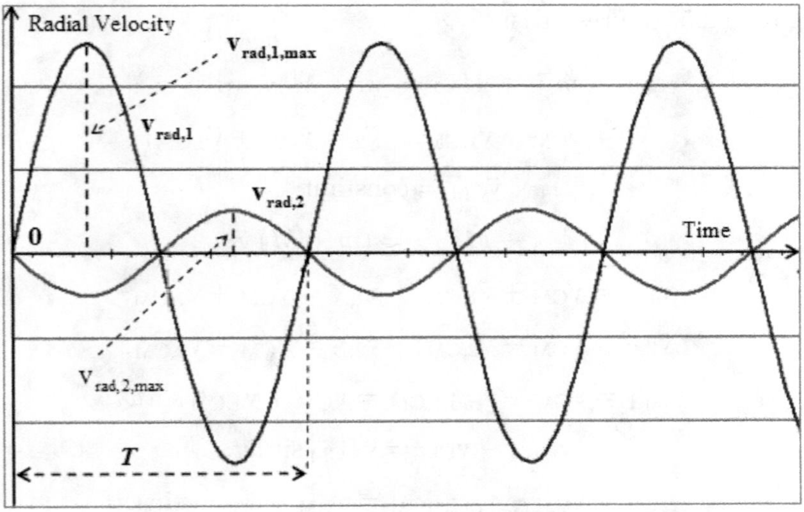


**Fig. T2.4**

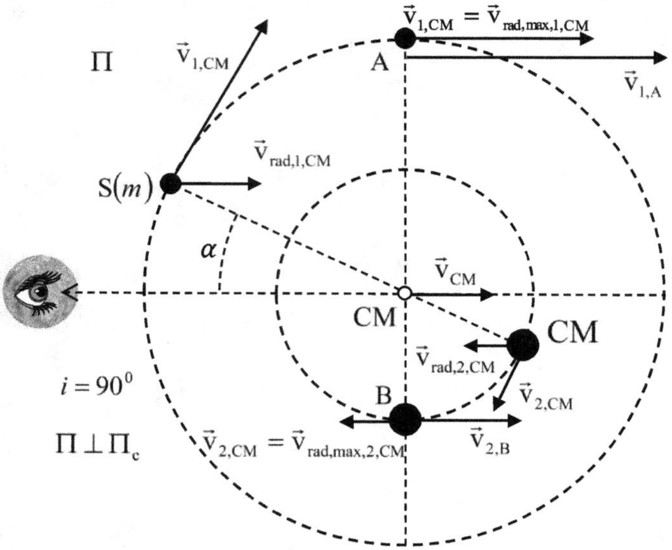


**Fig. T2.5**

are spectroscopic binary stars with two spectral lines, when the spectrum of both components is observed.

**3)** If the system's CM moves relative to the observer as presented in Figure T2.5, the result is:

$$m\vec{v}_1 + M\vec{v}_2 = (m + M)\vec{v}_{CM};$$

$$\vec{v}_1 = \vec{v}_{CM} + \vec{v}_{1,CM}; \quad \vec{v}_2 = \vec{v}_{CM} + \vec{v}_{2,CM};$$

$$\vec{v}_{CM} = \text{constant};$$

$$m\vec{v}_{1,A} + M\vec{v}_{2,B} = (m + M)\,\vec{v}_{CM};$$

$$\vec{v}_{1,A} = \vec{v}_{CM} + \vec{v}_{1,CM}; \quad v_{1,A} = v_{CM} + v_{1,CM};$$

$$\vec{v}_{2,B} = \vec{v}_{CM} + \vec{v}_{2,CM}; \quad v_{2,B} = v_{CM} - v_{2,CM};$$

$$v_{rad,1} = v_{CM} + v_{rad,1,CM} = v_{CM} + v_{1,CM}\sin\omega t;$$

$$v_{rad,1} - v_{CM} = v_{1,CM}\sin\omega t;$$

$$v_{rad,2} = v_{CM} - v_{rad,2,CM} = v_{CM} - v_{2,CM}\sin\omega t;$$

$$v_{rad,2} - v_{CM} = -v_{2,CM}\sin\omega t;$$

$$v_{rad,1,max} = v_{CM} + v_{1,CM};$$
$$v_{rad,2,max} = v_{CM} - v_{2,CM};$$
$$v_{2,CM} < v_{1,CM}; \quad \rightarrow v_{rad,1,max} < v_{rad,2,max}.$$

The graphs of these dependencies are those represented in Figure T2.6.

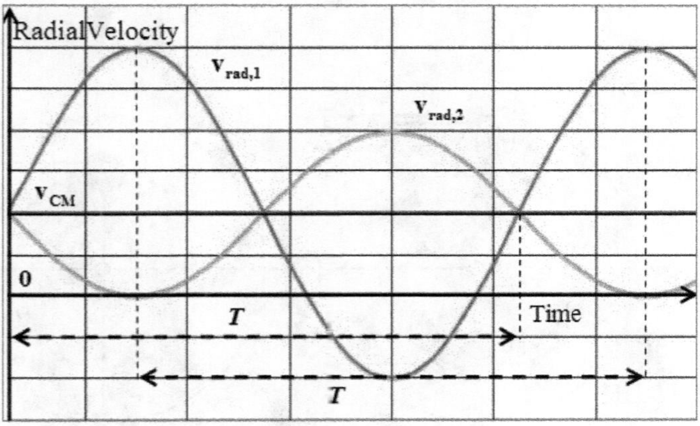


**Fig. T2.6**

If we analyze the system's evolution over half a period, as presented in Figure T2.7, the result is:

$$m\vec{v}_{1,A} + M\vec{v}_{2,B} = (m + M)\,\vec{v}_{CM};$$
$$mv_{1,A} + Mv_{2,B} = (m + M)\,v_{CM};$$
$$\vec{v}_{1,A} = (\vec{v}_{CM} + \vec{v}_{1,CM})_A \qquad \vec{v}_{2,B} = (\vec{v}_{CM} + \vec{v}_{2,CM})_B;$$
$$v_{1,A} = v_{CM} + v_{1,CM} \qquad v_{2,B} = v_{CM} - v_{2,CM};$$
$$m\,(v_{CM} + v_{1,CM}) + M\,(v_{CM} - v_{2,CM}) = (m + M)\,v_{CM};$$
$$mv_{1,CM} = Mv_{2,CM};$$
$$m\vec{v}_{1,C} + M\vec{v}_{2,D} = (m + M)\,\vec{v}_{CM};$$
$$mv_{1,C} + Mv_{2,D} = (m + M)\,v_{CM};$$

$$\vec{v}_{1,C} = (\vec{v}_{CM} + \vec{v}_{1,CM})_C; \quad \vec{v}_{2,D} = (\vec{v}_{CM} + \vec{v}_{2,CM})_D;$$

$$v_{1,C} = v_{CM} - v_{1,CM}; \quad v_{2,D} = v_{2,CM} + v_{CM};$$

$$m\,(v_{CM} - v_{1,CM}) + M\,(v_{CM} + v_{2,CM}) = (m + M)\,v_{CM};$$

$$mv_{1,CM} = Mv_{2,CM};$$

$$v_{1,CM} - v_{CM} \leq v_{rad,1,max} \leq v_{1,CM} + v_{CM};$$

$$v_{CM} - v_{2,CM} \leq v_{rad,1,max} \leq v_{2,CM} + v_{CM}.$$

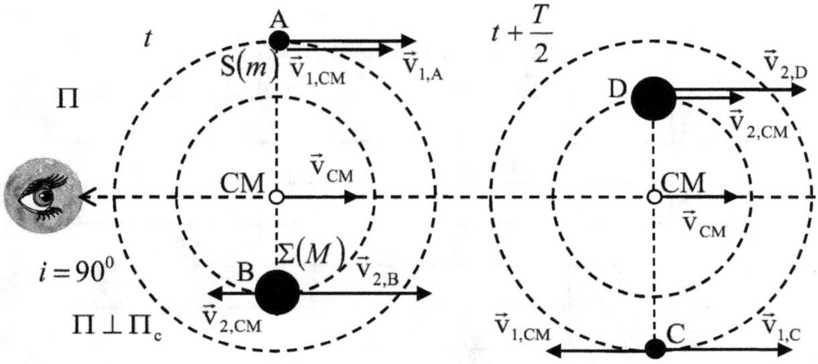


**Fig. T2.7**

**4)** We analyze now the case when the velocity $\vec{v}_{CM}$ of the system's mass center is not in the direction of the observer's view line, as presented in Figures T2.8 and T2.9:

$$m\vec{v}_1 + M\vec{v}_2 = (m + M)\,\vec{v}_{CM};$$

$$\vec{v}_1 = \vec{v}_{CM} + \vec{v}_{1,CM}; \quad \vec{v}_2 = \vec{v}_{CM} + \vec{v}_{2,CM};$$

$$mv_{rad,1} + Mv_{rad,2} = (m + M)\,v_{rad,CM};$$

$$m\vec{v}_1 + M\vec{v}_2 = (m + M)\,\vec{v}_{CM};$$

$$\vec{v}_1 = \vec{v}_{CM} + \vec{v}_{1,CM}; \quad \vec{v}_2 = \vec{v}_{CM} + \vec{v}_{2,CM};$$

$$m\,(\vec{v}_{CM} + \vec{v}_{1,CM}) + M\,(\vec{v}_{CM} + \vec{v}_{2,CM}) = (m + M)\,\vec{v}_{CM};$$

$$m\vec{v}_{CM} + M\vec{v}_{CM} + m\vec{v}_{1,CM} + M\vec{v}_{2,CM} = (m + M)\,\vec{v}_{CM};$$

$$(m + M)\,\vec{v}_{CM} + m\vec{v}_{1,CM} + M\vec{v}_{2,CM} = (m + M)\,\vec{v}_{CM};$$

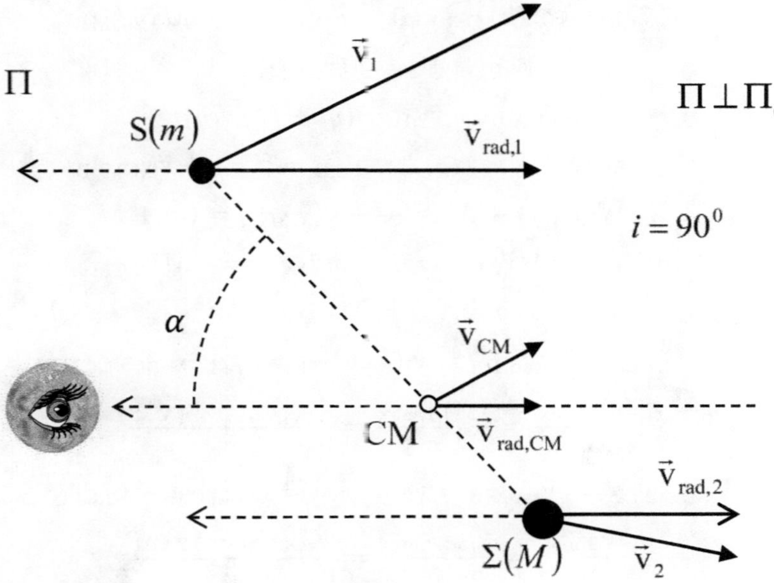


**Fig. T2.8**

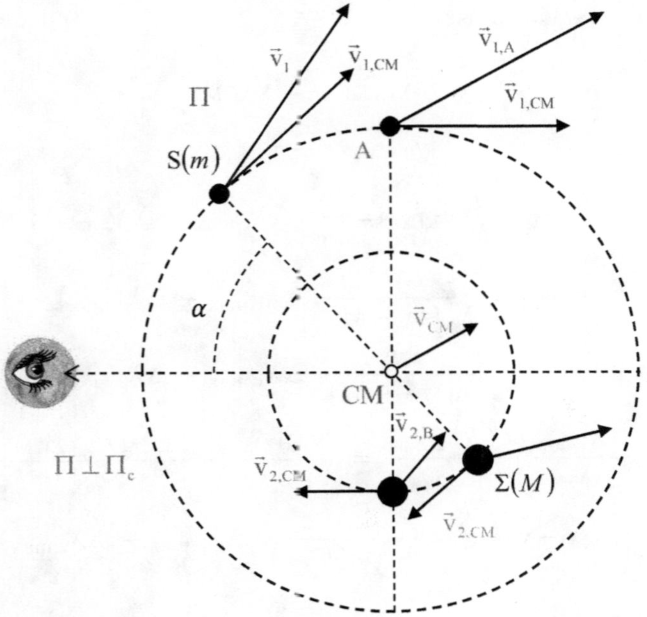


**Fig T2.9**

$$m\vec{v}_{1,\mathrm{CM}} + M\vec{v}_{2,\mathrm{CM}} = 0; \quad m\vec{v}_{1,\mathrm{CM}} = -M\vec{v}_{2,\mathrm{CM}};$$

$$m\mathrm{v}_{1,\mathrm{CM}} = M\mathrm{v}_{2,\mathrm{CM}};$$

$$m\vec{v}_{1,\mathrm{A}} + M\vec{v}_{2,\mathrm{B}} = (m+M)\,\vec{v}_{\mathrm{CM}};$$

$$\vec{v}_{1,\mathrm{A}} = (\vec{v}_{\mathrm{CM}} + \vec{v}_{1,\mathrm{CM}})_{\mathrm{A}}; \quad \vec{v}_{2,\mathrm{B}} = (\vec{v}_{\mathrm{CM}} + \vec{v}_{2,\mathrm{CM}})_{\mathrm{B}};$$

$$m\left(\vec{v}_{\mathrm{CM}} + \vec{v}_{1,\mathrm{CM}}\right)_A + M\left(\vec{v}_{\mathrm{CM}} + \vec{v}_{2,\mathrm{CM}}\right)_B = (m+M)\,\vec{v}_{\mathrm{CM}};$$

$$m\vec{v}_{1,\mathrm{CM}} + M\vec{v}_{2,\mathrm{CM}} = 0; \quad m\vec{v}_{1,\mathrm{CM}} = -M\vec{v}_{2,\mathrm{CM}};$$

$$m\mathrm{v}_{1,\mathrm{CM}} = M\mathrm{v}_{2,\mathrm{CM}};$$

$$\mathrm{v}_{\mathrm{rad,1,max}} = \mathrm{v}_{\mathrm{rad,1,A}} = \mathrm{v}_{1,\mathrm{A}}\cos\alpha_1 = \mathrm{v}_{\mathrm{rad,CM}} + \mathrm{v}_{1,\mathrm{CM}};$$

$$\frac{\Delta\lambda_{1,\mathrm{max}}}{\lambda_0} = \frac{\mathrm{v}_{\mathrm{rad,1,max}}}{c} = \frac{\mathrm{v}_{\mathrm{rad,CM}} + \mathrm{v}_{1,\mathrm{CM}}}{c};$$

$$\mathrm{v}_{\mathrm{rad,2,max}} = \mathrm{v}_{\mathrm{rad,2,B}} = \mathrm{v}_{2,\mathrm{B}}\cos\alpha_2 = \mathrm{v}_{\mathrm{rad,CM}} - \mathrm{v}_{2,\mathrm{CM}};$$

$$\frac{\Delta\lambda_{2,\mathrm{max}}}{\lambda_0} = \frac{\mathrm{v}_{\mathrm{rad,2,max}}}{c} = \frac{\mathrm{v}_{\mathrm{rad,CM}} - \mathrm{v}_{2,\mathrm{CM}}}{c};$$

$$\frac{\Delta\lambda_{1,\mathrm{max}} - \Delta\lambda_{2,\mathrm{max}}}{\lambda_0} = \frac{\mathrm{v}_{1,\mathrm{CM}} + \mathrm{v}_{2,\mathrm{CM}}}{c};$$

$$\mathrm{v}_{1,\mathrm{CM}} + \mathrm{v}_{2,\mathrm{CM}} = \frac{c}{\lambda_0}\left(\Delta\lambda_{1,\mathrm{max}} - \Delta\lambda_{2,\mathrm{max}}\right);$$

$$m\mathrm{v}_{1,\mathrm{CM}} = M\mathrm{v}_{2,\mathrm{CM}};$$

$$\mathrm{v}_{2,\mathrm{CM}} = \frac{m}{M}\mathrm{v}_{1,\mathrm{CM}};$$

$$\mathrm{v}_{1,\mathrm{CM}} + \frac{m}{M}\mathrm{v}_{1,\mathrm{CM}} = \frac{c}{\lambda_0}\left(\Delta\lambda_{1,\mathrm{max}} - \Delta\lambda_{2,\mathrm{max}}\right);$$

$$\mathrm{v}_{1,\mathrm{CM}} = \frac{cM}{\lambda_0\,(m+M)}\left(\Delta\lambda_{1,\mathrm{max}} - \Delta\lambda_{2,\mathrm{max}}\right);$$

$$\mathrm{v}_{2,\mathrm{CM}} = \frac{cm}{\lambda_0\,(m+M)}\left(\Delta\lambda_{1,\mathrm{max}} - \Delta\lambda_{2,\mathrm{max}}\right);$$

$$\frac{\Delta\lambda_{1,\mathrm{max}}}{\lambda_0} + \frac{\Delta\lambda_{2,\mathrm{max}}}{\lambda_0} = \frac{2\mathrm{v}_{\mathrm{rad,CM}}}{c} + \frac{\mathrm{v}_{1,\mathrm{CM}} - \mathrm{v}_{2,\mathrm{CM}}}{c};$$

$$\mathrm{v}_{1,\mathrm{CM}} - \mathrm{v}_{2,\mathrm{CM}} = \frac{cM}{\lambda_0\,(m+M)}\left(\Delta\lambda_{1,\mathrm{max}} - \Delta\lambda_{2,\mathrm{max}}\right) - \frac{cM}{\lambda_0\,(m+M)}\left(\Delta\lambda_{1,\mathrm{max}} - \Delta\lambda_{2,\mathrm{max}}\right);$$

$$\mathrm{v}_{1,\mathrm{CM}} - \mathrm{v}_{2,\mathrm{CM}} = \frac{c\,(M-m)}{\lambda_0\,(m+M)}\left(\Delta\lambda_{1,\max} - \Delta\lambda_{2,\max}\right);$$

$$\frac{\Delta\lambda_{1,\max}}{\lambda_0} = \frac{\mathrm{v}_{\mathrm{rad,CM}} + \mathrm{v}_{1,\mathrm{CM}}}{c}; \quad \frac{\Delta\lambda_{2,\max}}{\lambda_0} = \frac{\mathrm{v}_{\mathrm{rad,CM}} - \mathrm{v}_{2,\mathrm{CM}}}{c};$$

$$\frac{\Delta\lambda_{1,\max}}{\lambda_0} + \frac{\Delta\lambda_{2,\max}}{\lambda_0} = \frac{\mathrm{v}_{\mathrm{rad,CM}} + \mathrm{v}_{1,\mathrm{CM}}}{c} + \frac{\mathrm{v}_{\mathrm{rad,CM}} - \mathrm{v}_{2,\mathrm{CM}}}{c};$$

$$\frac{\Delta\lambda_{1,\max}}{\lambda_0} + \frac{\Delta\lambda_{2,\max}}{\lambda_0} = 2\frac{\mathrm{v}_{\mathrm{rad,CM}}}{c} + \frac{\mathrm{v}_{1,\mathrm{CM}} - \mathrm{v}_{2,\mathrm{CM}}}{c};$$

$$\frac{\Delta\lambda_{1,\max}}{\lambda_0} + \frac{\Delta\lambda_{2,\max}}{\lambda_0} - \frac{\mathrm{v}_{1,\mathrm{CM}} - \mathrm{v}_{2,\mathrm{CM}}}{c} = 2\frac{\mathrm{v}_{\mathrm{rad,CM}}}{c};$$

$$\frac{\Delta\lambda_{1,\max} + \Delta\lambda_{2,\max}}{\lambda_0} - \frac{c\,(M-m)}{\lambda_0\,(m+M)}\left(\Delta\lambda_{1,\max} - \Delta\lambda_{2,\max}\right) = 2\mathrm{v}_{\mathrm{rad,CM}};$$

$$\frac{c}{2\lambda_0}\left[\Delta\lambda_{1,\max} + \Delta\lambda_{2,\max} - \frac{M-m}{M+m}\left(\Delta\lambda_{1,\max} - \Delta\lambda_{2,\max}\right)\right] = \mathrm{v}_{\mathrm{rad,CM}};$$

$$\mathrm{v}_{\mathrm{rad,CM}} = \frac{c}{2\lambda_0}\left[\Delta\lambda_{1,\max} - \frac{M-m}{M+m}\Delta\lambda_{1,\max} + \Delta\lambda_{2,\max} + \frac{M-m}{M+m}\Delta\lambda_{2,\max}\right];$$

$$\mathrm{v}_{\mathrm{rad,CM}} = \frac{c}{\lambda_0}\left(\Delta\lambda_{1,\max} + \Delta\lambda_{2,\max}\right).$$

**5)** Let's suppose that the orbits of the two components of the binary visual stellar system relative to the CM are the ellipses presented in Figure T2.10. If the mass center moves with the constant velocity $\vec{\mathrm{v}}_{\mathrm{CM}}$ relative to the observer O on Earth, it means that the presented elliptic orbits are considered relative to an observer O′ that moves with a velocity $\vec{\mathrm{v}}_{\mathrm{CM}}$ relative to the observer O.

According to the notation from Figures T2.10, T2.11, T2.12 and T2.13, the results are:

$$\vec{\mathrm{v}}_{1,(\mathrm{O})} = \vec{\mathrm{v}}_{\mathrm{CM},(\mathrm{O})} + \vec{\mathrm{v}}_{1,\mathrm{CM}(\mathrm{O}')}; \quad \vec{\mathrm{v}}_{2,(\mathrm{O})} = \vec{\mathrm{v}}_{\mathrm{CM},(\mathrm{O})} + \vec{\mathrm{v}}_{2,\mathrm{CM}(\mathrm{O}')},$$

$$\vec{\mathrm{v}}_{1,\mathrm{A},(\mathrm{O})} = \vec{\mathrm{v}}_{\mathrm{CM},(\mathrm{O})} + \vec{\mathrm{v}}_{1,\mathrm{A},\mathrm{CM}(\mathrm{O}')}; \quad \vec{\mathrm{v}}_{2,\mathrm{B},(\mathrm{O})} = \vec{\mathrm{v}}_{\mathrm{CM},(\mathrm{O})} + \vec{\mathrm{v}}_{2,\mathrm{B},\mathrm{CM}(\mathrm{O}')};$$

$$\vec{\mathrm{v}}_{\mathrm{rad},1,(\mathrm{O})} = \vec{\mathrm{v}}_{\mathrm{CM}\,(\mathrm{O})} + \vec{\mathrm{v}}_{\mathrm{rad},1,\mathrm{CM}(\mathrm{O}')};$$

$$\mathrm{v}_{\mathrm{rad},1,(\mathrm{O})} = \mathrm{v}_{\mathrm{CM},(\mathrm{O})} + \mathrm{v}_{\mathrm{rad},1,\mathrm{CM}(\mathrm{O}')};$$

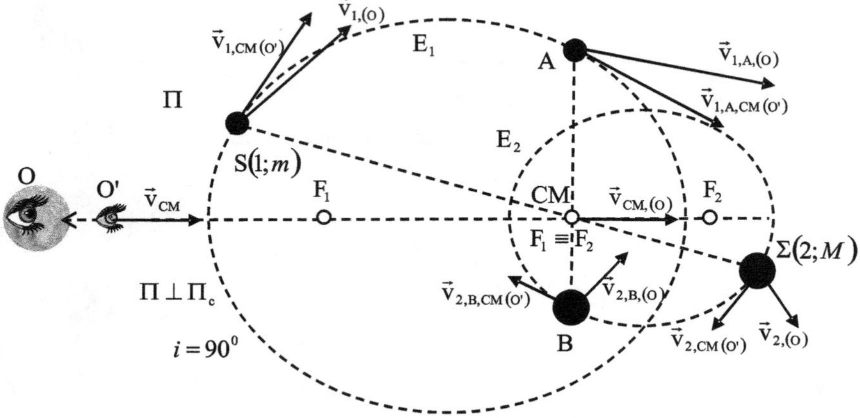


**Fig. T2.10**

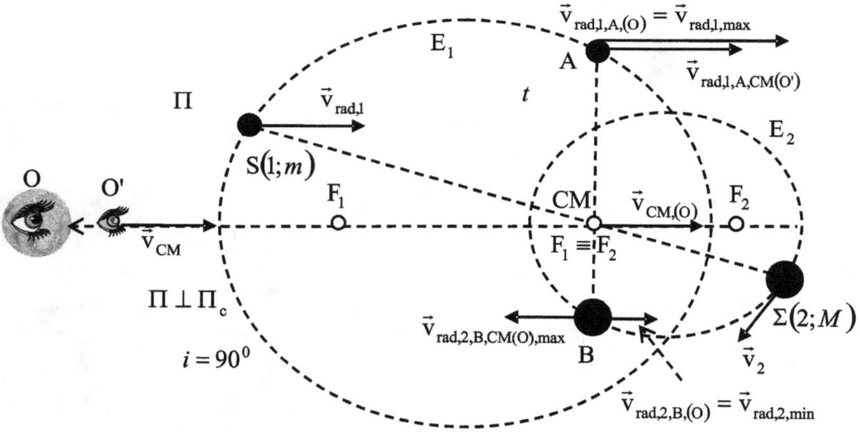


**Fig. T2.11**

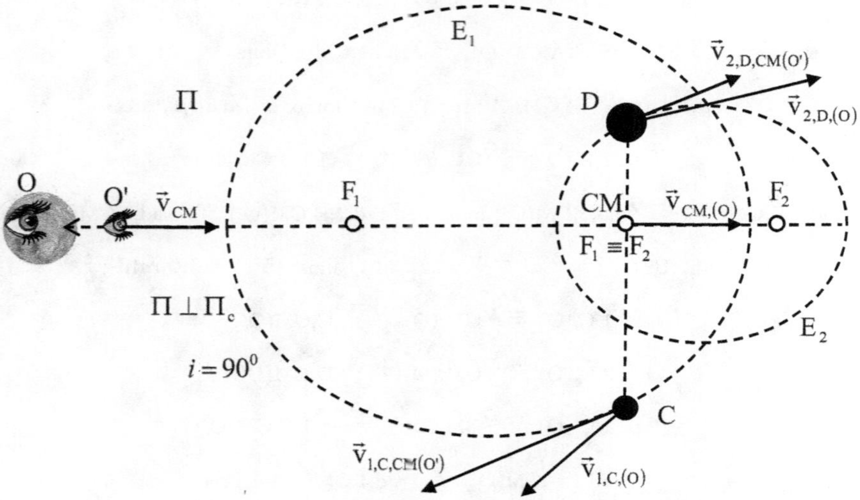


**Fig. T2.12**

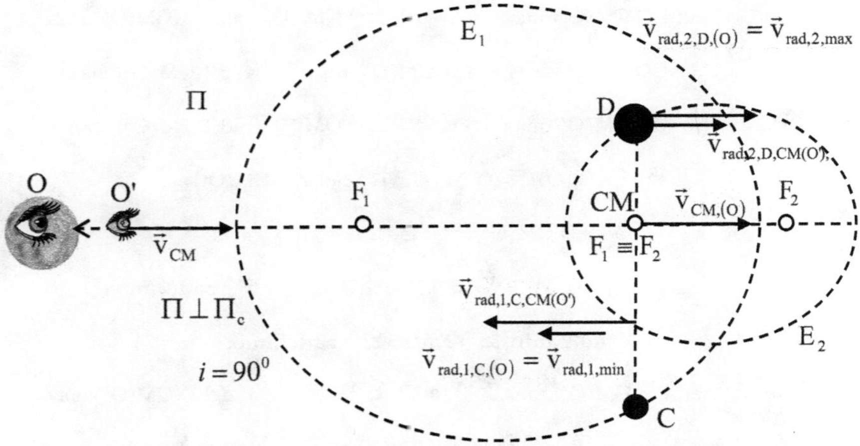


**Fig. T2.13**

$$\vec{v}_{rad,1,A,(O)} = \vec{v}_{CM,(O)} + \vec{v}_{rad,1,A,CM(O')};$$

$$\vec{v}_{rad,1,A,CM(O')} = \vec{v}_{rad,1,CM(O'),max};$$

$$v_{rad,1,A,(O)} = v_{CM} + v_{rad,1,CM(O'),max} = \mathbf{v_{rad,1,max}};$$

$$\vec{v}_{rad,2,B,(O)} = \vec{v}_{CM,(O)} + \vec{v}_{rad,2,B,CM(O')};$$

$$\vec{v}_{rad,2,B,CM(O')} = \vec{v}_{rad,2,CM(O'),max}; \quad v_{rad,2,B,CM(O')} = v_{rad,2,CM(O'),max};$$

$$v_{rad,2,B,(O)} = v_{CM} - v_{rad,2,CM(O'),max} = \mathbf{v_{rad,2,min}};$$

$$\vec{v}_{1,C,(O)} = \vec{v}_{CM,(O)} + \vec{v}_{1,C,CM(O')};$$

$$\vec{v}_{2,D,(O)} = \vec{v}_{CM,(O)} + \vec{v}_{2,D,CM(O')};$$

$$\vec{v}_{rad,1,C,(O)} = \vec{v}_{CM,(O)} + \vec{v}_{rad,1,C,CM(O')};$$

$$\vec{v}_{rad,1,C,CM(O')} = \vec{v}_{rad,1,CM(O'),max};$$

$$v_{rad,1,C,(O)} = v_{CM} - v_{rad,1,CM(O'),max} = \mathbf{v_{rad,1,min}};$$

$$\mathbf{v_{rad,1,min}} \le \mathbf{v_{rad,1}} \le \mathbf{v_{rad,1,max}};$$

$$v_{CM} - v_{rad,1,C,CM(O'),max} \le v_{rad,1} \le v_{CM} + v_{rad,1,A,CM(O'),max};$$

$$v_{rad,1,C,CM(O'),max} = v_{rad,1,A,CM(O'),max} = v_{rad,1,CM(O'),max};$$

$$v_{CM} - v_{rad,1,CM(O'),max} \le v_{rad,1} \le v_{CM} + v_{rad,1,CM(O'),max};$$

$$\vec{v}_{rad,2,D,(O)} = \vec{v}_{CM,(O)} + \vec{v}_{rad,2,D,CM(O')};$$

$$\vec{v}_{rad,2,D,CM(O')} = \vec{v}_{rad,2,D,CM(O'),max};$$

$$v_{rad,2,D,(O)} = v_{CM} + v_{rad,2,D,CM(O'),max} = \mathbf{v_{rad,2,max}};$$

$$\mathbf{v_{rad,2,min}} \le \mathbf{v_{rad,2}} \le \mathbf{v_{rad,2,max}};$$

$$v_{CM} - v_{rad,2,B,CM(O'),max} \le v_{rad,2} \le v_{CM} + v_{rad,2,D,CM(O'),max};$$

$$v_{rad,2,B,CM(O'),max} = v_{rad,2,D,CM(O'),max} = v_{rad,2,CM(O'),max};$$

$$v_{CM} - v_{rad,2,CM(O'),max} \le v_{rad,2} \le v_{CM} + v_{rad,2,CM(O'),max}.$$

In Figure T2.14, the graphs of $v_{rad}(t)$ (function of time) for the two components of the binary visual stellar system are presented.

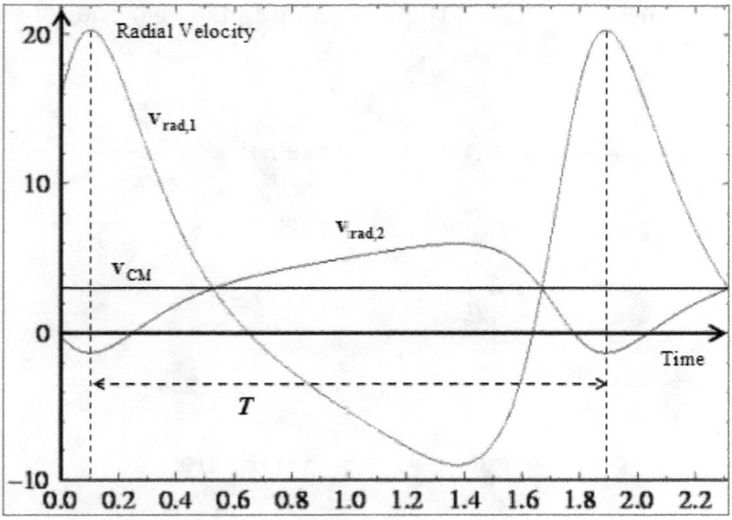


**Fig. T2.14**

**6)** Let's consider now that the Π plane of the circular orbits of the binary visual stellar system's components makes an angle relative to the mass center of $0 < i < 90°$ with the celestial plane $\Pi_c$, as presented in Figure T2.15. To simplify, we will consider that the system's CM is stationary relative to the observer on Earth.

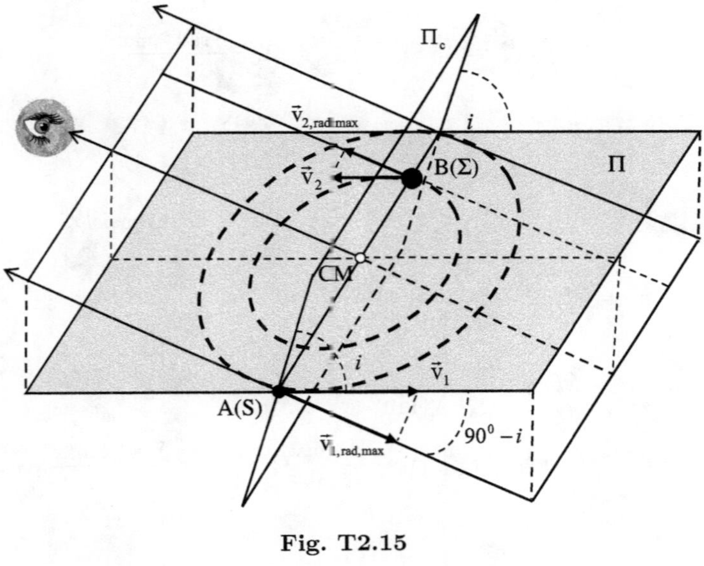


**Fig. T2.15**

Under these conditions, the maximum radial velocities of the two components are:

$$\mathrm{v}_{\mathrm{rad,1,max}} = \mathrm{v}_1 \cos\left(90^0 - i\right) = \mathrm{v}_1 \sin i; \quad \mathrm{v}_1 = \frac{\mathrm{v}_{\mathrm{rad,1,max}}}{\sin i};$$

$$\mathrm{v}_{\mathrm{rad,2,max}} = \mathrm{v}_2 \cos\left(90^0 - i\right) = \mathrm{v}_2 \sin i; \quad \mathrm{v}_2 = \frac{\mathrm{v}_{\mathrm{rad,2,max}}}{\sin i};$$

$$(m+M)\,T^2 = \frac{4\pi^2 a^3}{K};$$

$$\mathrm{v}_1 = \frac{2\pi a_1}{T}; \quad a_1 = \frac{\mathrm{v}_1 T}{2\pi}; \quad \mathrm{v}_2 = \frac{2\pi a_2}{T}; \quad a_2 = \frac{\mathrm{v}_2 T}{2\pi};$$

$$a = a_1 + a_2 = \frac{T}{2\pi}\left(\mathrm{v}_1 + \mathrm{v}_2\right);$$

$$(m+M)\,T^2 = \frac{(2\pi)^2}{K}\frac{T^3}{(2\pi)^3}\left(\mathrm{v}_1 + \mathrm{v}_2\right)^3;$$

$$m + M = \frac{T}{2\pi K \sin^3 i}\left(\mathrm{v}_{\mathrm{rad,1,max}} + \mathrm{v}_{\mathrm{rad,2,max}}\right)^3;$$

$$\Delta\lambda_{1,\mathrm{max}} = \lambda_{1,\mathrm{max}} - \lambda_0 = \lambda_0 \cdot \frac{\mathrm{v}_{\mathrm{rad,1,max}}}{c};$$

$$\mathrm{v}_{\mathrm{rad,1,max}} = \frac{c\Delta\lambda_{1,\mathrm{max}}}{\lambda_0};$$

$$\Delta\lambda_{2,\mathrm{max}} = \lambda_0 - \lambda_{2,\mathrm{max}} = \lambda_0 \cdot \frac{\mathrm{v}_{\mathrm{rad,2,max}}}{c};$$

$$\mathrm{v}_{\mathrm{rad,2,max}} = \frac{c\Delta\lambda_{2,\mathrm{max}}}{\lambda_0};$$

$$m + M = \frac{T}{2\pi K \sin^3 i}\left(\mathrm{v}_{\mathrm{rad,1,max}} + \mathrm{v}_{\mathrm{rad,2,max}}\right)^3;$$

$$m + M = \frac{T}{2\pi K \sin^3 i}\left(\frac{c\Delta\lambda_{1,\mathrm{max}}}{\lambda_0} + \frac{c\Delta\lambda_{2,\mathrm{max}}}{\lambda_0}\right)^3;$$

$$m + M = \frac{c^3 T}{2\pi K \lambda_0^3 \sin^3 i}\left(\Delta\lambda_{1,\mathrm{max}} + \Delta\lambda_{2,\mathrm{max}}\right)^3;$$

$$m\mathrm{v}_1 = M\mathrm{v}_2; \quad \mathrm{v}_1 = \frac{\mathrm{v}_{\mathrm{rad,1,max}}}{\sin i}; \quad \mathrm{v}_2 = \frac{\mathrm{v}_{\mathrm{rad,2,max}}}{\sin i};$$

$$\frac{m}{M} = \frac{v_2}{v_1} = \frac{v_{rad,2,max}}{v_{rad,2,max}} = \frac{\Delta\lambda_{2,max}}{\Delta\lambda_{1,max}};$$

$$\frac{m}{M} = \frac{\Delta\lambda_{2,max}}{\Delta\lambda_{1,max}}.$$

Or:

$$\frac{v_{rad,2,max}}{v_{rad,1,max}} = \frac{\Delta\lambda_{2,max}}{\Delta\lambda_{1,max}};$$

$$m + M = \frac{T}{2\pi K \sin^3 i} v^3_{rad,1,max} \left(1 + \frac{v_{rad,2,max}}{v_{rad,1,max}}\right)^3;$$

$$m + M = \frac{T}{2\pi K \sin^3 i} v^3_{rad,1,max} \left(1 + \frac{\Delta\lambda_{2,max}}{\Delta\lambda_{1,max}}\right)^3;$$

$$v_1 = \frac{v_{rad,1,max}}{\sin i};$$

$$m + M = \frac{T}{2\pi K} v_1^3 \left(1 + \frac{\Delta\lambda_{2,max}}{\Delta\lambda_{1,max}}\right)^3;$$

$$v_1 = \sqrt[3]{\frac{2\pi K (m - M)}{T}} \cdot \frac{1}{1 + \frac{\Delta\lambda_{2,max}}{\Delta\lambda_{1,max}}};$$

$$m v_1 = M v_2;$$

$$v_2 = \frac{m}{M} v_1 = \frac{m}{M} \cdot \sqrt[3]{\frac{2\pi K (m + M)}{T}} \cdot \frac{1}{1 + \frac{\Delta\lambda_{2,max}}{\Delta\lambda_{1,max}}}.$$

## The Mass–Luminosity Relation

In 1924, Arthur Eddington established that the relation between the luminosity $L$ of a star and its mass $M$ is:

$$\frac{L}{L_S} \approx 0.23 \left(\frac{M}{M_S}\right)^{2.3}; \quad M < 0.43 M_S,$$

where $L_S$ is the Sun's luminosity and $M_S$ is the Sun's mass;

$$\frac{L}{L_S} = \left(\frac{M}{M_S}\right); \quad 0.43 M_S < M < 2 M_S;$$

$$\frac{L}{L_S} \approx 1.5\left(\frac{M}{M_S}\right)^{3.5}; \quad 2M_S < M < 20M_S;$$

$$\frac{L}{L_S} \sim \frac{M}{M_S}; \quad M > 20M_S.$$

## Doppler Effect

**1)** A star $\Sigma$ moves further from the Earth in the observer's direction as presented in Figure T2.16. Its velocity relative to the observer is $v_{radial}$.

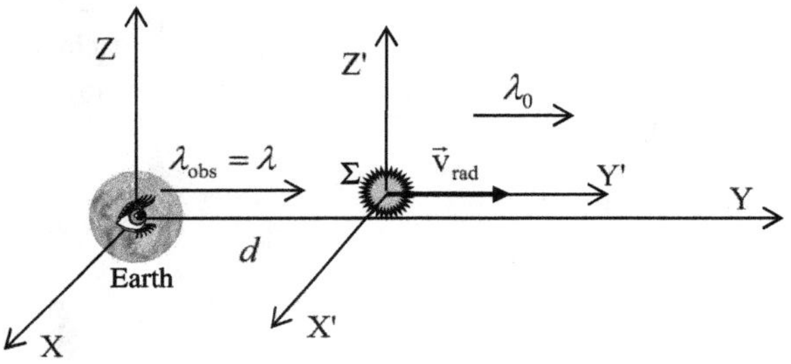


**Fig. T2.16**

The $\lambda_0$ wavelength of the radiation emitted by the star has a different wavelength $\lambda_{obs} \neq \lambda_0$ when reaching the observer. The value of the new wavelength depends on the radial velocity of the star (the star's velocity component along the observer's viewing direction). If the star moves further from the observer, the radiation's wavelength recorded by the observer will be:

$$\lambda_{obs} = \lambda = \lambda_0\sqrt{\frac{1+\frac{v_{rad}}{c}}{1-\frac{v_{rad}}{c}}} > \lambda_0;$$

$$\lambda = \lambda_0\frac{\left(1+\frac{v_{rad}}{c}\right)^{1/2}}{\left(1-\frac{v_{rad}}{c}\right)^{1/2}} = \lambda_0\left(1+\frac{v_{rad}}{c}\right)^{1/2}\left(1-\frac{v_{rad}}{c}\right)^{-1/2};$$

$$v_{rad} << c;$$

$$\lambda = \lambda_0 \left(1 + \frac{1}{2}\frac{v_{rad}}{c}\right)\left(1 + \frac{1}{2}\frac{v_{rad}}{c}\right) = \lambda_0 \left(1 + \frac{v_{rad}}{c} + \frac{1}{4}\frac{v_{rad}^2}{c^2}\right);$$

$$\lambda \approx \lambda_0 \left(1 + \frac{v_{rad}}{c}\right).$$

Thus:

$$\frac{\lambda - \lambda_0}{\lambda_0} = \frac{\Delta\lambda}{\lambda_0} = \frac{v_{rad}}{c};$$

$$v_{rad} = c\frac{\Delta\lambda}{\lambda_0},$$

representing the radial velocity of the star relative to the observer on Earth.

**2)** The density of the energetic flux at the observer's level on Earth (the star's brightness for the observer) represents the energy of all radiation from the star/from the Sun that reaches the observer crossing a unit surface area per unit time, that is:

$$\phi_{Star,obs} = \frac{L_{Star}}{4\pi d_{Star,obs}^2}; \quad \phi_{Sun,obs} = \frac{L_{Sun}}{4\pi d_{Sun,obs}^2};$$

$$\frac{\phi_{Star,obs}}{\phi_{Sun,obs}} = \frac{L_{Star}}{L_{Sun}}\left(\frac{d_{Sun,obs}}{d_{Star,obs}}\right)^2;$$

$$d_{Star,obs}^2 = d_{Sun,obs}^2 \frac{L_{Star}}{L_{Sun}}\frac{\phi_{Sun,obs}}{\phi_{Star,obs}}; \quad d_{Sun,obs} = 1\text{AU};$$

$$d_{Star,obs} = d_{Sun,obs}\sqrt{\frac{L_{Star}}{L_{Sun}}\frac{\phi_{Sun,obs}}{\phi_{Star,obs}}},$$

representing the relation for calculating the distance from the observer on the Earth to the star. The quantities under the square root are measurable (experimentally determined).

# Topic 3

# Double Stars

Figure T3.1 presents images of the apparent positions for a few visual binary stellar systems.

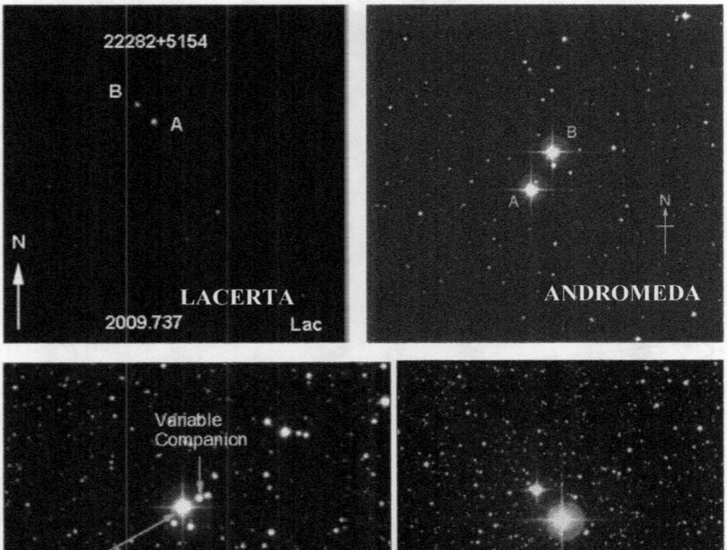


**Fig. T3.1**

In Figures T3.2 and T3.3, the possibilities for localizing, on the celestial plane, the apparent positions of the star S relative to $\Sigma$ (both pertaining to a visual binary stellar system) are represented using the following angular coordinates: $\theta$ – angular position (AP); $\rho$ – angular separation (AS).

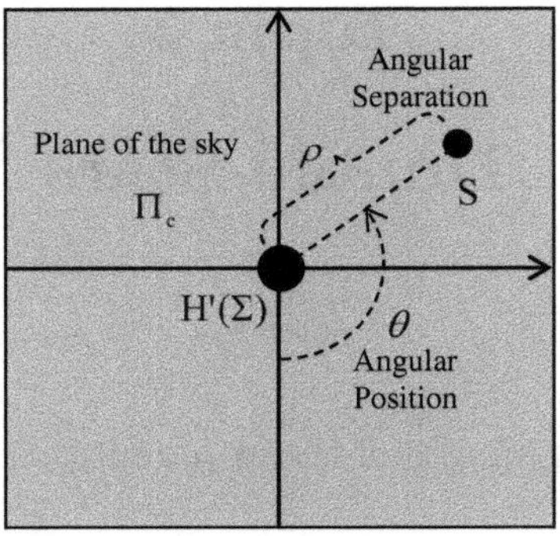


**Fig. T3.2**

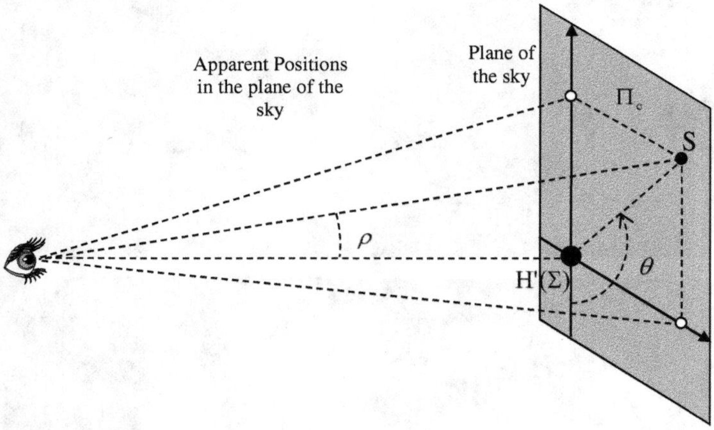


**Fig. T3.3**

Thus, based on the data presented in the following table, in Figure T3.4 the ellipse representing the apparent orbit of the companion star of the double star 85 Pegasi in the Pegasus constellation has been drawn.

| Year | 2005 | 2006 | 2007 | 2008 | 2009 | 2010 | 2011 | 2012 |
|---|---|---|---|---|---|---|---|---|
| Angular position $\vartheta$ (degrees) | 232 | 241 | 249 | 257 | 265 | 273 | 282 | 292 |
| Angular separation $\rho$ (arcsec) | 0.80 | 0.82 | 0.84 | 0.85 | 0.85 | 0.84 | 0.80 | 0.73 |

| Year | 2013 | 2014 | 2015 | 2016 | 2017 | 2018 | 2019 | 2020 |
|---|---|---|---|---|---|---|---|---|
| Angular position $\vartheta$ (degrees) | 304 | 323 | 356 | 44 | 79 | 99 | 112 | 123 |
| Angular separation $\rho$ (arcsec) | 0.62 | 0.49 | 0.36 | 0.36 | 0.48 | 0.80 | 0.70 | 0.75 |

| Year | 2021 | 2022 | 2023 | 2024 | 2025 | 2026 | 2027 | 2028 |
|---|---|---|---|---|---|---|---|---|
| Angular position $\vartheta$ (degrees) | 133 | 142 | 151 | 161 | 170 | 180 | 191 | 201 |
| Angular separation $\rho$ (arcsec) | 0.78 | 0.79 | 0.78 | 0.77 | 0.76 | 0.75 | 0.75 | 0.75 |

| Year | 2029 | 2030 |
|---|---|---|
| Angular position $\theta$ (degrees) | 211 | 221 |
| Angular separation $\rho$ (arcsec) | 0.76 | 0.78 |

Let us suppose a binary stellar system whose star S moves on an ellipse around the star $\Sigma$ that is located in one of its foci. Let us also consider that the plane $\Pi$ of the elliptic orbit (the orbit of S relative

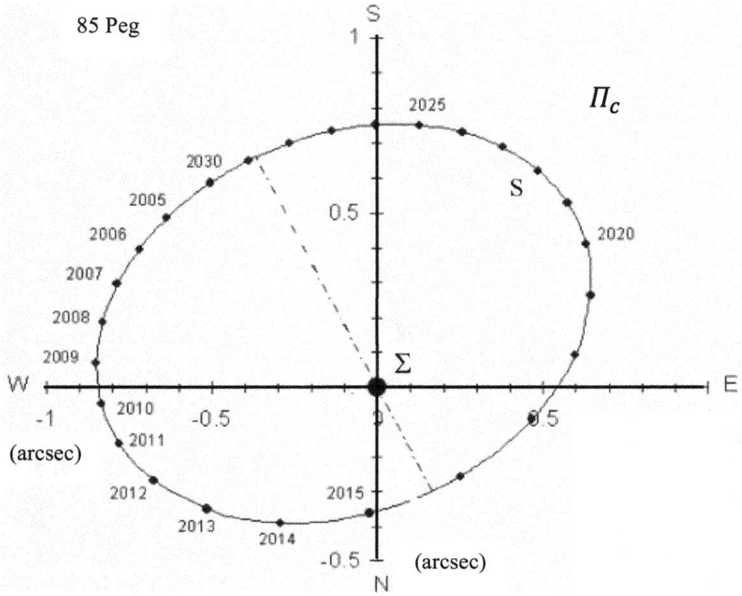


**Fig. T3.4**

to Σ) coincides with the plane of the local meridian, as presented in Figure T3.5. For the geocentric observer O, whose sightline is perpendicular to the celestial plane (the plane tangent to the celestial sphere at the observer's zenith), the shape of the apparent trajectory of S relative to Σ is the MN line segment. For the observer O, the apparent movement of S′ is an oscillatory movement in the north–south direction, to one side then the other of the star Σ.

Let's admit that the elliptical orbit (the orbit of S relative to Σ) is in the Π plane, parallel to the celestial plane ($\Pi_c$), as presented in Figure T3.6. For the observer in the center of the geocentric celestial sphere, the sky plane is a tangent to the geocentric celestial sphere at the point corresponding to the observer's zenith. For the observer on Earth whose sight line is perpendicular to the celestial plane, the apparent trajectory of S relative to Σ is an ellipse identical to the ellipse corresponding to the movement of S relative to Σ. The star Σ is located in the focus of each ellipse.

If the planes of the two orbits (Π and $\Pi_c$) are no longer parallel (see Figure T3.7), the relative elliptic orbit of star S around star Σ is not in the celestial plane. Thus, the observer's sight line is not

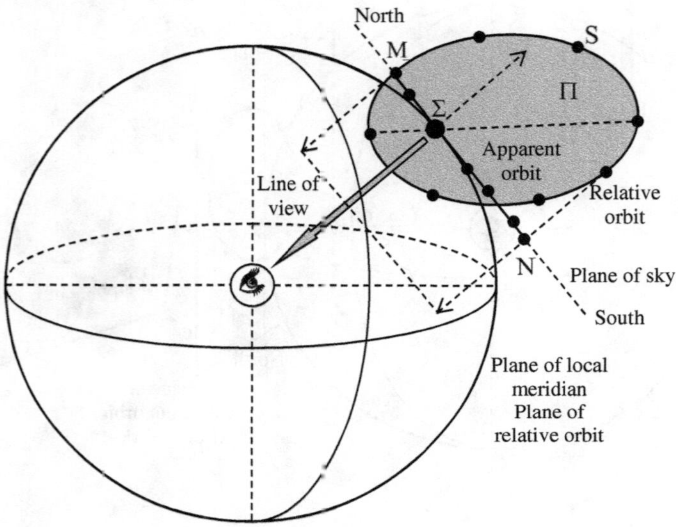


**Fig. T3.5**

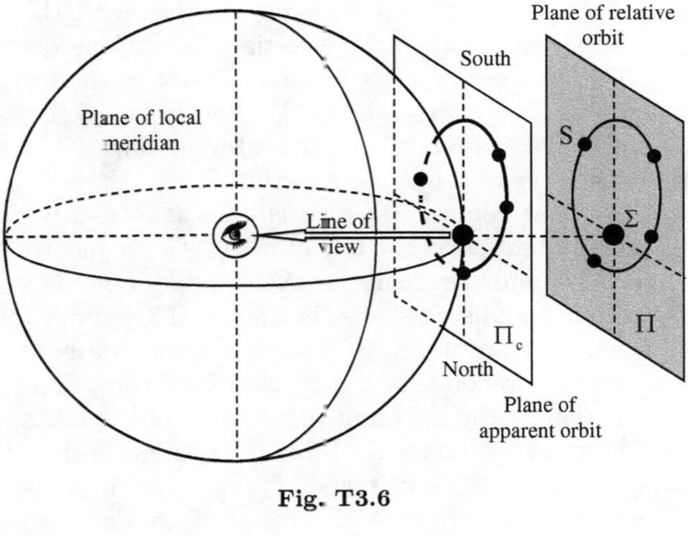


**Fig. T3.6**

perpendicular to the real elliptic orbit plane. The observer whose sight line is perpendicular to the celestial plane will register the shape of the apparent orbit of S′ around Σ as the projection of the real orbit in the celestial plane (the apparent plane).

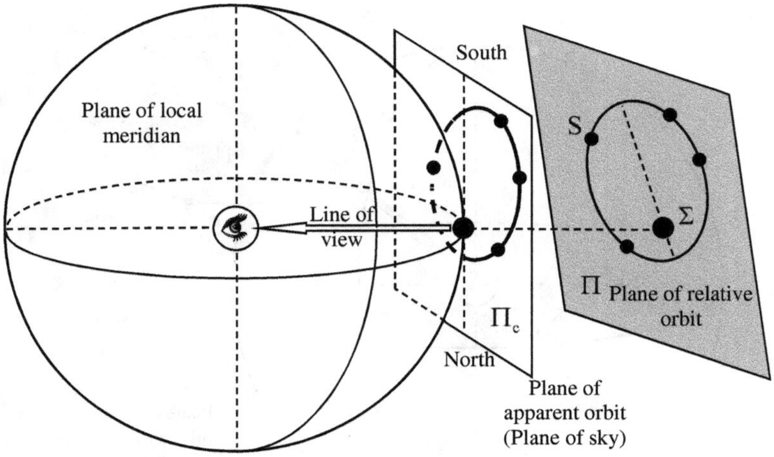


**Fig. T3.7**

The projection of the relative (real) elliptic orbit in the celestial plane is also an ellipse (the apparent orbit), but the projection of the relative (real) elliptic orbit does not overlap with the focus of the ellipse (apparent orbit) in the celestial plane. Consequently, the projection of star $\Sigma$ on the celestial plane is not in the focus of the apparent orbit of $S'$. As presented in the illustration of the problem, the apparent orbit of S relative to $\Sigma$ is also an ellipse, but the star $\Sigma$ is not in the focus of the apparent orbit.

The planes that contain the two ellipses (the relative and the apparent orbit) intersect on the line of nodes. Consequently, the two ellipses have a common segment: the $N_aN_d$ nodes line, on which the $\Pi$ star is also located, as presented in Figures T3.8 and T3.9.

It is known that any three collinear points in the relative orbit (ellipse) plane remain collinear in the apparent orbit (ellipse) plane.

The projection in the apparent orbit plane of the ellipse's (relative orbit) major axis (the $A-\Sigma-P$ line of apsides) is the $A'-\Sigma-P'$ segment in the apparent orbit plane. The projection of the relative orbit (ellipse) major axis (the $A-\Sigma-P$ line of apsides) on the $N_aN_d$ nodes line is the $A''$–$\Sigma$–$P''$ segment.

Thus, in the apparent orbit (ellipse) plane, two directions intersect: the nodes line ($N_a\Sigma N_d$) and the $A'\Sigma P'$ projection of the line of

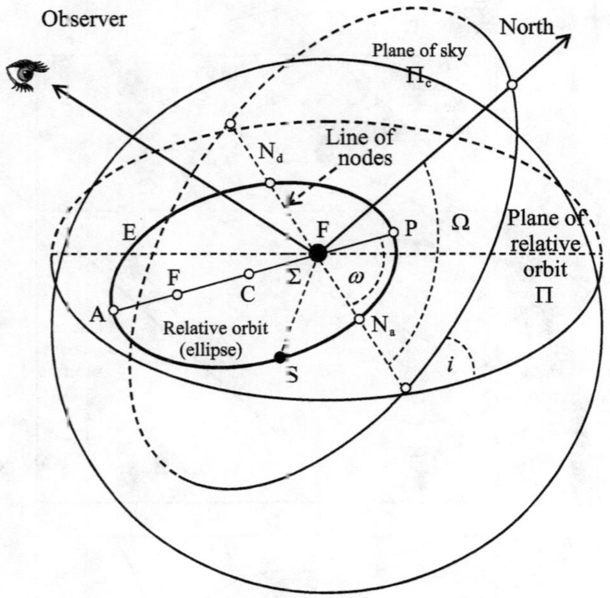


**Fig. T3.8**

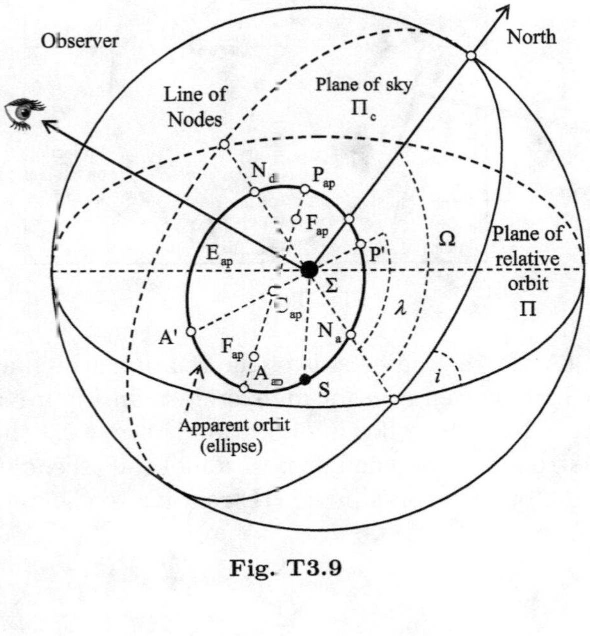


**Fig. T3.9**

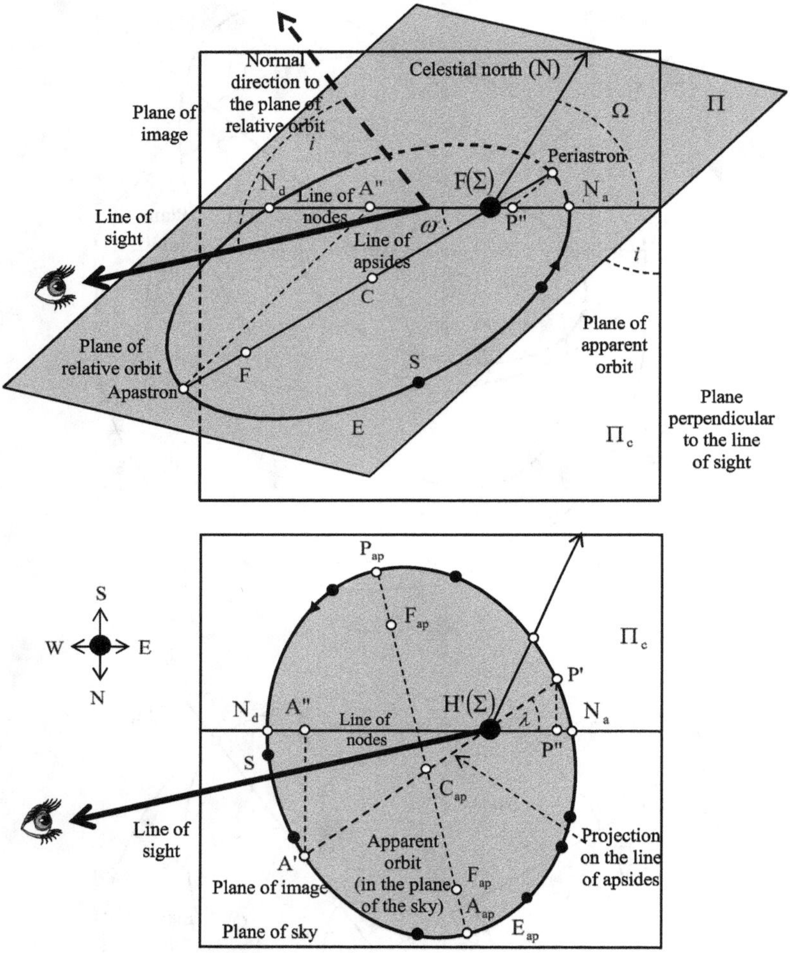


**Fig. T3.10**

the apsides (AΠP, the major axis of the relative orbit), as presented in Figure T3.10, as well as – for an exercise – in Figure T3.11.

In Figure T3.12, the following notation is used: $\omega$ – the argument of the periastron; $\Omega$ – the angular position of the ascendant node; $i$ – the inclination of the orbit's plane ($\Pi$) relative to the apparent orbit plane ($\Pi_c$).

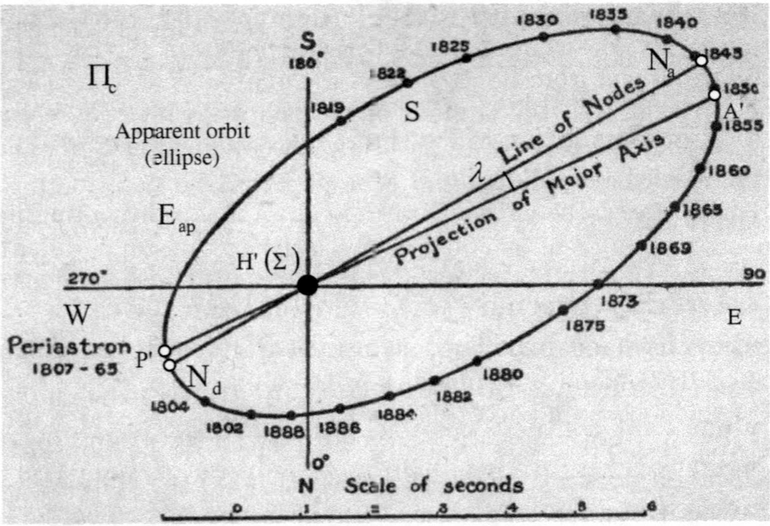


**Fig. T3.11**

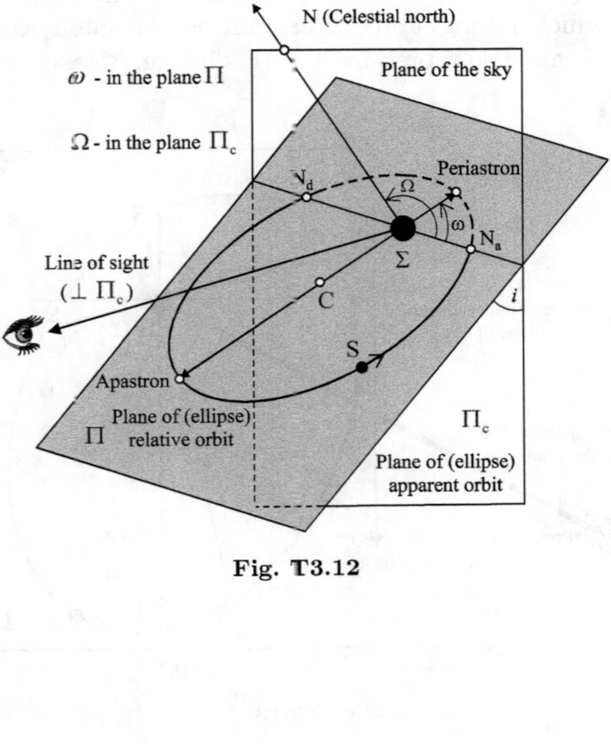


**Fig. T3.12**

Generally, when the movement of a star S around another star $\Sigma$ is studied, the $\Pi_c$ plane of the star S's apparent orbit (the celestial plane) is different from the $\Pi$ plane of the relative orbit (the real orbit plane). We say that the $\Pi$ plane of the relative orbit (the real orbit plane) is inclined relative to the $\Pi_c$ plane of the star S's apparent orbit (the celestial plane), i.e., $i \neq 0$.

Consequently, the elements of the ellipse $E_{ap}$ representing in the $\Pi_c$ plane the apparent orbit of star S relative to the star $\Sigma$ differ from the elements of the ellipse E representing in plane $\Pi$ the relative (real) orbit of star S around star $\Sigma$.

It is considered (can be demonstrated) that the projection of ellipse E from plane $\Pi$ to plane $\Pi_c$ is the ellipse $E_{ap}$.

For this reason and according to Kepler's laws, the star $\Sigma$ around which the star S orbits is located in the focus F of the ellipse E, but that location does not represent a focus ($F_{ap}$) of the ellipse $E_{ap}$.

The point $F_{ap}$ represents the apparent focus of the apparent orbit (ellipse) $E_{ap}$ in the celestial plane $\Pi_c$.

In Figure T3.13, the apparent orbit (ellipse) of the secondary star S relative to the principal star $\Sigma$ is presented. The directions within its plane which intersect at $\Sigma$, as well as the main axes and the ellipse's foci, are also represented in this image. Measuring distances

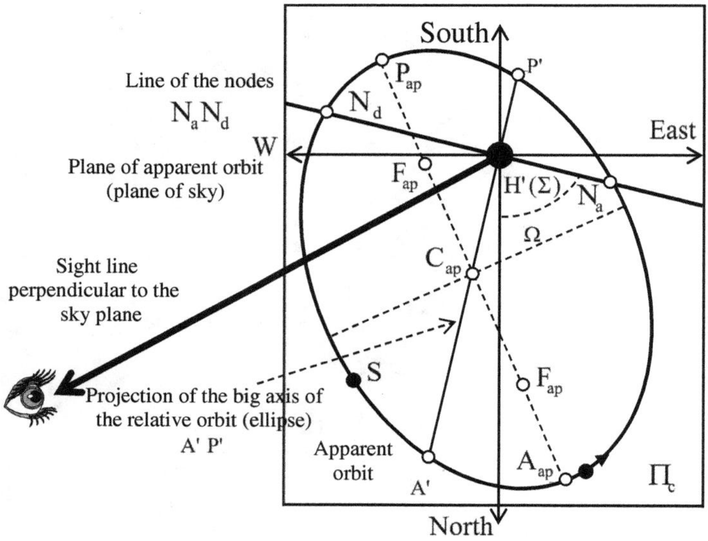


**Fig. T3.13**

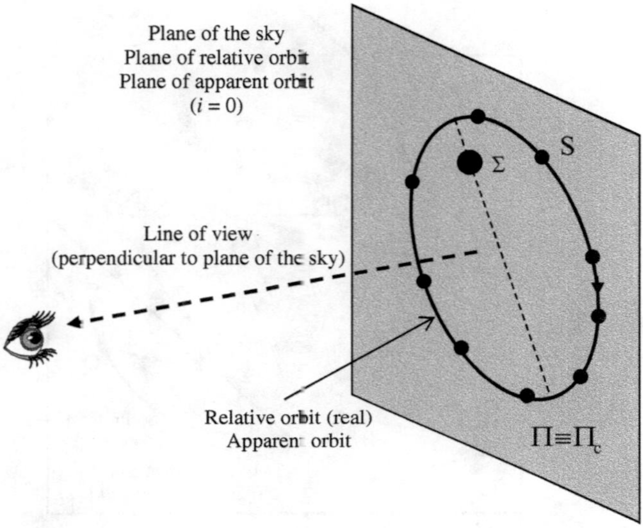


**Fig. T3.14**

on this diagram, the elements of the ellipse that represents the star S's orbit (ellipse) relative to the star Σ can be determined.

In particular, if $i = 0$, the two planes ($\Pi \equiv \Pi_c$) coincide, the two ellipses ($E \equiv E_{ap}$) coincide, the two foci ($F \equiv F_{ap}$) coincide, and thus the star Σ is localized in the common focus of the two ellipses as presented in Figure T3.14.

Since the apparent orbit (ellipse) in the $\Pi_c$ celestial plane is known, the elements of the relative orbit (ellipse) can be determined from its geometry and the ellipse E representing the relative orbit of the star S in the plane Π can be drawn.

Consequently, for the orbit in Π, the distance between a point Q of the relative orbit (the ellipse E) and the nodes line ($N_aN_d$) is QR $= x$ in the plane of the relative, then the distance between the $Q'$ point on the apparent orbit (the ellipse $E_{ap}$) and the nodes line is $Q'R = x \cos i$, as presented in Figure T3.15. The $Q'$ point in the $\Pi_c$ plane represents the projection of point Q on the Π plane. Projected on the $\Pi_c$ celestial plane, any segment from the Π plane that is perpendicular to the line of nodes is reduced by the same multiplier ($\cos i$).

In Figure T3.16, the following notation has been used: Σ – principal star; S – secondary star; **A** – apastron (the star S's apastron on the ellipse E relative to the star Σ that is located in the ellipse's

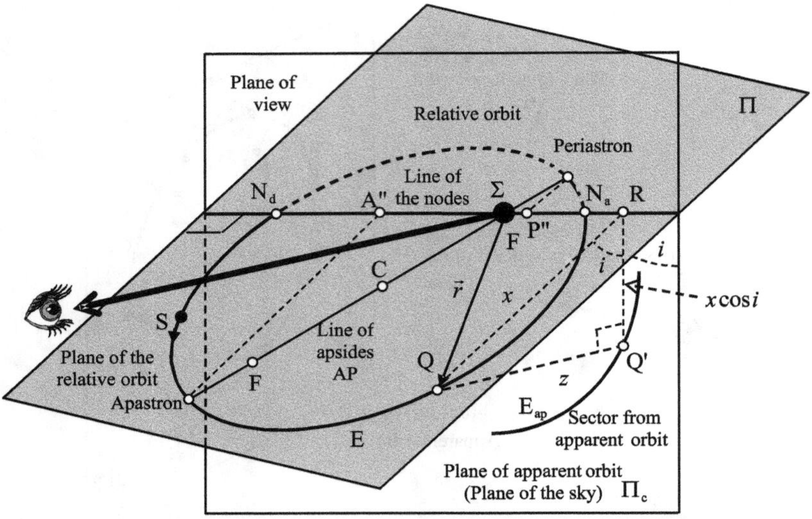


**Fig. T3.15**

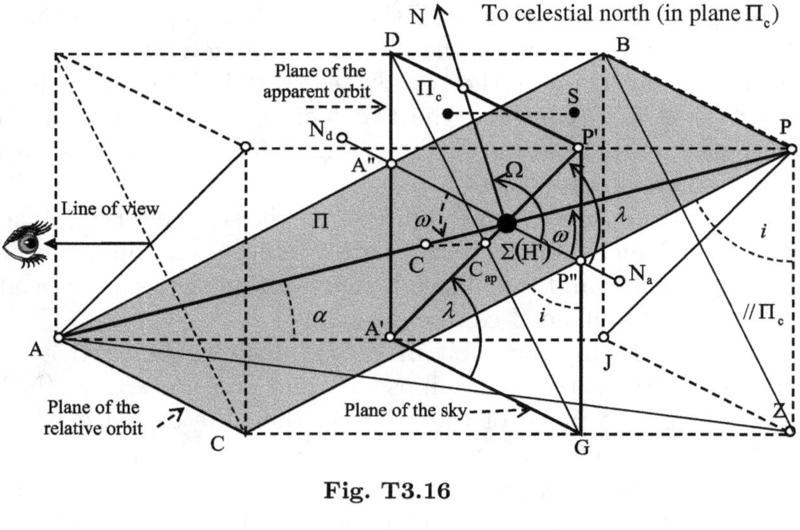


**Fig. T3.16**

focus); P – periastron (star S's periastron on the ellipse E relative to the star Σ); AP – the line of apsides (the major axis of the ellipse representing the relative orbit); A′P′ – the projection of the line of apsides on the celestial plane; $N_aN_d$ – the nodes line; $i$ – the angle between the relative orbit plane and the celestial plane; $\omega$ – the angle between the line of apsides and the nodes line; $\Pi(\mathrm{ABPC})$ – the relative orbit plane; $\Pi_c(\mathrm{DP'GA'})$ – the celestial plane (the apparent orbit plane); $2a$ – the distance between the apastron and the periastron (the major axis of the relative ellipse); $\mathrm{A''P''}$ – the projection on the nodes line of the major axis in the relative orbit (ellipse).

The orbit of star S relative to star $\Sigma$ is an ellipse (E) in the $\Pi(\mathrm{ABPC})$ plane. The apparent orbit of star S is the ellipse $E_{ap}$ in the $\Pi_c$ $(\mathrm{DP'GA'})$ celestial plane. The ellipse $E_{ap}$ is the projection of the ellipse E.

The results are:

$$\mathrm{AP} = 2a; \quad A''P'' = 2a \cdot \cos\omega;$$

$$\mathrm{AJ} = \mathrm{AP} \cdot \cos\alpha = 2a \cdot \cos\alpha = \mathrm{CZ};$$

$$\mathrm{CP} = \mathrm{AP} \cdot \sin\omega = 2a \cdot \sin\omega;$$

$$\mathrm{CZ} = \mathrm{CP} \cdot \sin i = 2a \cdot \sin\omega \cdot \sin i;$$

$$\mathrm{AJ} = \mathrm{CZ};$$

$$2a \cdot \cos\alpha = 2a \cdot \sin\omega \cdot \sin i;$$

$$\cos\alpha = \sin\omega \cdot \sin i;$$

$$d = \mathrm{JP} = \mathrm{AP} \cdot \sin\alpha = \mathrm{A'P'};$$

$$d = 2a \cdot \sin\alpha;$$

$$d = 2a \cdot \sqrt{1 - \cos^2\alpha};$$

$$d = 2a \cdot \sqrt{1 - \sin^2\omega \cdot \sin^2 i};$$

$$i = 0^0; \quad d = 2a;$$

$$i = 90^0; \quad d = 2a \cdot \sqrt{1 - \sin^2\omega} = 2a \cdot \cos\omega;$$

$$i = 90^0; \quad \omega = 0; \quad d = 2a;$$

$$i = 0; \quad \omega = 90^0; \quad d = 0;$$

$$a = \frac{d}{2 \cdot \sqrt{1 - \sin^2\omega \cdot \sin^2 i}},$$

representing the semi-major axis of the (secondary) star S's ellipse (orbit) relative to the principal star Σ;

$$\mathrm{A\Sigma} = r_{\max} = a(1+e); \quad \mathrm{AA'} = r_{\max}\ \cos\alpha;$$

$$\mathrm{P\Sigma} = r_{\min} = a\,(1-e)\,; \quad \mathrm{JA'} = r_{\min}\ \cos\alpha;$$

$$\mathrm{AA'} + \mathrm{JA'} = \mathrm{AJ} = (r_{\max} + r_{\min})\cos\alpha = 2a\cdot\cos\alpha;$$

$$\frac{\mathrm{A\Sigma}}{\mathrm{P\Sigma}} = \frac{r_{\max}}{r_{\min}} = \frac{\mathrm{A'\Sigma}}{\mathrm{P'\Sigma}} = k = \frac{1+e}{1-e};$$

$$\mathrm{A'P'} = \mathrm{A'\Sigma} + \mathrm{P'\Sigma};$$

$$\cos\alpha = \sin\,\omega\cdot\sin\,i;$$

$$d = 2a\cdot\sqrt{1-\sin^2\omega\cdot\sin^2 i};$$

$$\mathrm{A'\Sigma} = \mathrm{A\Sigma}\cdot\sin\alpha = \mathrm{A\Sigma}\cdot\sqrt{1-\cos^2\alpha};$$

$$\mathrm{P'\Sigma} = \mathrm{P\Sigma}\cdot\sin\alpha = \mathrm{P\Sigma}\cdot\sqrt{1-\cos^2\alpha};$$

$$\mathrm{A'P'} = (\mathrm{A\Sigma}+\mathrm{P\Sigma})\sin\alpha = \mathrm{AP}\cdot\sin\alpha = \mathrm{AP}\cdot\sqrt{1-\sin^2\omega\sin^2 i};$$

$$\mathrm{A'P'} = 2a\cdot\sqrt{1-\sin^2\omega\cdot\sin^2 i} = d;$$

$$\mathrm{A'\Sigma} = \mathrm{A\Sigma}\cdot\sqrt{1-\sin^2\omega\cdot\sin^2 i} = r_{\max}\cdot\sqrt{1-\sin^2\omega\cdot\sin^2 i};$$

$$\mathrm{P'\Sigma} = \mathrm{P\Sigma}\cdot\sqrt{1-\sin^2\omega\cdot\sin^2 i} = r_{\min}\cdot\sqrt{1-\sin^2\omega\cdot\sin^2 i};$$

$$\frac{\mathrm{A'\Sigma}}{\mathrm{P'\Sigma}} = \frac{\mathrm{A\Sigma}}{\mathrm{P\Sigma}} = \frac{r_{\max}\cdot\sqrt{1-\sin^2\omega\cdot\sin^2 i}}{r_{\min}\cdot\sqrt{1-\sin^2\omega\cdot\sin^2 i}} = \frac{r_{\max}}{r_{\min}}$$

$$= \frac{a\,(1+e)}{a\,(1-e)} = \frac{1+e}{1-e} = k;$$

$$k = \frac{1+e}{1-e};$$

$$e = \frac{k-1}{k+1}; \quad k = \frac{\mathrm{A'\Sigma}}{\mathrm{P'\Sigma}};$$

$$e = \sqrt{1-\frac{b^2}{a^2}}; \quad b = a\sqrt{1-e^2};$$

$$\lambda = \angle\left(\mathrm{N}_a\mathrm{N}_d;\ \mathrm{A}'\mathrm{P}'\right),\ \text{in plane } \Pi';$$

$$\tan\lambda = \frac{\mathrm{PZ}}{\mathrm{A}''\mathrm{P}''} = \frac{\mathrm{CP}\cdot\cos i}{\mathrm{AP}\cdot\cos\omega} = \frac{\mathrm{AP}\cdot\sin\omega\cdot\cos i}{\mathrm{AP}\cdot\cos\omega};$$

$$\tan\lambda = \tan\omega\cdot\cos i;$$

$$\tan\omega = \frac{\tan\lambda}{\cos i};$$

$$\mathrm{A}''P'' = \mathrm{AP}\cdot\cos\omega = \mathrm{A}'\mathrm{P}'\cdot\cos\lambda;$$

$$\mathrm{AP} = 2a; \quad A'P' = d;$$

$$a = \frac{d\cdot\cos\lambda}{2\cdot\cos\omega};$$

$$\tan\omega = \frac{\tan\lambda}{\cos i}; \quad \cos^2\omega = \frac{1}{1+\tan^2\omega}; \quad \cos\omega = \frac{1}{\sqrt{1+\tan^2\omega}};$$

$$\cos\omega = \frac{1}{\sqrt{1+\frac{\tan^2\lambda}{\cos^2 i}}} = \frac{\cos i}{\sqrt{\cos^2 i + \tan^2\lambda}};$$

$$\cos\lambda = \frac{1}{\sqrt{1+\tan^2\lambda}};$$

$$a = \frac{d}{2\cdot\cos i}\sqrt{\frac{\cos^2 i + \tan^2\lambda}{1+\tan^2\lambda}},$$

where $d$, $\lambda$ and $e$ are measured on the diagram of the apparent orbit (ellipse);

$$\frac{\mathrm{C_{ap}H}'}{\mathrm{C_{ap}P}'} = \frac{\mathrm{CH}'}{\mathrm{CP}} = \frac{\mathrm{CF}}{\mathrm{CP}} = \frac{ea}{a} = e;$$

$\cos i$ – demonstrated;

$$\cos i = \sqrt{1-e^2};$$

$a$ – calculated;

$T$ – known;

$$a = \frac{d}{2 \cdot \sqrt{1 - \sin^2 \omega \cdot \sin^2 i}};$$

$$\sin^2 \omega = \frac{\tan^2 \omega}{1 + \tan^2 \omega}; \quad \tan^2 \omega = \frac{\tan^2 \lambda}{\cos^2 i};$$

$$\sin^2 \omega = \frac{\frac{\tan^2 \lambda}{\cos^2 i}}{1 + \frac{\tan^2 \lambda}{\cos^2 i}} = \frac{\tan^2 \lambda}{\cos^2 i + \tan^2 \lambda};$$

$$a = \frac{d}{2 \cdot \sqrt{1 - \frac{\tan^2 \lambda}{\cos^2 i + \tan^2 \lambda} \cdot \sin^2 i}};$$

$$a = \frac{d}{2 \cdot \cos i} \cdot \sqrt{\frac{\cos^2 i + \tan^2 \lambda}{1 + \tan^2 \lambda}}.$$

Let's rotate the relative orbit (ellipse) plane around the line of nodes ($N_aN_d$) with an angle $i$ until the two planes overlap. Represented in the same plane (the celestial plane), the two ellipses, E and $E_{ap}$, that represent the relative and the apparent orbits overlap as presented in Figures T3.17, T3.18 and T3.19. Thus, at point $\Sigma$ the following directions intersect: the nodes' line ($N_aN_d$); the apsides' line AP; the projection of the line of apsides on the celestial plane (A′P′); the projection of the relative orbit's (ellipse's) major axis (the line of apsides) on the nodes' line (A″P″).

From these Figures, the following equation results:

$$A''P''A'P' \cdot \cos \lambda = AP \cdot \cos \omega.$$

For the relative orbit (ellipse) represented on the celestial plane ($\Pi_c$), the apparent orbit is obtained through points presented in Figures T3.17, T3.18, T3.19 and T3.20. Measuring the lengths of different $x \cos i$ segments perpendicular to the nodes' line and knowing the inclination value $i$, the segment lengths ($x$) can be determined. The locus of the exterior extremities of the $x$ segments represent the relative orbit (ellipse) in the celestial plane. For this orbit, the lengths of the semiaxes, $a$ and $b$, are determined. Then the eccentricity $e$ of the relative orbit (ellipse) can be obtained. Knowing the rotation period ($T$) of the secondary star around the principal star – obtained using the notation on the apparent orbit (ellipse) – and knowing the semi-major axis ($a$) of the relative orbit (ellipse), the mass $M$ of the principal star $\Sigma$ can be determined according to Kepler's laws.

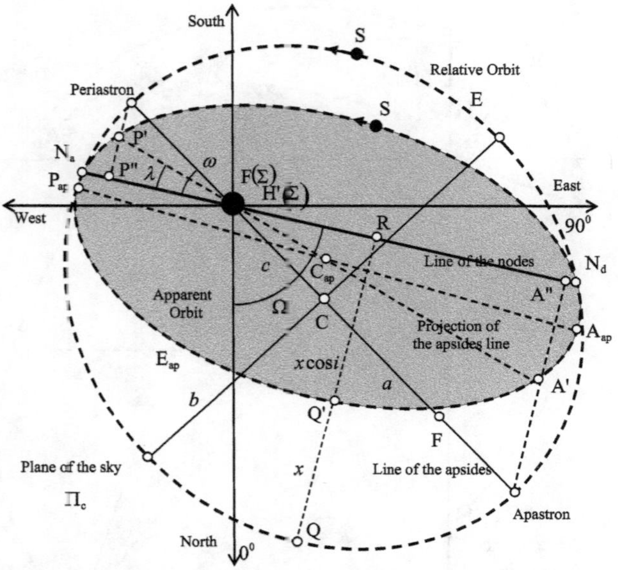


**Fig. T3.17**

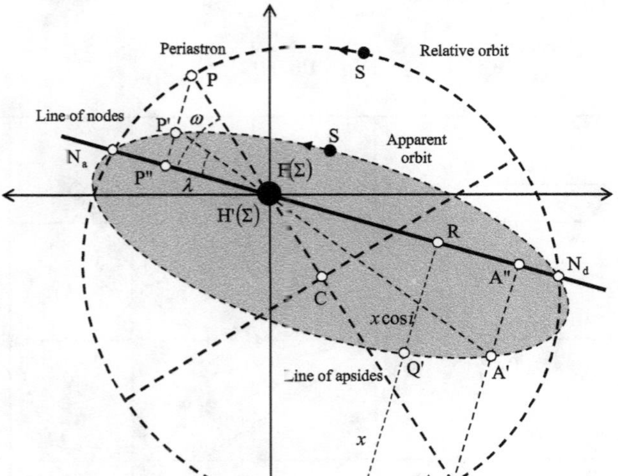


**Fig. T3.18**

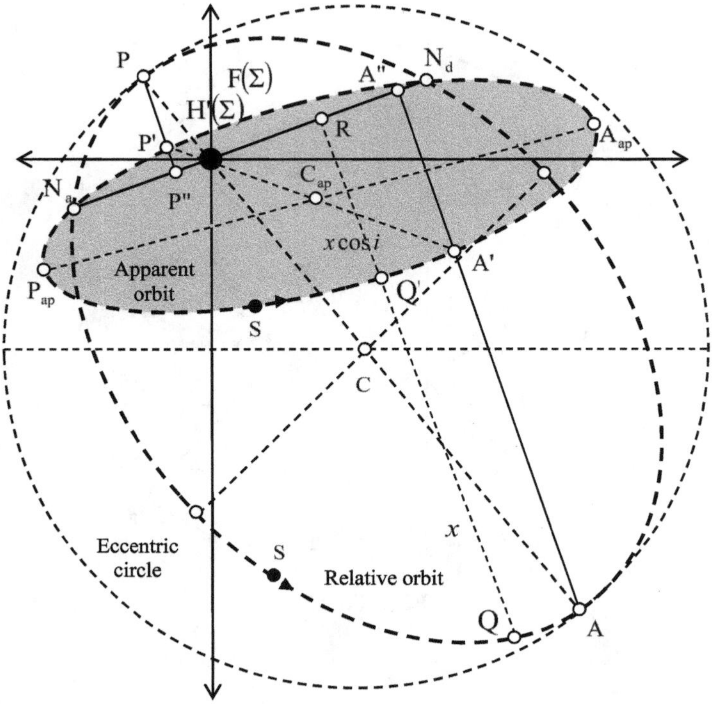


**Fig. T3.19**

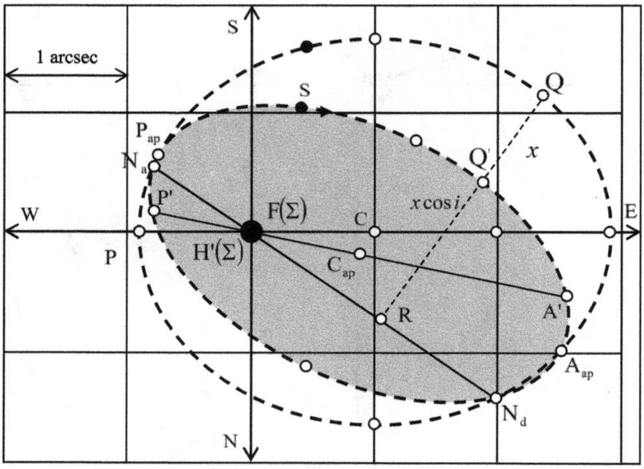


**Fig. T3.20**

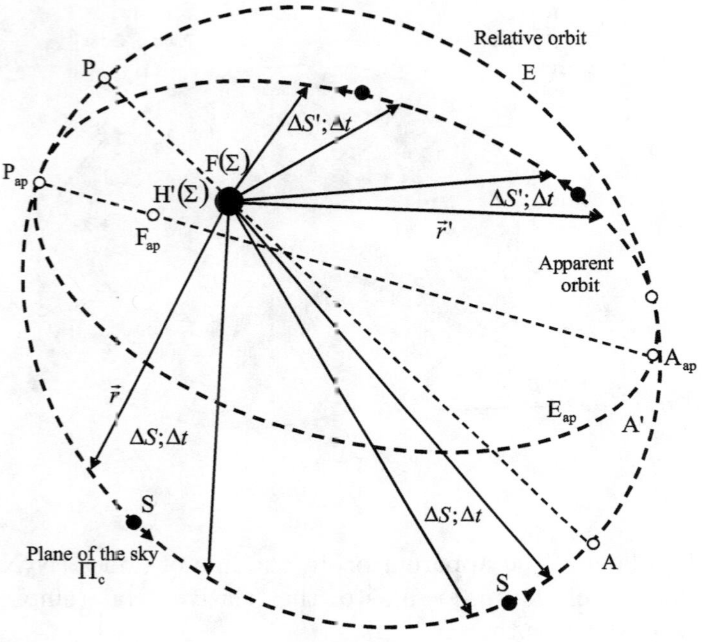


**Fig. T3.21**

In orthogonal projection on the celestial plane, all areas are reduced by the same factor ($\cos i$). Consequently, the radius vector of the secondary star on the apparent orbit sweeps equal areas within equal time intervals, even if the principal star is not located in the apparent ellipse's focus (Kepler's second law: the Law of Equal Areas), as presented in Figure T3.21.

The apparent movement of the secondary star around the principal star has an elliptic trajectory (specifically, a circle or a line segment). The primary star is always inside the apparent ellipse, but it is not always located in its focus. On the apparent orbit (ellipse), the vector radius of the secondary star relative to the principal star sweeps surfaces whose areas are directly proportional with the movement duration. Consequently, Kepler's second law (the Law of Equal Areas) is true also for binary stars.

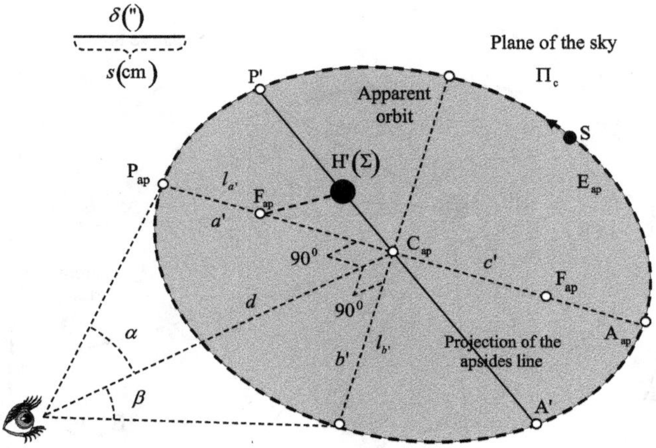


**Fig. T3.22**

In the plane of the apparent orbit, the line of nodes ($N_aN_d$) and the projection of the major axis of the relative orbit (ellipse) $P'A'$ are known as they intersect at $\Sigma$.

Corresponding to the notation in Figure T3.22, where $d$ is the distance from the observer to the stellar system, using the scale indicated in the Figure, the elements of the apparent orbit (ellipse) in the celestial plane will be determined.

$$s \ldots\ldots\ldots\ldots\ldots\ldots \delta;$$

$$l_{a'} \ldots\ldots\ldots\ldots\ldots \alpha = \frac{l_{a'}\delta}{s};$$

$$l_{b'} \ldots\ldots\ldots\ldots\ldots \beta = \frac{l_{b'}\delta}{s};$$

$$a' = \alpha d = \frac{l_{a'}\delta}{s}d; \quad b' = \beta d = \frac{l_{b'}\delta}{s}d;$$

$$e' = \sqrt{1 - \frac{b'^2}{a'^2}} = \sqrt{1 - \frac{l_{b'}^2}{l_{a'}^2}};$$

In Figures T3.23, T3.24 and T3.25, the apparent and the relative orbits are presented and the elements that can be measured for each orbit in each plane have been drawn. In none of the images is the angle representing the inclination ($i$) of the relative orbit relative to the celestial plane (the plane of the apparent orbit) marked. This angle is to be determined.

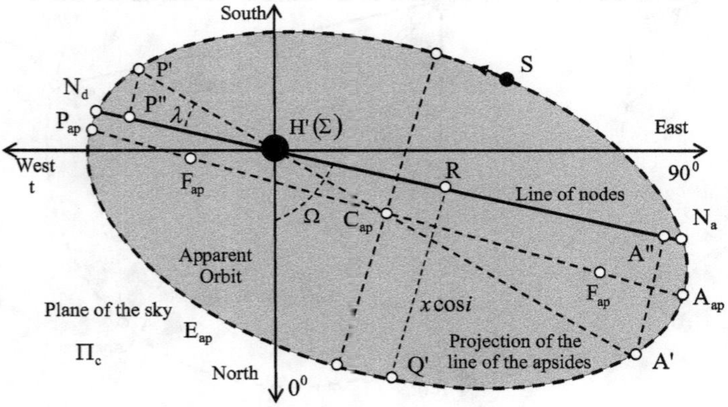


**Fig. T3.23**

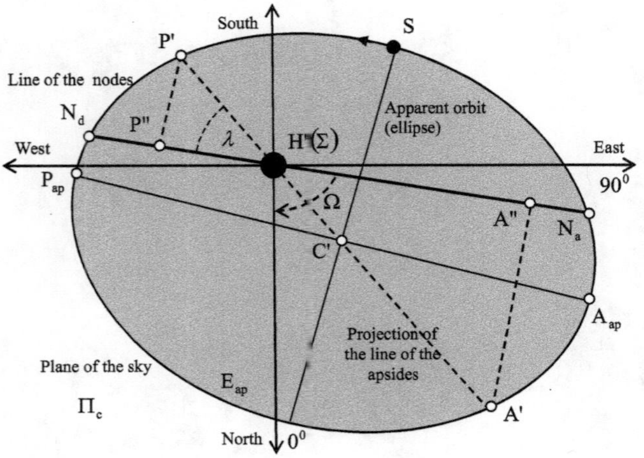


**Fig. T3.24**

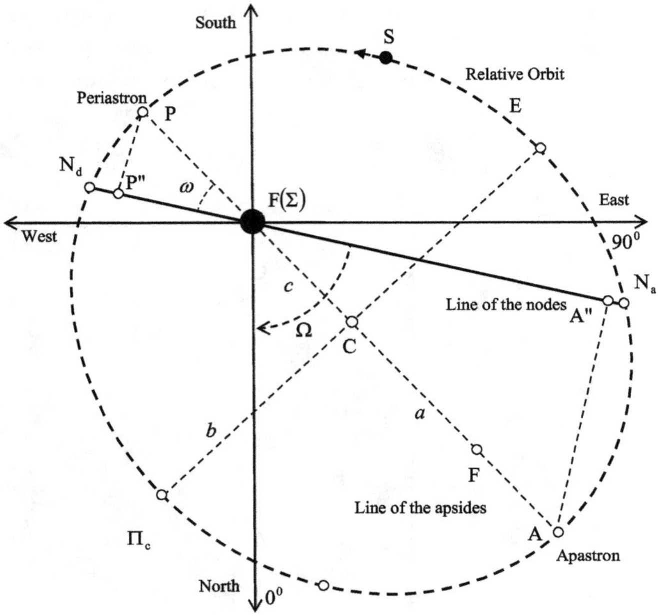
South
S
Relative Orbit
Periastron
P
E
$N_d$
P''
ω
F(Σ)
East
West
90⁰
$N_a$
c
Line of the nodes
A''
Ω
C
a
b
F
Line of the apsides
A
$\Pi_c$
Apastron
North
0⁰

**Fig. T3.25**

# Topic 4

# The Two-Body Problem

Two stars close to one another in space that interact through gravitational attraction forces represent a binary stellar system. In Figure T4.1, the position of the two components (S and Σ) of a binary stellar system is indicated relative to Earth. The center of mass and the two stars' velocities relative to the CM, as well as the CM's velocity relative to Earth are presented in the image below.

Corresponding to the gravitational interaction between the two stars, the result is:

$$F = K\frac{mM}{(r_{1,\mathrm{CM}} + r_{2,\mathrm{CM}})^2};$$

$$\vec{\mathrm{v}}_{1,\mathrm{P}} = \vec{\mathrm{v}}_{1,\mathrm{CM}} + \vec{\mathrm{v}}_{\mathrm{CM,P}} \quad \vec{\mathrm{v}}_{2,\mathrm{P}} = \vec{\mathrm{v}}_{2,\mathrm{CM}} + \vec{\mathrm{v}}_{\mathrm{CM,P}};$$

$$\vec{r}_{\mathrm{CM,P}} = \frac{m\vec{r}_{1,\mathrm{P}} + M\vec{r}_{2,\mathrm{P}}}{m+M};$$

$$\vec{r}_{1,\mathrm{P}} = \vec{r}_{\mathrm{CM,P}} + \vec{r}_{1,\mathrm{CM}}; \quad \vec{r}_{2,\mathrm{P}} = \vec{r}_{\mathrm{CM,P}} + \vec{r}_{2,\mathrm{CM}};$$

$$\vec{\mathrm{v}}_{\mathrm{CM,P}} = \frac{d\vec{r}_{\mathrm{CM,P}}}{dt} = \frac{m\vec{\mathrm{v}}_{1,\mathrm{P}} + M\vec{\mathrm{v}}_{2,\mathrm{P}}}{m+M};$$

$$\vec{H}_{\mathrm{CM,P}} = (m+M)\cdot\vec{\mathrm{v}}_{\mathrm{CM,P}} = m\vec{\mathrm{v}}_{1,\mathrm{P}} + M\vec{\mathrm{v}}_{2,\mathrm{P}};$$

$$\vec{H}_{\mathrm{CM,CM}} = m\vec{\mathrm{v}}_{1,\mathrm{CM}} + M\vec{\mathrm{v}}_{2,\mathrm{CM}} = 0;$$

$$\vec{\mathrm{v}}_{2,\mathrm{CM}} = -\frac{m}{M}\vec{\mathrm{v}}_{1,\mathrm{CM}}\vec{\mathrm{v}}_{2,\mathrm{CM}}//\vec{\mathrm{v}}_{1,CM};$$

$$m\mathrm{v}_{1,\mathrm{CM}} = M\mathrm{v}_{2,\mathrm{CM}};$$

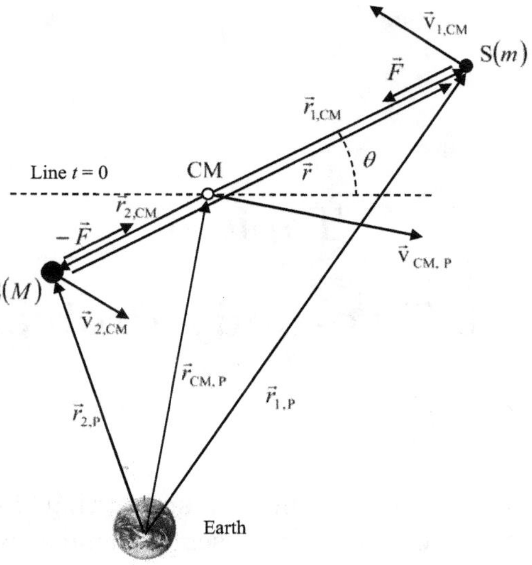


**Fig. T4.1**

$$\vec{r}_{\text{CM,CM}} = \frac{m\vec{r}_{1,\text{CM}} + M\vec{r}_{2,\text{CM}}}{m+M} = 0; \quad m\vec{r}_{1,\text{CM}} + M\vec{r}_{2,\text{CM}} = 0;$$

$$\vec{r}_{2,\text{CM}} = -\frac{m}{M}\vec{r}_{1,\text{CM}};$$

$$mr_{1,\text{CM}} = Mr_{2,\text{CM}}; \quad ma_1 = Ma_2;$$

$$\frac{v_{2,\text{CM}}}{v_{1,\text{CM}}} = \frac{r_{2,\text{CM}}}{r_{1,\text{CM}}} = \frac{a_2}{a_1} = \frac{m}{M};$$

$$\vec{r} = \vec{r}_{1,\text{P}} - \vec{r}_{2,\text{P}};$$

$$m\vec{r}_{1,\text{CM}} + M\vec{r}_{2,\text{CM}} = 0;$$

$$\vec{r} = \vec{r}_{1,\text{CM}} - \vec{r}_{2,\text{CM}};$$

$$\vec{r}_{1,\text{CM}} = \frac{M}{m+M}\vec{r}; \quad \vec{r}_{2,\text{CM}} = -\frac{m}{m+M}\vec{r},$$

representing the vector equations of the binary stellar system components' movement relative to the CM;

$$r_{1,\text{CM}}(t) = \frac{M}{m+M}r(t); \quad r_{2,\text{CM}}(t) = \frac{m}{m+M}r(t); \quad \theta = \theta(t),$$

representing the two ellipses, as presented in Figure T4.2.

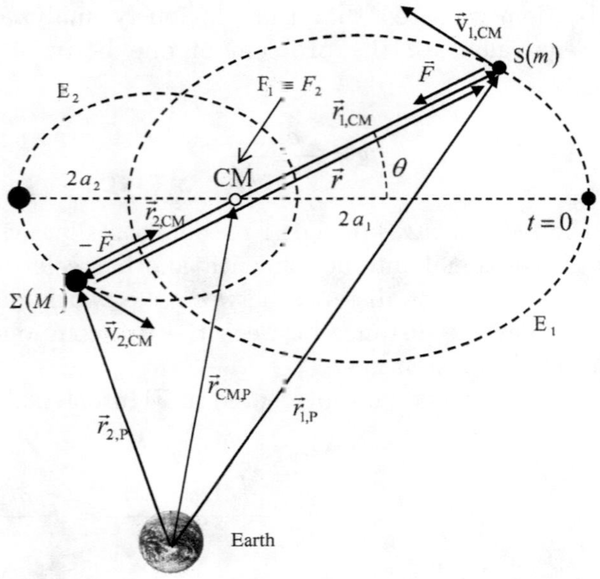


**Fig. T4.2**

The two components orbit on elliptic trajectories around the center of mass and together they move within our galaxy. The two stars' center of mass is located in the common focus of the two ellipses.

Let's consider the binary stellar system's center of mass to be stationary relative to the observer on Earth, as presented in Figure T4.2. Consequently, the orbits of the two stars relative to the CM and to the observer are the two ellipses presented in the following image.

Written in plane polar coordinates, the equations of the two elliptical orbits are:

$$r_{1,\mathrm{CM}} = \frac{p_1}{1 + e_1 \cos\theta} = \frac{a_1(1 - e_1^2)}{1 + e_1 \cos\theta};$$

$$r_{2,\mathrm{CM}} = \frac{p_2}{1 + e_2 \cos\theta} = \frac{a_2(1 - e_2^2)}{1 + e_2 \cos\theta}.$$

The problem that studies the movement of the two stars (S and $\Sigma$) of masses $m$ and $M$, respectively, which are gravitationally interacting relative to their center of mass, is known in mechanics as the *two-body problem.*

It can be demonstrated that the previously analyzed *two-body problem* is equivalent to the problem of one body of equivalent mass,

$$\mu = \frac{mM}{m+M},$$

also called the *reduced mass* of the given binary stellar system in the case of its gravitational interaction with another celestial body of mass $(m+M)$, when the distance between the two bodies ($S_0$ and $\Sigma_0$) is the same as the distance between the two components of the given binary stellar system.

For the equivalent system represented in Figure T4.3, it is known that:

$$F_{\text{equivalent}} = K\frac{\mu\,(m+M)}{r^2} = K\frac{\frac{mM}{m+M}\,(m+M)}{r^2} = K\frac{mM}{r^2} = F;$$

$$\mu\frac{\mathrm{d}^2\vec{r}}{\mathrm{d}t^2} = K\frac{\mu\,(m+M)}{r^2}\cdot\text{versor}\,\vec{F}_{\text{equivalent}} = -K\frac{\mu\,(m+M)}{r^2}\cdot\text{versor}\,\vec{r};$$

$$\mu\frac{\mathrm{d}^2\vec{r}}{\mathrm{d}t^2} = -K\frac{\mu\,(m+M)}{r^2}\cdot\frac{\vec{r}}{r} = -K\frac{\mu\,(m+M)}{r^3}\cdot\vec{r};$$

$$\frac{\mathrm{d}^2\vec{r}}{\mathrm{d}t^2} = -K\frac{(m+M)}{r^3}\cdot\vec{r}.$$

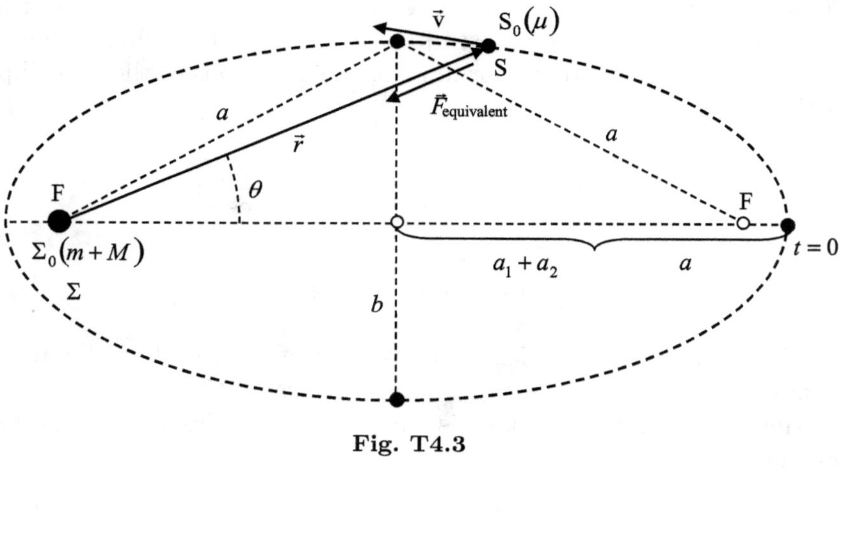


**Fig. T4.3**

Thus, the result is:

$$r = \frac{p}{1 + e\cos\theta} = \frac{a\left(1 - e^2\right)}{1 + e\cos\theta}; \quad T^2 = \frac{4\pi^2}{K\left(m + M\right)}a^3;$$

$$r_{1,\mathrm{CM}} = \frac{M}{m + M}r; \quad r_{2,\mathrm{CM}} = \frac{m}{m + M}r;$$

$$mr_{1,\mathrm{CM}} = Mr_{2,\mathrm{CM}};$$

$$mr_{1,\mathrm{CM}} = \frac{mM}{m + M}r = Mr_{2,\mathrm{CM}};$$

$$mr_{1,\mathrm{CM}} = \frac{mp_1}{1 + e_1\cos\theta} = \frac{ma_1\left(1 - e_1^2\right)}{1 + e_1\cos\theta} = \frac{mM}{m + M}\frac{p}{1 + e\cos\theta}$$

$$= \frac{mM}{m + M} \cdot \frac{a\left(1 - e^2\right)}{1 + e\cos\theta};$$

$$p_1 = \frac{M}{m + M}p;$$

$$Mr_{2,\mathrm{CM}} = \frac{Mp_2}{1 + e_2\cos\theta} = \frac{Ma_2\left(1 - e_2^2\right)}{1 + e_2\cos\theta} = \frac{mM}{m + M}\frac{p}{1 + e\cos\theta}$$

$$= \frac{mM}{m + M} \cdot \frac{a\left(1 - e^2\right)}{1 + e\cos\theta};$$

$$p_2 = \frac{m}{m + M}p;$$

$$\frac{ma_1\left(1 - e_1^2\right)}{1 + e_1\cos\theta} = \frac{Ma_2\left(1 - e_2^2\right)}{1 + e_2\cos\theta};$$

$$ma_1 = Ma_2;$$

$$\frac{\left(1 - e_1^2\right)}{1 + e_1\cos\theta} = \frac{\left(1 - e_2^2\right)}{1 + e_2\cos\theta};$$

$$\left(1 - e_1^2\right)\left(1 + e_2\cos\theta\right) = \left(1 - e_2^2\right)\left(1 + e_1\cos\theta\right);$$

$$e_2\left(1 - e_1^2\right)\cos\theta - e_1^2 = e_1\left(1 - e_2^2\right)\cos\theta - e_2^2,$$

which has to hold true for any $\theta$ value;

$$e_2\left(1 - e_1^2\right) = e_1\left(1 - e_2^2\right);$$

$$e_1 = e_2,$$

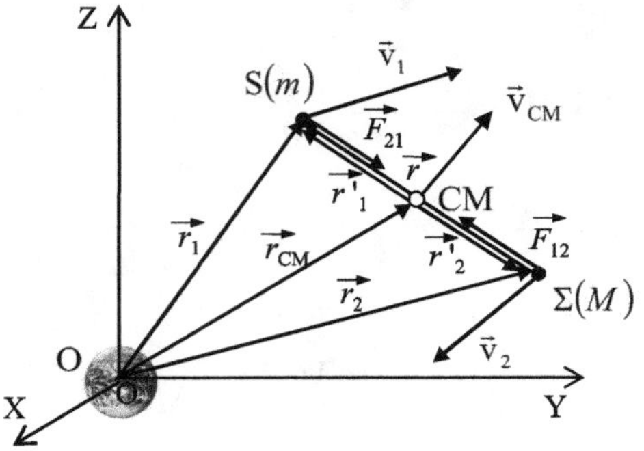


**Fig. T4.4**

i.e., the eccentricities of the two ellipses are identical;

$$\sqrt{1-\frac{b_1^2}{a_1^2}}=\sqrt{1-\frac{b_2^2}{a_2^2}};\quad \frac{b_1}{a_1}=\frac{b_2}{a_2}.$$

If at any moment $t$ the geometry of the binary stellar system is the one represented in Figure T4.4, where OXYZ is a stationary reference system, it results that:

$$F_{12}=F_{21}=K\frac{mM}{r^2};\quad \vec{F}_{12}=-\vec{F}_{21};\quad \vec{r}=\vec{r}_1-\vec{r}_2;$$

$$m\ddot{\vec{r}}_1=\vec{F}_{21}=K\frac{mM}{r^3}\left(\vec{r}_2-\vec{r}_1\right);$$

$$M\ddot{\vec{r}}_2=\vec{F}_{12}=K\frac{mM}{r^3}\left(\vec{r}_1-\vec{r}_2\right).$$

From the above, by projecting on the OXYZ system's axes, six scalar differential equations of the second order are obtained. By integrating these six scalar differential equations of the second order, as regards to the initial conditions, the required dependencies are determined, i.e., $\vec{r}_1(t)$, $\vec{r}_2(t)$, $\vec{\mathrm{v}}_1(t)$, $\vec{\mathrm{v}}_2(t)$, where $\vec{\mathrm{v}}_1$ and $\vec{\mathrm{v}}_2$ are the velocities of the two components relative to Earth.

From the previous two vector equations, it also results that:

$$m\ddot{\vec{r}}_1+M\ddot{\vec{r}}_2=0;$$

$$m\dot{\vec{\mathrm{v}}}_1+M\dot{\vec{\mathrm{v}}}_2=0;$$

$$\frac{\mathrm{d}}{\mathrm{d}t}\left(m\vec{\mathrm{v}}_1+M\vec{\mathrm{v}}_2\right)=0;\quad m\vec{\mathrm{v}}_1+M\vec{\mathrm{v}}_2=\text{constant}=\left(m+M\right)\vec{\mathrm{v}}_{\mathrm{CM}},$$

emphasizing the conservation of the total impulse of the insulated mechanical system consisting of the two stars, where $\vec{v}_{CM}$ is the velocity of the system's center of mass relative to the observer.

Let us consider a coordinates system $X_2Y_2Z_2$ with the origin $O_2$ at the point where the principal star ($\Sigma$) of mass $M$ is located. The axes of this system perform only translations relative to the stationary OXYZ system. Under these circumstances, by analyzing the movement of the secondary component (the star S of mass $m$) relative to the principal star ($\Sigma$), it results that

$$m\vec{a}_{\text{rel}} = m\vec{a}_{12} = \vec{F}_{21} + \vec{F}_{\text{tr}} + \vec{F}_{\text{Cor}},$$

representing the fundamental principle of the dynamics for the relative movement of a material point, where $\vec{F}_{\text{tr}}$ and $\vec{F}_{\text{Cor}}$ are the complementary forces of transport and Coriolis, respectively:

$$\vec{F}_{\text{tr}} = -m\ddot{\vec{r}}_2 - m\dot{\vec{\omega}} \times \vec{r} - \vec{\omega} \times (\vec{\omega} \times \vec{r})\, m;$$

$$\vec{F}_{\text{tr}} = -m\ddot{\vec{r}}_2;$$

$$\vec{F}_{\text{Cor}} = -2m\vec{\omega} \times \vec{v}_{\text{rel}} = -2m\vec{\omega} \times \vec{v}_{12} = 0,$$

since the $X_2Y_2Z_2$ mobile system does not move relative to the stationary system;

$$\vec{a}_{\text{rel}} = \vec{a}_{12} = \ddot{\vec{r}} = \ddot{\vec{r}}_1 - \ddot{\vec{r}}_2;$$

$$m\ddot{\vec{r}} = \vec{F}_{21} - m\frac{\vec{F}_{12}}{m_2} = \frac{m+M}{M}\vec{F}_{21};$$

$$\frac{mM}{m+M}\ddot{\vec{r}} = \vec{F}_{21};$$

$$\mu = \frac{mM}{m+M},$$

representing the reduced mass of the system;

$$\mu\ddot{\vec{r}} = \vec{F}_{21} = -F_{21}\frac{\vec{r}}{r},$$

that is, the movement of star S relative to star $\Sigma$ is equivalent to the absolute movement of one star ($S_0$) of mass $\mu$ due to the gravitational interaction with a star ($\Sigma_0$) of mass $(m + M)$. Stars $S_0$ and $\Sigma_0$ have the locations of the stars S and Σ, respectively, and are under the action of the equivalent central gravitational force:

$$F_{\text{equivalent}} = K\frac{\mu\,(m+M)}{r^2} = K\frac{\frac{mM}{m+M}(m+M)}{r^2} = K\frac{mM}{r^2} = F_{21},$$

whose direction permanently travels through star Σ's location.

$$\mu\ddot{\vec{r}} = \vec{F}_{\text{equivalent}} = K\frac{\mu\,(m+M)}{r^2}\cdot \text{versor}\,\vec{F}_{\text{equivalent}};$$

$$\text{versor}\,\vec{F}_{\text{equivalent}} = -\text{versor}\,\vec{r} = -\frac{\vec{r}}{r};$$

$$\mu\ddot{\vec{r}} = -K\frac{\mu\,(m+M)}{r^2}\cdot\frac{\vec{r}}{r} = -K\frac{\mu\,(m+M)}{r^3}\cdot\vec{r};$$

$$\ddot{\vec{r}} + K\frac{(m+M)}{r^3}\cdot\vec{r} = 0.$$

The same result is reached using the equations of absolute movement. Thus:

$$mM\ddot{\vec{r}}_1 = M\vec{F}_{21};$$

$$mM\ddot{\vec{r}}_2 = m\vec{F}_{12} = -m\vec{F}_{21};$$

$$mM\left(\ddot{\vec{r}}_1 - \ddot{\vec{r}}_2\right) = (m+M)\vec{F}_{21};$$

$$\vec{r} = \vec{r}_1 - \vec{r}_2;$$

$$\frac{mM}{m+M}\ddot{\vec{r}} = \vec{F}_{21} = -\frac{F_{21}}{r}\vec{r}.$$

This results in:

$$2\mu\frac{\mathrm{d}\vec{r}}{\mathrm{d}t}\frac{\mathrm{d}^2\vec{r}}{\mathrm{d}t^2} = -2K\frac{mM}{r^2}\frac{1}{r}\vec{r}\frac{\mathrm{d}\vec{r}}{\mathrm{d}t};$$

$$\vec{r}^2 = r^2; \quad \vec{r}\frac{\mathrm{d}\vec{r}}{\mathrm{d}t} = r\frac{\mathrm{d}r}{\mathrm{d}t};$$

$$\mu\frac{\mathrm{d}}{\mathrm{d}t}\left[\left(\frac{\mathrm{d}\vec{r}}{\mathrm{d}t}\right)^2\right] = -2K\frac{mM}{r^2}\frac{\mathrm{d}r}{\mathrm{d}t};$$

$$-\frac{1}{r^2}\frac{\mathrm{d}r}{\mathrm{d}t} = \frac{\mathrm{d}}{\mathrm{d}t}\left(\frac{1}{r}\right);$$

$$\frac{\mathrm{d}\vec{r}}{\mathrm{d}t} = \vec{\mathrm{v}}_{\mathrm{rel}} = \vec{\mathrm{v}}_{12};$$

$$\mu\frac{\mathrm{d}\left(\mathrm{v}_{\mathrm{rel}}^2\right)}{\mathrm{d}t} = 2KmM\frac{\mathrm{d}}{\mathrm{d}t}\left(\frac{1}{r}\right);$$

$$\frac{\mathrm{d}}{\mathrm{d}t}\left(\frac{\mu\mathrm{v}_{\mathrm{rel}}^2}{2}\right) = \frac{\mathrm{d}}{\mathrm{d}t}K\left(\frac{mM}{r}\right);$$

$$\frac{\mu\mathrm{v}_{\mathrm{rel}}^2}{2} - K\frac{mM}{r} = \frac{h}{2} = \text{constant},$$

representing the integral of the system's energy relative to the star $\Sigma$.

Similarly, using the vector equation of the relative movement, it results that:

$$\mu\vec{r} \times \ddot{\vec{r}} = -\frac{F_{21}}{r}\vec{r} \times \vec{r} = 0;$$

$$\vec{r} \times \frac{\mathrm{d}^2\vec{r}}{\mathrm{d}t^2} = 0; \quad \frac{\mathrm{d}}{\mathrm{d}t}\left(\vec{r} \times \frac{\mathrm{d}\vec{r}}{\mathrm{d}t}\right) = 0;$$

$$\vec{r} \times \vec{\mathrm{v}}_{\mathrm{rel}} = \vec{C},$$

representing the integral of the areas swept by the movement of the star S relative to the star $\Sigma$, under the central gravitational attraction force. This proves that this relative movement is planar.

If the plane where the star S moves relative to the star $\Sigma$ is the $\mathrm{O}_2\xi\eta$ plane presented in Figure T4.5, the result is:

$$S_{\mathrm{O}_2SS'} = \frac{1}{2}\left|\vec{r} \times \mathrm{d}\vec{r}\right| = \mathrm{d}S;$$

$$\mathrm{d}\vec{S} = \frac{1}{2}\left(\vec{r} \times \mathrm{d}\vec{r}\right);$$

$$\vec{\Omega} = \frac{\mathrm{d}\vec{S}}{\mathrm{d}t} = \frac{1}{2}\left(\vec{r} \times \vec{\mathrm{v}}_{\mathrm{rel}}\right); \quad \vec{C} = 2\vec{\Omega},$$

where $\vec{\Omega}$ is the areal velocity.

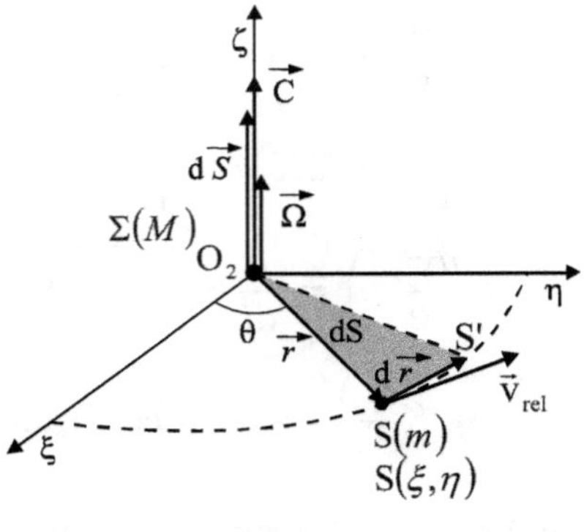


**Fig. T4.5**

Corresponding to the polar plane coordinates $(r, \theta)$, we have:

$$\xi = r\cos\theta; \quad \eta = r\sin\theta;$$

$$r^2\dot{\theta} = C;$$

$$\mathrm{v}_{\mathrm{rel}}^2 = \left(\frac{\mathrm{d}\xi}{\mathrm{d}t}\right)^2 + \left(\frac{\mathrm{d}\eta}{\mathrm{d}t}\right) = \dot{r}^2 + r^2\dot{\theta}^2;$$

$$\dot{r} = \frac{\mathrm{d}r}{\mathrm{d}t} = \dot{\theta}\frac{\mathrm{d}r}{\mathrm{d}\theta};$$

$$\mathrm{v}_{\mathrm{rel}}^2 = \frac{C^2}{r^4}\left(\frac{\mathrm{d}r}{\mathrm{d}\theta}\right)^2 + \frac{C^2}{r^2};$$

$$\mathrm{v}_{\mathrm{rel}}^2 = \left(\frac{C}{r^2}\frac{\mathrm{d}r}{\mathrm{d}\theta}\right)^2 + \frac{C^2}{r^2};$$

$$\mathrm{v}_{\mathrm{rel}}^2 = \left[\frac{\mathrm{d}}{\mathrm{d}\theta}\left(\frac{C}{r}\right)\right]^2 + \frac{C^2}{r^2};$$

$$\mathrm{v}_{\mathrm{rel}}^2 = \frac{2KmM}{\mu r} + \frac{h}{\mu};$$

$$\left[\frac{\mathrm{d}}{\mathrm{d}\theta}\left(\frac{C}{r}\right)^2\right] + \frac{C^2}{r^2} = \frac{2KmM}{\mu r} + \frac{h}{\mu};$$

$$\frac{\mathrm{d}}{\mathrm{d}\theta}\left(\frac{C}{r}\right)^2 = \pm\sqrt{\frac{2KmM}{\mu r} + \frac{h}{\mu} - \frac{C^2}{r^2}};$$

$$\frac{2KmM}{\mu r} + \frac{h}{\mu} - \frac{C^2}{r^2} = \frac{h}{\mu} + \frac{K^2m^2M^2}{\mu^2C^2} - \frac{K^2m^2M^2}{\mu^2C^2} + 2\frac{KmM}{\mu r} - \frac{C^2}{r^2}$$

$$= \frac{h}{\mu} + \frac{K^2m^2M^2}{\mu^2C^2} - \left(\frac{C}{r} - \frac{KmM}{\mu C}\right)^2;$$

$$\frac{\mathrm{d}}{\mathrm{d}\theta}\left(\frac{C}{r}\right) = \pm\sqrt{\frac{h}{\mu} + \frac{K^2m^2M^2}{\mu^2C^2} - \left(\frac{C}{r} - \frac{KmM}{\mu C}\right)^2};$$

$$\frac{\mathrm{d}\left(\dfrac{\frac{C}{r} - \frac{KmM}{\mu C}}{\sqrt{\frac{h}{\mu} + \frac{K^2m^2M^2}{\mu^2C^2}}}\right)}{\pm\sqrt{1 - \left(\dfrac{\frac{C}{r} - \frac{KmM}{\mu C}}{\sqrt{\frac{h}{\mu} + \frac{K^2m^2M^2}{\mu^2C^2}}}\right)^2}} = \mathrm{d}\theta.$$

Through integration, this results in:

$$\arccos\left(\dfrac{\frac{C}{r} - \frac{KmM}{\mu C}}{\sqrt{\frac{h}{\mu} + \frac{K^2m^2M^2}{\mu^2C^2}}}\right) = \theta - \theta_0;$$

$$\frac{C}{r} - \frac{KmM}{\mu C} = \sqrt{\frac{h}{\mu} + \frac{K^2m^2M^2}{\mu^2C^2}}\cos(\theta - \theta_0);$$

$$\frac{1}{r} = \frac{1 + \sqrt{1 + \frac{h\mu C^2}{K^2m^2M^2}}\cos(\theta - \theta_0)}{\frac{\mu C^2}{KmM}};$$

$$\sqrt{1 + \frac{h\mu C^2}{K^2m^2M^2}} = e; \quad \frac{\mu C^2}{K^2mM} = p;$$

$$r = \frac{p}{1 + e\cos(\theta - \theta_0)}.$$

This represents the equation of star S's trajectory relative to star $\Sigma$, expressed in polar plane coordinates; it is a conic in whose focus the star $\Sigma$ is located in the following variants:

$h < 0,\ e < 1,$ ellipse,

$h = 0,\ e = 1,$ parabola,

$h > 0,\ e > 1,$ hyperbola.

For the particular case of the movement on an ellipse, the result is:

$$p = a(1 - e^2); \quad b^2 = a^2(1 - e^2);$$

$$\Omega = \frac{\pi ab}{T}; \quad C = \frac{2\pi ab}{T};$$

$$C^2 = \frac{pKmM}{\mu} = \frac{a(1 - e^2)mMK}{\mu} = \frac{4\pi^2 a^4(1 - e^2)}{T^2};$$

$$\frac{T^2}{a^3} = \frac{4\pi^2}{K(m + M)} = \text{constant};$$

$$\frac{T^2}{a^3} = \frac{4\pi^2}{K(m + M)} = \text{constant};$$

$$m + M = \frac{4\pi^2}{KT^2}a^3.$$

*Visual binary stars are identified on the celestial sphere by the fact that their two components periodically switch their relative positions, in contrast to common stars whose apparent positions on the celestial sphere do not change.*

From the relationships previously demonstrated, if $T$ is the period of the apparent rotation of the star S around the star $\Sigma$ on an ellipse of semi-major axis $a_{12}$ that has $\Sigma$ in its focus, then:

$$\frac{T^2(m + M)}{a_{12}^3} = \frac{4\pi^2}{K},$$

representing Kepler's third law, where $m$ and $M$ are the masses of the two stellar components.

In the *two-body problem*, the two material points can be, for instance, considered to be the Earth and the Sun, if the gravitational interactions with other planets are not taken into account.

In particular, if the same law is written for the binary Earth–Sun system, we obtain

$$\frac{\tau^2(M_{\mathrm{E}} + M_{\mathrm{S}})}{a_{\mathrm{ES}}^3} = \frac{4\pi^2}{K},$$

where $\tau$ is the apparent rotation period of the Earth moving around the Sun on the ellipse of semi-major axis $a_{\mathrm{ES}}$. The Sun is located in the focus of the Earth's elliptical trajectory and $M_{\mathrm{E}}$ and $M_{\mathrm{S}}$ represent the Earth's and the Sun's masses. From the previous equation, the result is

$$m + M = \frac{\tau^2}{T^2}\frac{a_{12}^3}{a_{\mathrm{ES}}^3}(M_{\mathrm{E}} + M_{\mathrm{S}}),$$

representing the total mass of a visual binary stellar system.

The experimental astronomical observations do not allow us to determine the length of the semi-major axis $a_{12}$, but, as presented in image b of Figure T4.6, only its angular value (opening) $\alpha$. Under these conditions, if the principal star's parallax (the angle under which the semi-major axis of the ellipse in which the Earth is moving around the Sun is seen when watching from the center of the principal star) is $\beta$ and if $\Delta$ represents the distance from the Sun to the principal star $\Sigma$, it results in the following:

$$a_{12} \approx \alpha\Delta; \quad a_{\mathrm{ES}} \approx \beta\Delta;$$

$$m_+ M = \frac{\tau^2}{T^2}\frac{\alpha^3}{\beta^3}(M_{\mathrm{E}} + M_{\mathrm{S}}).$$

This relation allows us to calculate the total mass of a visual binary stellar system if the parallax of the principal star is known.

If absolute astronomical observations are made, following the movement of each component relative to the system's CM and if $a_1$ and $a_2$, respectively, are the semi-major axis of the ellipses described by the two components relative to the CM, and $\alpha_1$ and $\alpha_2$ represent the angles at which the two semi-major axis are seen from the Sun's center, we have:

$$a_1 \approx \alpha_1\Delta; \quad a_2 \approx \alpha_2\Delta;$$

$$a = a_1 + a_2; \quad \alpha = \alpha_1 + \alpha_2;$$

$$a_1 m = a_2 M; \quad \alpha_1 m = \alpha_2 M;$$

$$\frac{\alpha_1}{\alpha} = \frac{M}{m + M}; \quad \frac{\alpha_2}{\alpha} = \frac{m}{m + M}.$$

Thus, for the mass of each component of the visual binary stellar system, the result is:

$$m = \alpha_2 \frac{\tau^2}{T^2}\frac{\alpha^2}{\beta^3}(M_E + M_S);$$

$$M = \alpha_1 \frac{\tau^2}{T^2}\frac{\alpha^2}{\beta^3}(M_E + M_S).$$

In particular, considering that the absolute trajectories of the two components relative to the CM are concentric circles (see image c, Figure T4.6), the result is:

$$K\frac{mM}{(a_1 + a_2)^2} = ma_1\omega^2 = Ma_2\omega^2;$$

$$\omega = \frac{2\pi}{T}.$$

Thus the maximum angular movements of the two components, observed with a telescope from the Earth as noted in image d of

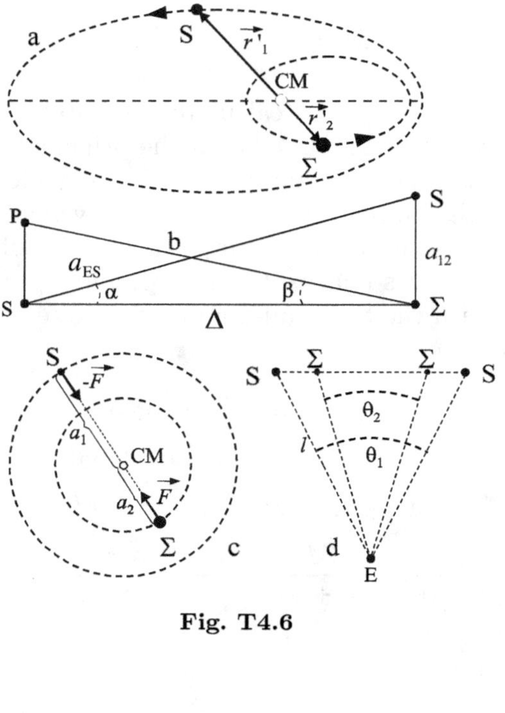


**Fig. T4.6**

Figure T4.3, we obtain:

$$a_1 \approx l\frac{\theta_1}{2}; \quad a_2 \approx l\frac{\theta_2}{2},$$

where $l$ is the distance from the Earth to the visual binary stellar system;

$$l^3 = \frac{2KT^2M}{\pi^2\theta_1 (\theta_1 + \theta_2)^2};$$

$$l^3 = \frac{2K\alpha_1 T^2 \alpha^2 (M_{\mathrm{E}} + M_{\mathrm{S}})}{\pi^2\theta_1 (\theta_1 + \theta_2)^2 \beta^3}.$$

Astronomical observations have shown that there are binary stellar systems whose components are too close to one another and for this reason they cannot be seen separately even with the strongest telescope. They have been named *spectroscopic binary stellar systems.*

Finally, if the two components' orbital planes contain the Sun, and if the two components are so close that they cannot be seen separately, then the binary stellar system appears as a single star of periodically variable brightness, since the two components reciprocally eclipse each other. They have been named *photometric binary stellar systems.*

# Topic 5

# The Mass of a Binary Stellar System and the Virial Theorem

For the binary stellar system represented in Figure T5.1, the result is:

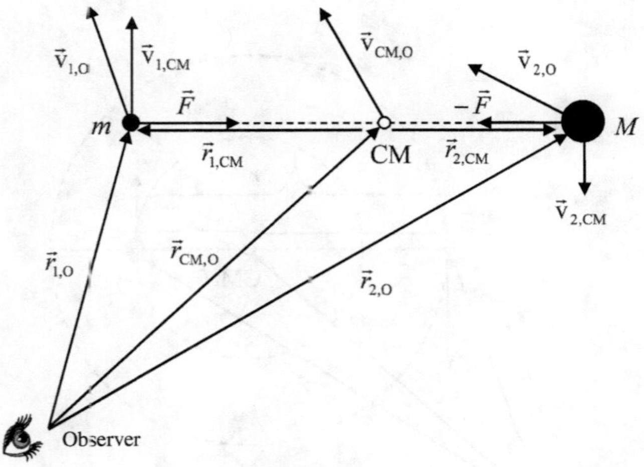


**Fig. T5.1**

$$r_{\text{CM,O}} = R\frac{m\vec{r}_{1,\text{O}} + M\vec{r}_{2,\text{O}}}{m+M}; \quad \vec{\text{v}}_{\text{CM,O}} = \frac{m\vec{\text{v}}_{1,\text{O}} + M\vec{\text{v}}_{2,\text{O}}}{m+M};$$

$$\vec{\text{v}}_{1,\text{O}} = \vec{\text{v}}_{1,\text{CM}} + \vec{\text{v}}_{\text{CM,O}}; \quad \vec{\text{v}}_{2,\text{O}} = \vec{\text{v}}_{2,\text{CM}} + \vec{\text{v}}_{\text{CM,O}};$$

$$\vec{\text{v}}_{\text{CM,O}} = \frac{m\vec{\text{v}}_{1,\text{CM}} + m\vec{\text{v}}_{\text{CM,O}} + M\vec{\text{v}}_{2,\text{CM}} + M\vec{\text{v}}_{\text{CM,O}}}{m+M};$$

$$m\vec{r}_{1,\text{CM}} + M\vec{r}_{2,\text{CM}} = 0; \quad m\vec{\text{v}}_{1,\text{CM}} + M\vec{\text{v}}_{2,\text{CM}} = 0;$$

$$mr_{1,\text{CM}} = Mr_{2,\text{CM}}; \quad m\text{v}_{1,\text{CM}} = M\text{v}_{2,\text{CM}}.$$

If the two components of the binary stellar system are of masses $M$ and $m$, according to Figure T5.2, the movements of the two stars relative to their center of mass are uniform and take place in concentric circles, and the center of mass is placed in the common center of the two trajectories. If $\vec{\text{v}}_1$ and $\vec{\text{v}}_2$ are the velocities of the two stars relative to the CM, the two stars continuously being in diametrically opposed positions, corresponding to the position vectors $\vec{r}_1$ and $\vec{r}_2$, respectively, it results that:

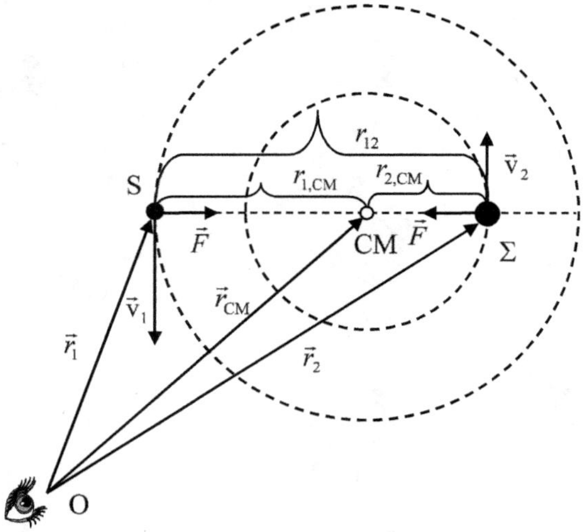


**Fig. T5.2**

$$\vec{r}_{\mathrm{CM}} = \frac{m\vec{r}_1 + M\vec{r}_2}{m+M} = \text{constant}; \quad \vec{\mathrm{v}}_{\mathrm{CM}} = \frac{m\vec{\mathrm{v}}_1 + M\vec{\mathrm{v}}_2}{m+M} = 0;$$

$$\vec{r}_1 = \vec{r}_{\mathrm{CM}} + \vec{r}_{1,\mathrm{CM}}; \quad \vec{r}_2 = \vec{r}_{\mathrm{CM}} + \vec{r}_{2,\mathrm{CM}};$$

$$\vec{r}_{\mathrm{CM}} = \frac{m\left(\vec{r}_{\mathrm{CM}} + \vec{r}_{1,\mathrm{CM}}\right) + M\left(\vec{r}_{\mathrm{CM}} + \vec{r}_{2,\mathrm{CM}}\right)}{m+M}$$

$$= \frac{m\vec{r}_{1,\mathrm{CM}} + M\vec{r}_{2,\mathrm{CM}} + (m+M)\,\vec{r}_{\mathrm{CM}}}{m+M};$$

$$\vec{r}_{\mathrm{CM}} = \frac{m\vec{r}_{1,\mathrm{CM}} + M\vec{r}_{2,\mathrm{CM}}}{m+M} + \vec{r}_{\mathrm{CM}};$$

$$m\vec{r}_{1,\mathrm{CM}} + M\vec{r}_{2,\mathrm{CM}} = 0;$$

$$m\vec{r}_1 + M\vec{r}_2 = 0; \quad m\vec{\mathrm{v}}_1 + M\vec{\mathrm{v}}_2 = 0,$$

which cannot be accepted unless the two vectors, $\vec{\mathrm{v}}_1$ and $\vec{\mathrm{v}}_2$, are parallel and have opposite directions;

$$m\mathrm{v}_1 = M\mathrm{v}_2; \quad \vec{\mathrm{v}}_1 = \vec{\omega}\,x\,\vec{r}_1; \quad \mathrm{v}_1 = \omega r_1; \quad \vec{\mathrm{v}}_2 = \vec{\omega}\,x\,\vec{r}_2; \quad \mathrm{v}_2 = \omega r_2;$$

$$m r_1 = M r_2;$$

$$F = K\frac{mM}{\left(r_1 + r_2\right)^2} = m\omega^2 r_1 = M\omega^2 r_2;$$

$$r_1 + r_2 = r_{12}; \quad r_2 = \frac{m}{M}r_1; \quad r_1 + \frac{m}{M}r_1 = r_{12}; \quad r_1 = \frac{M}{m+M}r_{12};$$

$$r_2 = \frac{m}{m+M}r_{12};$$

$$K\frac{mM}{\left(r_1 + r_2\right)^2} = m\omega^2\frac{M}{m+M}r_{12} = M\omega^2\frac{m}{m+M}r_{12};$$

$$K\frac{mM}{\left(r_1 + r_2\right)^2} = \frac{4\pi^2}{T^2}\frac{mM}{m+M}r_{12};$$

$$K\frac{mM}{r_{12}^2} = \frac{4\pi^2}{T^2}\frac{mM}{m+M}r_{12};$$

$$T^2 = \frac{4\pi^2}{K(m+M)}(r_1+r_2)^3; \quad T^2 = \frac{4\pi^2}{K(m+M)}r_{12}^3,$$

representing Kepler's third law for the common rotation period of the two stellar components relative to the CM in the format proposed by Newton.

In Figure T5.3 the two stellar components are represented orbiting on elliptical trajectories around the center of mass, in non-uniform movements under the action of gravitational attraction forces.

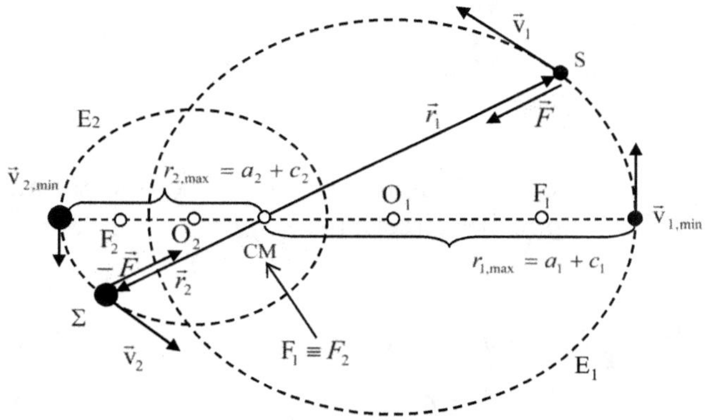


**Fig. T5.3**

According to *the virial theorem*, the non-uniform movement of the secondary star S around the center of mass on the ellipse $E_1$ of semi-major axis $a_1$ represented in Figure T5.4 is equivalent to its uniform movement on the circle $C_1$ having its center in the stellar system's CM and a radius equal to the ellipse's semi-major axis $a_1$. The speed of the secondary star moving uniformly on a circular orbit is equal to its speed on the ellipse $E_1$ at point $B_1$, which also equals the average speed of the secondary star S on the entire ellipse $E_1$.

Similarly, the non-uniform movement of star $\Sigma$ on ellipse $E_2$ of semi-major axis $a_2$ (as presented in image b of Figure T5.4) is equivalent to its uniform movement on the circle $C_2$ with its center in the stellar system's CM and of a radius equal to the ellipse's semi-major axis $a_2$. The speed of the principal star moving uniformly on a circular orbit is equal to its speed on the ellipse $E_2$ at point $B_2$, which also equals the average speed of the principal star $\Sigma$ on the entire ellipse $E_2$.

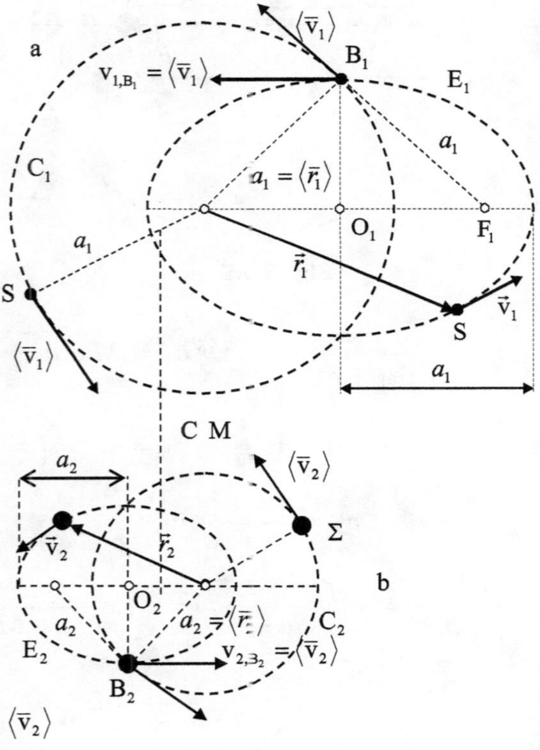


**Fig. T5.4**

In Figure T5.5 the elements of the two stars' uniform circular movements on elliptical orbits are represented. The movement takes place under gravitational attraction. Under these conditions, it results that:

$$m\mathrm{v}_1 = M\mathrm{v}_2; \quad \mathrm{v}_1 = \omega a_1; \quad \mathrm{v}_2 = \omega a_2;$$

$$ma_1 = Ma_2;$$

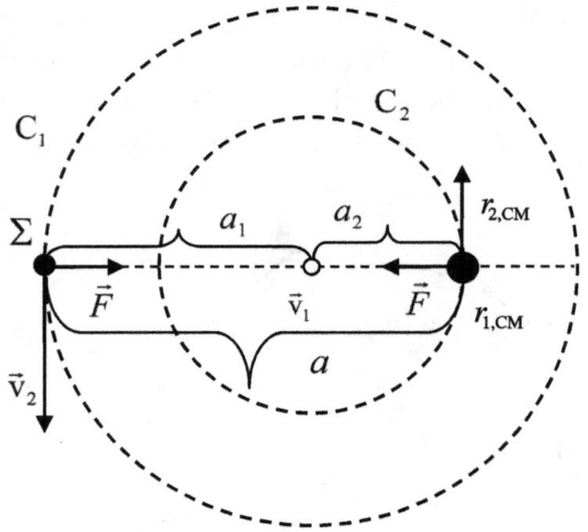


**Fig. T5.5**

$$F = K\frac{mM}{(a_1+a_2)^2} = m\omega^2 a_1 = M\omega^2 a_2;$$

$$a_1 + a_2 = a; \quad a_2 = \frac{m}{M}a_1; \quad a_1 + \frac{m}{M}a_1 = a; \quad a_1 = \frac{M}{m+M}a;$$

$$a_2 = \frac{m}{m+M}a;$$

$$K\frac{mM}{(a_1+a_2)^2} = m\omega^2\frac{M}{m+M}a = M\omega^2\frac{m}{m+M}a;$$

$$K\frac{mM}{(a_1+a_2)^2} = \frac{4\pi^2}{T^2}\frac{mM}{m+M}a;$$

$$K\frac{mM}{a^2} = \frac{4\pi^2}{T^2}\frac{mM}{m+M}a;$$

$$T^2 = \frac{4\pi^2}{K(m+M)}(a_1+a_2)^3; \quad T^2 = \frac{4\pi^2}{K(m+M)}a^3;$$

$$m + M = \frac{4\pi^2 a^3}{KT^2},$$

representing the possibility of determining the total mass of the binary stellar system, if the two stars' common rotation periods ($T$) and the distance between the two stars ($a$) are known.

# Topic 6

# The Masses of the Capella Star's Components

Capella ($\alpha$ Aurigae; the brightest star in the Auriga constellation) is one of the visual binary stars close to Earth. In Figure T6.1 the apparent orbit of the star's secondary component S is presented. This was determined after many years of observation by different observatories, including the Special Astrophysical Observatory (SAO, Figure T6.2) of the USSR Academy of Sciences.

In Figure T6.1, the points obtained by SAO are marked. The position of the principal component $\Sigma$ is marked, and it is linked to the periastron of star S's trajectory.

The SAO observations, made with a telescope whose mirror is 6 m in diameter, aimed to determine the stellar masses.

In Figure T6.3 the diagrams of the two components' radial velocities relative to the system's CM are presented. The following are known: the Capella star's secular parallax $p_C = 0.077''$; the orbital period of the Capella star's components, $T_C = 104$ days.

*Let's suppose* a tridimensional model for the respective system, especially for the eccentric orbit and the inclination of this orbit's plane relative to the observation line. *Estimate* the values of the two components of the Capella star using Kepler's third law. *Specify* the causes of possible errors.

Capella is a stellar system made of two pairs of binary stars. In the first pair there are two bright gigantic stars (Aa and Ab) orbiting one around the other, each with a diameter ten times larger than the Sun's diameter and with a distance between them of 0.72 AU.

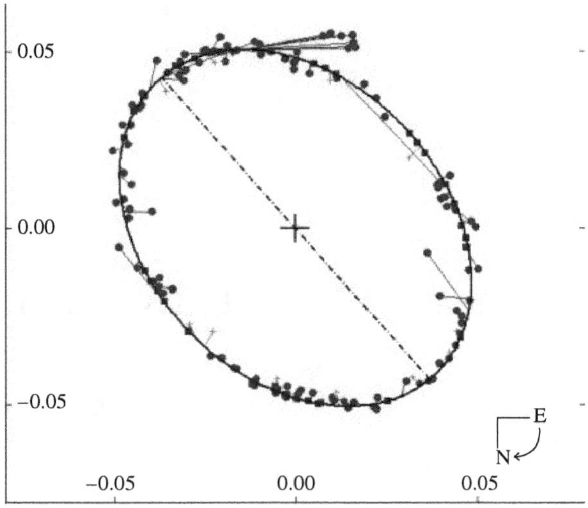


**Fig. T6.1**

**Fig. T6.2**

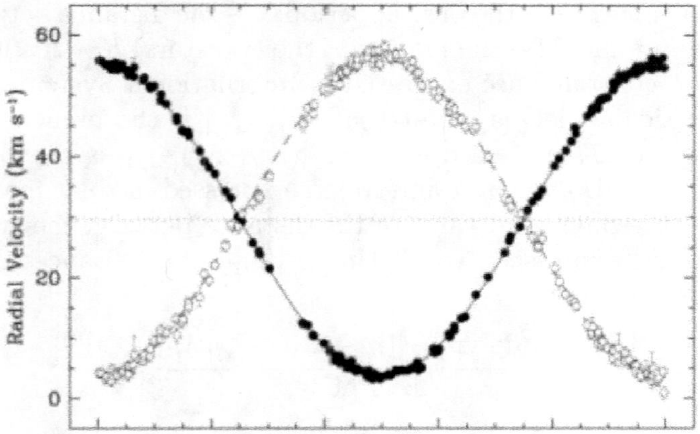


**Fig. T6.3**

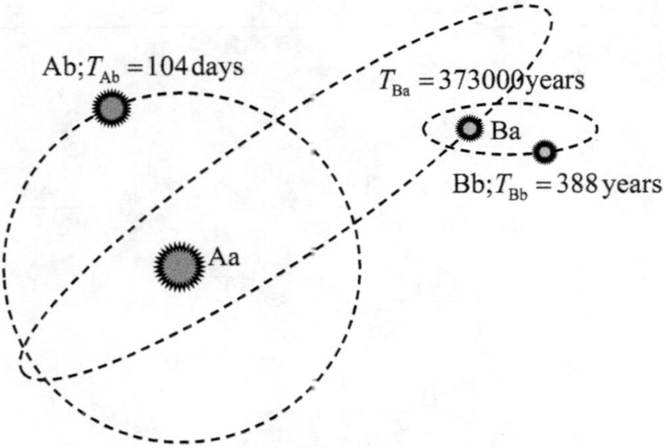


**Fig. T6.4**

The second pair (Ba and Bb) is at a distance of 10 000 AU from the first pair and consists of two red dwarf stars. The four stars' movement in the Capella system is represented in Figure T6.4.

For a binary stellar system whose components orbit around the mass center, Kepler's third law is

$$\frac{T^2(m+M)}{a^3} = \frac{4\pi^2}{K},$$

where all values ($T$ – the orbital period; $a$ – the distance between the two stars; $m$ and $M$– the masses of the two stars; $K$ – the universal attraction constant) are expressed in International System units.

In particular, let us admit that: $|T_{(\text{years})}|$ is the numerical value of the period, $T$, expressed in years; $|(m+M)_{(M_S)}|$ is the numerical value of $(m+M)$ when $m$ and $M$ are expressed in solar mass ($M_S$); $|a_{(\text{AU})}|$ is the numerical value of the distance between the two stars, $a$, when it is expressed in AU. Under these circumstances, Kepler's third law becomes:

$$\frac{|T_{(\text{years})}|^2\,(1\,\text{yr})^2 \cdot |(m+M_B)_{M_S})|\,M_S}{|a_{(\text{AU})}|^3\,(1\,\text{AU})^3} = \frac{4\pi^2}{K};$$

$$\frac{|T_{(\text{years})}|^2 \cdot |(m+M)_{(M_S)}|}{|a_{(\text{AU})}|^3} \cdot \frac{(1\,\text{yr})^2 \cdot M_S}{(1\,\text{AU})^3} = \frac{4\pi^2}{K};$$

$$\frac{(1\text{ yr})^2 \cdot M_S}{(1\,\text{AU})^3} = \frac{(365 \cdot 24 \cdot 3600)^2\,\text{s}^2 \cdot 1.989 \cdot 10^{30}\,\text{kg}}{(15 \cdot 10^{10})^3\,\text{m}^3}$$

$$\approx 5.86 \cdot 10^{11}\,\frac{\text{s}^2\,\text{kg}}{\text{m}^3};$$

$$\frac{4\pi^2}{K} = \frac{4 \cdot 3.14 \cdot 3.14}{6.67 \cdot 10^{-11}\,\text{Nm}^2\text{kg}^{-2}} \approx 5.91 \cdot 10^{11}\,\frac{\text{s}^2\,\text{kg}}{\text{m}^3};$$

$$\frac{(1\,\text{yr})^2 \cdot M_S}{(1\text{AU})^3} \approx \frac{4\pi^2}{K};$$

$$\frac{\left|T_{(\text{years})}\right|^2 \cdot |(m+M)_{(M_S)}|}{\left|a_{(\text{AU})}\right|^3} = 1.$$

Similarly, for the movement of the Earth–Sun system, Kepler's third law is

$$\frac{\left|\tau_{(\text{years})}\right|^2 \cdot \left|(M_E+M_S)_{(M_S)}\right|}{\left|r_{(\text{AU})}\right|^3} = 1,$$

where: $\tau = 1$ year is the orbital period of the Earth–Sun system; $|\tau_{\text{years}}| = 1$; $M_E$ is the Earth's mass; $M_S$ is the Sun's mass; $|(M_E + M_S)_{(M_S)}|$ is the numeric value of the $(M_E + M_S)$ sum expressed in $M_S$ units; $|r_{(\text{AU})}|$ is the numeric value of the Earth–Sun distance expressed in AU; $r = 1\,\text{AU}$; $|r_{(\text{AU})}| = 1$.

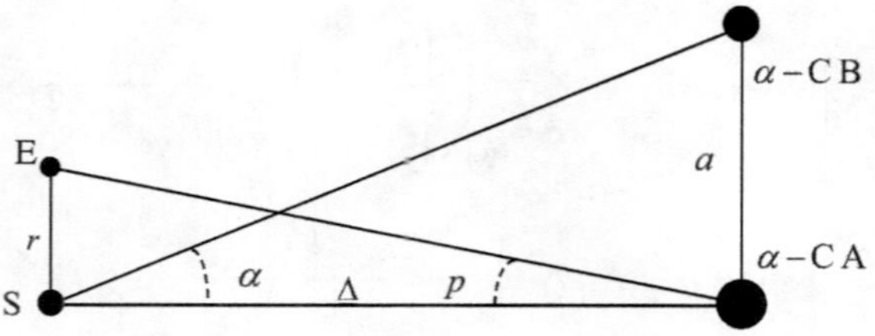


**Fig. T6.5**

The result is:

$$\frac{\left|T_{(\text{years})}\right|^2 \cdot \left|(m+M)_{(M_S)}\right|}{\left|a_{(\text{AU})}\right|^3} = \frac{\left|\tau_{(\text{years})}\right|^2 \cdot \left|(M_E+M_S)_{(M_S)}\right|}{\left|r_{(\text{AU})}\right|^3};$$

$$\frac{\left|T_{(\text{years})}\right|^2 \cdot \left|(m+M)_{(M_S)}\right|}{\left|(M_E+M_S)_{(M_S)}\right|} = \frac{\left|\tau_{(\text{years})}\right|^2 \cdot \left|a_{(\text{AU})}\right|^3}{\left|r_{(\text{AU})}\right|^3};$$

$$M_E << M_S; \quad \left|(M_E+M_S)_{(M_S)}\right| \approx \left|(M_S)_{(M_S)}\right| = 1;$$

$$\left(\frac{\left|a_{(\text{AU})}\right|}{\left|r_{(\text{AU})}\right|}\right)^3 = \left|T_{(\text{years})}\right|^2 \cdot \left|(m+M)_{(M_S)}\right|,$$

where $\left|a_{(\text{AU})}\right|$ represents the numerical (absolute) value (expressed in AU) of the distance between the two stars that cannot be directly determined through experimental observations. From these observations only the angular distance between the two stars ($\alpha$) is determined.

In Figure T6.5: $\Delta$ – the distance between the Sun and the binary star system; $a$ – the distance between the stars; $\alpha$ – the angular distance between the stars; $r$ – the distance between the Earth and the Sun; $p$ – the principal star's parallax (the angle at which the distance between the Earth and the Sun is seen from the center of the principal star). Under the above conditions, and using the Figure, it results in:

$$a = \alpha\Delta; \quad r = p\Delta;$$

$$\left(\frac{\left|\alpha_{('')}\right|}{\left|p_{('')}\right|}\right)^3 = \left|T_{(\text{years})}\right|^2 \cdot \left|(M_A+M_B)_{(M_S)}\right|;$$

$$\left|(m+M)_{(M_S)}\right| = \left(\frac{\left|\alpha_{('')}\right|}{\left|p_{('')}\right|}\right)^3 \cdot \frac{1}{\left|T_{(\text{years})}\right|^2};$$

$$\left|(m+M)_{(M_S)}\right| = \frac{\left|\alpha_{('')}\right|^3}{\left|p_{('')}\right|^3 \cdot \left|T_{(\text{years})}\right|^2},$$

where $|p_{('')}|$ represents the numerical value of the principal star's parallax, $p$, when it is expressed in arcseconds.

For any visual binary stellar system consisting of the stars $\sigma_1$ and $\sigma_2$, the *mass function* of the system is defined as

$$f\left(M_1; M_2\right) = \frac{M_2^3 \sin^3 i}{\left(M_1 + M_2\right)^2},$$

where $M_1$ and $M_2$ are the masses of the stars $\sigma_1$ and $\sigma_2$, respectively, and $i$ is the angle between the plane of the relative orbit and the plane of the apparent orbit (the angle between the line of sight and the normal to the plane of the relative orbit).

*Determine* the masses of the two stars if the following are known: the system's period, $T$; the radius of the two stars' luminosities $k = L_2/L_1 > 1$; the gravitational constant, $K$; the speed of the star $\sigma_1$ relative to the system's mass center $\mathrm{v}_{1,\mathrm{CM}}$.

When the movement of star $\sigma_1$ relative to star $\sigma_2$ is studied, the relative orbit proves to be an ellipse, as presented in Figure T6.6.

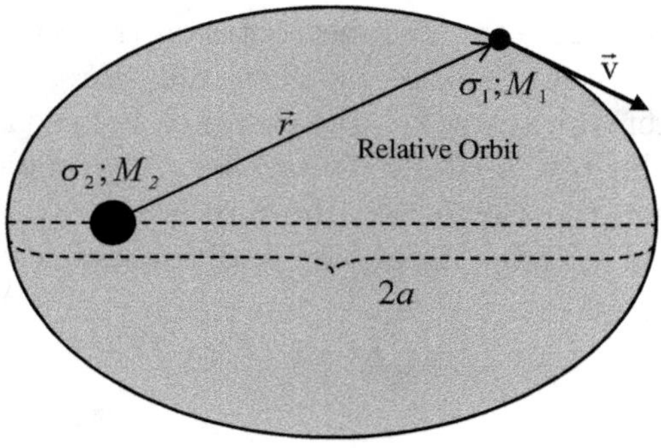


**Fig. T6.6**

Under these conditions, Kepler's third law is

$$\frac{T^2}{a^3} = \frac{4\pi^2}{K(M_1 + M_2)},$$

where $a$ is the semi-major axis of the ellipse that represents the relative orbit.

In Figure T6.7 the same binary system and its CM are represented. The velocities of the two stars relative to the observer at the moment when their orientations are in the line of sight direction, as well as the CM's velocity relative to the observer on the Earth – $\vec{v}_1$, $\vec{v}_2$, $\vec{v}_{CM}$ – are marked. The velocities of the two stars relative to the CM are also indicated in the image:

$$\vec{v}_{1,CM} = \vec{v}_1 - \vec{v}_{CM}; \quad \vec{v}_{2,CM} = \vec{v}_2 - \vec{v}_{CM}.$$

Thus:

$$\vec{v}_1 = \vec{v}_{1,CM} + \vec{v}_{CM}; \quad \vec{v}_2 = \vec{v}_{2,CM} + \vec{v}_{CM}.$$

The stars $\sigma_1$ and $\sigma_2$ that represent a visual binary system move on concentric circles around the common center of mass (CM) and are observed as presented in Figure T6.7. Since the planes of their orbits form a 90° angle with the perpendicular plane in the observation direction ($i = 90°$), the result is:

$$a = a_1 + a_2;$$

$$v_{1,CM} = \frac{2\pi a_1}{T}; \quad v_{2,CM} = \frac{2\pi a_2}{T}.$$

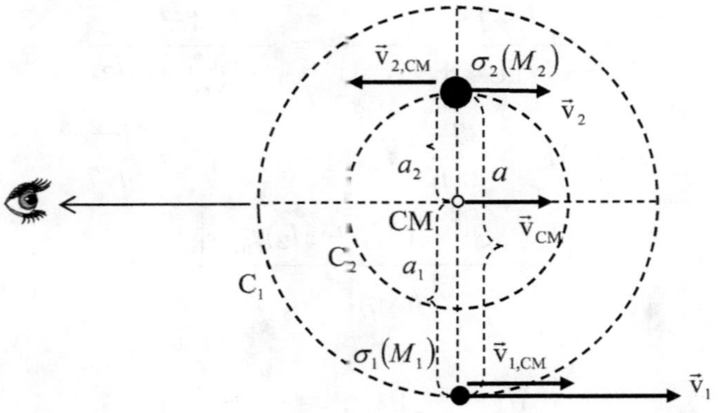


**Fig. T6.7**

The rotation period, $T$, of the two stars relative to the CM is the same as the period $T$ of star $\sigma_1$'s movement relative to star $\sigma_2$. Hence:

$$a_1 = \frac{v_{1,\mathrm{CM}} T}{2\pi}; \quad a_2 = \frac{v_{2,\mathrm{CM}} T}{2\pi};$$

$$a_1 + a_2 = \frac{T}{2\pi}(v_{1,\mathrm{CM}} + v_{2,\mathrm{CM}}) = a,$$

and so, in the CM reference system, the distance between the two stars is constant.

In the star $\sigma_1$'s relative movement, the distance between the two stars is variable, but the average value of this distance is equal to the ellipse's semi-major axis. In the movement of the star $\sigma_1$ relative to the star $\sigma_2$, there is a moment when the distance between the two stars is equal to the semi-major axis of the ellipse that represents the relative orbit.

As a consequence, the distance between the two stars calculated in the SRCM is $a_1 + a_2$ and can be considered to be equal to the semi-major axis of the relative orbit. Thus:

$$a = a_1 + a_2;$$

$$\frac{T^2}{a^3} = \frac{4\pi^2}{K(M_1 + M_2)};$$

$$\frac{T^2}{(a_1 + a_2)^3} = \frac{4\pi^2}{K(M_1 + M_2)};$$

$$\frac{T^2}{\frac{T^3}{(2\pi)^3}(v_{1,\mathrm{CM}} + v_{2,\mathrm{CM}})^3} = \frac{4\pi^2}{K(M_1 + M_2)};$$

$$M_1 + M_2 = \frac{T}{2\pi K}(v_{1,\mathrm{CM}} + v_{2,\mathrm{CM}})^3 = \frac{4\pi^2 a^3}{KT^2};$$

$$\frac{\left|T_{(\mathrm{years})}\right|^2 \cdot \left|(M_1 + M_2)_{(M_\mathrm{S})}\right|}{\left|a_{(\mathrm{AU})}\right|^3} = 1;$$

$$\left|(M_1 + M_2)_{(M_\mathrm{S})}\right| = \frac{\left|a_{(\mathrm{AU})}\right|^3}{\left|T_{(\mathrm{years})}\right|^2}.$$

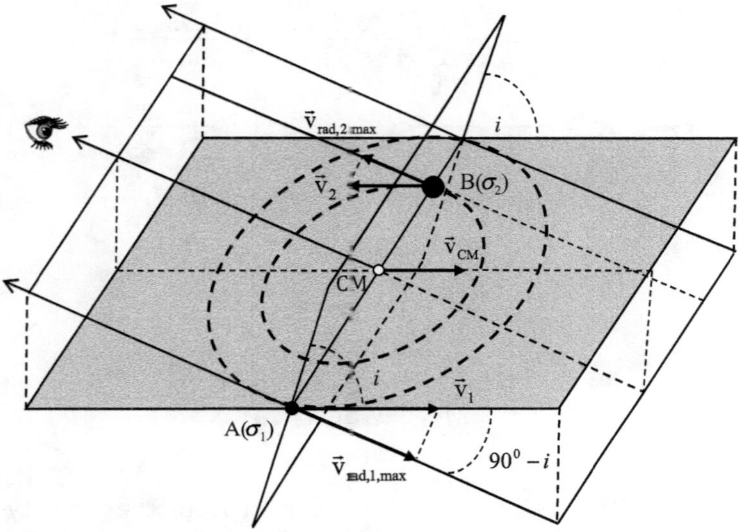


**Fig. T6.8**

If, as presented in Figure T6.8, the observation of the two stars takes place when the orbits' plane makes an $i < 90°$ angle with the plane perpendicular to the observation direction, this results in:

$$\vec{v}_{CM} = \frac{M_1\vec{v}_1 + M_2\vec{v}_2}{M_1 + M_2} = \frac{M_1\left(\vec{v}_{1,CM} + \vec{v}_{CM}\right) + M_2\left(\vec{v}_{CM} + \vec{v}_{2,CM}\right)}{M_1 + M_2};$$

$$M_1\vec{v}_{1,CM} + M_2\vec{v}_{2,CM} = 0; \quad M_1 v_{1,CM} = M_2 v_{2,CM}; \quad \frac{M_1}{M_2} = \frac{v_{2,CM}}{v_{1,CM}};$$

$$v_{rad,1,max} = v_1 \cos\left(90° - i\right) = v_1 \sin i = \left(v_{1,CM} + v_{CM}\right)\sin i;$$

$$v_{1,CM} = \frac{v_{rad,1,max}}{\sin i} - v_{CM};$$

$$v_{rad,2,max} = v_2 \cos\left(90° - i\right) = v_2 \sin i = \left(v_{CM} - v_{2,CM}\right)\sin i;$$

$$v_{2,CM} = v_{CM} - \frac{v_{rad,2,max}}{\sin i};$$

$$M_1 + M_2 = \frac{T}{2\pi K}\left(v_{1,CM} + v_{2,CM}\right)^3;$$

$$M_1 v_{1,CM} = M_2 v_{2,CM};$$

$$M_1 + M_2 = \frac{T}{2\pi K}\left(\frac{\mathrm{v}_{\mathrm{rad,1,max}}}{\sin i} - \frac{\mathrm{v}_{\mathrm{rad,2.\,max}}}{\sin i}\right)^3;$$

$$M_1 + M_2 = \frac{T}{2\pi K \cdot \sin^3 i} \cdot \mathrm{v}^3_{\mathrm{rad,1,max}}\left(1 - \frac{\mathrm{v}_{\mathrm{rad,2,max}}}{\mathrm{v}_{\mathrm{rad,1,max}}}\right)^3;$$

$$\vec{H}_{\mathrm{CM}} = \vec{H}_{1,\mathrm{CM}} + \vec{H}_{2,\mathrm{CM}} = M_1\vec{\mathrm{v}}_{1,\mathrm{CM}} + M_2\vec{\mathrm{v}}_{2,\mathrm{CM}} = 0;$$

$$\vec{\mathrm{v}}_{\mathrm{rad,\,1,max}}$$

$$M_1\frac{\mathrm{v}_{\mathrm{rad,1,max}}}{\sin i} = M_2\frac{\mathrm{v}_{\mathrm{rad,2,max}}}{\sin i};$$

$$M_1\mathrm{v}_{\mathrm{rad,1,max}} = M_2\mathrm{v}_{\mathrm{rad,2,max}};$$

$$\frac{M_1}{M_2} = \frac{\mathrm{v}_{\mathrm{rad,2,max}}}{\mathrm{v}_{\mathrm{rad,1,max}}}.$$

The value of this ratio can be determined from the velocity–time graph for the two stars, represented in Figure T6.9.

Under these conditions, using the equation

$$\left|(M_1 + M_2)_{(M_\mathrm{S})}\right| = \frac{\left|a_{(\mathrm{AU})}\right|^3}{\left|T_{(\mathrm{years})}\right|^2},$$

the masses ($M_1$ and $M_2$) of the two components of the studied binary stellar system can be determined.

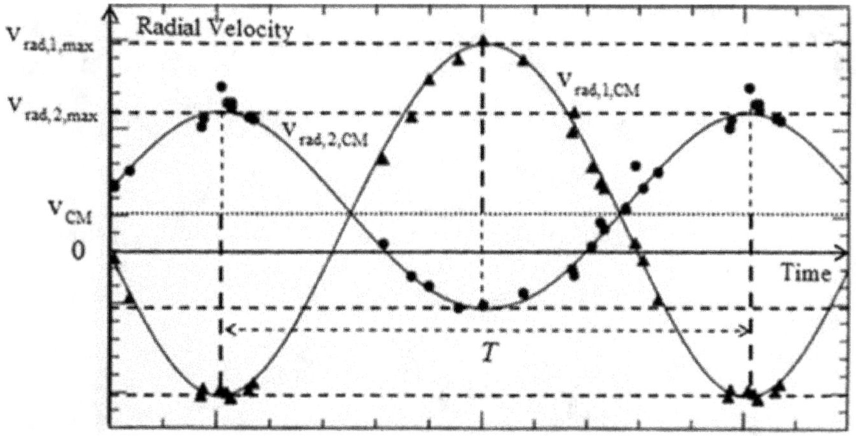


**Fig. T6.9**

Also:

$$\frac{v_{rad,2,max}}{v_{rad,1,max}} = \frac{M_1}{M_2} = \frac{(v_{CM} - v_{2,CM}) \sin i}{(v_{1,CM} + v_{CM}) \sin i} = \frac{v_{CM} - v_{2,CM}}{v_{1,CM} + v_{CM}};$$

$$\frac{M_1}{M_2} = \frac{v_{CM} - v_{2,CM}}{v_{1,CM} + v_{CM}};$$

$$\frac{T}{2\pi K} (v_{1,CM} + v_{2,CM})^3 = M_1 + M_2;$$

$$v_{1,CM} + v_{2,CM} = \sqrt[3]{\frac{2\pi K (M_1 + M_2)}{T}};$$

$$M_1 v_{1,CM} = M_2 v_{2,CM}.$$

The $v_{1,CM}$ and $v_{2,CM}$ velocities can be determined from the last two equations.

Further, the equations

$$v_{rad,1,max} = (v_{1,CM} + v_{CM}) \sin i$$

$$v_{rad,2,max} = (v_{CM} - v_{2,CM}) \sin i$$

result in

$$\sin i = \frac{v_{rad,1,max}}{v_{1,CM} + v_{CM}} = \frac{v_{rad,2,max}}{v_{CM} - v_{2,CM}},$$

where: $v_{1,CM}$ and $v_{2,CM}$ are known from the previous system solution, and $v_{rad,1,max}$, $v_{rad,2,max}$ and $v_{CM}$ are known from the graphs of radial velocities.

Using the mass function for the system results in:

$$M_1 + M_2 = \frac{T}{2\pi K \cdot \sin^3 i} \cdot v^3_{rad,1,max} \left(1 + \frac{M_1}{M_2}\right)^3;$$

$$v_{rad,1,max} = (v_{1,CM} + v_{CM}) \sin i;$$

$$M_1 + M_2 = \frac{T}{2\pi K \cdot \sin^3 i} \cdot v^3_{1,rad,max} \frac{(M_1 + M_2)^3}{M_2^3};$$

$$\frac{M_2^3 \sin^3 i}{(M_1 + M_2)^2} = \frac{T}{2\pi K} \cdot v^3_{rad,1,max} = \frac{T}{2\pi K} (v_{1,CM} \cdot \sin i)^3$$

$$= f(M_1; M_2),$$

representing the mass function for the visual binary stellar system;

$$\frac{M_2^3 \sin^3 i}{(M_1 + M_2)^2} = \frac{T}{2\pi K} (\mathrm{v}_{1,\mathrm{CM}} \cdot \sin i)^3 ;$$

$$\frac{M_2^3}{(M_1 + M_2)^2} = \frac{T}{2\pi K} \cdot \mathrm{v}_{1,\mathrm{CM}}^3;$$

$$L_1 = qM_1^4; \quad L_2 = qM_2^4;$$

$$\frac{L_2}{L_1} = k = \left(\frac{M_2}{M_1}\right)^4; \quad \frac{M_2}{M_1} = \sqrt[4]{k}; \quad M_2 = \sqrt[4]{k} \cdot M_1;$$

$$\frac{k^{3/4} \cdot M_1^3}{M_1^2 \left(1 + \sqrt[4]{k}\right)^2} = \frac{T}{2\pi K} \cdot \mathrm{v}_{1,\mathrm{CM}}^3;$$

$$M_1 = \frac{T}{2\pi K} \cdot \frac{(1 + k^{1/4})^2}{k^{3/4}} \cdot \mathrm{v}_{1,\mathrm{CM}}^3;$$

$$M_2 = \frac{T}{2\pi K} \cdot \frac{(1 + k^{3/4})^2}{k^{-1/4}} \cdot \mathrm{v}_{1,\mathrm{CM}}^3 = \frac{T}{2\pi K} \cdot k^{1/4} \cdot (1 + k^{3/4})^2.$$

In Figure T6.10, the elements, S and $\Sigma$, of the binary stellar system are represented corresponding to the moment $t$, when their velocities relative to a stationary observer are $\vec{\mathrm{v}}_1$ and $\vec{\mathrm{v}}_2$, respectively. These velocities ($\vec{\mathrm{v}}_1$ and $\vec{\mathrm{v}}_2$) are the result of gravitational interaction between the two stars. It is known that the two stars move on the same plane, $\Pi$, generally different from the plane of the system's observation. Since the binary stellar system is considered to be an insulated system, its center of mass will uniformly move on a rectilinear trajectory, while the relative movements of the two components will be variant and coplanar.

This results in the following:

$$m\vec{\mathrm{v}}_1 + M\vec{\mathrm{v}}_2 = (m + M)\, \vec{\mathrm{v}}_{\mathrm{CM}};$$

$$\vec{\mathrm{v}}_{\mathrm{CM}} = \frac{m\vec{\mathrm{v}}_1 + M\vec{\mathrm{v}}_2}{m + M} = \text{constant}.$$

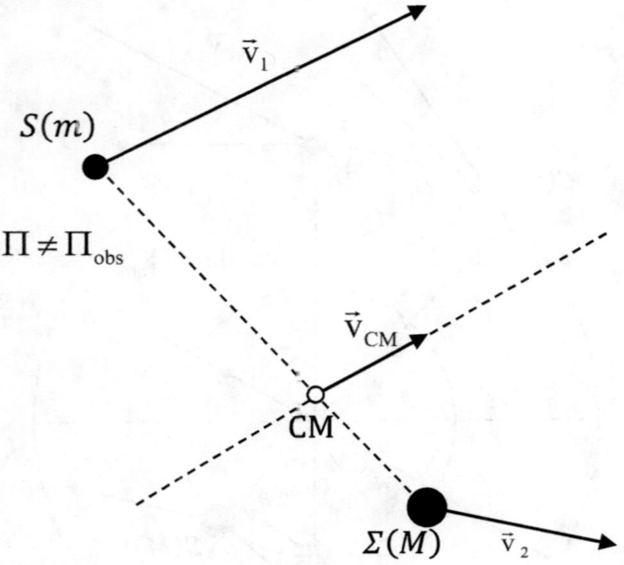


**Fig. T6.10**

Let us admit that the orbits of the two components relative to the CM are concentric circles in the same plane, Π, as presented in Figure T6.11. Thus:

$$\vec{v}_1 = \vec{v}_{CM} + \vec{v}_{1,CM}; \quad \vec{v}_2 = \vec{v}_{CM} + \vec{v}_{2,CM};$$

$$m\left(\vec{v}_{CM} + \vec{v}_{1,CM}\right) + M\left(\vec{v}_{CM} + \vec{v}_{2,CM}\right) = (m+M)\,\vec{v}_{CM};$$

$$m\vec{v}_{CM} + M\vec{v}_{CM} + m\vec{v}_{1,CM} + M\vec{v}_{2,CM} = (m+M)\,\vec{v}_{CM};$$

$$(m+M)\,\vec{v}_{CM} + m\vec{v}_{1,CM} + M\vec{v}_{2,CM} = (m+M)\,\vec{v}_{CM};$$

$$m\vec{v}_{1,CM} + M\vec{v}_{2,CM} = 0; \quad m\vec{v}_{1,CM} = -M\vec{v}_{2,CM};$$

$$m\mathrm{v}_{1,CM} = M\mathrm{v}_{2,CM}.$$

In a subsequent moment, $t + \Delta t$, the two stars have reached the points A and B, respectively, as presented in Figure T6.12. At that time, their velocities relative to the CM have changed only their orientations, and the velocities of the two stars relative to the stationary observer have changed both their orientations and their moduli. Thus, the CM remains in a uniform rectilinear movement.

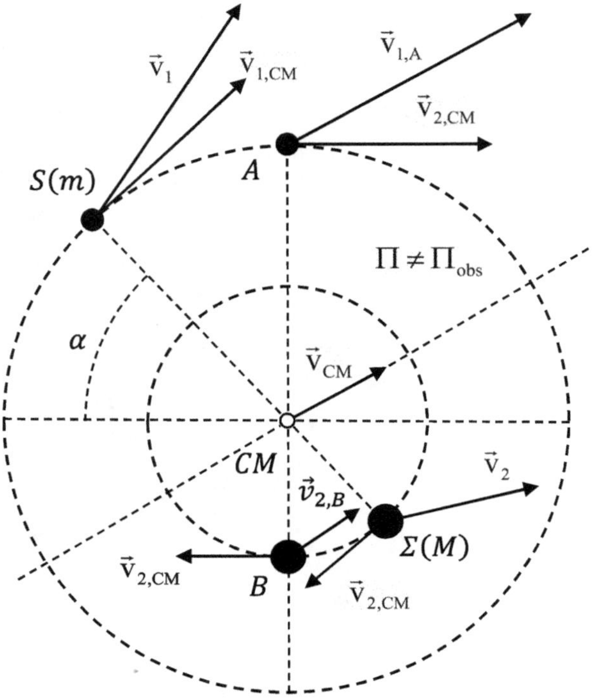


**Fig. T6.11**

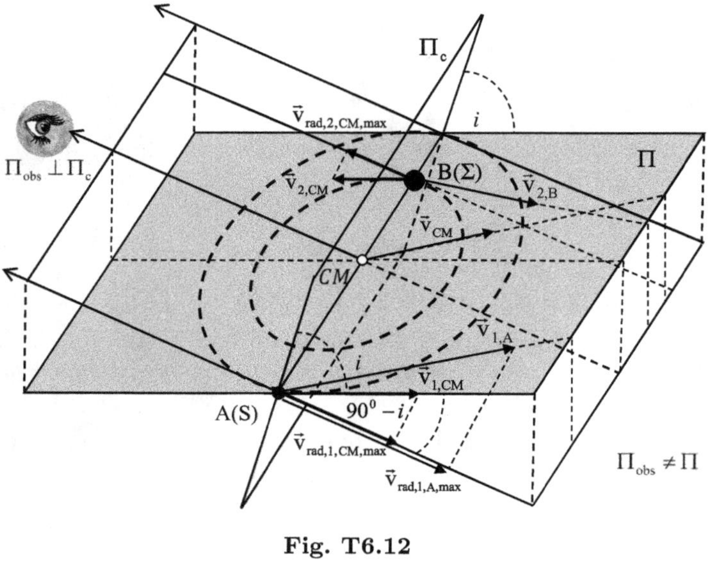


**Fig. T6.12**

The result is:

$$m\vec{v}_{1,A} + M\vec{v}_{2,B} = (m+M)\,\vec{v}_{CM};$$

$$\vec{v}_{1,A} = (\vec{v}_{CM} + \vec{v}_{1,CM})_A; \quad \vec{v}_{2,B} = (\vec{v}_{CM} + \vec{v}_{2,CM})_B;$$

$$m\,(\vec{v}_{CM} + \vec{v}_{1,CM})_A + M\,(\vec{v}_{CM} + \vec{v}_{2,CM})_B = (m+M)\,\vec{v}_{CM};$$

$$m\vec{v}_{1,CM} + M\vec{v}_{2,CM} = 0; \quad m\vec{v}_{1,CM} = -M\vec{v}_{2,CM}; \quad m v_{1,CM} = M v_{2,CM};$$

$$\frac{m}{M} = \frac{v_{2,CM}}{v_{1,CM}}.$$

$$v_{rad,1,max} = v_{rad,1,A} = v_{1,A}\cos\alpha_1 = v_{rad,CM} + v_{1,CM};$$

$$v_{rad,2,max} = v_{rad,2,B} = v_{2,B}\cos\alpha_2 = v_{rad,CM} - v_{2,CM}.$$

# Topic 7

# Radial Velocities

For the situation represented in Figure T7.1, considering that at the initial moment the secondary star (S) is at the periastron, and taking into account the details of Figure T7.2, the result is:

$$0 < \theta < 180^0;$$

$$\sin i = \frac{z}{x}; \quad z = x \sin i;$$

$$\sin\left[\pi - (\theta + \omega)\right] = \frac{x}{r} = -\cos\pi \cdot \sin(\theta + \omega) = \sin(\theta + \omega);$$

$$x = r \cdot \sin(\theta + \omega);$$

$$z = r \cdot \sin(\theta + \omega) \cdot \sin i,$$

where $z$ is the distance from the secondary star (S) to the celestial plane ($\Pi_c$), which means that the S's coordinates correspond to the axis $\Sigma Z \perp \Pi_c$; thus:

$$\mathrm{v_{rad}} = \frac{\mathrm{d}z}{\mathrm{d}t} = \frac{\mathrm{d}}{\mathrm{d}t}\left[r\ \sin(\theta + \omega)\ \sin i\right]; \quad \theta = \theta(t); \quad r = r(t);$$

$$i = \text{constant} \quad \omega = \text{constant};$$

$$\mathrm{v_{rad}} = r\frac{\mathrm{d}}{\mathrm{d}t}\left[\sin(\theta + \omega)\sin i\right] + \sin(\theta + \omega)\sin i\frac{\mathrm{d}r}{\mathrm{d}t};$$

$$\mathrm{v_{rad}} = r\ \sin(\theta + \omega)\frac{\mathrm{d}}{\mathrm{d}t}(\sin i) + r\sin i\frac{\mathrm{d}}{\mathrm{d}t}\left[\sin(\theta + \omega)\right]$$

$$+ \sin(\theta + \omega)\sin i\ \frac{\mathrm{d}r}{\mathrm{d}t};$$

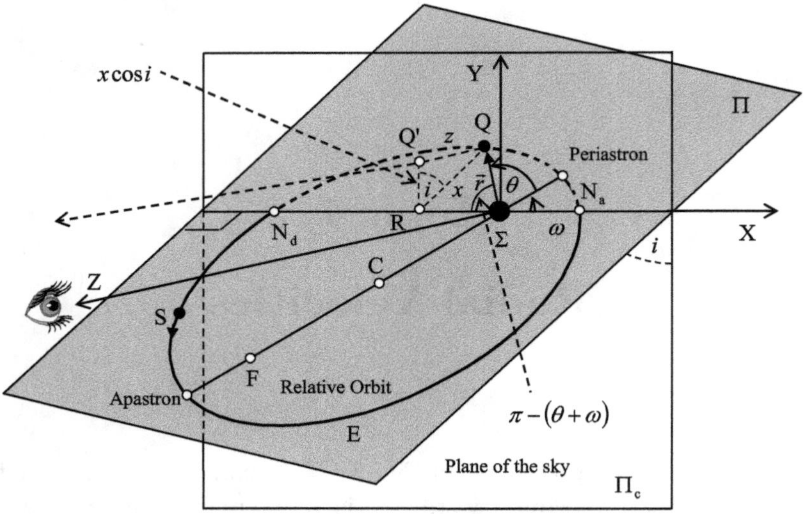


**Fig. T7.1**

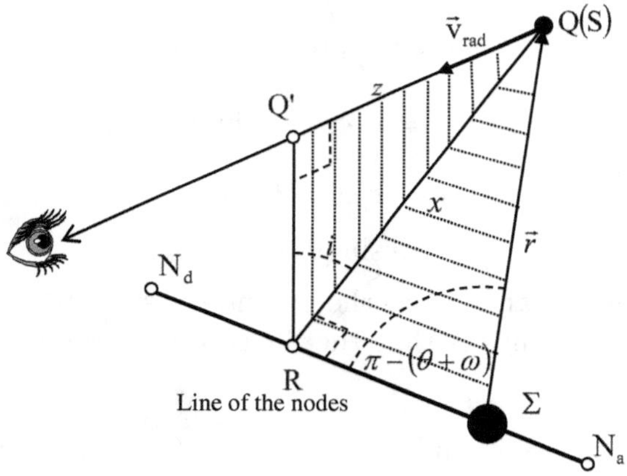


**Fig. T7.2**

$$\mathrm{v_{rad}} = r\sin i\cos(\theta+\omega)\ \frac{\mathrm{d}}{\mathrm{d}t}(\theta+\omega) + \sin(\theta+\omega)\sin i\ \frac{\mathrm{d}r}{\mathrm{d}t};$$

$$\mathrm{v_{rad}} = r\sin i\ \cos(\theta+\omega)\ \frac{\mathrm{d}\theta}{\mathrm{d}t} + \sin(\theta+\omega)\ \sin i\frac{\mathrm{d}r}{\mathrm{d}t};$$

$$\mathrm{v_{rad}} = r\sin i\cos(\theta+\omega)\,\dot{\theta} + \sin(\theta+\omega)\sin i\,\dot{r};$$

$$\mathrm{v_{rad}} = \left[r\,\dot{\theta}\,\cos(\theta+\omega) + \dot{r}\,\sin(\theta+\omega)\right]\sin i;$$

$$r = \frac{p}{1+e\,\cos\theta} = \frac{a\,(1-e^2)}{1+e\cos\theta};$$

$$\dot{r} = \frac{\mathrm{d}r}{\mathrm{d}t} = \frac{\mathrm{d}}{\mathrm{d}t}\left[\frac{a\,(1-e^2)}{1+e\,\cos\theta}\right];$$

$$\dot{r} = \frac{\mathrm{d}r}{\mathrm{d}t} = \frac{(1+e\,\cos\theta)\,\frac{\mathrm{d}}{\mathrm{d}t}\left[a\,(1-e^2)\right] - a\,(1-e^2)\,\frac{\mathrm{d}}{\mathrm{d}t}\,(1+e\,\cos\theta)}{(1+e\,\cos\theta)^2};$$

$$\dot{r} = \frac{\mathrm{d}r}{\mathrm{d}t} = \frac{a\,(1-e^2)\;e\sin\theta\,\frac{\mathrm{d}\theta}{\mathrm{d}t}}{(1+e\,\cos\theta)^2};$$

$$\dot{r} = \frac{\mathrm{d}r}{\mathrm{d}t} = \frac{a\,(1-e^2)}{1+e\cos\theta}\,\frac{e\,\frac{\mathrm{d}\theta}{\mathrm{d}t}\sin\theta}{1+e\cos\theta};$$

$$r = \frac{p}{1+e\,\cos\theta} = \frac{a\,(1-e^2)}{1+e\cos\theta};$$

$$\dot{r} = \frac{r\,e\,\dot{\theta}\,\sin\theta}{1+e\,\cos\theta};$$

$$\frac{\mathrm{d}A}{\mathrm{d}t} = \frac{1}{2}\,r^2\dot{\theta};$$

$$\frac{A}{T} = \frac{1}{2}\,r^2\dot{\theta};$$

$$A = \pi ab; \quad b = a\sqrt{1-e^2};$$

$$A = \pi a^2\sqrt{1-e^2};$$

$$\frac{\pi a^2\sqrt{1-e^2}}{T} = \frac{1}{2}\,r^2\dot{\theta};$$

$$r\,\dot{\theta} = \frac{2\pi a^2\sqrt{1-e^2}}{rT}; \quad r\,\dot{\theta} = \frac{1}{r}\,\frac{2\pi a^2\sqrt{1-e^2}}{T};$$

$$r\,\dot{\theta} = \frac{1+e\,\cos\theta}{a\,(1-e^2)}\,\frac{2\pi a^2\sqrt{1-e^2}}{T};$$

$$r\dot{\theta} = \frac{2\pi a\,(1+e\,\cos\theta)}{T\sqrt{1-e^2}};$$

$$\dot{r} = \frac{r\,e\,\dot{\theta}\,\sin\theta}{1+e\,\cos\theta} = r\dot{\theta}\,\frac{e\,\sin\theta}{1+e\,\cos\theta};$$

$$\dot{r} = \frac{2\pi a\,(1+e\,\cos\theta)}{T\sqrt{1-e^2}}\,\frac{e\,\sin\theta}{1+e\,\cos\theta};$$

$$\dot{r} = \frac{2\pi\,a\,e\,\sin\theta}{T\sqrt{1-e^2}};$$

$$\mathrm{v_{rad}} = \left[r\,\dot{\theta}\,\cos(\theta+\omega) + \dot{r}\,\sin(\theta+\omega)\right]\,\sin i;$$

$$\mathrm{v_{rad}} = \left[\frac{2\pi a\,(1+e\,\cos\theta)}{T\sqrt{1-e^2}}\,\cos(\theta+\omega) + \frac{2\pi a e\sin\theta}{T\sqrt{1-e^2}}\,\sin(\theta+\omega)\right]\sin i;$$

$$\mathrm{v_{rad}} = \frac{2\pi a\sin i}{T\sqrt{1-e^2}}\,\left[(1+e\cos\theta)\,\cos(\theta+\omega) + e\,\sin\theta\,\sin(\theta+\omega)\right];$$

$$\mathrm{v_{rad}} = \frac{2\pi a\sin i}{T\sqrt{1-e^2}}[\cos(\theta+\omega) + e\,\cos\theta\,\cos(\theta+\omega)$$

$$+\,e\,\sin\theta\,\sin(\theta+\omega)];$$

$$\cos(\theta+\omega) = \cos\theta\,\cos\omega - \sin\theta\,\sin\omega;$$

$$\sin(\theta+\omega) = \sin\theta\,\cos\omega + \cos\theta\,\sin\omega;$$

$$[\cos(\theta+\omega) + e\,\cos\theta\,\cos(\theta+\omega) + e\,\sin\theta\,\sin(\theta+\omega)] =$$

$$\cos\theta\,\cos\omega - \sin\theta\,\sin\omega + e\,\cos\omega = \cos(\theta+\omega) + e\,\cos\omega;$$

$$\mathrm{v_{rad}} = \frac{2\pi\,a\,\sin i}{T\sqrt{1-e^2}}\,[\cos(\theta+\omega) + e\,\cos\omega]\,.$$

For the version represented in Figure T7.3, considering that at the initial moment the secondary star (S) is at the periastron and taking into account the details in Figure T7.4, the result is:

$$180^0 < \theta < 360^0;$$

$$\sin i = \frac{z}{x}; \quad z = x\sin i;$$

$$\sin[2\pi - (\theta+\omega)] = \frac{x}{r} = -\cos 2\pi\cdot\sin(\theta+\omega) = -\sin(\theta+\omega)\,;$$

$$x = -r \cdot \sin(\theta + \omega);$$

$$z = -r \cdot \sin(\theta + \omega) \cdot \sin i;$$

$$\mathrm{v_{rad}} = -\frac{\mathrm{d}z}{\mathrm{d}t} = \frac{\mathrm{d}}{\mathrm{d}t}\left[r\ \sin(\theta + \omega)\ \sin i\right];$$

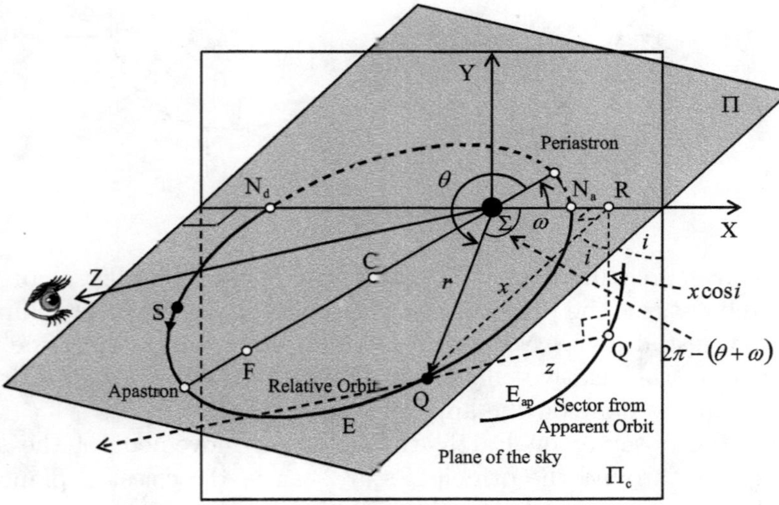


**Fig. T7.3**

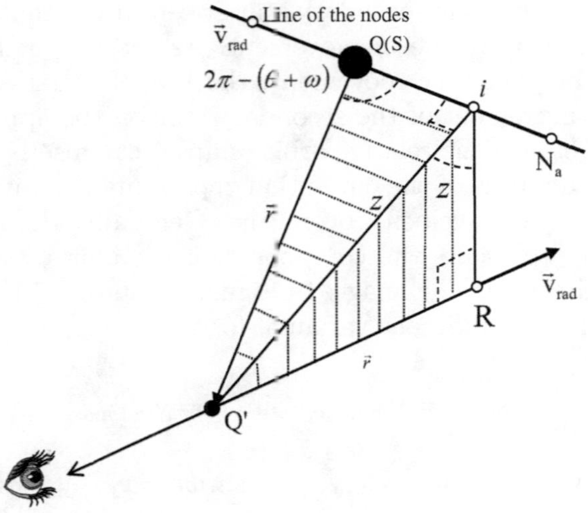


**Fig. T7.4**

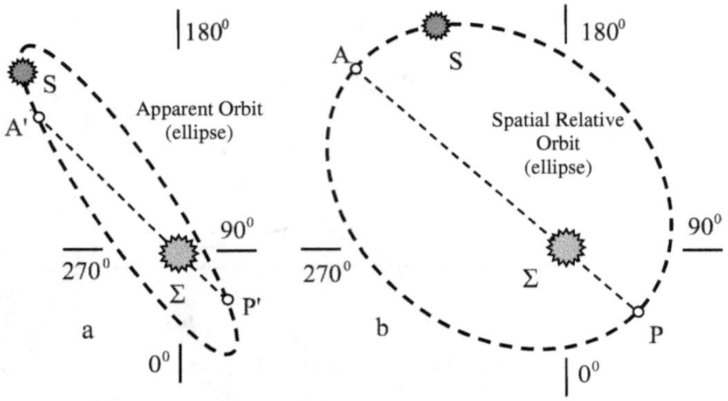


**Fig. T7.5**

As presented in Figure T7.5, the apparent orbit (ellipse) of the secondary star is the projection of the relative (actual) orbit (ellipse) on the celestial plane. Numerous methods allow us to determine the elements of the relative ellipse using the information resulting from measurements done on the apparent orbit (ellipse).

For the observer on Earth, the apparent movement of the secondary star around the principal star, seen in the celestial plane, is an elliptic trajectory (the apparent orbit), in particular a circle or a line segment. The primary (principal) star is always inside the apparent ellipse, but not always in its focus. On the apparent orbit (ellipse), the radius vector of the secondary star sweeps areas that are directly proportional to the time of movement. As a consequence, Kepler's second law of planetary movement, the law of equal areas, is also true for the movement of the secondary star on the apparent orbit.

The elements of the relative orbit (ellipse) can also be determined through the analysis of the curve that represents the variation of the second star's radial velocity over time. Generally, the radial velocity of a star represents the component of the star's velocity in the observer's direction. The images in Figures T7.6 to T7.10 present the radial velocities in different variants, for which:

$$\mathrm{v_{rad}} = v \cdot \sin\alpha = \mathrm{v_{rad,max}} \cdot \sin\omega t = \mathrm{v_{rad,max}} \cdot \sin\frac{2\pi}{T}t;$$

$$\mathrm{v_{rad}} = \mathrm{v} \cdot \sin i \cdot \sin\alpha = \mathrm{v_{rad,max}} \cdot \sin\omega t = \mathrm{v_{rad,max}} \cdot \sin\frac{2\pi}{T}t;$$

$$\mathrm{v_{rad,max}} = \mathrm{v} \cdot \sin i.$$

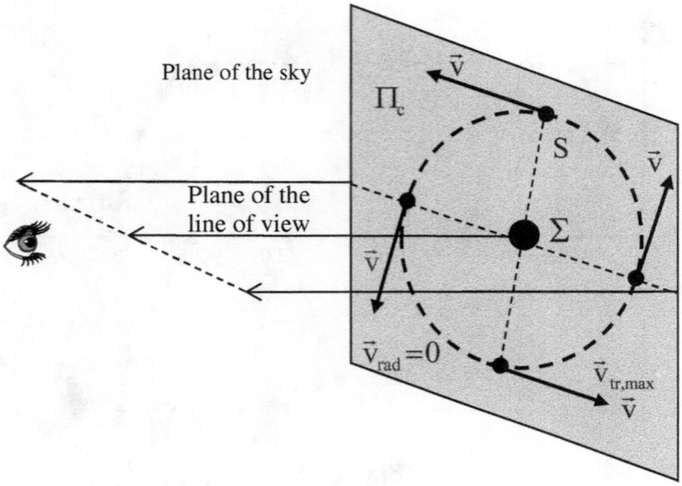


**Fig. T7.6**

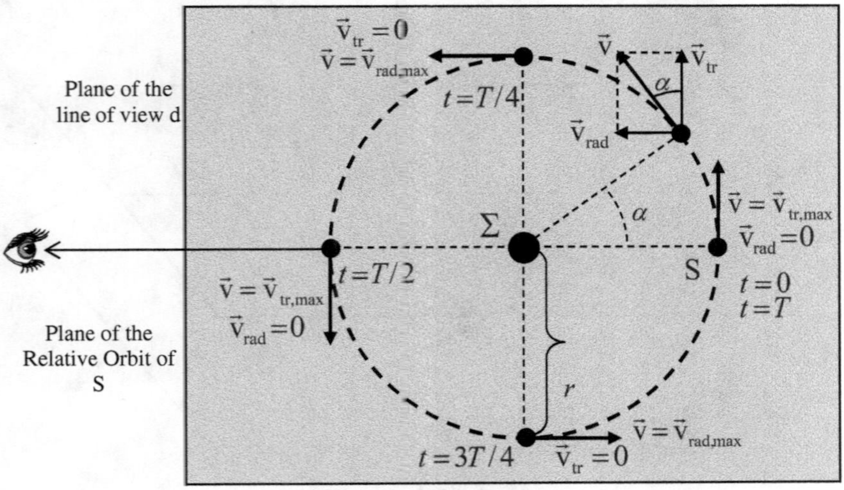


**Fig. T7.7**

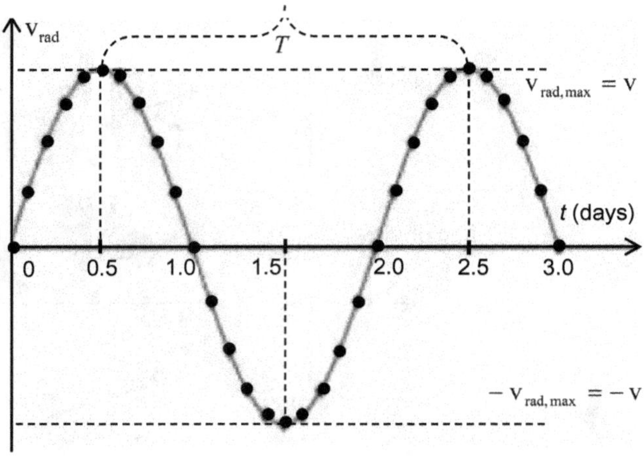


**Fig. T7.8**

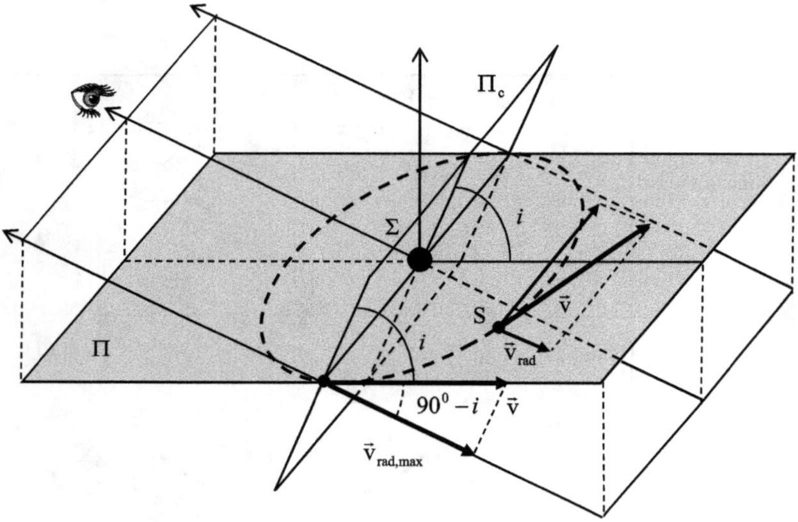


**Fig. T7.9**

If $i \neq 90^0$, the amplitude of the radial velocity variation is reduced by the factor $\sin i$.

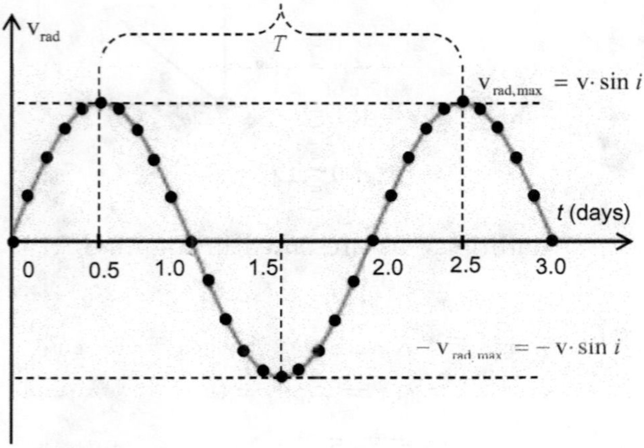


**Fig. T7.10**

The elliptical orbit of the star S around the star Σ is represented in Figure T7.11, where the system's observation line is also indicated.

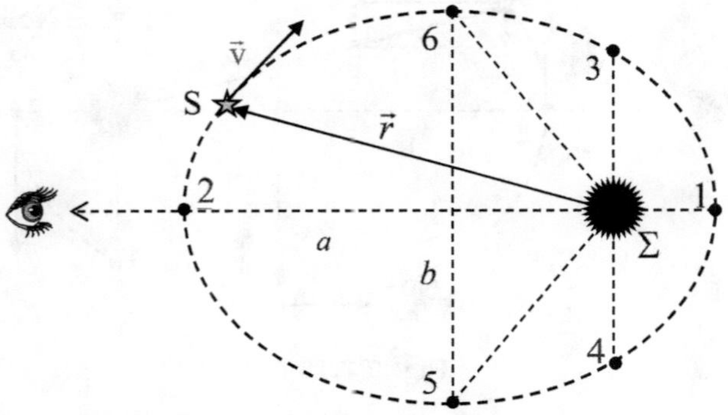


**Fig. T7.11**

For the secondary star (S), which at a certain moment has the velocity $\vec{v}$ relative to the observer O, as presented in Figure T7.12, we define the radial velocity, $\vec{v}_{rad}$, as the component of velocity along the star's observation direction and the transversal velocity, $\vec{v}_{tr}$, as the component of velocity perpendicular to the star's observation direction.

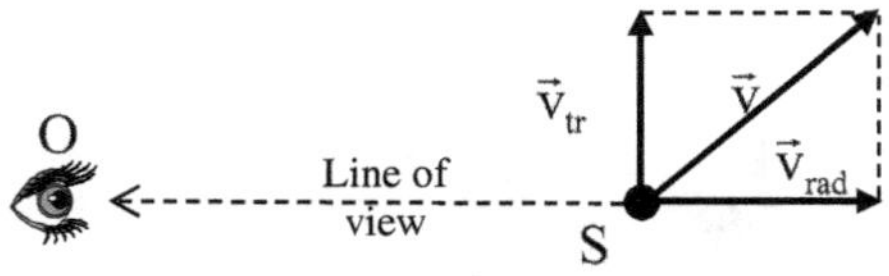


**Fig. T7.12**

Under these conditions, as presented in Figure T7.13, the result is:

$$v_1 = v_{max} = v_{tr.\,max}; \quad v_2 = v_{min} = v_{tr.\,min};$$

$$v_{rad,1} = v_{rad,2} = 0;$$

$$v_5 = v_6 = v = v_{rad}.$$

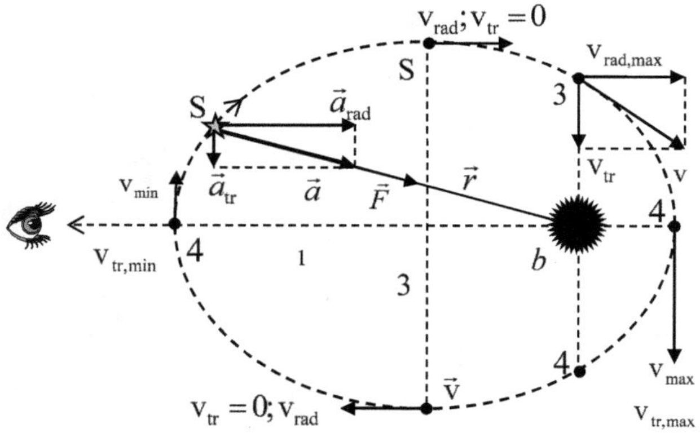


**Fig. T7.13**

The acceleration of star S due to the central gravitational force, $\vec{a} = \frac{\vec{F}}{m}$, exerted on star S by star Σ can be decomposed into a transversal and a radial component, as presented in Figure T7.13:

$$\vec{a} = \vec{a}_{rad} + \vec{a}_{tr},$$

of which only the radial component, $\vec{a}_{rad}$, determines the variation of the radial component of the secondary star's velocity.

In Figure T7.14 is presented the evolution of the radial and transversal components of the velocity and acceleration vectors relative to the observer when the line of sight is in the orbit's plane.

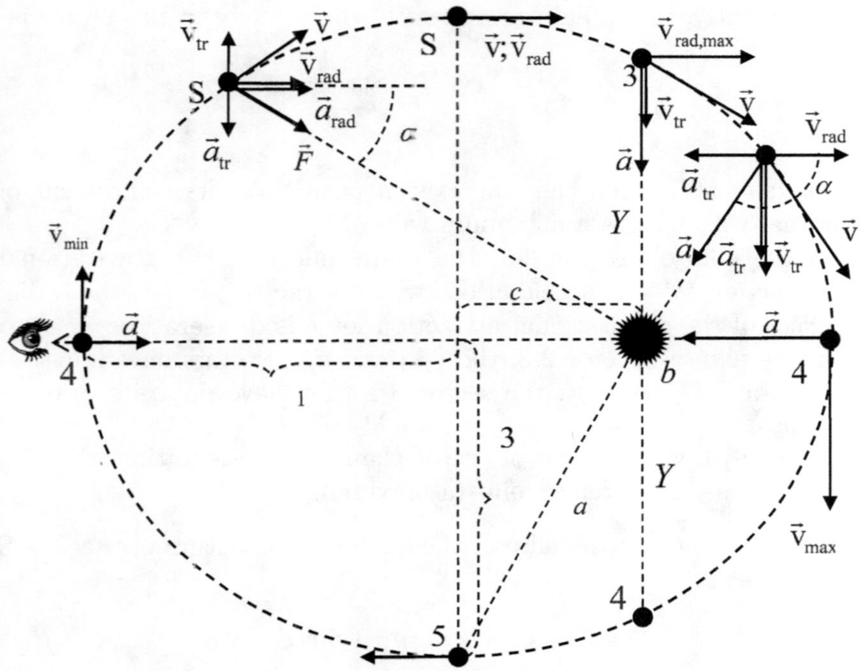


**Fig. T7.14**

In the ellipse's sector 2–6–3, the angle $\alpha$ between the acceleration vector ($\vec{a}$) and the radial velocity vector ($\vec{v}_{rad}$) is

$$0 \leq \alpha \leq 90°.$$

The acceleration has an accelerating effect (the effect of the gravitational attraction force) on the radial component of the velocity. Consequently, the radial component of the velocity in this sector is

$$0 \leq v_{rad} \leq v_{rad,max}.$$

In the ellipse's sector 3–1, the angle $\alpha$ between the acceleration vector ($\vec{a}$) and the radial velocity vector ($\vec{v}_{rad}$) is

$$90 \leq \alpha \leq 180°.$$

The acceleration has a decelerating effect (the effect of the gravitational attraction force) on the radial component of the velocity.

Consequently, the radial component of the velocity in this sector is

$$0 \leq \mathrm{v}_{\mathrm{rad}} \leq \mathrm{v}_{\mathrm{rad,max}}.$$

Conclusions:

- for $\alpha = 90°$, when the star S is in position 3, its component of radial velocity has a maximum value;
- in the ellipse's sector 2-3, the radial effect of the gravitational attraction force is acceleration, while in the sector 3-1, the radial effect of the gravitational attraction force is deceleration;
- in the ellipse's sector 2-3, the $\vec{\mathrm{v}}_{\mathrm{rad}}$ and $\vec{a}_{\mathrm{rad}}$ vectors have identical orientations, while in the sector 3-1 they have opposite orientations;
- at point 3, where the $\vec{a}_{\mathrm{rad}}$ vector changes its orientation, the $\vec{\mathrm{v}}_{\mathrm{rad}}$ vector has an extreme point (a maximum).

At any point on the ellipse, the angular momentum of the star S is:

$$\vec{L} = \vec{r} x m \vec{\mathrm{v}}; \quad L = rmv \cdot \sin(\vec{r}; \quad \vec{\mathrm{v}}).$$

Thus, according to the angular momentum conservation law, it results that:

$$\vec{L} = \text{constant}; \quad L = rmv \cdot \sin(\vec{r}; \quad \vec{\mathrm{v}}) = r_{\min} m \mathrm{v}_{\max} = r_{\max} m \mathrm{v}_{\min};$$

$$r_{\min} = \frac{p}{1+e}; \quad \mathrm{v}_{\max} = \sqrt{\frac{KM(1+e)}{1-e}};$$

$$r_{\min} = \frac{p}{1-e}; \quad \mathrm{v}_{\min} = \sqrt{\frac{KM(1-e)}{1+e}};$$

$$p = a\left(1 - e^2\right); \quad p = b\sqrt{1 - e^2};$$

$$L = m\sqrt{\frac{KMa^2(1-e)^2(1+e)}{a(1-e)}} = mb\sqrt{\frac{KM}{a}}.$$

Corresponding to position 3 of the star S when its angular momentum is

$$L = Ym\mathrm{v}_{\mathrm{rad,max}},$$

it results in:

$$Ym\mathrm{v}_{\mathrm{rad,max}} = mb\sqrt{\frac{KM}{a}}; \quad \mathrm{v}_{\mathrm{rad,max}} = \frac{b}{Y}\cdot\sqrt{\frac{KM}{a}};$$

$$\frac{x^2}{a^2} + \frac{y^2}{b^2} = 1;$$

$$x = c; \quad y = Y; \quad \frac{c^2}{a^2} + \frac{Y^2}{b^2} = 1; \quad c^2 = a^2 - b^2; \quad Y = \frac{b^2}{a};$$

$$\mathrm{v}_{\mathrm{rad,max}} = \frac{a}{b}\cdot\sqrt{\frac{KM}{a}}.$$

If $\tau_1$ is the time interval during which the radial component of star S's velocity increases from zero to the maximum value and if $\tau_2$ is the time interval during which the same component decreases from the maximum value to zero, it results in:

$$\Delta\mathrm{v}_{\mathrm{rad,23}} = \mathrm{v}_{\mathrm{rad,max}} - 0 = \mathrm{v}_{\mathrm{rad,max}}; \quad \Delta t_{23} = \tau_1;$$

$$\Delta\mathrm{v}_{\mathrm{rad,31}} = 0 - \mathrm{v}_{\mathrm{rad,max}} = -\mathrm{v}_{\mathrm{rad,max}}; \quad \Delta t_{31} = \tau_2;$$

$$\frac{\Delta \mathrm{S}_1}{\tau_1} = \frac{\Delta \mathrm{S}_2}{\tau_2} = \frac{\mathrm{S}_{\mathrm{ellipse}}}{T} = \frac{\pi ab}{T}; \quad \Delta \mathrm{S}_1 = \pi ab\cdot\frac{\tau_1}{T}; \quad \Delta \mathrm{S}_2 = \pi ab\cdot\frac{\tau_2}{T};$$

$$\Delta \mathrm{S}_1 + \Delta \mathrm{S}_2 = \frac{1}{2}\cdot \mathrm{S}_{\mathrm{ellipse}}; \quad \pi ab\cdot\frac{\tau_1}{T} + \pi ab\cdot\frac{\tau_2}{T} = \frac{1}{2}\cdot\pi ab;$$

$$\tau_1 + \tau_2 = \frac{1}{2}T.$$

In Figure T7.15, such curves are presented. Their shape depends on the shape of the relative orbit and on its position relative to the observer's line of sight.

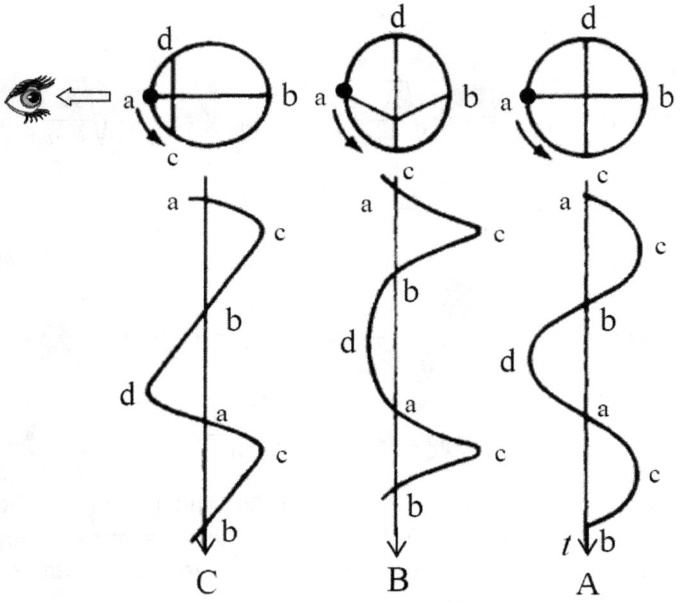


**Fig. T7.15**

# Topic 8

# Light Curves

If the plane of the line of sight coincides with a binary star orbit's plane (the orbit plane that is perpendicular to the celestial plane), reciprocal eclipses of the two components can be periodically observed, as presented in Figures T8.1 and T8.2. Depending on the component's dimensions (radii) and on their brightness, the total brightness and magnitude will have several minimum values, more or less wide or deep: primary minimum values (the hot star is eclipsed by the cold star) and secondary minimum values (the cold star is eclipsed by the hot star). By studying the light curve, the elements of the binary star's orbit can be deduced.

The period of binary stars' reciprocal eclipses is determined by the distance between the two stars and by their masses. If the two components are close, a transfer of substance takes place from one star to the other, and thus variations of the eclipses' period can be observed. This constitutes a proof of substance transfer from one star to the other.

The Algol star ($\beta$ Persei) is one of the best-known variable stars in the sky. It belongs to the Perseus constellation. Algol is a binary star with two components of different brightness. The orbital plane of this binary star is very close to the observer's line of sight. When the two components are clearly separated, as presented in image A of Figure T8.3, the observer receives light rays from both stars.

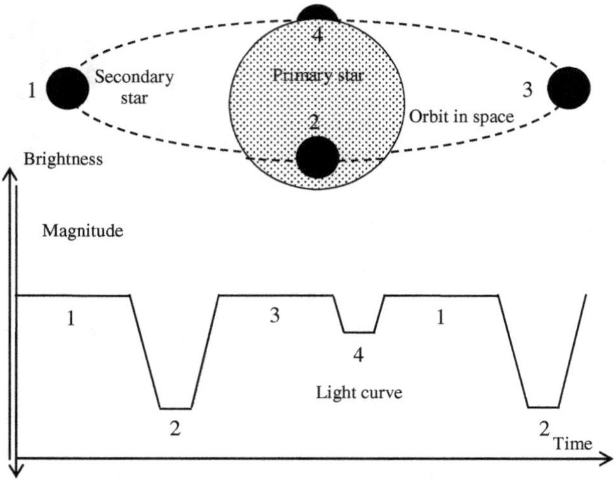


**Fig. T8.1**

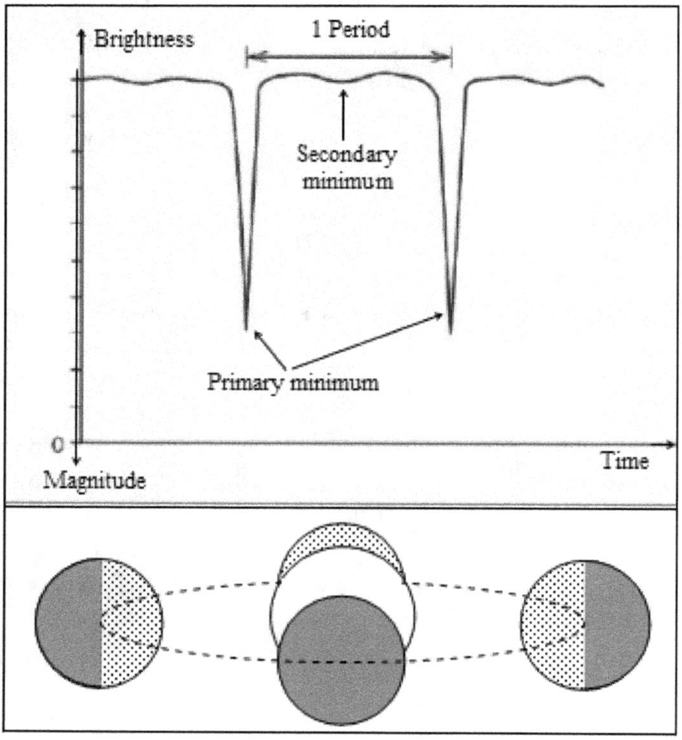


**Fig. T8.2**

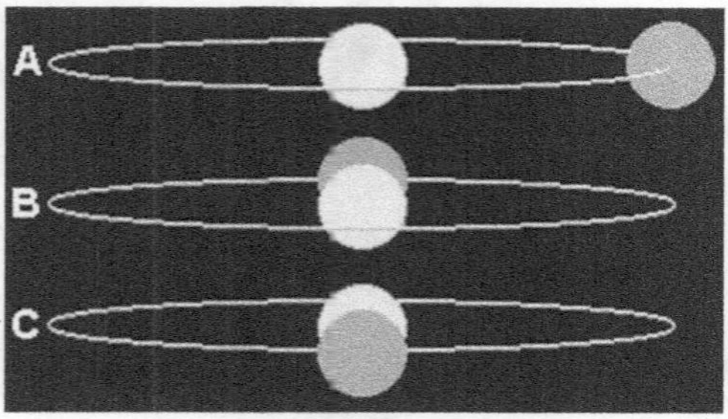


**Fig. T8.3**

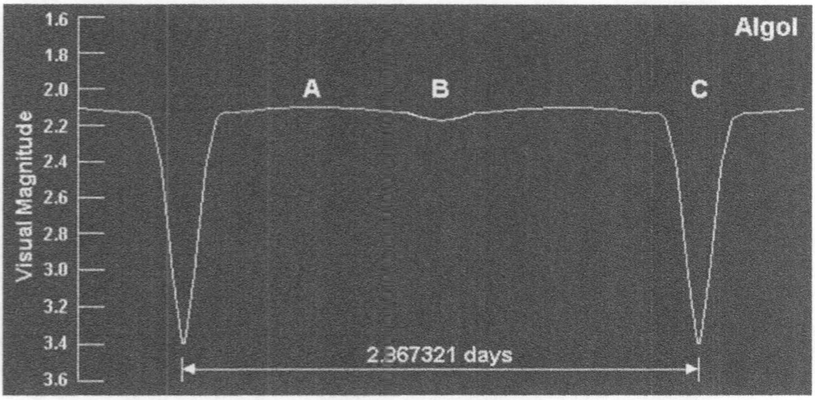


**Fig. T8.4**

When the less bright star is behind the brighter star, as presented in image B, a part of the light emitted by the less bright star cannot reach the observer; thus, the light intensity perceived by the observer slightly diminishes and a secondary minimum is observed. When the less bright star is in front of the brightest star, as presented in image C, the light intensity perceived by the observer is significantly diminished and the primary (deeper) minimum is observed.

The light curve of the Algol system is presented in Figure T8.4, where: A – the observer receives light from both stars; B – the observer receives slightly less light than in situation A since the hot component eclipses the cold component; C – the observer receives significantly less light than in situation B since the cold component eclipses the hot one.

# Topic 9

# Exoplanets

Exoplanets, also known as extrasolar planets, are planets outside the solar system that orbit around stars other than the Sun. Their existence has been confirmed since 1988.

The direct identification and localization of exoplanets is difficult since they do not have their own light and the intensity of the light they reflect is very low in comparison with the intensity of the light from the host stars. However, a state-of-the-art telescope can detect an exoplanet, or a gas giant, if it moves at a very large distance from the host star and if its temperature is high enough for it to be a strong infrared emitter.

## 9.1. Astrometry

Detecting an exoplanet through astrometric methods implies locating a star in the sky and observing the way its position changes. If the host star has (an invisible) planet, due to their gravitational interaction, the host star will change its position in time. The planet and the host star will move on different circular/elliptical orbits around their center of mass. The planet's circular/elliptical orbit is large and the host star's circular/elliptic orbit is small, since $M_{\text{Planet}} \ll M_{\text{Star}}$. The method is efficient if the plane of the relative orbits coincides exactly with the celestial plane, as presented in Figure T9.1.

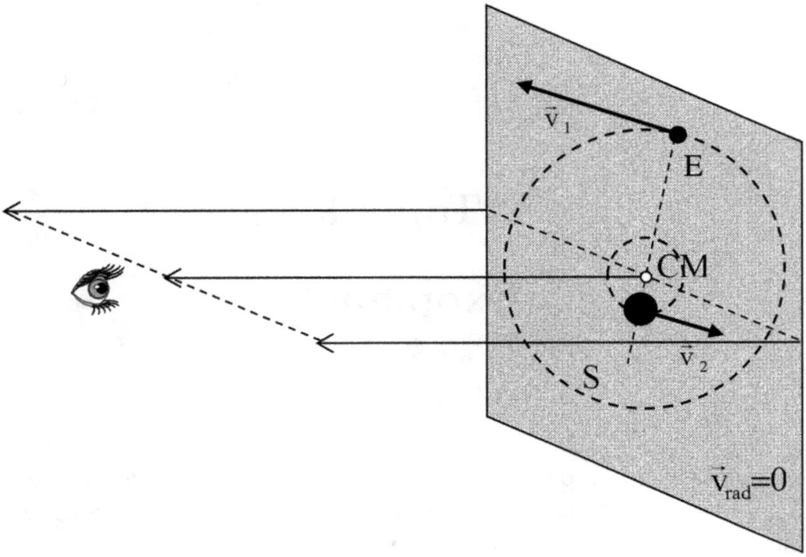


**Fig. T9.1**

## 9.2. Radial Velocity and Doppler Spectroscopy

The method is efficient if the plane of the relative orbits is perpendicular to the celestial plane, and thus the observation direction is along the plane of the relative orbits, as presented in Figure T9.2.

Under these conditions, the radial velocity of the host star relative to the observer is variable, and according to the Doppler effect, the wavelength of the radiation received by the observer is affected by the distance between the star and the observer (blueshift or redshift):

$$\frac{\Delta\lambda}{\lambda_0} = \frac{v_{rad}}{c}; \quad \frac{\Delta\lambda_{max}}{\lambda_0} = \frac{v_{rad,max}}{c}; \quad v_{rad,max} = v_2 = \frac{2\pi r_{Star}}{T}.$$

When the planet is in front of the host star, the light from the star heading towards the observer crosses the planet's atmosphere and it is partially absorbed by this atmosphere (depending on the gas molecules the atmosphere is made of). On its orbit around the host star, the invisible planet moves closer to or further from the observer on the Earth. Consequently, the spectral lines of absorption from

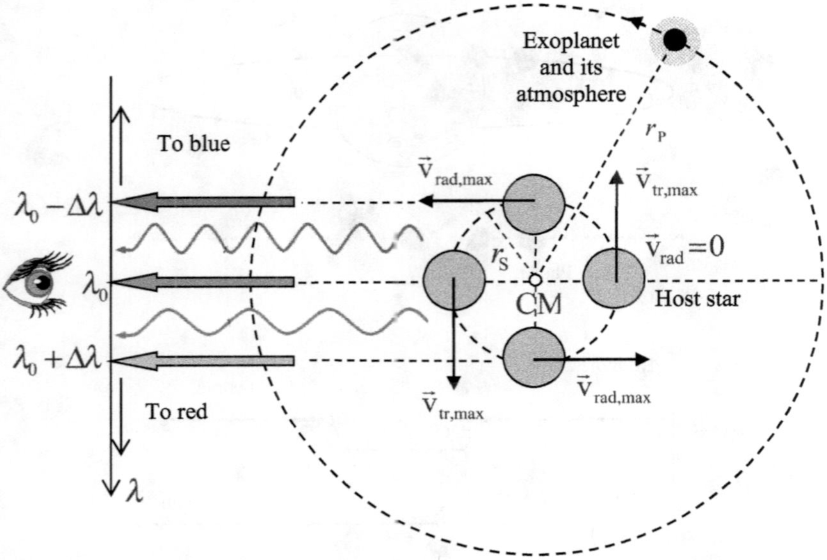


**Fig. T9.2**

the planet's atmosphere will be shifted towards blue (shorter wavelengths) or towards red (longer wavelengths), respectively. Measuring the spectral shifts of the planet's atmospheric absorption lines, the orbital movement of the planet around the star can be determined.

## 9.3. The Transit of an Exoplanet and the Light Curve

When an exoplanet transits the host star, an event equivalent to a partial eclipse, the star's brightness slightly decreases, as presented in the light curve graph (Figure T9.3). The decrease in the host star's brightness during the exoplanet's transit depends on the ratio of the two celestial bodies' disk surfaces. From the analysis of the light curve graph, the exopanet's radius can be determined. The mass of the exoplanet is determined from the radial velocity graph. By combining these two studies, the density of the exoplanet can be determined.

The high-resolution spectrum of the light received from the host star, obtained after the light has crossed the exoplanet's atmosphere during this transit, allows the identification of chemical elements in the exoplanet's atmosphere.

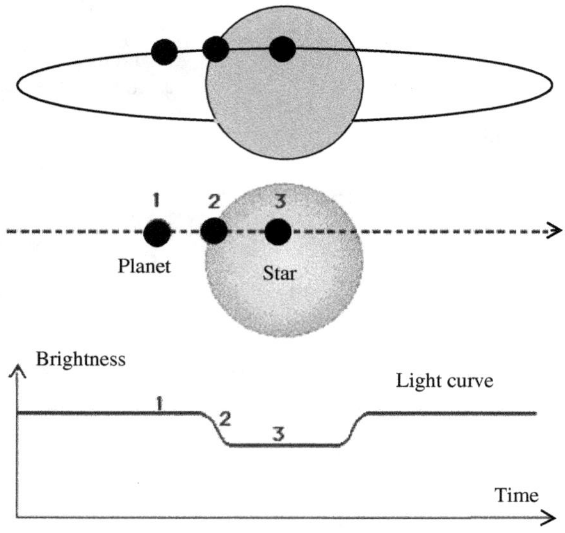


**Fig. T9.3**

The exoplanet's period is determined as the time interval between two consecutive eclipses. The orbital velocity of the exoplanet is estimated from the duration of one individual eclipse.

The transit of the exoplanet behind the host star (secondary eclipse) offers the possibility of determining the exoplanet's temperature. For this purpose, the difference between the intensity of the radiation received from the host star and the exoplanet before the exoplanet begins its transit and the intensity of the radiation received from the host star when the exoplanet is behind the host star is established. This difference represents the intensity of the radiation received from the exoplanet, which allows us to determine the exoplanet's temperature.

By using the light curve graph resulting from the exoplanet's transit in front of the host star, the fraction of the host star's disk surface covered by the exoplanet's disk may be determined.

Thus:

$$\frac{B_{\text{min}}}{B_{\text{max}}} = \frac{S_{\text{star disk}} - S_{\text{planet disk}}}{S_{\text{star disk}}} = 1 - \frac{S_{\text{planet disk}}}{S_{\text{star disk}}};$$

$$\frac{S_{\text{planet disk}}}{S_{\text{star disk}}} = 1 - \frac{B_{\text{min}}}{B_{\text{max}}},$$

where $B_{min}$ and $B_{max}$, expressed in conventional units, are obtained from the light curve graph by measuring with a ruler.

## 9.4. Pulsar Synchronization

A pulsar is not a pulsing star! A pulsar ("pulse" + "star" = "pulsar") is a neutron star of very small radius (15 km $< R <$ 20 km) and of high density that has its own very rapid rotation movement (1.4 ms $< T <$ 8.5 s) and a very intense magnetic field ($10^{14}$ Gs $< B < 10^{15}$ Gs) concentrated at the star's magnetic poles. The rotation axis of a pulsar does not coincide with its magnetic axis. Consequently, the radiation produced by this neutron star is focused by the pulsar's magnetic field as two beams that sweep the sky in opposite directions, as presented in Figure T9.4. If the beam of radiation meets the Earth once per rotation of the pulsar, the observer will record short and regular (rhythmic) pulses.

This happened in 1967, when Jocelyn Bell Burnell and Antony Hewish from Cambridge University discovered the first pulsar. They detected regular radio signals, at equal time intervals (a few seconds in length). These signals represent electromagnetic (radio) radiation pulses with the frequency of $v = 81$ MHz. A pulsar can be detected only when its radiation flux is oriented towards the Earth. When the pulsar is moving towards the Earth, the time interval between successive pulses decreases, and when the pulsar moves away from the Earth, the time interval between successive pulses increases.

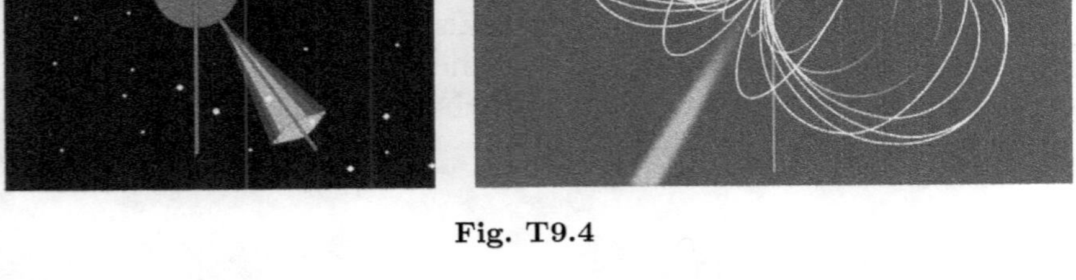


**Fig. T9.4**

If there is a planet orbiting around the pulsar, the pulsar and the planet orbit around their common center of mass. The pulsar moves very close to the center of mass if its mass is considerably larger than the planet's mass. Due to the gravitational action of the planet on the pulsar, the regularity (synchronicity) of the radiofrequency pulse emission is affected by small abnormalities. These abnormalities are determined by the existence of the planet; thus, the results of these observations lead to the evaluation of the planet's orbital parameters and of other data related to the planet.

It is known that the Sun and many stars have dipolar magnetic fields. Inside any star there is ionized gas, which is a very good electrical conductor. Consequently, the ionized particles inside the star have to move along the magnetic field's lines.

When the core of a star gravitationally collapses from $R_0 = 10^9$ m to $R = 10^4$ m, its magnetic field flux through the equatorial transversal section of the spherical core,

$$\Phi = \int \vec{B} \cdot d\vec{S} = \int \vec{B} \cdot \vec{n} \cdot dS,$$

must preserve itself. Corresponding to Figure T9.5, this is the result:

$$\Phi = \vec{B}_0 \cdot \vec{S}_0 = \vec{B} \cdot \vec{S};$$

$$B_0 \cdot S_0 = B \cdot S;$$

$$\frac{B}{B_0} = \frac{S_0}{S} = \frac{R_0^2}{R^2} = \frac{10^{18}}{10^8} = 10^{10};$$

$$B = 10^{10} B_0,$$

representing the intensity of the star's magnetic field after the gravitational collapse of its core. Consequently, for an initial magnetic field of $B_0 = 100$ gauss, after the previously mentioned gravitational collapse, the intensity of the pulsar's magnetic field becomes $B = 10^{10} \cdot 10^2$ gauss $= 10^{12}$ gauss, which explains the pulsar's very strong magnetic field resulting from the gravitational collapse of a neutron star.

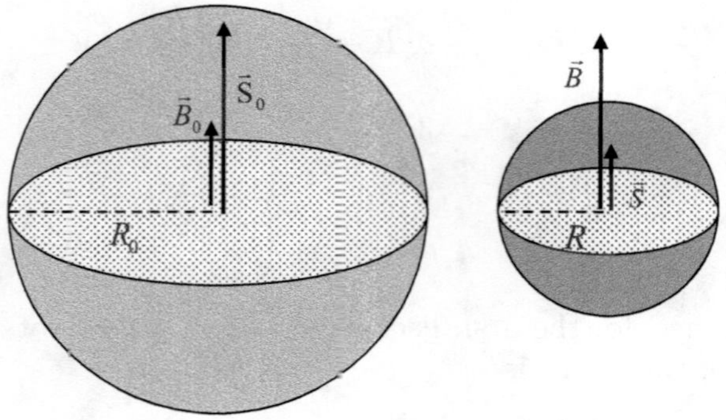


**Fig. T9.5**

The gravitational collapse also respects the angular momentum conservation law:

$$L = I_0\omega_0 = I\omega;$$

$$\frac{2}{5}MR_0^2\omega_0 = \frac{2}{5}MR^2\omega;$$

$$R_0^2\omega_0 = R^2\omega;$$

$$\frac{\omega}{\omega_0} = \frac{R_0^2}{R^2} = 10^{10};$$

$$\omega = 10^{10} \cdot \omega_0.$$

This justifies the very high value of the pulsar's angular velocity after the gravitational collapse of the neutron star. Following the gravitational collapse of the neutron star, the multiplication factor of the angular velocity is the same as the magnetic field intensity multiplication factor.

The rotation of a pulsar is very rapid, but the period of such rotation is limited by a value determined by the pulsar's density. This limit value can be determined from the condition that the centripetal acceleration at any point of the pulsar's equator must not be greater than the gravitational acceleration at that point. That is,

$$a_{\text{cp}} < g;$$

$$\omega^2 R < K\frac{M}{R^2}; \quad \frac{4\pi^2}{T^2}R < K\frac{M}{R^2};$$

$$\frac{4\pi R^3}{3}\cdot\frac{3\pi}{T^2} < KM; \quad \frac{3\pi}{T^2} < K\frac{M}{\frac{4\pi R^3}{3}}; \quad \frac{4\pi R^3}{3} = V; \quad \frac{M}{V} = \rho;$$

$$\frac{3\pi}{T^2} < K\rho;$$

$$\rho > \frac{3\pi}{KT^2}.$$

For instance, for the first discovered pulsar, whose rotation period is $T = 1.3$ s, the result is

$$\rho > \frac{3\cdot 3.14}{6.67\cdot 10^{-11}\ \mathrm{Nm^2kg^{-2}}\cdot (1.3)^2\mathrm{s}^2} \approx 0.83\cdot 10^{11}\frac{\mathrm{kg}}{\mathrm{m}^3} = 0.83\cdot 10^{8}\frac{\mathrm{g}}{\mathrm{cm}^3}.$$

## 9.5. Gravitational Microlensing

As presented in Figure T9.6, gravitational microlensing is the effect a star–planet system has on the background star's light on its way to the observer. As can be observed, this gravitational effect is identical (similar) to the effect of a convergent optical lens on a light beam emitted by a distant (far away) source of light. According to the General Relativity Theory, the gravitational field of the star–planet system bends the trajectory of the light rays from the background star. Thus, the intensity of the light that reaches the observer increases. Consequently, the background star appears brighter than in the absence of the star–planet system, which proves the existence of the star–planet system.

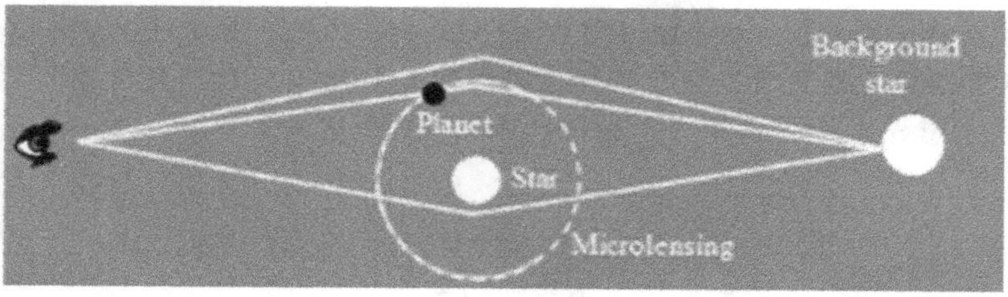


**Fig. T9.6**

# Topic 10

# The Apparent Orbit of a Secondary Star

Let's consider a binary stellar system consisting of stars Σ and S, where Σ is the primary star and S is the secondary star. The (real) orbit of the secondary star relative to the primary star considered stationary relative to the observer is an ellipse that has the primary star in its focus, as presented in Figure T10.1.

According to the gravitational attraction law corresponding to Newton's laws, the following relations can be demonstrated:

$$F = K\frac{mM}{r^2};$$

$$r = \frac{p}{1 + e\cos\theta}; \quad e = \sqrt{1 - \frac{b^2}{a^2}} < 1;$$

$$p = \frac{b^2}{a} = a\left(1 - e^2\right) = b\sqrt{1 - e^2};$$

$$r_{\min} = a\,(1 - e)\,; \quad v_{\max} = \sqrt{\frac{KM\,(1 + e)}{1 - e}};$$

$$r_{\max} = a\,(1 + e)\,; \quad v_{\min} = \sqrt{\frac{KM\,(1 - e)}{1 + e}};$$

$$E = -K\frac{mM}{2a}; \quad L = mb\sqrt{\frac{KM}{a}};$$

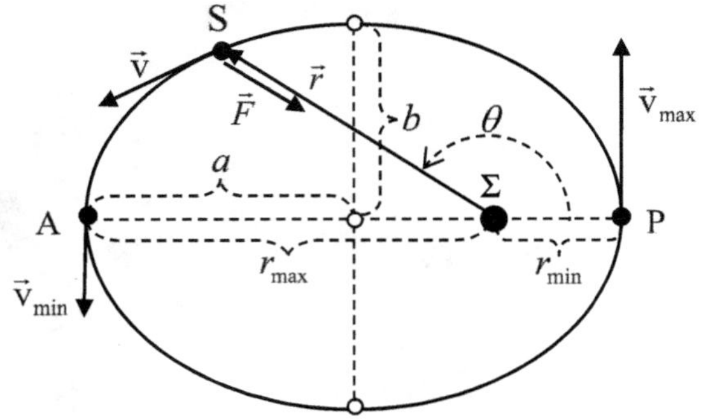


**Fig. T10.1**

$$T^2 = \frac{4\pi^2}{KM}a^3,$$

which represents Kepler's third law.

From this relation, the mass $M$ of the primary star can be determined if the following are known: $T$ – the rotation period of the secondary star around the primary star; $a$ – the semi-major axis of the relative orbit.

In most cases of visual binary systems, the observer's view line is not perpendicular to the plane of the secondary star's relative (real) orbit, as presented in Figures T10.2 and T10.3. From the elements of the observed (apparent) orbit represented in Figure T10.4, knowing the semi-major axis, $a$, of the relative orbit (ellipse) is not possible. Thus, the mass $M$ of the primary star $\Sigma$ of the considered binary stellar system cannot be directly determined, even if the period $T$ can be easily determined.

When the movement of the secondary star (S) around the primary star ($\Sigma$) is studied, as presented in Figure T10.2, the $\Pi_c$ plane of the apparent orbit (the celestial plane) is generally different from the $\Pi$ plane of the relative orbit (the real orbital plane). We say that the $\Pi$ plane of the relative orbit (the real orbital plane) is inclined relative to the $\Pi_c$ plane of the apparent orbit (the sky plane), the inclination being $i \neq 0$.

As a consequence, the elements of the ellipse $E_{ap}$ (in the $\Pi_c$ plane) that represents the apparent orbit of the star S relative to the star $\Sigma$ differ from the elements of the ellipse E (in plane $\Pi$) that represents the (real) orbit of the star S relative to the star $\Sigma$.

It is known (can be demonstrated) that the projection on the $\Pi_c$ plane of the ellipse E from the $\Pi$ plane is the ellipse $E_{ap}$.

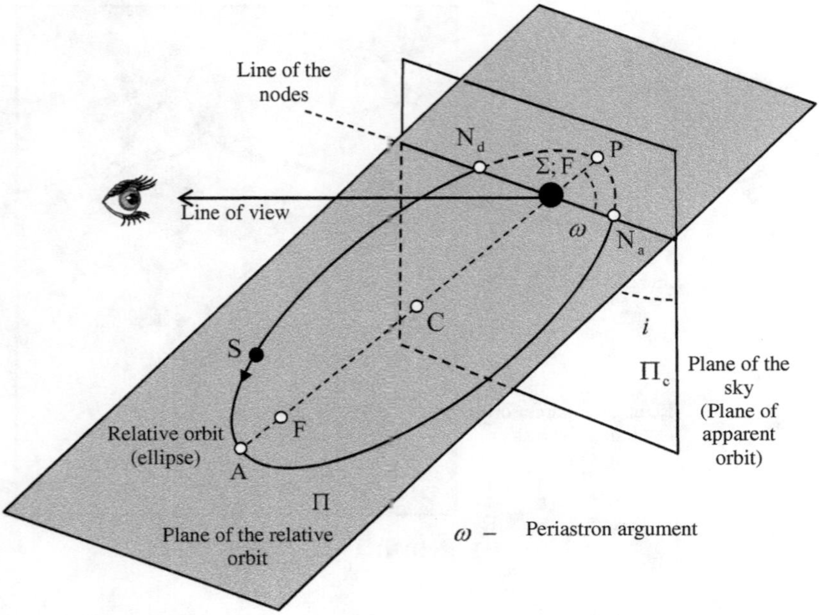


**Fig. T10.2**

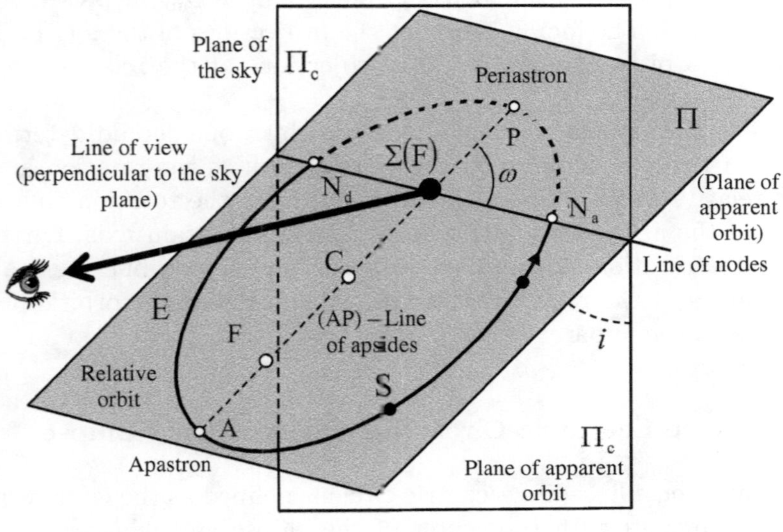


**Fig. T10.3**

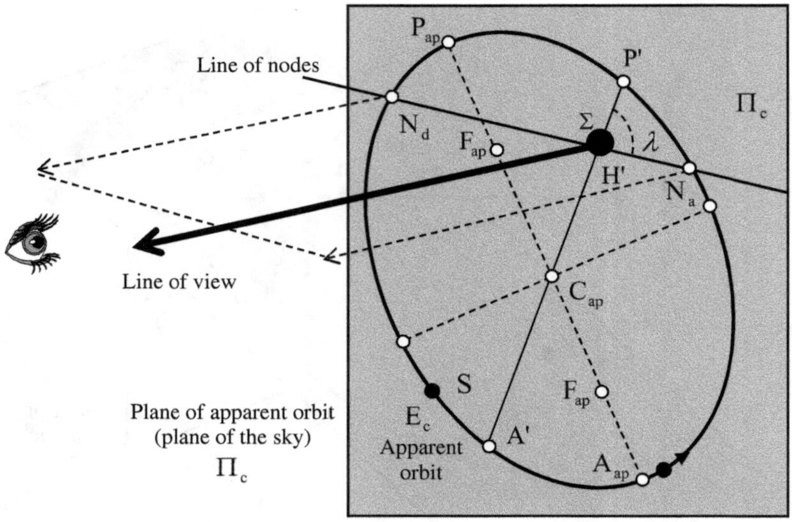


**Fig. T10.4**

According to Kepler's laws, the star Σ around which the star S orbits is in the focus F of the ellipse E. The star Σ (or its projection on plane $\Pi_c$) is not in the focus $F_{ap}$ of the ellipse $E_{ap}$, as presented in Figure T10.4. The foci $F_{ap}$ are not the projections of the foci F. The apparent orbit's axes are not the projections of the relative orbit's axes.

Using the elements of the apparent orbits, one should determine the rotation axis of the relative orbits as well as the rotation angle. The relative orbit (ellipse) should result from the rotation (inclination) of the apparent orbit (ellipse) around a certain axis. Furthermore, the rotation axis and the rotation angle determine the spatial orientation of the relative orbit (the inclination of the orbit's plane relative to the apparent orbit's plane).

## 10.1. The Eccentric Circle and the Auxiliary Ellipse

For any given ellipse, its eccentric circle is defined as the circle whose center coincides with the center of the ellipse and whose radius is equal to the ellipse's semi-major axis, as presented in Figure T10.5. The circle circumscribes the given ellipse.

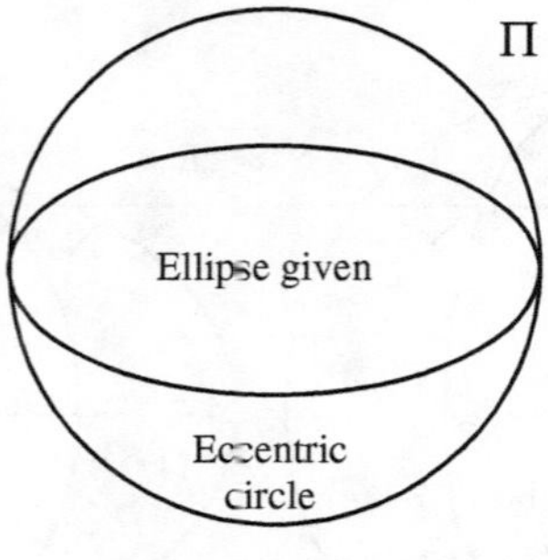


**Fig. T10.5**

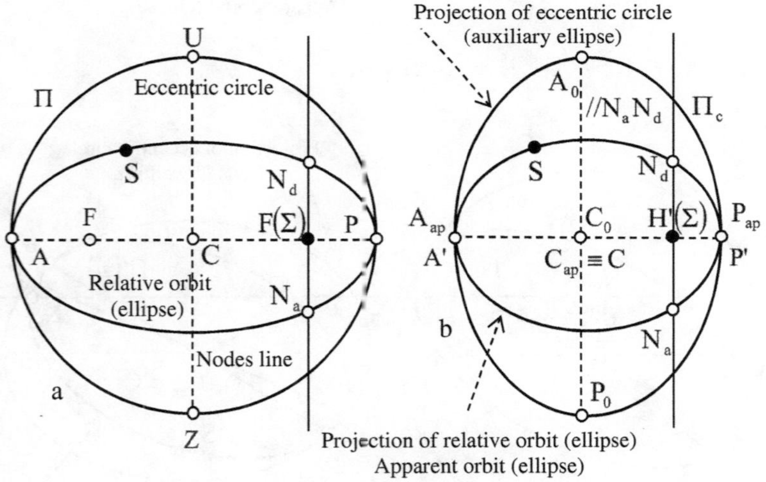


**Fig. T10.6**

In the Π plane (the image plane) presented in Figure T10.6, the relative orbit of the secondary star (S), its ellipse, comes around to the primary star (Σ) and its eccentric circle. If the given relative orbit (ellipse) and its eccentric circle are projected on a different plane ($\Pi_c$ – the celestial plane), we obtain two other ellipses, as presented in Figure T10.6(b). The intersection of the two planes Π and $\Pi_c$ is the $N_aN_d$ line of nodes, an axis inclined relative to the major axis (the line of apsides, AP) of the relative orbit (ellipse), at an angle $\omega$, as presented in Figures T10.2 and T10.3. The inclination of the plane Π relative to the plane $\Pi_c$ is at an angle $i$.

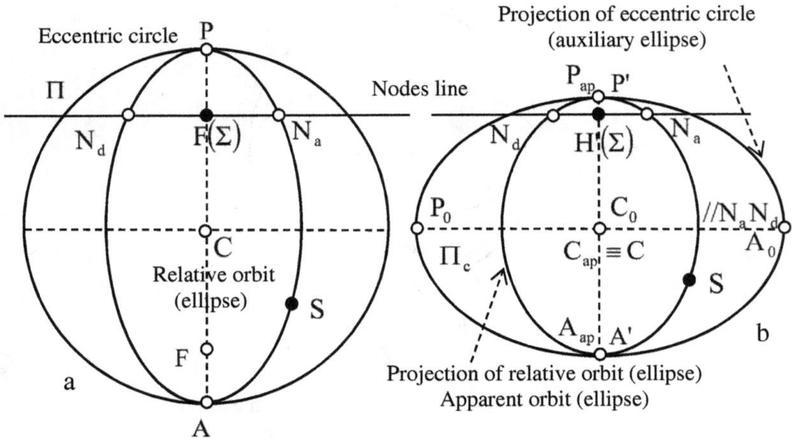


**Fig. T10.7**

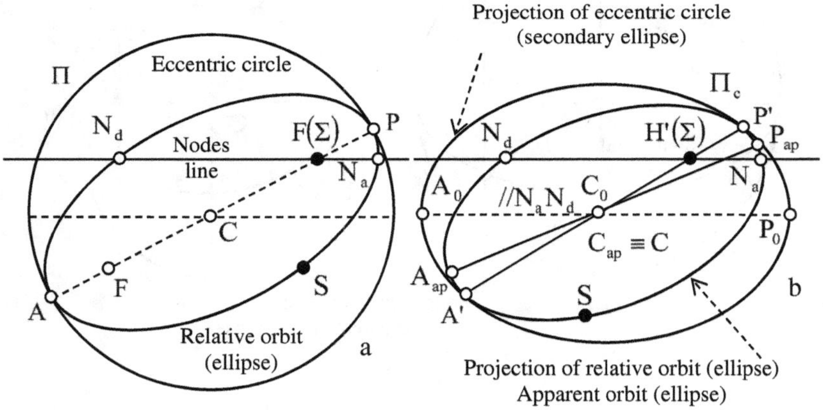


**Fig. T10.8**

Presented in Figures T10.7, T10.8 and T10.9 are variants of the nodes line position and of the relative orbit (ellipse). For each variant, the positions of the auxiliary and of the apparent ellipses are presented.

In Figure T10.10, for the Π plane of the relative ellipse (orbit), it is known that:

$$\frac{\mathrm{CF}}{\mathrm{CP}} = \frac{ea}{a} = e,$$

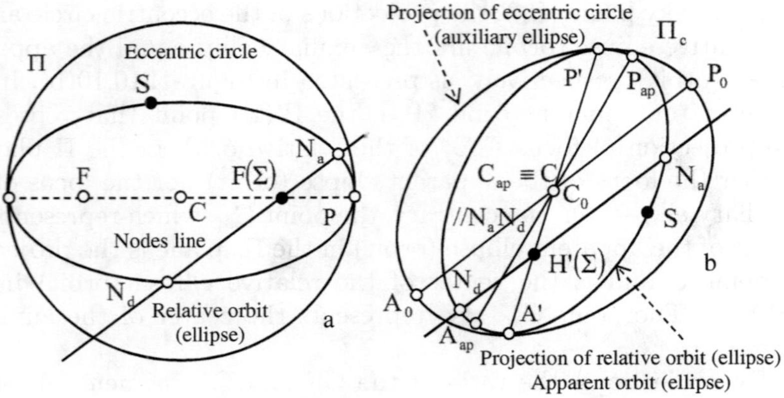


**Fig. T10.9**

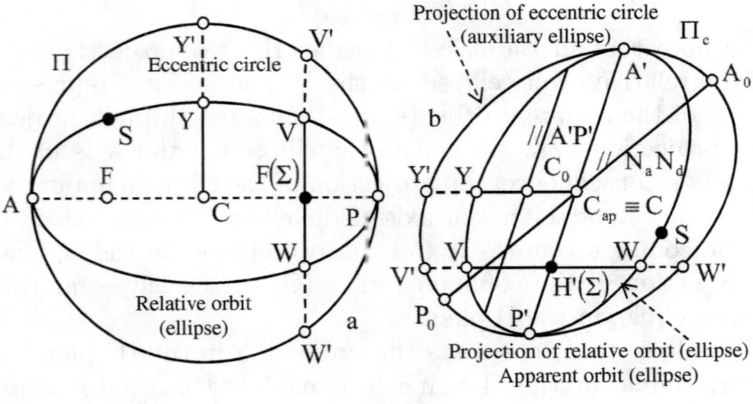


**Fig. T10.10**

representing the eccentricity of the relative ellipse (orbit);

$$\frac{\mathrm{CY}}{\mathrm{CP}} = \frac{b}{a} = \sqrt{1 - e^2}.$$

This value is the same for any ratio of two segments that represent the ordinates of the points on the relative ellipse (orbit) and on the auxiliary circle, respectively, corresponding to the same abscissa.

For instance,

$$\frac{\mathrm{FV}}{\mathrm{FV'}} = \sqrt{1 - e^2}.$$

In the sky plane ($\Pi_c$), the projections of the eccentric circle and of the relative ellipse (orbit) are the auxiliary ellipse and the apparent ellipse (orbit), respectively, as presented in Figure T10.10(b). In the plane of the apparent orbit ($\Pi_c$), the $H'(\Sigma)$ point that represents the projection of focus $F(\Sigma)$ of the relative orbit in the $\Pi$ plane is neither the focus of the apparent ellipse (orbit) nor the focus of the auxiliary ellipse. On the contrary, the point $C_{ap}$ which represents the center of the apparent ellipse (orbit) in the $\Pi_c$ plane is the projection of point C and is the center of the relative ellipse (orbit) in the $\Pi$ plane. The point $C_{ap}$ also represents the center of the auxiliary ellipse.

By projections, the ratio of the CF and CP segments does not change. Thus:

$$\frac{\mathrm{CF}}{\mathrm{CP}} = e; \quad \frac{\mathrm{C_{ap}H'}}{\mathrm{C_{ap}P'}} = e.$$

We note that in the celestial plane, $\Pi_c$, the projections of foci F of the relative orbit (ellipse) in the $\Pi$ plane do not represent the foci $F_{ap}$ of the apparent orbit (ellipse) obtained through projection. These projections, $H'$, are not on the ellipse's major axis in the $\Pi_c$ plane. As a consequence, the projection of the ellipse's major axis on the $\Pi$ plane is not the major axis of the ellipse's major axis in plane $\Pi_c$. The common center, $C_{ap}$, of the two ellipses in the $\Pi_c$ plane is the projection of the common center (C) of the ellipse and of the eccentric circle, in the $\Pi$ plane.

The ellipse that represents the projection in the $\Pi_c$ plane of the eccentric circle in the $\Pi$ plane is named the *auxiliary ellipse.* It touches on two points, $A'$ and $P'$, of the ellipse in the $\Pi_c$ plane that represents the projection on the $\Pi$ plane of the relative orbit (ellipse). The $A_0P_0$ segment is the major axis of the auxiliary ellipse and it is parallel to the nodes line $N_aN_d$.

The $N_aN_d$ line of nodes is the line that represents the intersection of the apparent orbit's plane ($\Pi_c$) with the relative orbit plane $\Pi$, as presented in Figures T10.2 and T10.3.

## 10.2. The Apparent Orbit (Ellipse)

Using observational (experimental) values available for the *angular position* and for the *angular separation* of the two components of a

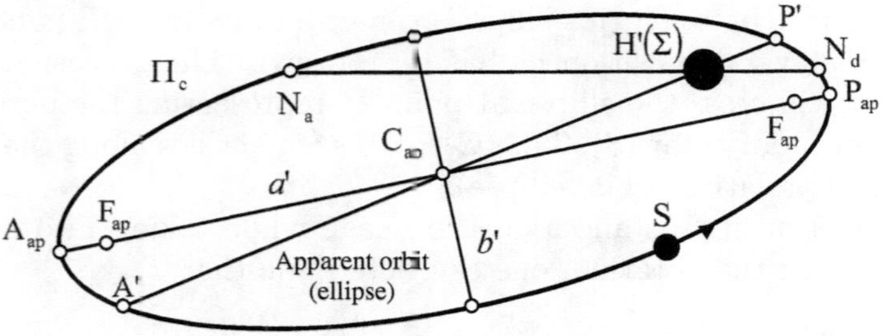


Fig. T10.11

visual binary stellar system, the apparent orbit (ellipse) of the secondary star relative to the primary star is represented in the celestial plane $\Pi_c$. The ellipse is presented in Figure T10.11, where $F_{ap}$ represent the foci of the apparent orbit (ellipse). These foci are not the projections of the foci F of the relative orbit (ellipse).

The center of the apparent orbit (ellipse) $C_{ap}$ on the celestial plane $\Pi_c$ is the projection of the relative orbit's (ellipse's) center C from plane Π.

## 10.3. The Projection of the Major Axis and Eccentricity of the Relative (Real) Orbit (Ellipse)

In Figure T10.12, the presented ellipse is the relative orbit of the secondary star S around the primary star Σ in the Π plane.

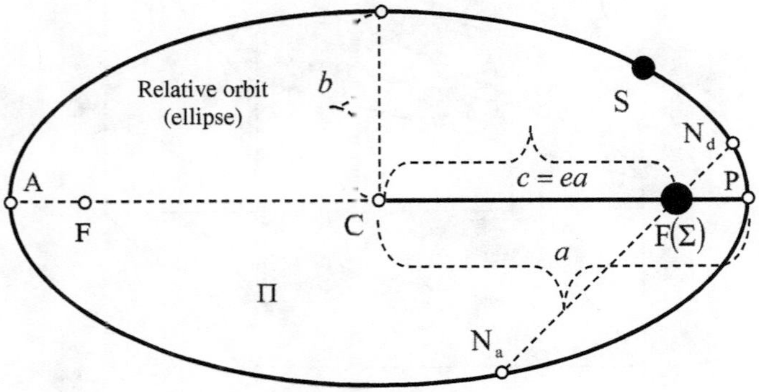


Fig. T10.12

The segment between this ellipse's center and its focus F (where the primary star $\Sigma$ is positioned) has been drawn. The extension of the segment will cross the ellipse at point P, representing the periastron of the secondary star (S). The (C, F, P) segment lies along the major axis of the relative orbit (ellipse).

By measuring distances on the image while taking into account its scale and the notation, one can determine that

$$\frac{\mathrm{CF}}{\mathrm{CP}} = \frac{ea}{a} = e,$$

representing the eccentricity of the relative orbit. But this ellipse (the relative orbit) is not known.

The three collinear points C, F, and P corresponding to the relative orbit (ellipse) in the $\Pi$ plane remain collinear after being projected onto the $\Pi_c$ plane. Their projections will have the notations $C_{ap}$, H′, and P′, respectively, and will maintain the same relative positions, as presented in Figure T10.13.

The point $C_{ap}$ on the apparent orbit (ellipse) plane is obtained as the projection of point C, the center of the relative orbit (ellipse). $C_{ap}$ is the center of the apparent orbit (ellipse). Consequently, on the ellipse (apparent orbit) obtained through projection on the celestial plane, $\Pi_c$, the line of these three points ($C_{ap}$, H′, P′) can be drawn. Thus, the ratio of the two segments' lengths measured in Figure T10.14 will also represent the eccentricity of the relative (real) orbit (ellipse).

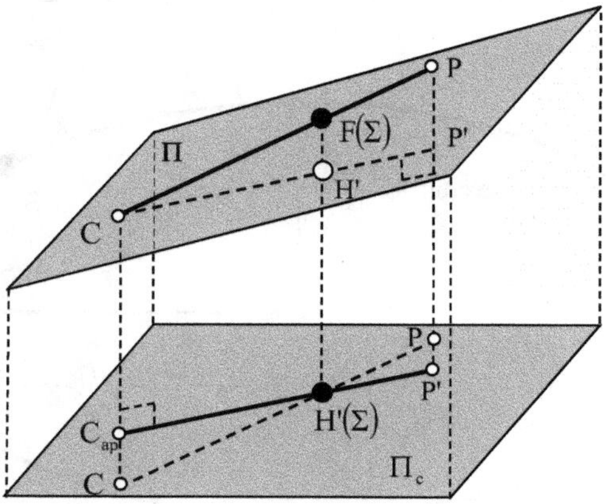


**Fig. T10.13**

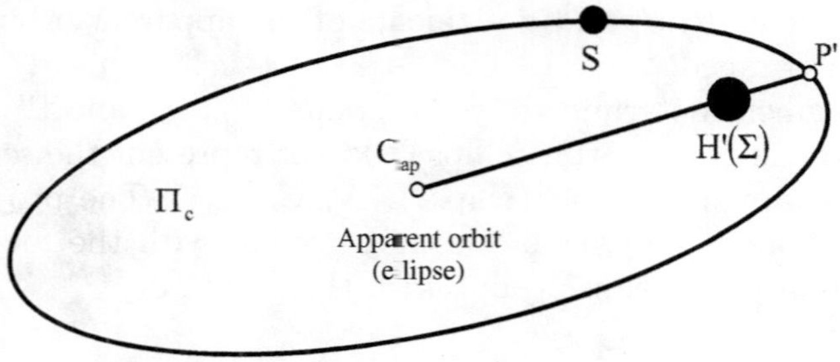


**Fig. T10.14**

The similitude of square triangles CFH′ and CPP′ results in

$$\frac{\mathrm{C_{ap}H'}}{\mathrm{C_{ap}P'}} = \frac{\mathrm{CH'}}{\mathrm{CP}} = \frac{\mathrm{CF}}{\mathrm{CP}} = \frac{ea}{a} = e.$$

The eccentricity ($e$) of the relative orbit (ellipse) is determined by measurements from the apparent orbit (ellipse). The inclination $i$ of the relative orbit in relation to the apparent orbit can be determined by calculus, as shown below.

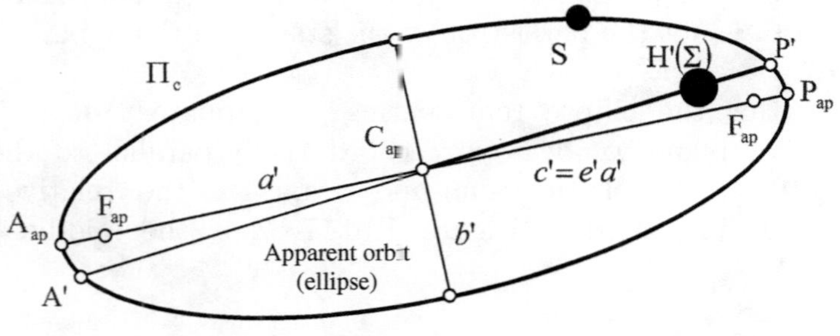


**Fig. T10.15**

In Figure T10.15 it is shown that the projection $\mathrm{A'C_{ap}P'}$ on the celestial plane ($\Pi_c$) of the relative major axis ACP from the $\Pi$ plane (the plane of the relative orbit) does not identify with the major axis of the apparent orbit (ellipse) $\mathrm{A_{ap}F_{ap}P_{ap}}$, from plane $\Pi'$. The star $\Sigma$ does not appear to be localized in the focus of the apparent orbit (ellipse). The projection of focus F of the relative orbit (ellipse) is not in the focus $\mathrm{F_{ap}}$ of the apparent orbit (ellipse). Using the measurements for the apparent orbit (ellipse), corresponding to its scale, the $a'$, $b'$, $e'$, and $c'$ elements of the apparent orbit (ellipse) can be determined.

The segment determined by the points $C_{ap}$, $H'$, and $P'$ in the $\Pi_c$ plane of the apparent orbit (ellipse) do not represent the semi-major axis of the apparent orbit (ellipse) ($A_{ap}C_{ap}P_{ap}$). The projection of the star $\Sigma$ on the $\Pi_c$ plane does not overlap with the focus $F_{ap}$ of the apparent orbit (ellipse), but with the point $H'$.

## 10.4. The Projection of the Minor Axis of the Real Orbit (Ellipse)

If $2b$ is the minor axis of the relative orbit (ellipse) in the $\Pi$ plane, we will prepare the representation of its projection on the celestial plane ($\Pi_c$).

First, on the ellipse representing the apparent orbit of the secondary star in the celestial plane ($\Pi_c$), the $C_{ap}$, $H'$, and $P'$ segment can be drawn. As we already know, it represents the projection of the semi-major axis of the relative orbit (ellipse): see Figure T10.16. This projection does not overlap with the semi-major axis of the apparent orbit (ellipse). $C_{ap}P'$ is not a semi-major axis in the apparent orbit (ellipse). $P'$ is not the periastron of the star $\Sigma$ on the apparent orbit (ellipse).

Then, for the ellipse representing the apparent orbit in the $\Pi_c$ celestial plane we draw any chord (NT) parallel to the projection ($C_{ap}H'P'$) of the semi-major axis in the relative orbit (ellipse), as presented in Figure T10.17. Z is the middle of the chord NT.

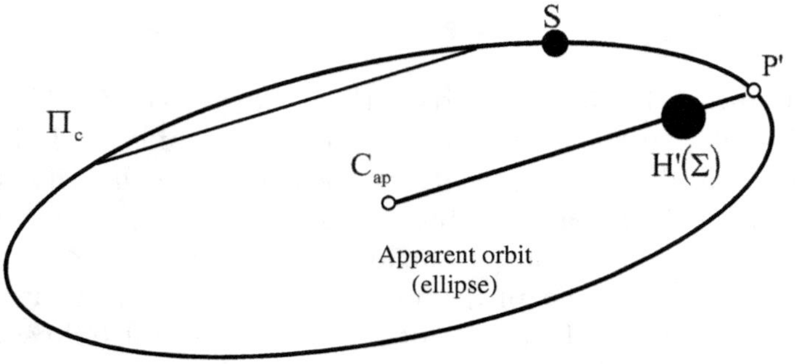


**Fig. T10.16**

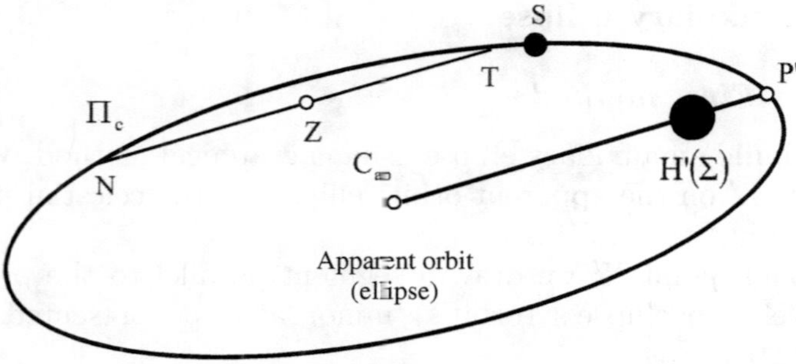


**Fig. T10.17**

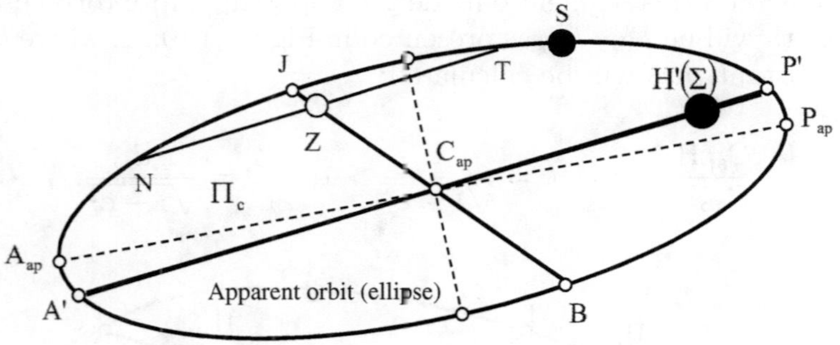


**Fig. T10.18**

We draw a segment that links the middle point of the chord to the center of the ellipse representing the apparent orbit of the secondary star in the celestial plane, and we prolong this segment until it intersects with the ellipse (representing the apparent orbit of the secondary star). We obtain the projection on the celestial plane of the minor axis of the relative ellipse (orbit), as presented in Figure T10.18. The projections on the celestial plane of the relative ellipse's (orbit's) two axes remain two conjugate segments.

The segment JB (see Figure T10.18) represents in the celestial plane $\Pi_c$ on the apparent orbit (ellipse) the projection of the minor axis of the relative orbit (ellipse) in the $\Pi$ plane. The segment $A'P'$ represents in the celestial plane $\Pi_c$ on the apparent ellipse (orbit) the projection of the major axis of the relative orbit (ellipse) on the $\Pi$ plane. The projections in the celestial plane $\Pi_c$ of the relative orbit's axes from the $\Pi$ plane are not perpendicular and do not coincide with the axes of the apparent ellipse (orbit).

## 10.5. Auxiliary Ellipse

### 10.5.1. *First method*

We will build an auxiliary ellipse using a graphical method. We mark the point X′ on the apparent orbit (ellipse) in the celestial plane, as presented in Figure T10.19.

Through point X′ we draw a segment parallel to the projection of the relative ellipse's (orbit's) minor axis, as presented in Figure T10.20.

We measure and consider the length of this segment to be $d$, as presented in Figure T10.21.

We extend this segment outside the apparent ellipse (orbit); thus, its length will be $D = kd$, as presented in Figure T10.22, where $k > 1$ is a constant that will be calculated:

$$\frac{\mathrm{C_{ap}H'}}{\mathrm{C_{ap}P'}} = e; \quad k = \frac{1}{\sqrt{1-e^2}} > 1; \quad D = \frac{d}{\sqrt{1-e^2}}.$$

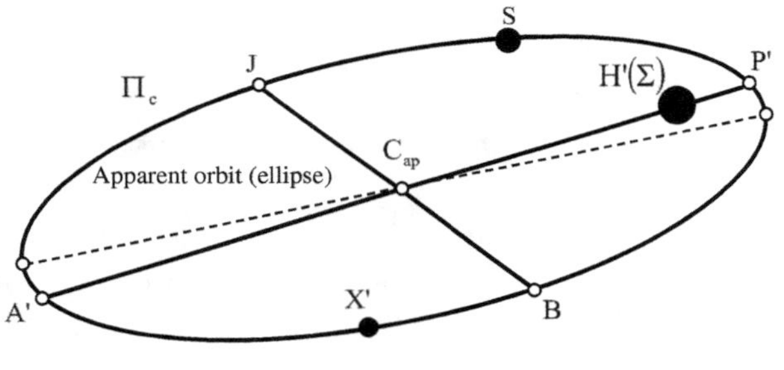


**Fig. T10.19**

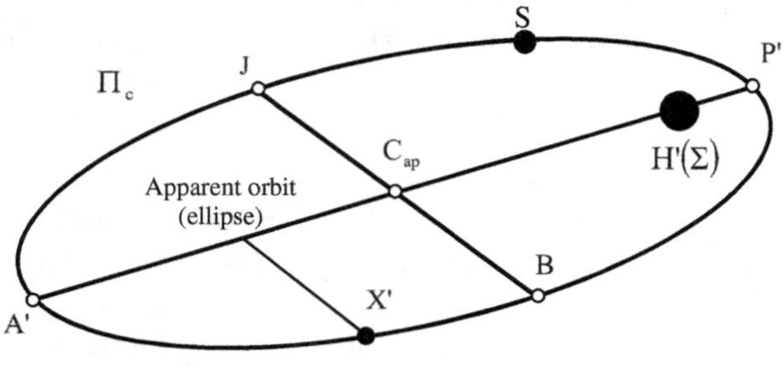


**Fig. T10.20**

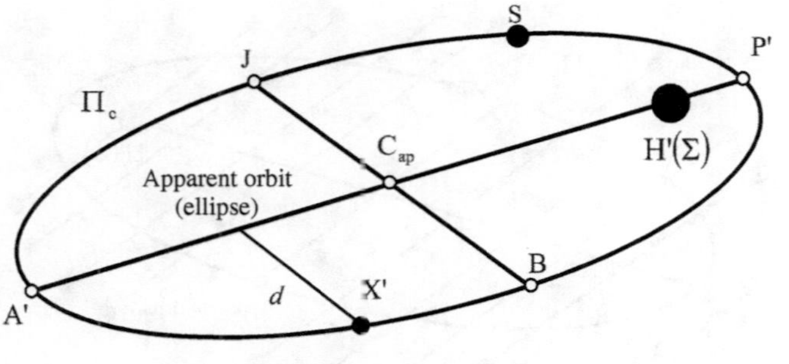


**Fig. T10.21**

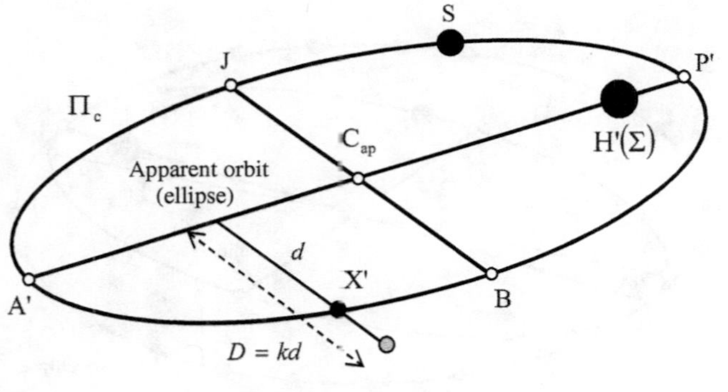


**Fig. T10.22**

We repeat this construction for many other points on the (observed) apparent orbit (ellipse), obtaining the exterior points of the apparent ellipse (orbit) indicated in Figure T10.23.

The value of the constant $k$ from the $D = kd$ equation must be calculated such that the connections of the points outside the apparent orbit (ellipse) – that is, the locus of those points – will be exactly the auxiliary ellipse known from Figure T10.6 and represented in Figure T10.24.

*Note*: the center ($C_0$) of the auxiliary ellipse coincides with the center ($C_{ap}$) of the apparent orbit (ellipse); the auxiliary ellipse is tangent to the apparent ellipse (orbit) at the extremities of the relative ellipse's major axis projection, and not at the extremities of the apparent ellipse's major axis; the main axes of the auxiliary ellipse (orbit) are generally rotated relative to the main axes of the apparent ellipse (orbit).

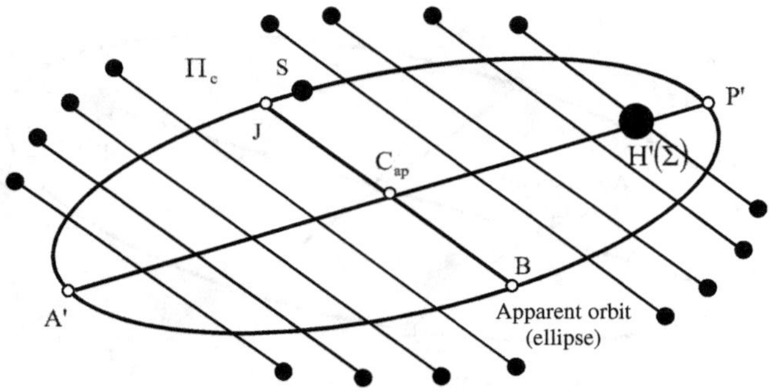


**Fig. T10.23**

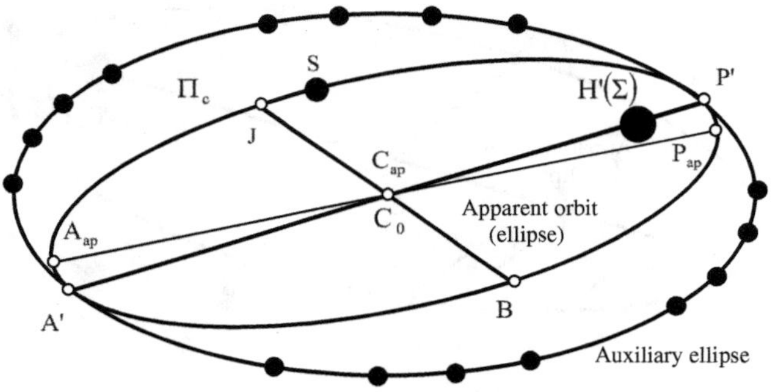


**Fig. T10.24**

### 10.5.2. *Second method*

In Figure T10.25, whose plane is the celestial plane $\Pi_c$, the apparent ellipse (orbit) of star S moving around the primary star $\Sigma$ is represented.

*Notation*: $C_{ap}$ – the center of the apparent ellipse, obtained as the projection of the center C of the relative orbit; $A_{ap}P_{ap}$ – the major axis of the apparent ellipse (orbit); $A'P'$ – the projection of the major axis AP (the line of the apsides) of the relative ellipse from the plane $\Pi$ on the celestial plane $\Pi_c$; $H'(\Sigma)$ – the projection of the star $\Sigma$ located in the focus F of the relative ellipse from the $\Pi$ plane on the celestial plane $\Pi_c$.

In Figure T10.26, the segment BJ represents the projection on the celestial plane of the relative ellipse's (orbit's) minor axis obtained as the conjugate diameter of the projection $A'P'$.

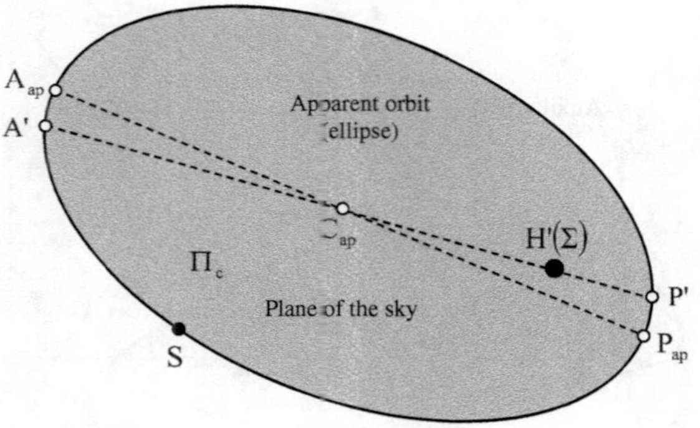


**Fig. T10.25**

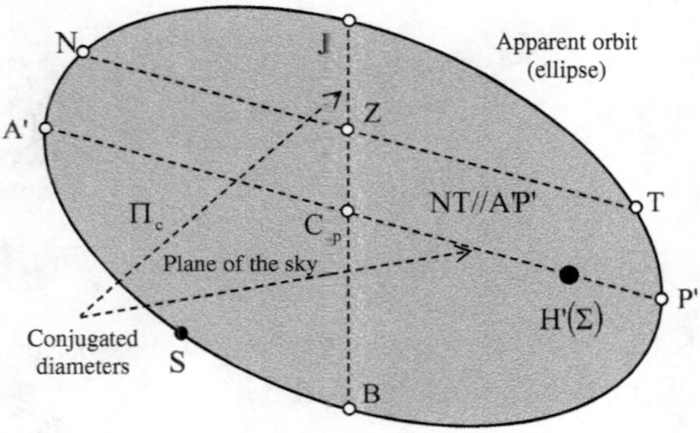


**Fig. T10.26**

According to the geometry presented in Figure T10.27, we present a graphical method to draw the auxiliary ellipse, using the apparent ellipse (orbit) of the star S relative to the primary star Σ.

**1)** For this, on the conjugate diameter BJ we mark the points D and R; thus, the following conditions must be fulfilled:

$$JD = BR;$$

$$\frac{\mathrm{C_{ap}D}}{\mathrm{C_{ap}J}} = \frac{a}{b} = \frac{1}{\sqrt{1-e^2}} = \frac{\mathrm{C_{ap}P'}}{\sqrt{(\mathrm{C_{ap}P'})^2 - (\mathrm{C_{ap}H'})^2}}$$

$$= \frac{1}{\sqrt{1 - \left(\frac{\mathrm{C_{ap}H'}}{\mathrm{C_{ap}P'}}\right)^2}},$$

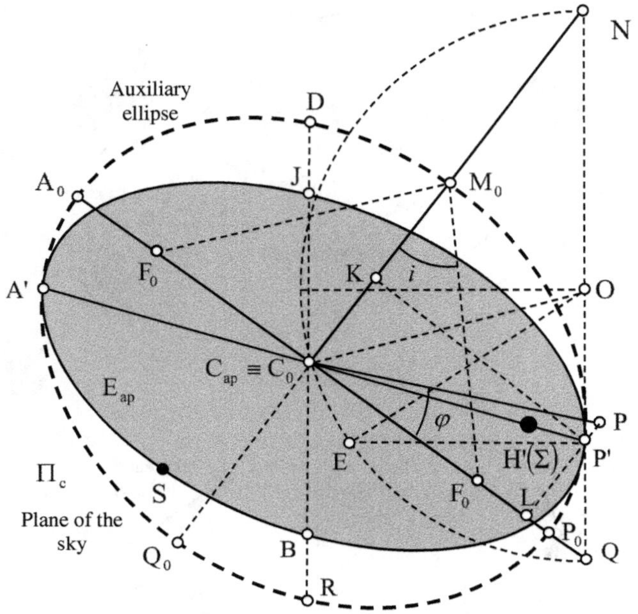


**Fig. T10.27**

where $a$ and $b$ are the semiaxes of the relative orbit and $e$ is the eccentricity of the relative ellipse (orbit);

$$e = \frac{\mathrm{C_{ap}H'}}{\mathrm{C_{ap}P'}},$$

representing the eccentricity of the relative orbit (ellipse), whose value can be determined using the measurements for the apparent orbit (ellipse).

The result is as follows:

$$\frac{\mathrm{C_{ap}D}}{\mathrm{C_{ap}J}} = \frac{1}{\sqrt{1-e^2}}; \quad \mathrm{C_{ap}D} = \frac{\mathrm{C_{ap}J}}{\sqrt{1-e^2}}; \quad \mathrm{C_{ap}D} > \mathrm{C_{ap}J},$$

where $\mathrm{C_{ap}J}$ is measured on the apparent ellipse (orbit). Thus, the previous relation allows the localization of point J in plane $\Pi_c$ of the apparent ellipse (orbit).

**2)** We draw the tangent to the apparent ellipse (orbit) at point P′. This tangent is parallel to the conjugate diameter BJ of the apparent ellipse (orbit). At point P′, perpendicular to the tangent to the apparent ellipse (orbit), we trace the segment $\mathrm{P'E}// = \mathrm{C_{ap}D}$.

**3)** On the tangent to the apparent ellipse (orbit) traced at point $P'$, we search for point O, representing the center of the circle that contains the points E and $C_{ap}$. Q and N are the intersections of this circle with the tangent to the apparent orbit (ellipse) traced at point $P'$.

**4)** Let's trace the segments $C_{ap}Q$ and $C_{ap}N$, which are obviously perpendicular at point $C_{ap}$. The directions of these two segments are also the directions of the auxiliary ellipse's axes that will eventually be drawn.

**5)** Let's trace the segments $P'L \perp C_{ap}Q$ and $P'K \perp C_{ap}N$.

**6)** On the segment $C_{ap}Q$ we localize the point $P_0$, corresponding to the geometric mean condition:

$$C_{ap}P_0 = \sqrt{(C_{ap}Q) \cdot (C_{ap}L)},$$

where $C_{ap}Q$ and $C_{ap}L$ are measured in the apparent orbit (ellipse) plane. Thus, the position of the point $P_0$ in the plane of the apparent orbit (ellipse) is determined.

Similarly, on the segment $C_{ap}N$ we localize the point $M_0$ corresponding to the geometric mean condition:

$$C_{ap}M_0 = \sqrt{(C_{ap}K) \cdot (C_{ap}N)},$$

where $C_{ap}K$ and $C_{ap}N$ are measured in the apparent orbit (ellipse) plane. Thus, the position of the point $M_0$ in the plane of the apparent orbit (ellipse) is determined.

Under these conditions, the segments $C_{ap}P_0$ and $C_{ap}M_0$, respectively, represent the semi-axes of the auxiliary ellipse that will eventually be drawn:

$$C_{ap}P_0 = a_{aux}; \quad C_{ap}M_0 = b_{aux}$$

(the lengths of these segments can be measured on the apparent ellipse (orbit));

$$e_{aux} = \sqrt{1 - \frac{b_{aux}}{a_{aux}}},$$

representing the eccentricity of the auxiliary ellipse, whose value can be determined.

**7)** The auxiliary ellipse can be drawn to link the points $P_0$, $M_0$ and D and to be tangent to the apparent orbit (ellipse) at points P′ and A′, while its center is the point $C_0 \equiv C_{ap}$.

**8)** The foci of the auxiliary ellipse are placed on its major axis and represent the points $F_0$ for which:

$$C_0F_0 = c_0 = e_{aux}a_{aux}.$$

Or, they represent the points $F_0$ for which, according to the ellipse's properties, the following equations hold:

$$M_0F_0 = C_0P_0 = C_0A_0 = a_{aux}.$$

**9)** The auxiliary ellipse in the celestial plane $\Pi_c$ coincides with the relative orbit (ellipse) in plane Π, which projected on the celestial plane $\Pi_c$ represents the apparent orbit (ellipse). According to the scale used, the semi-major axis $a_{aux}$ can be measured on the auxiliary ellipse. It will be identified with the semi-major axis of the relative orbit (ellipse), $a_{aux} = a$. Similarly, it can be shown that $b_{aux} = b = a\cos i$.

The auxiliary ellipse on the celestial plane is the projection of the eccentric circle in the Π plane of the relative orbit (ellipse). The angle $i$ between the plane of the eccentric circle (the plane Π of the relative orbit) and the plane of the apparent orbit (ellipse) (the celestial plane $\Pi_c$) represents the inclination of plane Π relative to plane $\Pi_c$, as presented in Figure T10.28.

It results that:

$$Q_0M_0 = UZ \cdot \cos i; \quad 2b_{aux} = 2a \cdot \cos i;$$

$$\cos i = \frac{b_{aux}}{a} = \frac{b}{a},$$

representing the inclination of the relative orbit's (ellipse's) plane Π, relative to the apparent orbit's (ellipse's) plane $\Pi_c$, where $a$ and $b$ are the semi-axes of the relative ellipse (orbit) seen as the auxiliary ellipse.

The intersection of the two planes Π and $\Pi_c$, is the nodes line $N_aN_d$. As a consequence, the major axis of the auxiliary ellipse $A_0P_0$ is parallel to the nodes line $N_aN_d$, as presented in Figure T10.29,

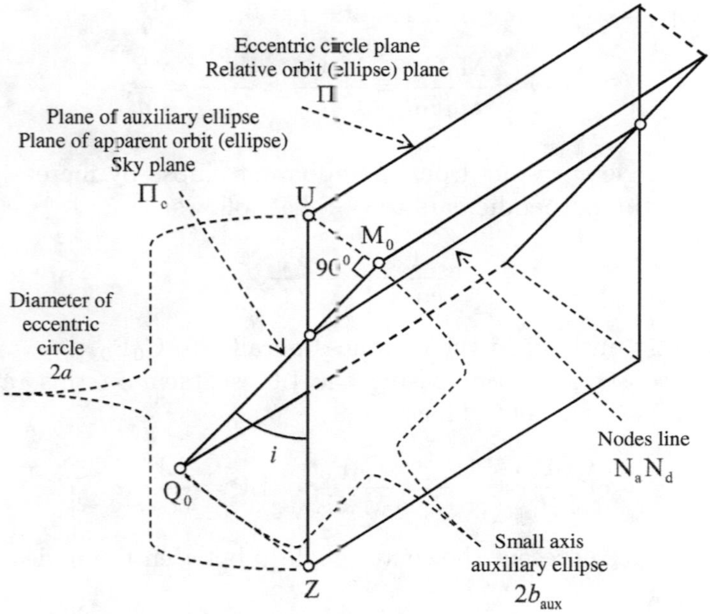


**Fig. T10.28**

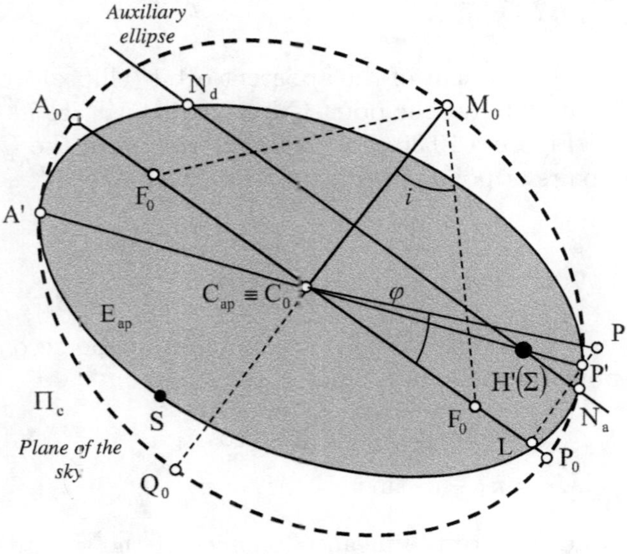


**Fig. T10.29**

where for $i = \angle(\mathrm{C_0M_0F_0})$, it results that

$$\cos i = \frac{\mathrm{M_0C_0}}{\mathrm{M_0F_0}} = \frac{\mathrm{M_0C_0}}{\mathrm{C_0P_0}} = \frac{b_{\mathrm{aux}}}{a_{\mathrm{aux}}} = \frac{b}{a}.$$

**10)** The angle $\varphi$ results from the apparent ellipse by increasing the lengths of the perpendiculars to $\mathrm{C_0P_0}$ as follows:

$$\frac{1}{\cos i} = \frac{\mathrm{C_0P_0}}{\mathrm{M_0C_0}},$$

maintaining unchanged the distances parallel to $\mathrm{C_0P_0}$.

As a consequence, increasing the $\mathrm{LP'}$ segment in this ratio we obtain the LP segment. Thus:

$$\frac{\mathrm{LP}}{\mathrm{LP'}} = \frac{1}{\cos i} = \frac{\mathrm{C_0P_0}}{\mathrm{M_0C_0}}; \quad \mathrm{LP} = \frac{\mathrm{LP'}}{\cos i}.$$

$\angle(\mathrm{LC_0P})$ will represent the center angle $\varphi$ between the node and the periastron.

$$\mathrm{C_0P} = a = \mathrm{C_0P_0};$$

thus, knowing $\varphi$ and $\mathrm{C_0P}$, the point P (the periastron) can be localized.

**11)** On the $\mathrm{A'P'}$ segment of the apparent orbit (ellipse) we trace the circle with the center at the point $\mathrm{C_{ap}}$ and with $\mathrm{A'P'}$ as its diameter, presented in Figure T10.30. On this circle we mark the $\mathrm{C_1}$–$\mathrm{G_1}$ and the $\mathrm{C_2}$–$\mathrm{G_2}$ pairs of points, symmetrical relative to $\mathrm{A'P'}$.

$$\angle\left(\mathrm{P'C_{ap}C_1}\right) = u_1 = \angle\left(\mathrm{P'C_{ap}G_1}\right);$$
$$\angle\left(\mathrm{P'C_{ap}C_2}\right) = u_2 = \angle\left(\mathrm{P'C_{ap}G_2}\right),$$

where $u_1$ and $u_2$ are the eccentric anomalies of the secondary star (S) corresponding to times $t_1$ and $t_2$, respectively;

$$\mathrm{C_{ap}}D = \mathrm{C_{ap}}C_1 \cdot \cos u_1;$$
$$M_1 = u_1 - e \cdot \sin u_1; \quad M_2 = u_2 - e \cdot \sin u_2,$$

where $M_1$ and $M_2$ are the mean anomalies of the secondary star S corresponding to $t_1$ and $t_2$, respectively.

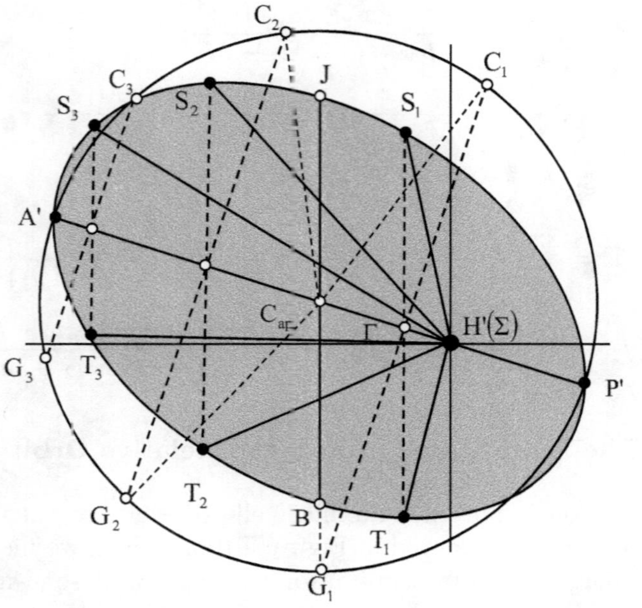


**Fig. Γ10.30**

According to the definition of the mean anomaly, if $T$ is the rotation period of the secondary star (S) around the primary star (Σ) and $\tau$ is the moment when the secondary star S reaches the periastron, then it results in the following:

$$M = u - e \cdot \sin u = n\,(t - \tau) = \frac{2\pi}{T}\,(t - \tau)\,;$$

$$M_1 = u_1 - e \cdot \sin u_1 = n\,(t_1 - \tau) = \frac{2\pi}{T}\,(t_1 - \tau)\,;$$

$$M_2 = u_2 - e \cdot \sin u_2 = n\,(t_2 - \tau) = \frac{2\pi}{T}\,(t_2 - \tau)\,;$$

$$M_2 - M_1 = \frac{2\pi}{T}\,(t_2 - t_1)\,;$$

$$\frac{T}{t_2 - t_1} = \frac{2\pi}{M_2 - M_1};$$

$$t_1 - \tau = \frac{T}{2\pi} M_1;$$

$$\frac{t_1 - \tau}{t_2 - t_1} = \frac{M_1}{M_2 - M_1};$$

$$\frac{T}{t_2 - t_1} = \frac{2\pi}{M_2 - M_1}; \quad \frac{t_1 - \tau}{t_2 - t_1} = \frac{M_1}{M_2 - M_1}.$$

Furthermore:

$$T = \frac{2\pi\,(t_2 - t_1)}{M_2 - M_1} = \frac{2\pi\,(t_2 - t_1)}{(u_2 - u_1) + e\,(\sin u_2 - \sin u_1)};$$

$$\tau = t_1 - \frac{M_1\,(t_2 - t_1)}{M_2 - M_1} = t_1 - \frac{(u_1 - e \cdot \sin u_1) \cdot (t_2 - t_1)}{(u_2 - u_1) + e\,(\sin u_2 - \sin u_1)}.$$

## 10.6. The Semi-Major Axis of the Relative Orbit (Ellipse)

For the previously obtained auxiliary ellipse, we draw the major and the minor axes as presented in Figure T10.31; then, we measure and note the lengths for its semi-major axis $a_{\text{aux}}$ and semi-minor axis $b_{\text{aux}}$.

We are reminded that the auxiliary ellipse is the projection of the eccentric circle from the plane $\Pi$ on the celestial plane $\Pi_c$. The eccentric circle is the one that circumscribes the relative ellipse (orbit) in plane $\Pi$. The radius of the eccentric circle is equal to the semi-major axis $a$ of the relative ellipse (orbit). Under these circumstances, the relative ellipse's (orbit's) semi-major axis is equal to the auxiliary ellipse's semi-major axis, $a = a_{\text{aux}}$.

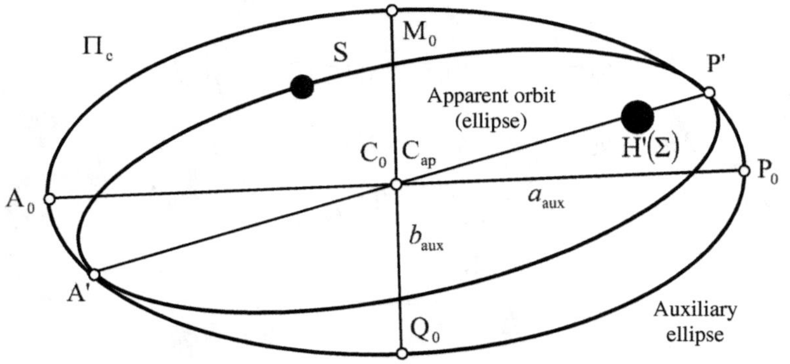


**Fig. T10.31**

As a consequence, the auxiliary ellipse in the celestial plane $\Pi_c$ identifies with the relative orbit (ellipse) in the $\Pi$ plane. The projection of the relative orbit (ellipse) on the celestial plane $\Pi_c$ represents the apparent orbit (ellipse). According to the scale used, on the auxiliary ellipse the semi-major axis $a_{aux}$ is measured and identified with the semi-major axis of the relative orbit (ellipse), $a_{aux} = a$. Similarly, it can be considered that $b_{aux} = b = a \cos i$.

Conclusion: knowing $T$ and $a$, the mass of the visual binary stellar system can be determined using Kepler's third law.

## 10.7. The Angular Inclination $i$

The eccentric circle circumscribes the relative (real) ellipse (orbit). When the eccentric circle is projected from its plane onto the celestial plane, the angle between the two planes represents the inclination angle $i$. The respective circle deforms and it becomes the auxiliary ellipse. The maximum deformation is on the axis perpendicular to the rotation axis, where the original radius $a$ is determined by the $\cos i$ factor, and it becomes the semi-minor axis ($b_{aux} = a \cos i$) of the auxiliary ellipse. Along the rotation axis, the eccentric circle radius does not change; thus, the original radius $a$ remains unchanged and it is equal to the semi-major axis of the auxiliary ellipse, $a_{aux} = a$.

Under these conditions, we note, measure, and calculate

$$\frac{b_{aux}}{a_{aux}} = \frac{a \cos i}{a} = \cos i,$$

where $i$ is the angle between the relative orbit plane and the apparent orbit plane (the inclination of the relative orbit in relation to the apparent orbit), and $a_{aux}$ and $b_{aux}$ are the semi-axes of the auxiliary ellipse.

Under the condition that the auxiliary ellipse overlaps with the relative orbit (ellipse), the result is:

$$\frac{\mathrm{CF}}{\mathrm{CP}} = \frac{ea}{a} = e = \sqrt{1 - \frac{b^2}{a^2}};$$

$$b_{aux} = a \cos i; \quad a_{aux} = a;$$

$$e = \sqrt{1 - \frac{b_{\text{aux}}^2}{a_{\text{aux}}^2}} = \sqrt{1 - \cos^2 i};$$

$$\cos i = \sqrt{1 - e^2};$$

$$d = D \cos i;$$

$$D = \frac{d}{\cos i} = \frac{d}{\sqrt{1 - e^2}} kd; \quad k = \frac{1}{\sqrt{1 - e^2}} > 1.$$

## 10.8. The Nodes Line

To determine the orientation of the relative (ellipse) in space, we must identify the axis around which the relative orbit (ellipse) has been inclined with the inclination angle $i$. This axis is to be projected on the celestial plane and represents the line of nodes. How can this axis be localized taking into account the apparent (observed) orbit (ellipse)?

Let's consider again the relative orbit (ellipse) when it is observed in a direction perpendicular to its plane, as presented in Figure T10.32.

The $N_a N_d$ line of nodes always contains the position of the primary star $\Sigma$. Corresponding to the primary star located in the ellipse's focus F, the relative orbit (ellipse) of the secondary star is represented.

In Figure T10.33, $\omega$ (the argument of the periastron) represents the angle between the periastron's position vector and the position

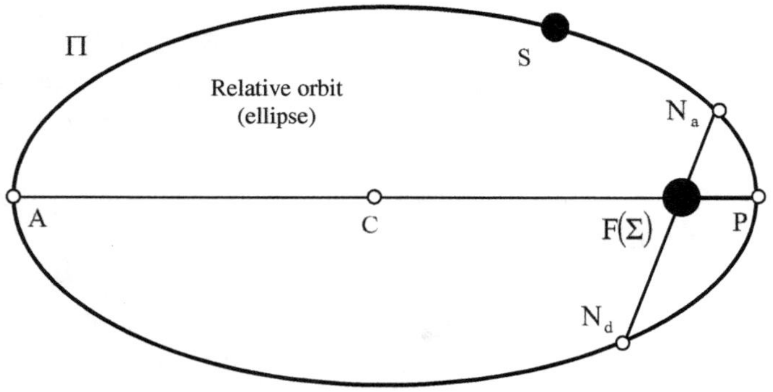


**Fig. T10.32**

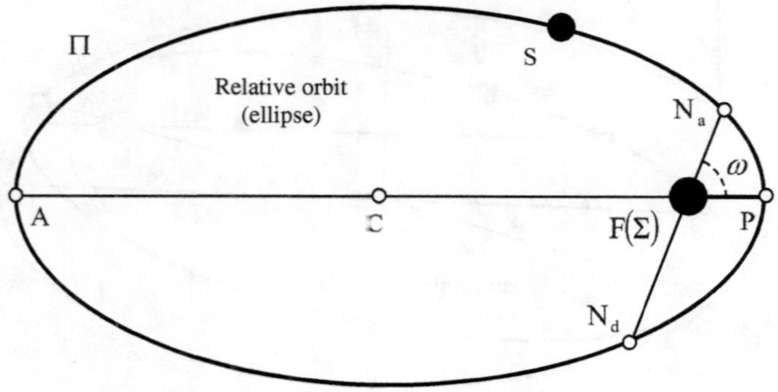


**Fig. T10.33**

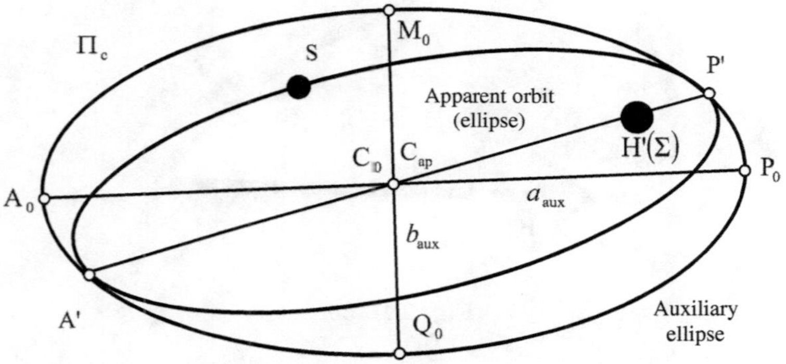


**Fig. T10.34**

vector corresponding to the closest node. The origins of these two position vectors coincide with the relative ellipse's focus where the primary star $\Sigma$ is located. The arguments of the periastron ($\omega$) are the angle between the $N_aN_d$ line of nodes and the line of apsides (the major axis of the relative orbit, AP, measured in the $\Pi$ plane).

To determine the value of the angle $\omega$ we return to the diagram presenting the apparent orbit (ellipse) and the auxiliary ellipse: see Figure T10.34.

Since the inclination (the rotation) took place around the line of nodes, the major axis of the auxiliary ellipse is parallel to the line of nodes. Consequently, the line parallel to the major axis of the auxiliary ellipse that contains the primary star $\Sigma$ has to be the line

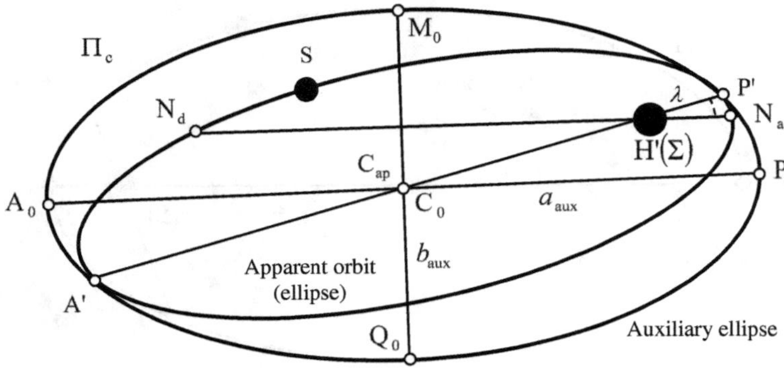


**Fig. T10.35**

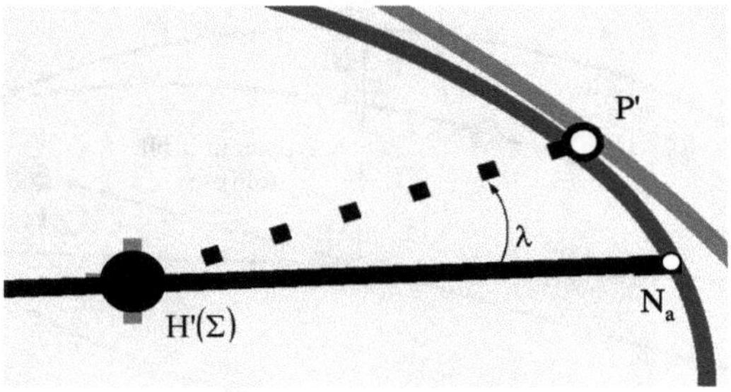


**Fig. T10.36**

of nodes. Let's draw the line on the apparent orbit (ellipse) that will contain the position of Σ in plane $\Pi_c$, as presented in Figure T10.35.

In Figure T10.36, a portion of the orbit close to the periastron is presented. The line of nodes intersects the apparent ellipse (orbit) at point $N_a$. In this ellipse's plane we can measure the angle $\lambda$ between $H'N_a$ and $H'P'$.

Using Figures T10.37 and T10.38 and applying one of the cotangent formulas for the spherical triangle ABC's edges and angles, it results that:

$$\sin a \cdot \cot c = \cos a \cdot \cos B + \sin B \cdot \cot C;$$

$$\sin \lambda \cdot \cot \omega = \cos \lambda \cdot \cos i + \sin i \cdot \cot 90^0;$$

$$\sin \lambda \cdot \cot \omega = \cos \lambda \cdot \cos i;$$

$$\frac{\sin\lambda}{\cos\lambda} = \frac{\cos i}{\cot\omega} = \cos i \cdot \tan\omega = \tan\lambda;$$

$$\tan\omega = \frac{\tan\lambda}{\cos i}.$$

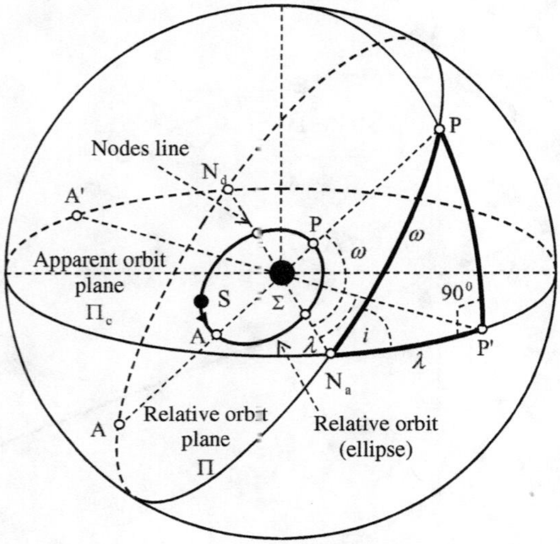


Fig. T10.37

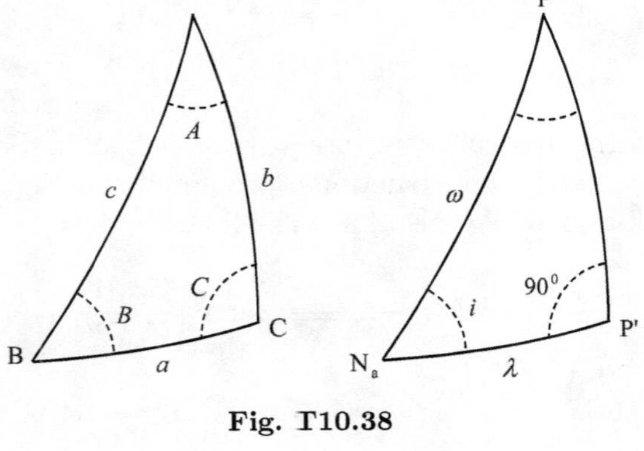


Fig. T10.38

## 10.9. Applications

**1)** *Determine* the elements of the relative orbit and *represent* the relative orbit of Sirius B, knowing the apparent orbit of Sirius B relative to Sirius A, presented in Figure T10.39. *Determine* mass of Sirius A. Sirius A is considered stationary relative to the observer. The distance from the Earth to the Sirius system is $\Delta = 8.6$ ly.

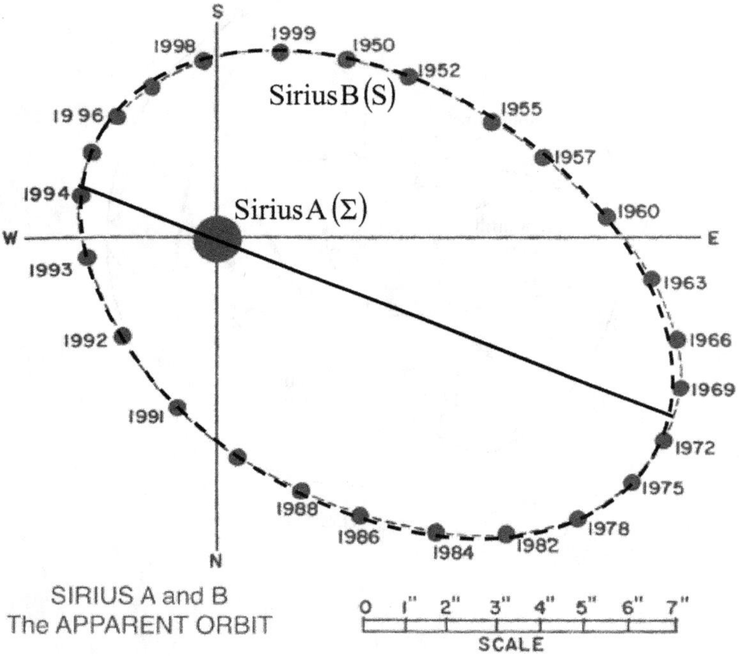


**Fig. T10.39**

Following the instructions (stages) described in Sections 10.1–10.8, the geometric constructions presented in Figures T10.40–T10.47 are obtained. We also have the following:

$$D = kd = \frac{d}{\sqrt{1-e^2}}; \quad e = \frac{C_{ap}H'}{C_{ap}P'}.$$

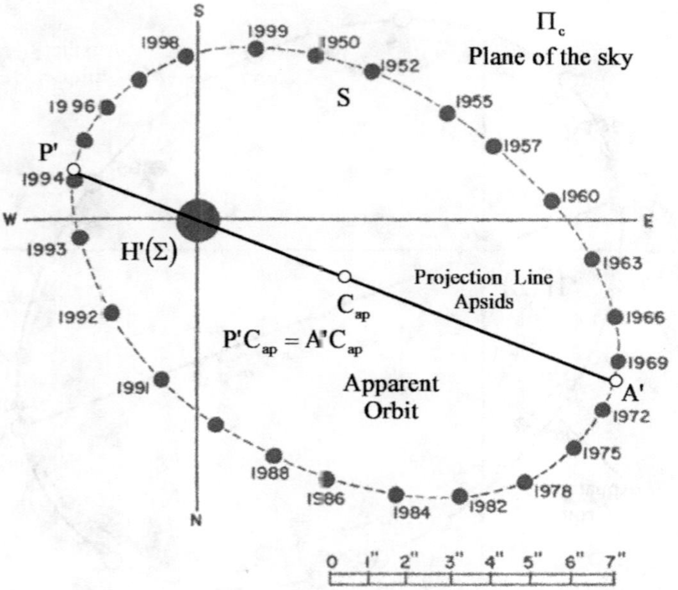


Fig. T10.40

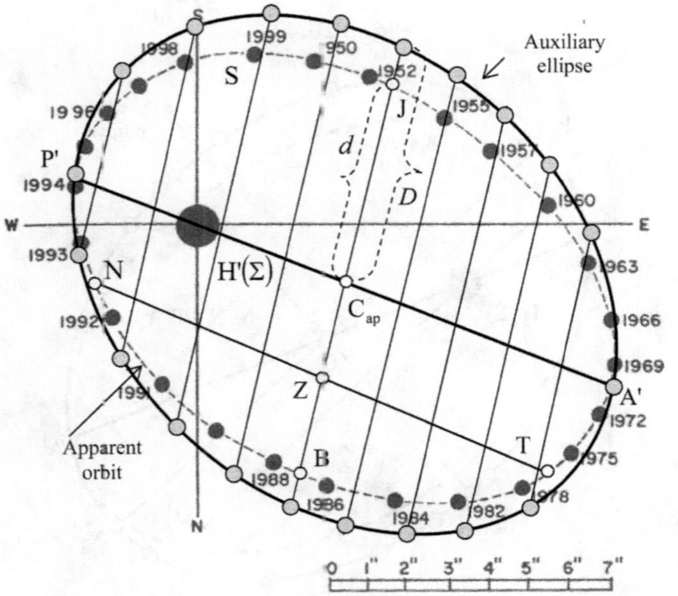


Fig. T10.41

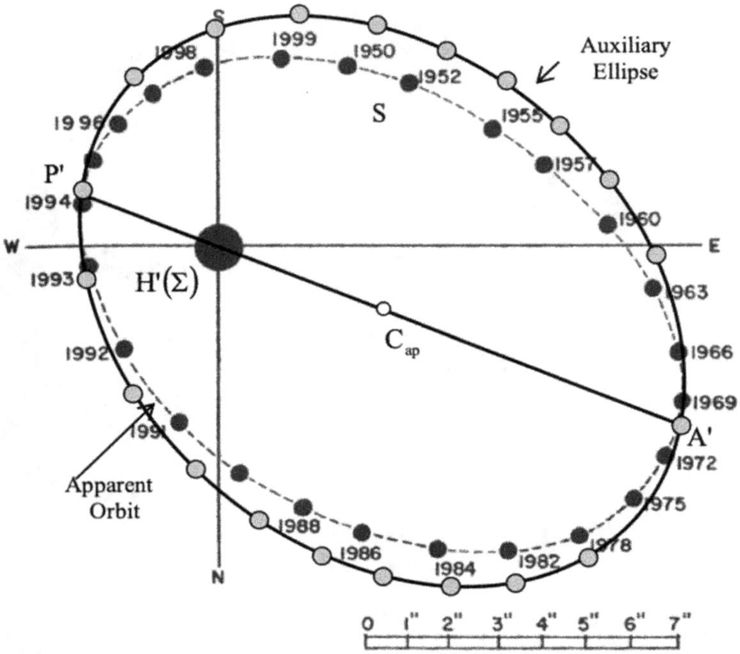


Fig. T10.42

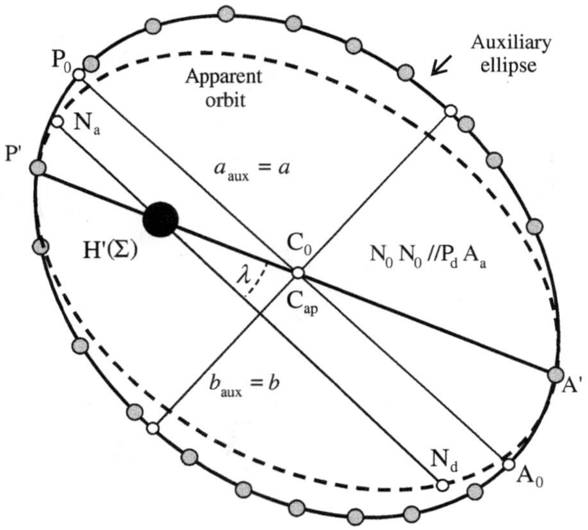


Fig. T10.43

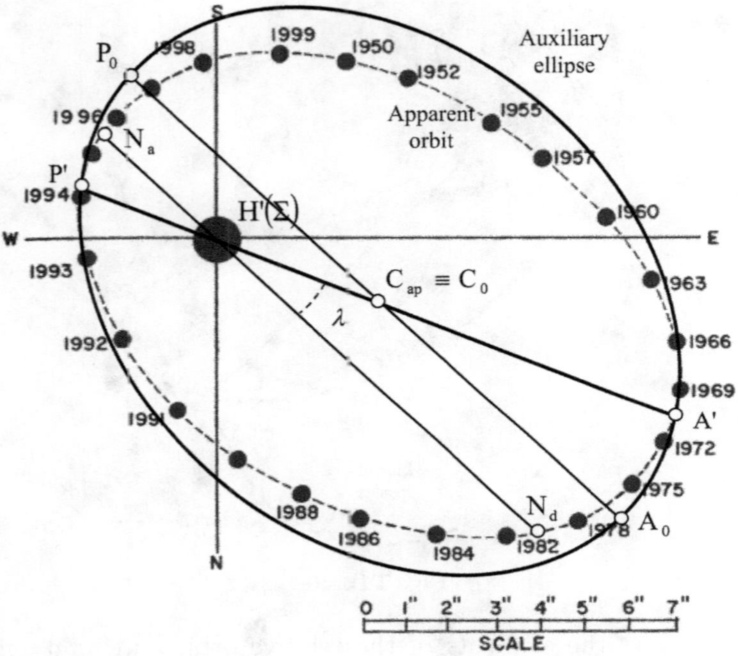


Fig. T10.44

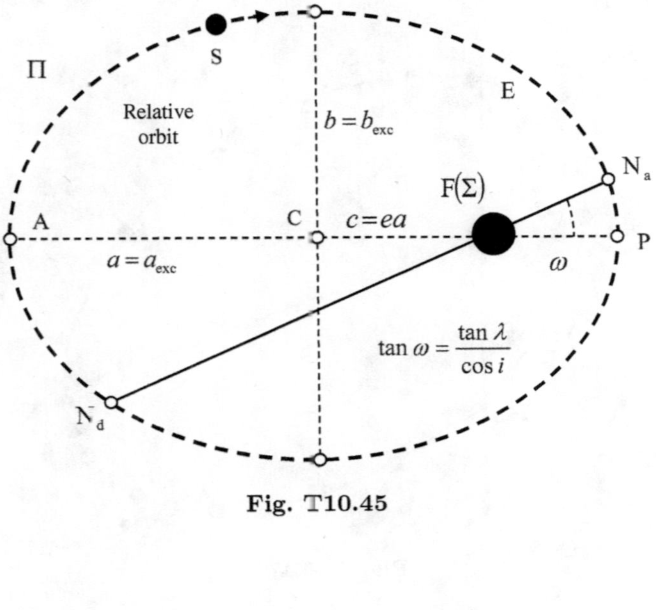


Fig. T10.45

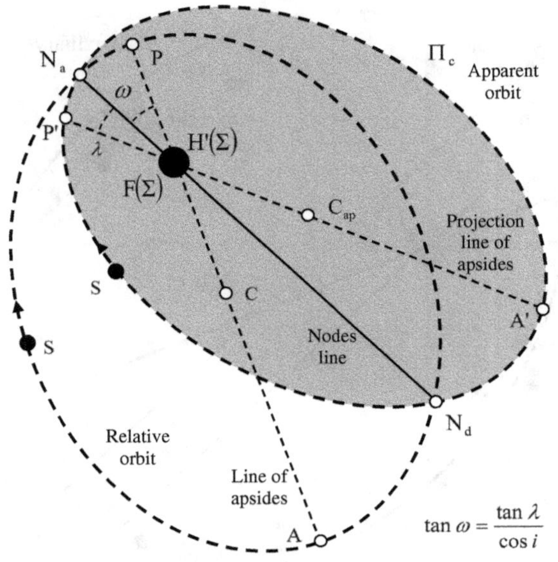


**Fig. T10.46**

**2)** *Determine* the elements of the relative orbit and *represent* the relative orbit of the secondary star S, knowing the apparent orbit of star S relative to the primary star Σ represented in Figure T10.47. *Determine* the mass of star Σ. Σ is considered stationary relative to the observer.

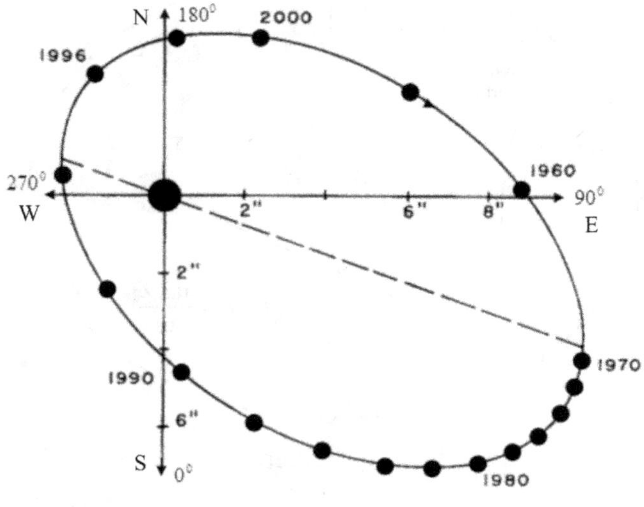


**Fig. T10.47**

Following the instructions (stages) described in Sections 10.1–10.8, the geometric constructions presented in Figures T10.48–T10.54 are obtained.

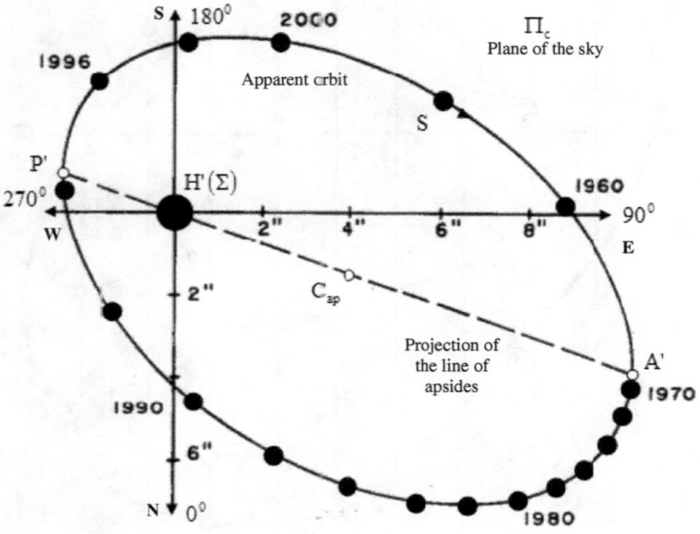


Fig. T10.48

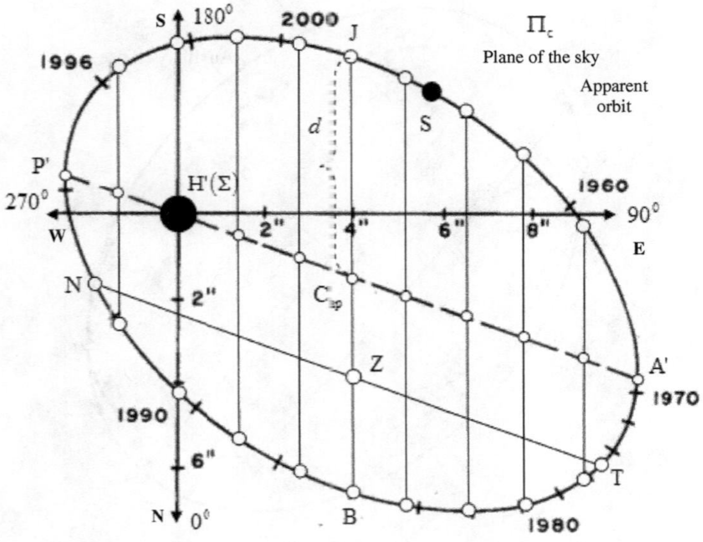


Fig. T10.49

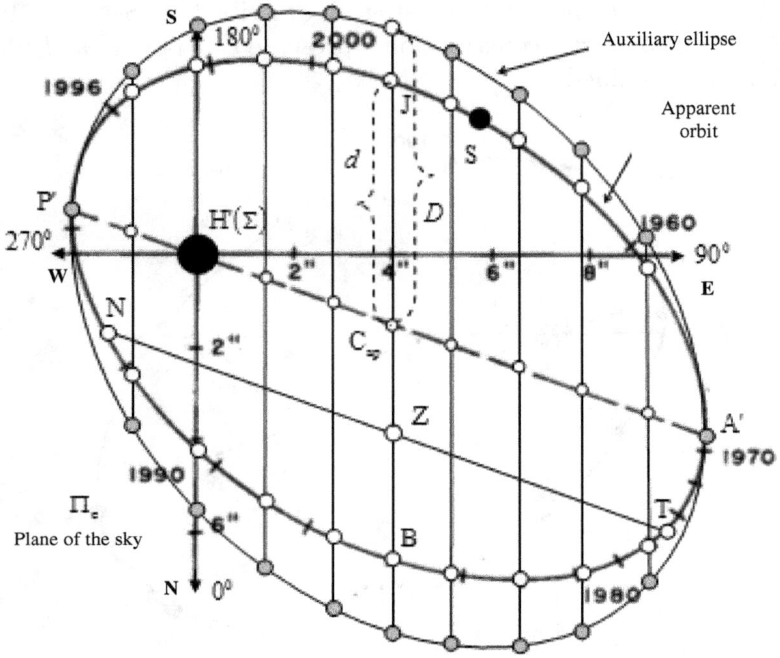


**Fig. T10.50**

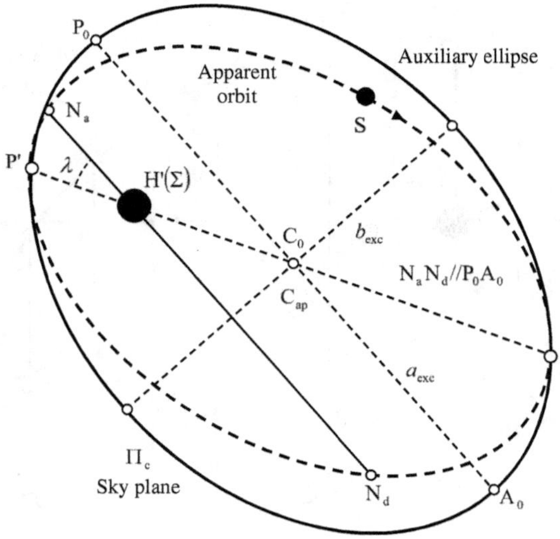


**Fig. T10.51**

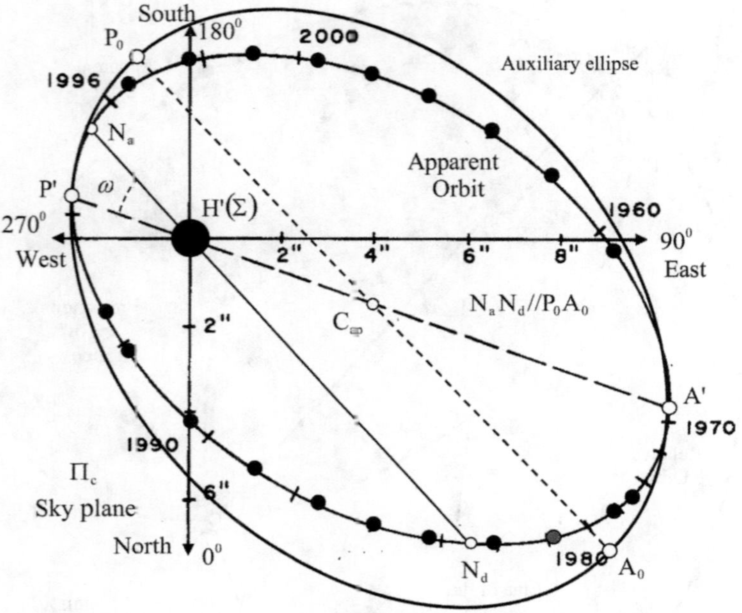


Fig. T10.52

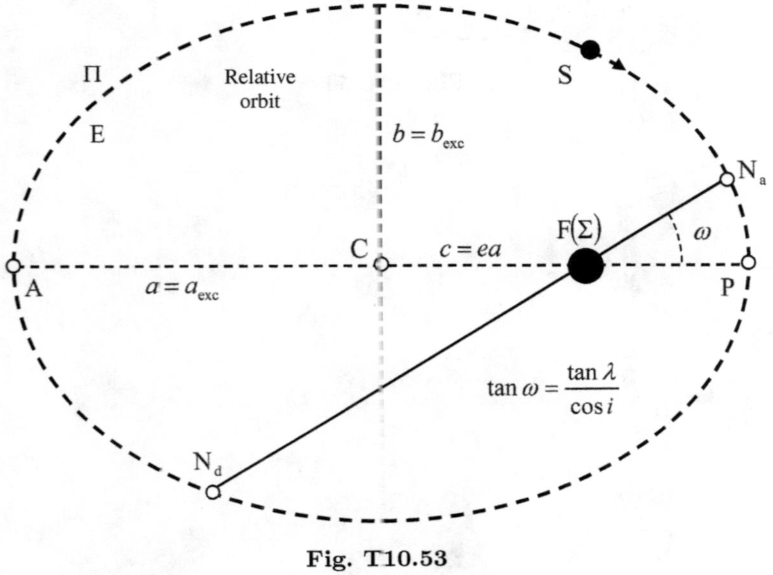


Fig. T10.53

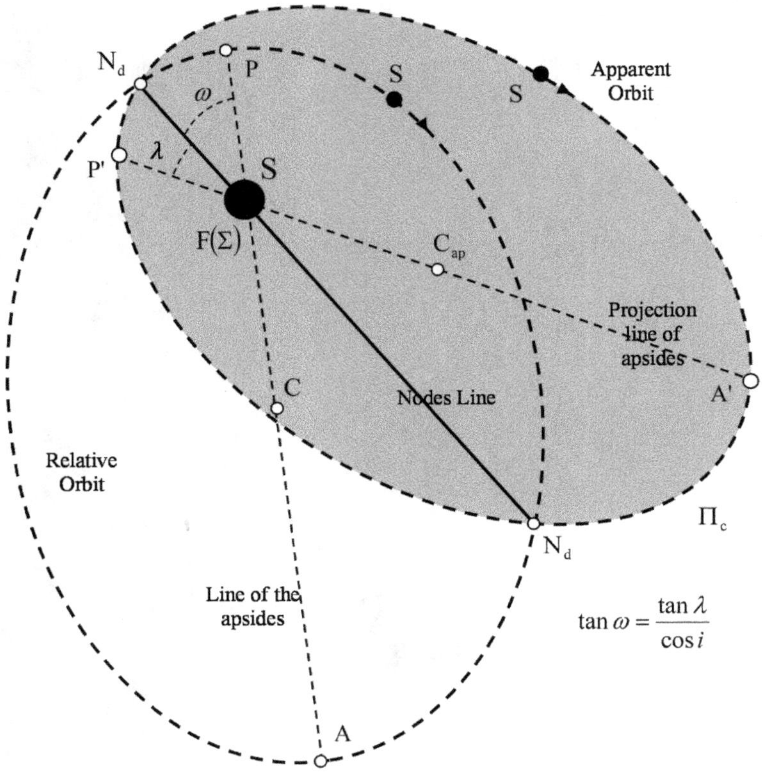

$N_d$
P
S
S
Apparent Orbit
$\omega$
$\lambda$
P'
S
$F(\Sigma)$
$C_{ap}$
Projection line of apsides
A'
C
Nodes Line
Relative Orbit
$\Pi_c$
$N_d$
Line of the apsides
$\tan\omega = \dfrac{\tan\lambda}{\cos i}$
A


**Fig. T10.54**

# Topic 11

# The Equations of the Eclipses

If the orbits of the stars in a binary system relative to the CM are concentric circles, their position coordinates relative to the CM can be determined using Figure T11.1, as follows:

$$\sigma_1\sigma_2 = a; \quad O\sigma_1 = a_1; \quad O\sigma_2 = a_2;$$

$$M_1 a_1 = M_2 a_2; \quad a_1 + a_2 = a;$$

$$a_1 = \frac{aM_2}{M_1 + M_2} = \frac{a}{1 + \frac{M_1}{M_2}}; \quad \frac{M_1}{M_2} = q; \quad a_1 = \frac{aM_2}{M_1 + M_2} = \frac{a}{1 + \frac{M_1}{M_2}};$$

$$a_1 = \frac{a}{1 + q};$$

$$a_2 = \frac{aM_1}{M_1 + M_2} = \frac{a}{1 + \frac{M_2}{M_1}}; \quad \frac{M_1}{M_2} = q; \quad a_2 = \frac{aM_1}{M_1 + M_2} = \frac{a}{1 + \frac{M_2}{M_1}};$$

$$a_2 = \frac{a}{1 + q^{-1}};$$

$$a_X = a \sin\theta \cos\varphi; \quad a_Y = a \sin\theta \sin\varphi; \quad a_Z = a \cos\theta,$$

representing the projection of the distance between the two stars, $a$, on the three coordinate axes;

$$x_1 = -a_1 \sin\theta \cos\varphi = -a_1 \frac{a_X}{a} = -\frac{a_X}{1 + q};$$

$$y_1 = -a_1 \sin\theta \sin\varphi = -a_1 \frac{a_Y}{a} = -\frac{a_Y}{1 + q};$$

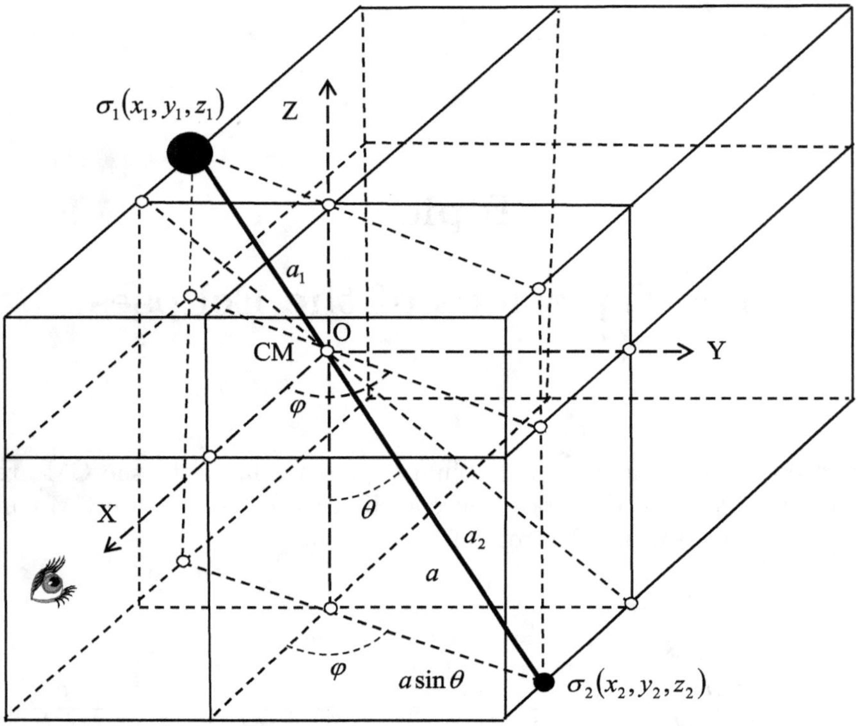


**Fig. T11.1**

$$z_1 = a_1 \cos\theta = a_1 \frac{a_Z}{a} = \frac{a_Z}{1+q};$$

$$x_2 = a_2 \sin\theta \cos\varphi = a_2 \frac{a_X}{a} = \frac{a_X}{1+q^{-1}};$$

$$y_2 = a_2 \sin\theta \sin\varphi = a_2 \frac{a_Y}{a} = \frac{a_Y}{1+q^{-1}};$$

$$z_2 = -a_2 \cos\theta = -a_2 \frac{a_Z}{a} = -\frac{a_Z}{1+q^{-1}}.$$

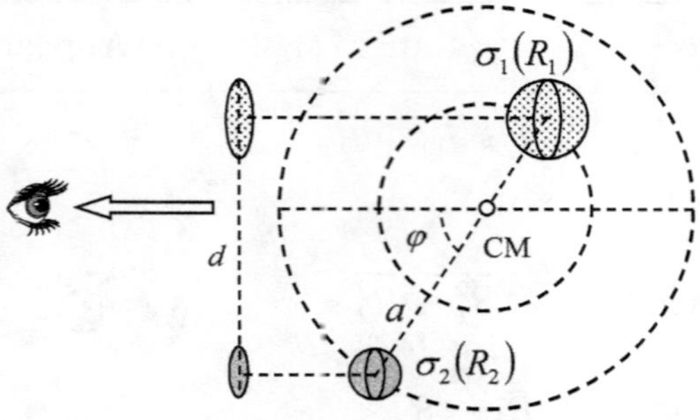


**Fig. T11.2**

The $y$ and $z$ coordinates of the two stars are needed to establish the apparent positions of the two stars on the celestial plane, and the $x$ coordinate of each star is necessary to establish which of the two stars eclipses the other (which one is in front and which one is behind during the eclipse).

If $YOZ \equiv \Pi_c$ is the celestial plane, and OX is the line of observation (line of sight), then the distance between the apparent disks of the two stars, as they appear to the observer in projection on the celestial plane, is

$$d = \sqrt{(y_2 - y_1)^2 + (z_2 - z_1)^2}.$$

Let us admit that $\theta = 0$. The plane of the two stars' orbits relative to the CM is the XOY plane, and the observer's line of sight is the OX axis. Under these circumstances, the binary stellar system under consideration is eclipsing, as presented in Figure T11.2.

For the observer on Earth, the movement of the two star's apparent disks during the eclipse is shown in the sequences presented in the table below. The geometrical meaning of the distance $d$ between the centers of the two disks on the celestial plane is represented in Figure T11.3.

To calculate the surfaces of the free and covered/eclipsed sectors of the apparent circular disks during the eclipses, the geometry of

| Stage | Range | Appearance |
|---|---|---|
| No eclipse | $d > R_1 + R_2$ | 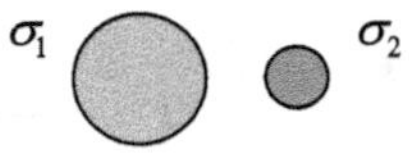  |
| Shallow partial eclipse | $\sqrt{R_1^2 - R_2^2} < d < R_1 + R_2$ | 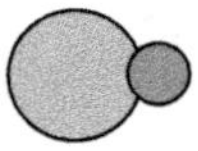 or 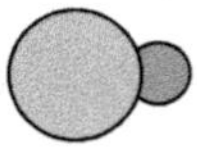 |
| Deep partial eclipse | $R_1 - R_2 < d < \sqrt{R_1^2 - R_2^2}$ | 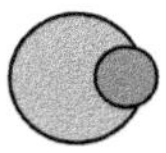 or 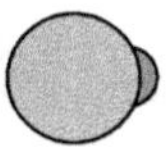 |
| Annular or total eclipse | $d < R_1 - R_2$ | 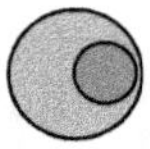 or  |

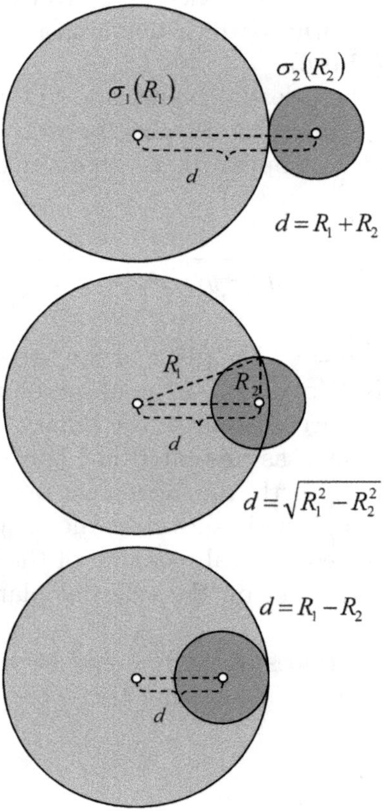


**Fig. T11.3**

the eclipses presented in sequences a and b of Figure T11.4 will be used. It results that:

$$\theta < \pi; \quad \theta = \pi - \alpha;$$

$$\Delta A = A_{\text{ACBDA}} = A_{\text{OACBO}} - A_{\text{OADBO}}$$
$$= \frac{\theta R^2}{2} - \frac{R^2}{2}\sin\theta = \frac{1}{2}R^2(\theta - \sin\theta);$$
$$\Delta A = \frac{1}{2}R^2(\theta - \sin\theta); \quad \theta < \pi,$$

where: $R$ – the radius of the circular disk; $\theta$ – the central angle corresponding to the AB segment;

$$\Delta A_1 = \frac{1}{2}R_1^2\,(\theta_1 - \sin\theta_1); \quad \Delta A_2 = \frac{1}{2}R_2^2\,(\theta_2 - \sin\theta_2);$$

$$\theta > \pi; \quad \theta = \pi + \alpha;$$

$$\beta < \pi; \quad \beta = \pi - \alpha;$$

$$\Delta A' = A_{\text{ADBEA}} = \frac{1}{2}R^2\,(\beta - \sin\beta);$$

$$\Delta A = A_{\text{ACBDA}} = \pi R^2 - \Delta A';$$

$$\Delta A = \pi R^2 - \frac{1}{2}R^2\,(\beta - \sin\beta);$$

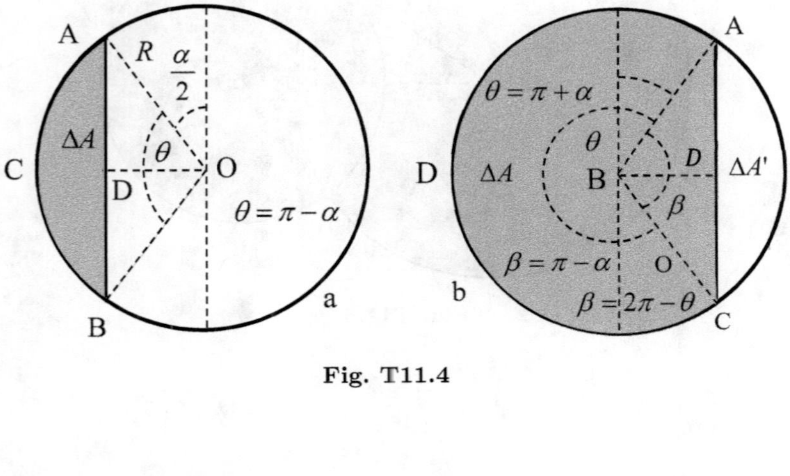


**Fig. T11.4**

$$\Delta A_1 = \pi R_1^2 - \frac{1}{2}R_1^2(\beta_1 - \sin\beta_1); \quad \Delta A_2 = \pi R_2^2 - \frac{1}{2}R_2^2(\beta_2 - \sin\beta_2);$$

$$\beta = 2\pi - \theta; \quad \theta > \pi;$$

$$\Delta A = \pi R^2 - \frac{1}{2}R^2(2\pi - \theta - \sin(2\pi - \theta));$$

$$\Delta A = \frac{1}{2}R^2(\theta - \sin\theta); \quad \theta > \pi;$$

$$\Delta A_1 = \frac{1}{2}R_1^2(\theta_1 - \sin\theta_1); \quad \Delta A_2 = \frac{1}{2}R_2^2(\theta_2 - \sin\theta_2).$$

Using Figure T11.5, the general relations between the radii of the two disks and the distance between the disks' centers in the celestial plane will be:

$$R_2^2 = R_1^2 + d^2 - 2R_1 d \cdot \cos\frac{\theta_1}{2};$$

$$R_1^2 = R_2^2 + d^2 - 2R_2 d \cdot \cos\frac{\theta_2}{2}.$$

If $x_1 > 0$ and $x_2 < 0$, it means that during the eclipse, the star $\sigma_1$ is permanently in front, while the star $\sigma_2$ passes behind it and then appears again, as shown in the sequences presented in the next

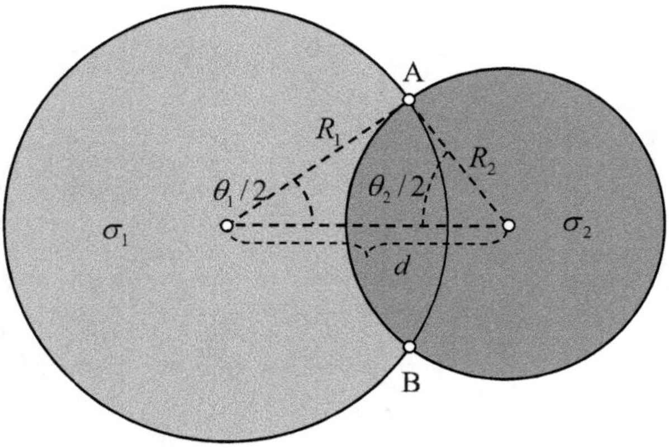


**Fig. T11.5**

table. Consequently, during the entire eclipse, the observer receives light from the entire surface of star $\sigma_1$'s disk, i.e., $A_1 = \pi R_1^2$. The surface of the star $\sigma_2$'s disk from which the observer receives light during the entire eclipse is variable: $0 \leq \Delta A_2 \leq \pi R_2^2$.

| | $x_1 > 0$ | $x_2 < 0$ | |
|---|---|---|---|
| Stage | $\sigma_1(\Delta A_1)$ | $\sigma_2(\Delta A_2)$ | Appearance |
| No eclipse | $\pi R_1^2$ | $\pi R_2^2$ | 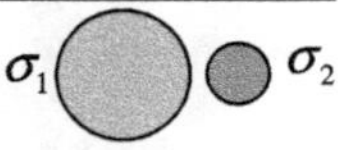  |
| Shallow partial eclipse | $\pi R_1^2$ | $\Delta A_{2,\text{Shallow}}$ | 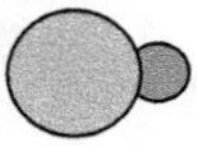 |
| Deep partial eclipse | $\pi R_1^2$ | $\Delta A_{2,\text{Deep}}$ | 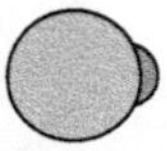 |
| Annular or total eclipse | $\pi R_1^2$ | 0 |  |

Using Figures T11.6 and T11.7 to calculate the area of the free surface sector of the star $\sigma_2$'s disk, in the shallow partial eclipse and deep partial eclipse cases, we obtain the following:

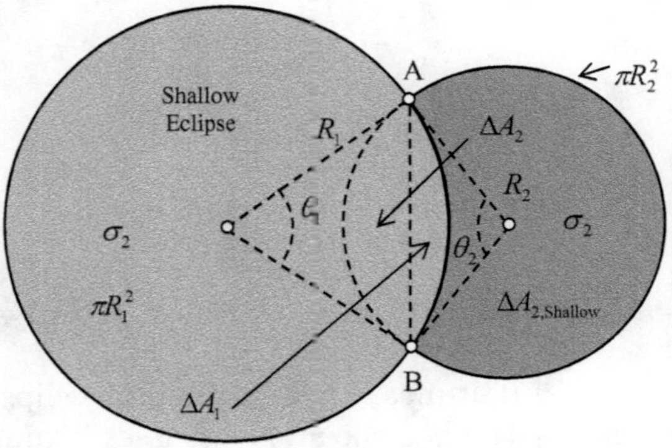


**Fig. T11.6**

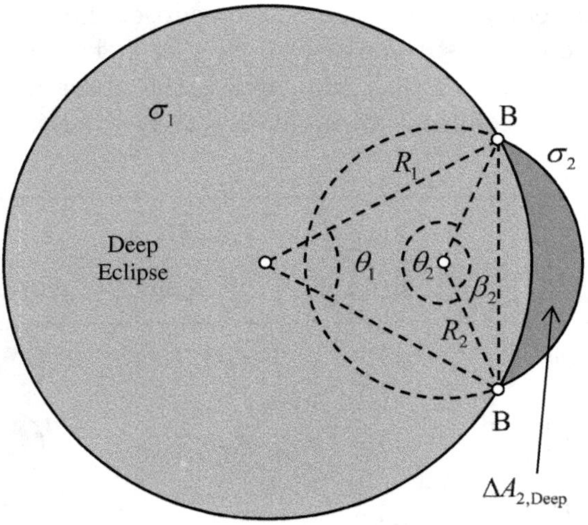


**Fig. T11.7**

$$\theta_1 < \pi; \quad \theta_2 < \pi;$$

$$\Delta A_{2,\text{Shallow}} = \pi R_2^2 - \Delta A_1 - \Delta A_2;$$

$$\theta_1 < \pi; \quad \theta_2 < \pi;$$

$$\Delta A_1 = \frac{1}{2} R_1^2 (\theta_1 - \sin\theta_1); \quad \Delta A_2 = \frac{1}{2} R_2^2 (\theta_2 - \sin\theta_2);$$

$$\theta_1 < \pi; \quad \theta_2 > \pi; \quad \beta_2 = 2\pi - \theta_2 < \pi;$$

$$\Delta A_{2,\text{Deep}} = \Delta A_2 - \Delta A_1;$$

$$\Delta A_1 = \frac{1}{2} R_1^2 (\theta_1 - \sin\theta_1);$$

$$\Delta A_2 = \frac{1}{2} R_2^2 (\theta_2 - \sin\theta_2); \quad \Delta A_2 = \pi R_2^2 - \frac{1}{2} R_2^2 (\beta_2 - \sin\beta_2).$$

If $x_2 > 0$ and $x_1 < 0$, it means that during the eclipse, the star $\sigma_2$ is permanently in front, while the star $\sigma_1$ passes behind it and then reappears, as shown in the sequences presented in the next table. The variation of each solar disk's free surface seen by the observer during the eclipse is shown for different stages of the eclipses in this table. Consequently, during the eclipse the observer receives light from the entire surface of star $\sigma_2$'s disk, that is, $A_2 = \pi R_2^2$. The surface of the star $\sigma_1$'s disk from which the observer receives light during the (entire) eclipse is variable: $\pi R_1^2 - \pi R_2^2 \leq \Delta A_1 \leq \pi R_1^2$.

| | $x_1 < 0$ | $x_2 > 0$ | |
|---|---|---|---|
| Stage | $\sigma_1(\Delta A_1)$ | $\sigma_2(\Delta A_2)$ | Appearance |
| No eclipse | $\sigma_1$ | $\pi R_2^2$ | 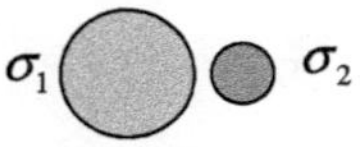 |
| Shallow partial eclipse | $\Delta S_{1,\text{Shallow}}$ | $\pi R_2^2$ | 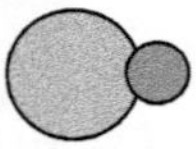 |
| Deep partial eclipse | $\Delta S_{1,\text{Deep}}$ | $\pi R_2^2$ | 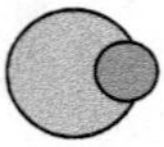 |
| Annular or total eclipse | $\pi R_1^2 - \pi R_2^2$ | $\pi R_2^2$ | 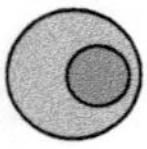 |

Figures T11.8 and T11.9 are used to calculate the area of the free surface sector of the star $\sigma_1$'s disk, in the shallow partial eclipse and deep partial eclipse cases. It results that:

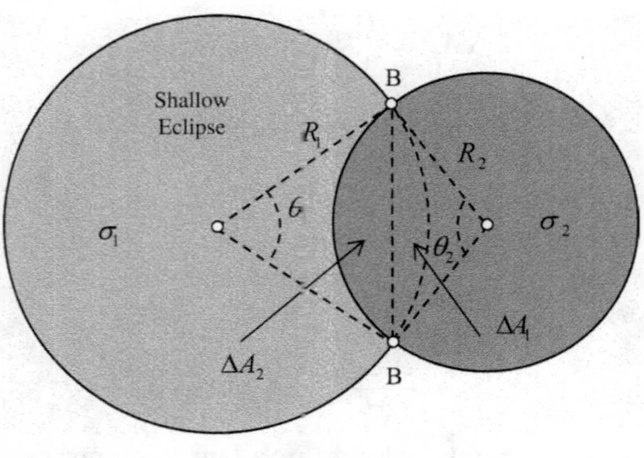


**Fig. T11.8**

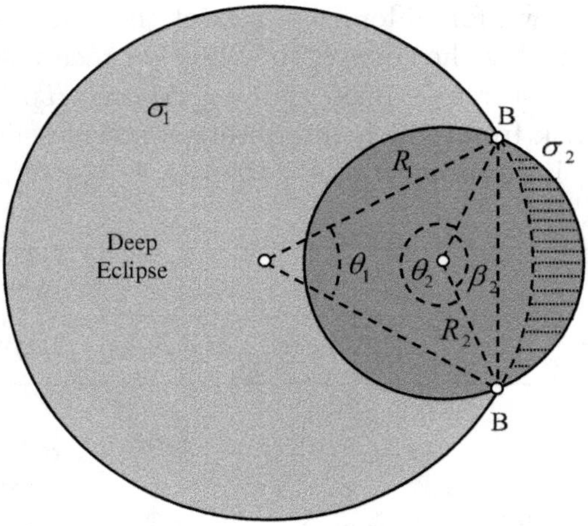


**Fig. T11.9**

$$\theta_1 < \pi; \quad \theta_2 < \pi;$$

$$\Delta A_{1,\text{Shallow}} = \pi R_1^2 - \Delta A_1 - \Delta A_2;$$

$$\Delta A_1 = \frac{1}{2} R_1^2 \left(\theta_1 - \sin\theta_1\right); \quad \Delta A_2 = \frac{1}{2} R_2^2 \left(\theta_2 - \sin\theta_2\right);$$

$$\theta_1 < \pi; \quad \theta_2 > \pi; \quad \beta_2 = 2\pi - \theta_2 < \pi;$$

$$\Delta A_{1,\text{Deep}} = \pi R_1^2 - \Delta A_1 - \Delta A_2;$$

$$\Delta A_1 = \frac{1}{2} R_1^2 (\theta_1 - \sin\theta_1);$$

$$\Delta A_2 = \frac{1}{2} R_2^2 (\theta_2 - \sin\theta_2); \quad \Delta A_2 = \pi R_2^2 - \frac{1}{2} R_2^2 (\beta_2 - \sin\beta_2).$$

Considering that the energy released by the entire spherical surface ($\Sigma$) of the star in a time interval $\Delta t$ is $\Delta E$, the luminosity of each star in the binary system is defined as the energy released through the star's surface per unit time:

$$L_1 = \frac{\Delta E_1}{\Delta t}; \quad L_2 = \frac{\Delta E_2}{\Delta t}.$$

According to the Stefan–Boltzmann law, the energies corresponding to all wavelengths released by each of the two stars per unit time

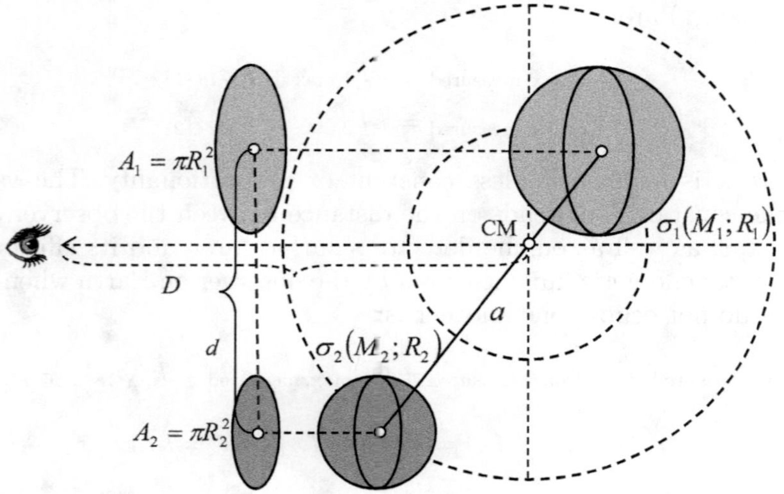


**Fig. T11.10**

per unit sector (the radiance, or energetic flux densities, at the stars' surfaces) are:

$$\varphi_1 = \frac{\Delta E_1}{\Delta t \cdot S_1} = \frac{\Delta E_1}{\Delta t \cdot 4\pi R_1^2} = \frac{L_1}{4\pi R_1^2} = \sigma T_1^4 = Q_1;$$

$$\varphi_2 = \frac{\Delta E_2}{\Delta t \cdot S_2} = \frac{\Delta E_2}{\Delta t \cdot 4\pi R_2^2} = \frac{L_2}{4\pi R_2^2} = \sigma T_2^4 = Q_2.$$

The energies that cross the apparent stellar disks of areas $A_1 = \pi R_1^2$ and $A_2 = \pi R_2^2$, respectively, per unit time (the energy flux) when the stars do not eclipse each other, as presented in Figure T11.10, have maximum values and can be expressed as:

$$F_{1,\max} = \varphi_1 A_1 = \frac{L_1}{4\pi R_1^2}\pi R_1^2 = \sigma\pi T_1^4 R_1^2;$$

$$F_{2,\max} = \varphi_2 A_2 = \frac{L_2}{4\pi R_2^2}\pi R_2^2 = \sigma\pi T_2^4 R_2^2.$$

The energies of the radiation received and measured by the observer on Earth at a distance $D$ per unit time (the measured flux energy) are:

$$\Phi_{1,\text{max, measured}} = kF_{1,\text{max}} = k\varphi_1 A_1;$$
$$\Phi_{2,\text{max, measured}} = kF_{2,\text{max}} = k\varphi_2 A_2,$$

where $k$ is a dimensionless constant of proportionality. The value of the constant $k$ depends on the distance between the observer and the star, as well as on the detector's surface area and its efficiency. The total energetic flux measured by the observer on Earth when the stars do not eclipse one another is:

$$\Phi_{\text{max, measured}} = \Phi_{1,\text{max, measured}} + \Phi_{2,\text{max, measured}} = k\left(\varphi_1 A_1 + \varphi_2 A_2\right)$$
$$= \frac{k}{4}(L_1 + L_2) = k'(L_1 + L_2); \quad k' = k/4;$$
$$\Phi_{\text{max, measured}} = k(\varphi_1 A_1 + \varphi_2 A_2) = k\sigma\pi\left(T_1^4 R_1^2 + T_2^4 R_2^4\right)$$
$$= k''\left(T_1^4 R_1^2 + T_2^4 R_2^2\right);$$
$$k'' = k\sigma\pi.$$

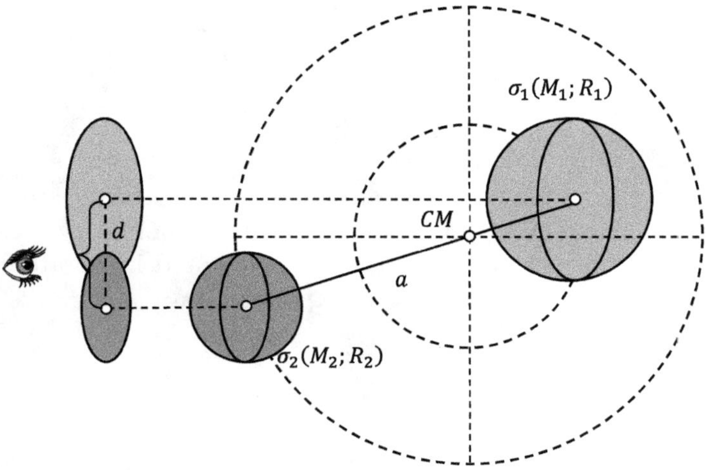


**Fig. T11.11**

When the components of the binary stellar system eclipse one another as presented in Figure T11.11, the apparent circular disks of the two stars overlap more or less. The areas of the free (uneclipsed) sectors of the stellar disks visible for the observer on Earth ($\Delta A_1$ and $\Delta A_2$, respectively) are variable.

The energies that cross the apparent stellar disks of areas $\Delta A_1$ and $\Delta A_2$ per unit time (the energy flux) when the stars eclipse one another are, respectively:

$$F_1 = \varphi_1 \Delta A_1; \quad F_2 = \varphi_2 \Delta A_2.$$

The energies of radiation reaching the observer's detector on Earth, at distance $D$, per unit time and measured by that detector (the measured energetic flux) are:

$$\Phi_{1,\,\text{measured}} = kF_1 = k\varphi_1 \Delta A_1 \quad \Phi_{2,\,\text{measured}} = kF_2 = k\varphi_2 \Delta A_2,$$

where $k$ is a dimensionless proportionality constant, whose value depends on the distance between the observer and the star, and on the detector's surface area and efficiency. The total energy flux measured when the stars eclipse one another is:

$$\Phi_{\text{measured}} = \Phi_{1,\,\text{measured}} + \Phi_{2,\,\text{measured}} = k(\varphi_1 \Delta A_1 + \varphi_2 \Delta A_2);$$

$$\Phi_{\text{measured}} = k\left(\varphi_1 \Delta A_1 + \varphi_2 \Delta A_2\right);$$

$$= k\left(\frac{L_1}{4\pi R_1^2}\Delta A_1 + \frac{L_2}{4\pi R_2^2}\Delta A_2\right) = k'\left(\frac{L_1}{R_1^2}\Delta A_1 + \frac{L_2}{R_2^2}\Delta A_2\right);$$

$$k' = \frac{k}{4\pi};$$

$$\Phi_{\text{measured}} = k\left(\varphi_1 \Delta A_1 + \varphi_2 \Delta A_2\right) = k\sigma\left(T_1^4 \Delta A_1 + T_2^4 \Delta A_2\right)$$

$$= k''\left(T_1^4 \Delta A_1 + T_2^4 \Delta A_2\right);$$

$$k'' = k\sigma.$$

## Suggested Exercise

There are two components ($\sigma_1$ and $\sigma_2$) of a binary stellar system with eclipse orbits on circular trajectories around the common center of mass. The observation line is in the plane of the two stars' orbital' centers. Relative to the observer on Earth, the system's center of mass is stationary.

*Determine* the difference between the apparent visual magnitudes of this binary stellar system in eclipse, corresponding to the following moments:

**a)** when the apparent disks of the two stars completely overlap, as in variant a and b in Figure T11.12;

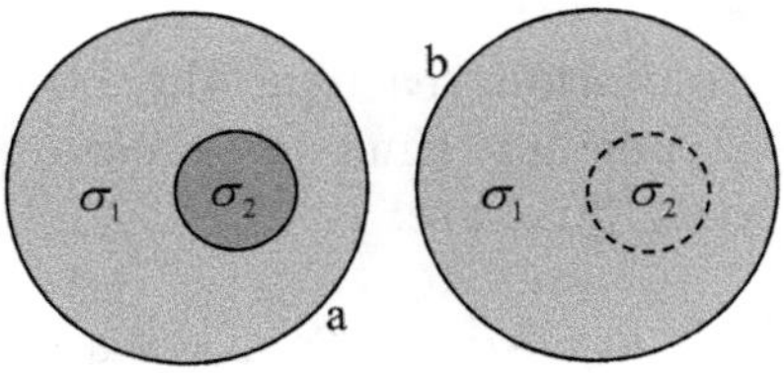


**Fig. T11.12**

**b)** when the apparent disks of the two stars are tangent, as in variants a and b of Figure T11.13;

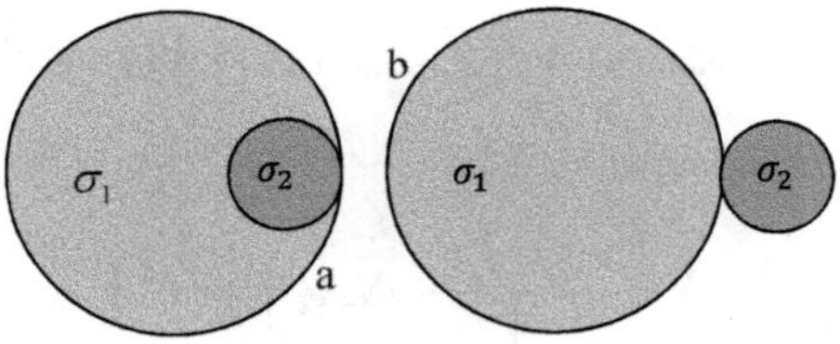


**Fig. T11.13**

**c)** when the centers of the two stars' apparent disks are at distances

$$\sqrt{R_1^2 - R_2^2} < d < R_1 + R_2,$$

as in variants a and b in Figure T11.14;

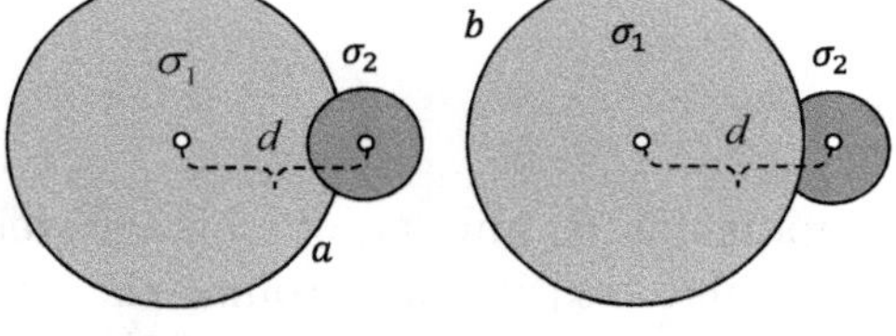


**Fig. T11.14**

**d)** when the centers of the two stars' apparent disks are at distances

$$R_1 - R_2 < d < \sqrt{R_1^2 - R_2^2},$$

as in variants a and b in Figure T11.15.

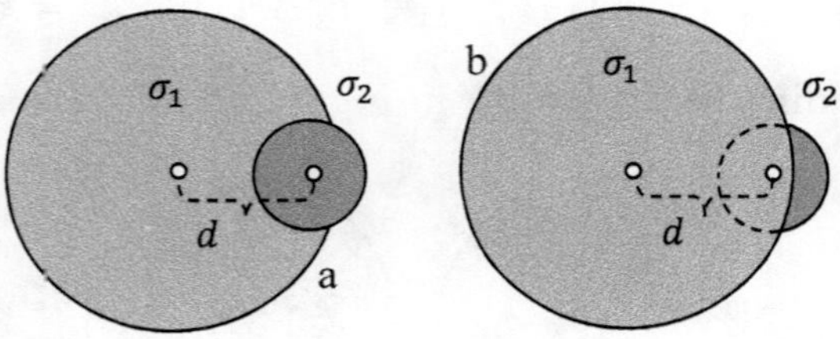


**Fig. T11.15**

The following are known: ($R_1$; $R_2 < R_1$) – the two stars' radii; ($T_1$; $T_2$) – the absolute temperature on the surface of the two stars; ($\theta_1$; $\theta_2$) – the center angle of each stellar disk subtended by the arc defined by the intersection points of the two stellar disks.

## Solution

Using Pogson's formula, the results are:

$$\log \frac{\Phi_{\text{measured, a}}}{\Phi_{\text{measured, b}}} = -0.4(m_{\text{a}} - m_{\text{b}});$$

$$m_{\text{a}} - m_{\text{b}} = 2.5 \log \frac{\Phi_{\text{measured, b}}}{\Phi_{\text{measured, a}}}.$$

When the components of the binary stellar system eclipse one another, the apparent circular disks of the two stars overlap more or less. The areas of the free (uneclipsed) sectors of the stellar disks visible for the observer on the Earth ($\Delta A_1$ and $\Delta A_2$, respectively) are variable.

The energy from the binary stellar system that reaches the detector of the observer on the Earth at distance $D$ per unit time and is measured by that detector (the total measured energy flux) is:

$$\Phi_{\text{measured}} = k\left(\varphi_1 \Delta A_1 + \varphi_2 \Delta A_2\right);$$

$$\Phi_{\text{measured}} = k'\left(\frac{L_1}{R_1^2}\Delta A_1 + \frac{L_2}{R_2^2}\Delta A_2\right); \quad k' = \frac{k}{4\pi};$$

$$\Phi_{\text{measured}} = k''\left(T_1^4 \Delta A_1 + T_2^4 \Delta A_2\right); \quad k'' = k\sigma.$$

**a)** Corresponding to the details in Figure T11.16, the results are:

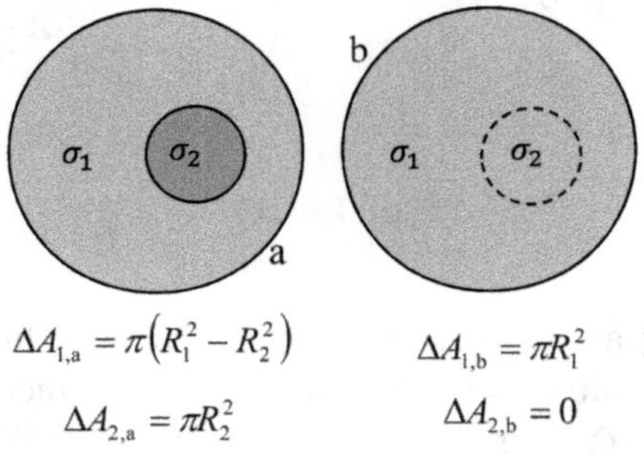


**Fig. T11.16**

$$\Phi_{\text{measured,a}} = k''(T_1^4 \Delta A_{1,\text{a}} + T_2^4 \Delta A_{2,\text{a}}) = k''[T_1^4 \pi(R_1^2 - R_2^2) + T_2^4 \pi R_2^2];$$

$$\Phi_{\text{measured,b}} = k''(T_1^4 \Delta A_{1,\text{b}} + T_2^4 \Delta A_{2,\text{b}}) = k'' T_1^4 \pi R_1^2;$$

$$m_{\text{a}} - m_{\text{b}} = 2.5 \log \frac{T_1^4 R_1^2}{T_1^4(R_1^2 - R_2^2) + T_2^4 R_2^2}.$$

**b)** Corresponding to the details in Figure T11.17, the results are:

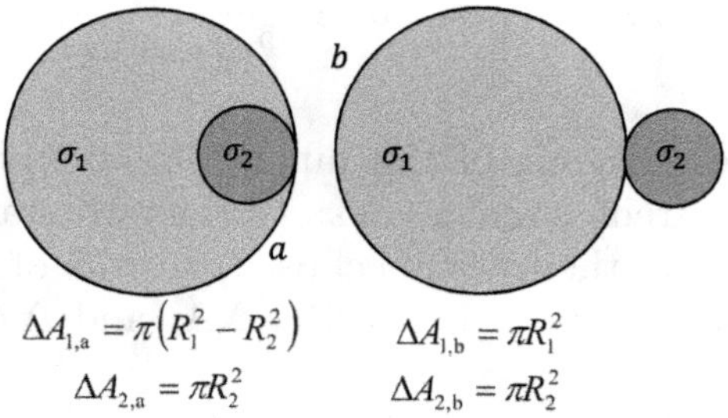


**Fig. T11.17**

$$\Phi_{\text{measured,a}} = k''\left(T_1^4 \Delta A_{1,\text{a}} + T_2^4 \Delta A_{2,\text{a}}\right)$$
$$= k''[T_1^4 \pi (R_1^2 - R_2^2) + T_2^4 \pi R_2^2];$$

$$\Phi_{\text{measured,b}} = k''(T_1^4 \Delta A_{1,\text{b}} + T_2^4 \Delta A_{2,\text{b}}) = k''\left(T_1^4 \pi R_1^2 + T_2^4 \pi R_2^2\right);$$

$$m_{\text{a}} - m_{\text{b}} = 2.5 \log \frac{T_1^4 (R_1^2 - R_2^2) + T_2^4 R_2^2}{T_1^4 R_1^2 + T_2^4 R_2^2}.$$

**c)** Corresponding to the details in Figure T11.18, the results are:

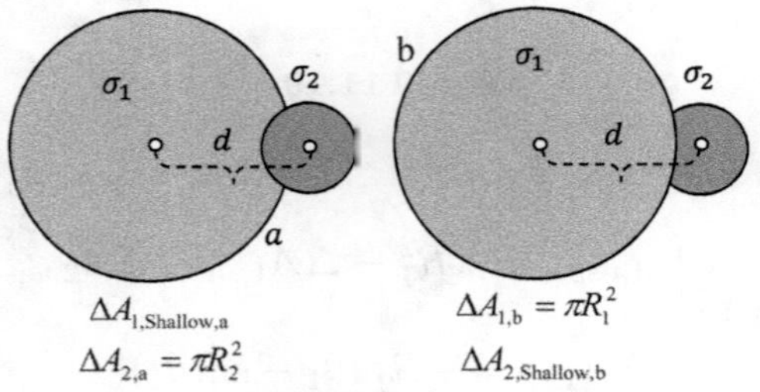


**Fig. T11.18**

$$\Delta A_{1,\text{Shallow,a}} = \pi R_1^2 - \Delta A_{1,\text{aa}} - \Delta A_{2,\text{aa}};$$

$$\Delta A_{1,\text{aa}} = \frac{1}{2} R_1^2 (\theta_1 - \sin\theta_1); \quad \Delta A_{2,\text{aa}} = \frac{1}{2} R_2^2 (\theta_2 - \sin\theta_2);$$

$$\Phi_{\text{measured,a}} = k''\left(T_1^4 \Delta A_{1,\text{Shallow,a}} + T_2^4 \Delta A_{2,\text{a}}\right)$$
$$= k''[T_1^4(\pi R_1^2 - \Delta A_{1,\text{aa}} - \Delta A_{2,\text{aa}}) + T_2^4 \pi R_2^2];$$

$$\Phi_{\text{measured,a}} = k''[T_1^4(\pi R_1^2 - \Delta A_{1,\text{aa}} - \Delta A_{2,\text{aa}}) + T_2^4 \pi R_2^2];$$

$$\Delta A_{2,\text{Shallow,b}} = \pi R_2^2 - \Delta A_{1,\text{bb}} - \Delta A_{2,\text{bb}};$$

$$\Delta A_{1,\text{bb}} = \frac{1}{2} R_1^2 (\theta_1 - \sin\theta_1); \quad \Delta A_{2,\text{bb}} = \frac{1}{2} R_2^2 (\theta_2 - \sin\theta_2);$$

$$\Phi_{\text{measured,b}} = k''(T_1^4 \Delta A_{1,\text{b}} + T_2^4 \Delta A_{2,\text{Shallow,b}})$$
$$= k''[T_1^4 \pi R_1^2 + T_2^4(\pi R_2^2 - \Delta A_{1,\text{bb}} - \Delta A_{2,\text{bb}})];$$

$$m_{\text{a}} - m_{\text{b}} = 2.5 \log \frac{T_1^4 \pi R_1^2 + T_2^4 (\pi R_2^2 - \Delta A_{1,\text{bb}} - \Delta A_{2,\text{bb}})}{T_1^4 (\pi R_1^2 - \Delta A_{1,\text{aa}} - \Delta A_{2,\text{aa}}) + T_2^4 \pi R_2^2}.$$

**d)** Corresponding to the details in Figure T11.19, the results are:

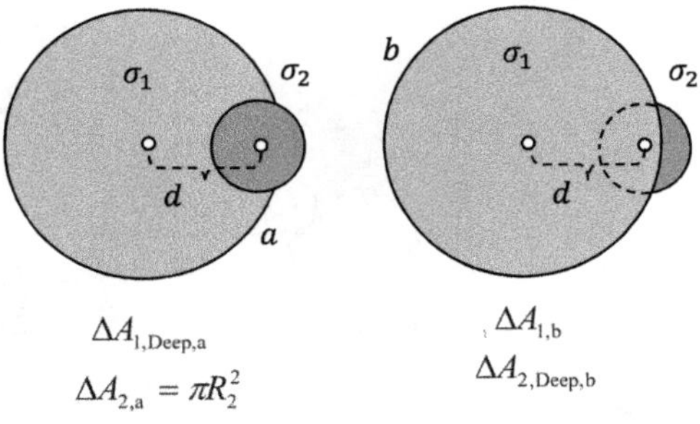


**Fig. T11.19**

$$\theta_1 < \pi; \quad \theta_2 > \pi; \quad \beta_2 = 2\pi - \theta_2 < \pi;$$

$$\Delta A_{1,\mathrm{Deep,a}} = \pi R_1^2 - \Delta A_{1,\mathrm{aa}} - \Delta A_{2,\mathrm{aa}};$$

$$\Delta A_{1,\mathrm{aa}} = \frac{1}{2} R_1^2 (\theta_1 - \sin\theta_1);$$

$$\Delta A_{2,\mathrm{aa}} = \frac{1}{2} R_2^2 (\theta_2 - \sin\theta_2); \quad \Delta A_{2,\mathrm{aa}} = \pi R_2^2 - \frac{1}{2} R_2^2 (\beta_2 - \sin\beta_2);$$

$$\Phi_{\mathrm{measured,a}} = k'' \left(T_1^4 \Delta A_{1,\mathrm{Deep,a}} + T_2^4 \Delta A_{2,\mathrm{a}}\right);$$

$$\Phi_{\mathrm{measured,a}} = k''[T_1^4(\pi R_1^2 - \Delta A_{1,\mathrm{aa}} - \Delta A_{2,\mathrm{aa}}) + T_2^4 \pi R_2^2];$$

$$\theta_1 < \pi; \quad \theta_2 > \pi; \quad \beta_2 = 2\pi - \theta_2 < \pi;$$

$$\Delta A_{2,\mathrm{Deep,b}} = \Delta A_{2,\mathrm{bb}} - \Delta A_{1,\mathrm{bb}};$$

$$\Delta A_{1,\mathrm{bb}} = \frac{1}{2} R_1^2 (\theta_1 - \sin\theta_1);$$

$$\Delta A_{2,\mathrm{bb}} = \frac{1}{2} R_2^2 (\theta_2 - \sin\theta_2); \quad \Delta A_{2,\mathrm{bb}} = \pi R_2^2 - \frac{1}{2} R_2^2 (\beta_2 - \sin\beta_2);$$

$$\Phi_{\mathrm{measured,b}} = k'' \left(T_1^4 \Delta A_{1,\mathrm{b}} + T_2^4 \Delta A_{2,\mathrm{Deep,b}}\right);$$

$$\Phi_{\mathrm{measured,b}} = k'' \left[T_1^4 \pi R_1^2 + T_2^4 (\Delta A_{2,\mathrm{bb}} - \Delta A_{1,\mathrm{bb}})\right];$$

$$m_{\mathrm{a}} - m_{\mathrm{b}} = 2.5 \log \frac{T_1^4 \pi R_1^2 + T_2^4 (\Delta A_{2,\mathrm{bb}} - \Delta A_{1,\mathrm{bb}})}{T_1^4 (\pi R_1^2 - \Delta A_{1,\mathrm{aa}} - \Delta A_{2,\mathrm{aa}}) + T_2^4 \pi R_2^2}.$$

# Topic 12

# Bolometric Magnitudes

Not long ago, telescopes could directly discern only the annual parallaxes of the stars located at relatively short distances from the Earth (at most 300 light years, or ly, away). For larger distances, using the same telescopes, the values of the parallaxes could not be directly determined, since they are extremely low.

Using a network of four telescopes (interferometers) available since 2007, the team led by Mareki Honma has directly determined very low values of the parallax for some stars inside our galaxy located at distances of 1000 ly from the Earth (Sun). Each radio telescope has a 20 m diameter mirror. They are installed in Japanese territory, as presented in Figure T12.1. The telescopes belong to NAOJ (the National Astronomical Observatory of Japan), employ VLBI (Very Long Baseline Interferometry) technology and are included in the VERA project (VLBI Exploration of Radio Astrometry). Their success is due to the fact that the simultaneous observation of a star by four telescopes is equivalent to the observation of the same star by a single telescope with a 2300 km diameter lens.

Figure T12.2 presents how a star's annual parallax is defined and determined by observing a celestial body on its orbit around the Sun, from two opposite locations on the Earth.

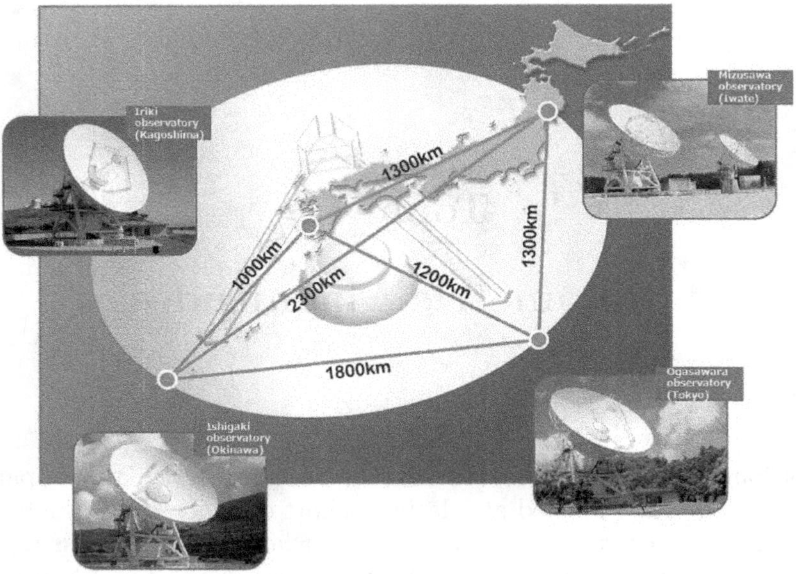


**Fig. T12.1** (Credit: NAOJ)

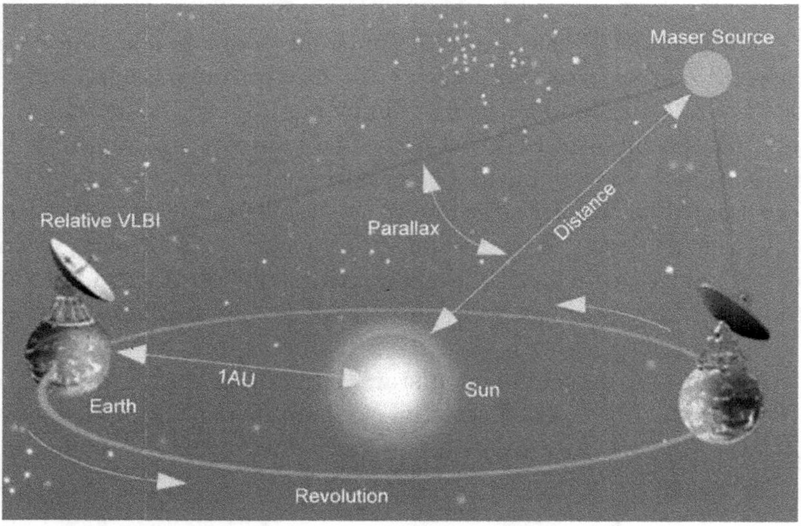


**Fig. T12.2** (Credit: NAOJ)

Any dimension that characterizes a star and that is directly determined through optical methods is affected by the radiation extinction in the interstellar medium. The effect of radiation extinction also influences the measurements derived from those directly determined. The extinction phenomenon can be ignored (neglected) for nearby stars.

In the table below, the values of several physical quantities that correspond to six stars are presented. The values affected by interstellar radiation extinction are marked with an asterisk (*).

*The following are known:* the Sun's luminosity, $L_{\mathrm{Sun}} = 3.828 \cdot 10^{26}$ W; the constant in the Stefan–Boltzmann law, $\sigma = 5.67 \cdot 10^{-8}$ $\frac{\mathrm{J}}{\mathrm{sm^2K^4}}$; the Earth's radius, $R_{\mathrm{Earth}} = 6378.16\,\mathrm{km}$; the Sun's radius, $R_{\mathrm{Sun}} = 109\ R_{\mathrm{Earth}}$; the constant in Wien's law, $C \approx 3 \cdot 10^{-3}\,\mathrm{m} \cdot \mathrm{K}$; Ballesteros' formula for the effective temperature at the surface of a star, $T_{\mathrm{eff}} = f(\mathrm{B-V}) = 4600 \left(\frac{1}{0.92(\mathrm{B-V})+1.7} + \frac{1}{0.92(\mathrm{B-V})+0.62}\right)$ K.

*Determine* the values for all the other physical quantities corresponding to the six stars, presented in the table below.

| Star | κ Velorum (Markeb) | β Tauri (Elnath) | Sirius A | Procyon A | Sun | Barnard's Star |
|---|---|---|---|---|---|---|
| Annual parallax $p^*$($10^{-3}$ arcsec) | 6.05 | 24.89 | 379.2 | 286.05 | – | 549.3 |
| Distance to the Sun $\Delta^*$ (pc) | | | | | | |
| Interstellar extinction in the V band, $A_V$ (mag) | 0.20 | 0.08 | Negligible | Negligible | – | Negligible |
| $10^{0.2 \cdot A_V}$ | | | | | | |
| Annual parallax $p$($10^{-3}$ arcsec) | | | | | | |
| The distance to the Sun $\Delta$ (pc) | | | | | 1 AU Earth | |
| Distance coefficient $\mu = m - M$ (mag) | | | | | – 31.57 | |
| Apparent visual magnitude V, $m^*$ (mag) | 2.86 | 1.68 | – 1.47 | 0.34 | – 26.73 | 9.54 |
| Apparent visual magnitude V, $m$ (mag) | | | | | | |

(*Continued*)

(*Continued*)

| Star | $\kappa$ Velorum (Markeb) | $\beta$ Tauri (Elnath) | Sirius A | Procyon A | Sun | Barnard's Star |
|---|---|---|---|---|---|---|
| Absolute visual magnitude, $M_V$ (mag) | | | | | | |
| Color index (B − V)* (mag) | − 0.14 | − 0.06 | + 0.01 | + 0.40 | +0.65 | + 1.74 |
| Interstellar reddening degree (color excess) | | | | | | |
| Selective extinction $E_{B-V}$ (mag) | | | | | | |
| Color index (B − V) (mag) | | | | | | |
| Effective temperature $T_{eff} = f$ (B − V); (K) | | | | | | |
| $\lambda_m$ (nm) | | | | | | |
| Radius (solar radius, $R_S$) | 9.1 | 4.6 | 1.711 | 2.048 | 1.00 | from 0.15 to 0.20 |
| Absolute bolometric magnitude $M_{bol}$ (mag) | | | | | 4.64 | |
| Total luminosity (solar luminosity, $L_S$) | | | | | 1.00 | |
| Bolometric correction, BC, for the V band (mag) | | | | | −0.20 | |

## Solution

**1)** In the plane of the eclipse presented in Figure T12.3, $\sigma$ represents a distant star. The circular orbit of the Earth around the Sun is also marked. On its circular orbit, the Earth is marked in two diametrically opposed positions $P_1$ and $P_2$, corresponding to two moments separated by a 6-month interval. We consider that the distant star $\sigma$ does not significantly change its position relative to the Sun, being stationary relative to the Sun. The observer on Earth can determine

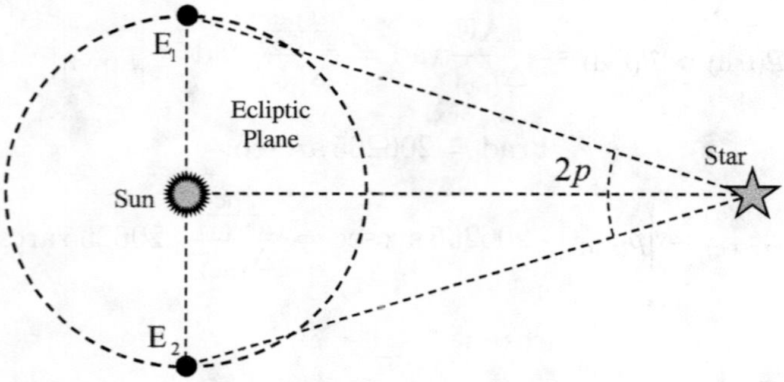


**Fig. T12.3**

the angle $2p$ between the directions $P_1\sigma$ and $P_2\sigma$ through optical methods.

The annual parallax of the star $\sigma$ is the angle $p$ subtended at the star $\sigma$ by the radius of the Earth's orbit around the Sun, considering that $\sigma S \perp SP_1$, and $S\sigma$ is the bisector of the angle $P_1\sigma P_2$. From the Earth, the parallax of the star $\sigma$ can be determined as half of the angle between the two viewing directions of the star from the two diametrically opposed positions on the Earth considered ($E_1$ and $E_2$, respectively).

According to the notation in Figure T12.4, to establish the relation between the parallax of a star and the distance from the star to the observer when the interstellar extinction is taken into account, we have:

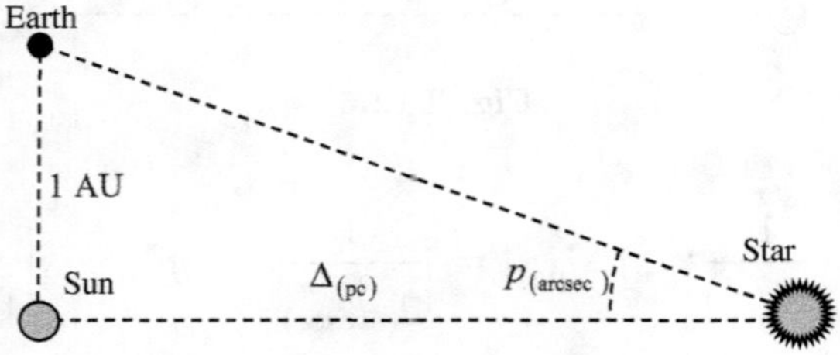


**Fig. T12.4**

$$\sin p_{(\mathrm{rad})} \approx p_{(\mathrm{rad})} = \frac{1\,\mathrm{AU}}{\Delta_{(\mathrm{pc})}}\,\mathrm{rad} = \frac{\frac{1\,\mathrm{pc}}{206265}}{\Delta_{(\mathrm{pc})}}\,\mathrm{rad} = \left|p_{(\mathrm{rad})}\right| \cdot 1\mathrm{rad};$$

$$1\,\mathrm{rad} = 206265\,\mathrm{arcsec};$$

$$p_{(\mathrm{arcsec})} = \left|p_{(\mathrm{rad})}\right| \cdot 206265\,\mathrm{arcsec} = \frac{\frac{1\,\mathrm{pc}}{206265}}{\Delta_{(\mathrm{pc})}} \cdot 206265\,\mathrm{arcsec}$$

$$= \frac{1\,\mathrm{pc}}{\Delta_{(\mathrm{pc})}}\,\mathrm{arcsec};$$

$$p_{(\mathrm{arcsec})} = \frac{1\,\mathrm{pc}}{\Delta_{(\mathrm{pc})}}\,\mathrm{arcsec}; \quad \Delta_{(\mathrm{pc})} = \left|\Delta_{(\mathrm{pc})}\right| \cdot 1\,\mathrm{pc};$$

$$p_{(\mathrm{arcsec})} = \frac{1\,\mathrm{pc}}{\left|\Delta_{(\mathrm{pc})}\right| \cdot 1\,\mathrm{pc}}\,\mathrm{arcsec} = \frac{1}{\left|\Delta_{(\mathrm{pc})}\right|}\,\mathrm{arcsec};$$

$$\left|p_{(\mathrm{arcsec})}\right| = \frac{1}{\left|\Delta_{(\mathrm{pc})}\right|}; \quad \left|\Delta_{(\mathrm{pc})}\right| = \frac{1}{\left|p_{(\mathrm{arcsec})}\right|}; \quad \left|p_{(\mathrm{arcsec})}\right| \cdot \left|\Delta_{(\mathrm{pc})}\right| = 1.$$

According to the notation in Figure T12.5, if we consider the interstellar extinction of the radiation, similar equations can be written:

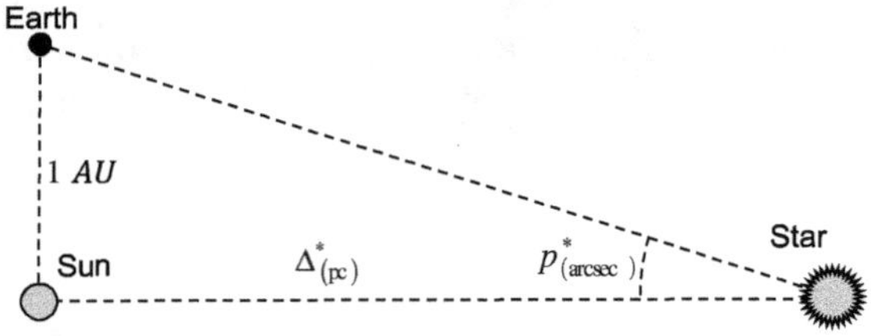


**Fig. T12.5**

$$\left|p^*_{(\mathrm{arcsec})}\right| = \frac{1}{\left|\Delta^*_{(\mathrm{pc})}\right|}; \quad \left|\Delta^*_{(\mathrm{pc})}\right| = \frac{1}{\left|p^*_{(\mathrm{arcsec})}\right|}; \quad \left|p^*_{(\mathrm{arcsec})}\right| \cdot \left|\Delta^*_{(\mathrm{pc})}\right| = 1.$$

**2)** For the intrinsic brightness of a star, astronomers consider its absolute magnitude. The absolute magnitude of a star represents its apparent magnitude unaffected by the radiation extinction phenomenon, if the star were placed at a standard distance $\Delta_{\mathrm{st}} = 10\,\mathrm{ps}$

from the observer. Knowing the apparent magnitude of the star unaffected by the radiation extinction phenomenon $m$, we have the following equation:

$$M = m + 5 - 5 \cdot \log \left|\Delta_{(\text{pc})}\right| ;$$

$$M = m + 5 - 5 \cdot \log \frac{1}{\left|p_{(\text{arcsec})}\right|} ; \quad M = m + 5 + 5 \cdot \log \left|p_{(\text{arcsec})}\right| ,$$

where $|\Delta_{(\text{pc})}|$ represents the absolute value of the real distance $\Delta_{(\text{pc})}$ between the observer and the star expressed in parsecs, and $|p_{(\text{arcsec})}|$ is the absolute value of the star's real parallax, $p_{(\text{arcsec})}$, expressed in arcsecs. Thus:

$$\log \left|\Delta_{(\text{pc})}\right| = \frac{m - M + 5}{5} = 0.2\,(m - M + 5) ;$$

$$\left|\Delta_{(\text{pc})}\right| = 10^{0.2(m-M+5)} ; \quad \left|p_{(\text{arcsec})}\right| = 10^{0.2(-m+M-5)} ;$$

$$\left|\Delta_{(\text{pc})}\right| \cdot \left|p_{(\text{arcsec})}\right| = 1.$$

If the observation of the star is affected by the phenomenon of radiation extinction due to the dust in interstellar space, corrections must be applied to the above equations to calculate the real distance between the star and the observer. Since the visual apparent magnitude determined by the observer under the conditions of the radiation extinction phenomenon is $m^* \neq m$, we have

$$m^* = m + A_{\text{abs}},$$

where the extinction by absorption, $A_{\text{abs}}$, represents the correction that must be introduced in the previous equation,

$$M = m + 5 - 5 \cdot \log \left|\Delta_{(\text{pc})}\right| ,$$

to calculate the real distance between the star and the observer:

$$M = m^* + 5 - 5 \cdot \log |\Delta^*_{(\text{pc})}|.$$

In both equations, the same absolute magnitude $M$ appears, since it is defined under the conditions of a standard distance ($\Delta_{\text{st}} = 10\,\text{pc}$) and in the absence of interstellar extinction.

Under these conditions, we discuss the distance affected by the interstellar extinction $\Delta^*_{(\mathrm{pc})} \neq \Delta_{(\mathrm{pc})}$ and the parallax measured under the conditions of interstellar extinction, $p^*_{(\mathrm{arcsec})} \neq p_{(\mathrm{arcsec})}$:

$$\log\left|\Delta^*_{(\mathrm{pc})}\right| = \frac{m^* - M + 5}{5} = 0.2\,(m^* - M + 5),$$

$$\left|\Delta^*_{(\mathrm{pc})}\right| = 10^{0.2(m^* - M + 5)}; \quad \left|\Delta^*_{(\mathrm{pc})}\right| = 10^{0.2(m + A_{\mathrm{abs}} - M + 5)};$$

$$\left|\Delta^*_{(\mathrm{pc})}\right| = 10^{0.2(m - M + 5)} \cdot 10^{0.2 \cdot A_{\mathrm{abs}}};$$

$$\left|\Delta_{(\mathrm{pc})}\right| = 10^{0.2(m - M + 5)};$$

$$\left|\Delta^*_{(\mathrm{pc})}\right| = \left|\Delta_{(\mathrm{pc})}\right| \cdot 10^{0.2 \cdot A_{\mathrm{abs}}};$$

$$0 < A_{\mathrm{abs}} < 1; \quad 0 < 0.2 \cdot A_{\mathrm{abs}} < 1; \quad 10^{0.2 \cdot A_{\mathrm{abs}}} > 1;$$

$$\left|\Delta^*_{(\mathrm{pc})}\right| > \left|\Delta_{(\mathrm{pc})}\right|;$$

$$\left|p^*_{(\mathrm{arcsec})}\right| = \frac{1}{\left|\Delta^*_{(\mathrm{pc})}\right|}; \quad \left|p^*_{(\mathrm{arcsec})}\right| = \frac{1}{\left|\Delta_{(\mathrm{pc})}\right|} \cdot \frac{1}{10^{0.2 \cdot A_{\mathrm{abs}}}} = \frac{\left|p_{(\mathrm{arcsec})}\right|}{10^{0.2 \cdot A_{\mathrm{abs}}}};$$

$$\left|p_{(\mathrm{arcsec})}\right| = \left|p^*_{(\mathrm{arcsec})}\right| \cdot 10^{0.2 \cdot A_{\mathrm{abs}}};$$

$$10^{0.2 \cdot A_{\mathrm{abs}}} > 1; \quad \left|p_{(\mathrm{arcsec})}\right| > \left|p^*_{(\mathrm{arcsec})}\right|;$$

$$\left|p^*_{(\mathrm{arcsec})}\right| < \left|p_{(\mathrm{arcsec})}\right|;$$

$$\left|p^*_{(\mathrm{arcsec})}\right| \cdot \left|\Delta^*_{(\mathrm{pc})}\right| = \frac{\left|p_{(\mathrm{arcsec})}\right|}{10^{0.2 \cdot A_{\mathrm{abs}}}} \cdot \left|\Delta_{(\mathrm{pc})}\right| \cdot 10^{0.2 \cdot A_{\mathrm{abs}}}$$

$$\left|p_{(\mathrm{arcsec})}\right| \cdot \left|\Delta_{(\mathrm{pc})}\right| = 1.$$

The existence of extinction determines $m^* > m$, which is equivalent to $\Delta^*_{(\mathrm{pc})} > \Delta_{(\mathrm{pc})}$ and $p^*_{(\mathrm{arcsec})} < p_{(\mathrm{arcsec})}$.

**3)** Using Figure T12.6, for the study of stellar radiation extinction due to interstellar dust absorption, the result is:

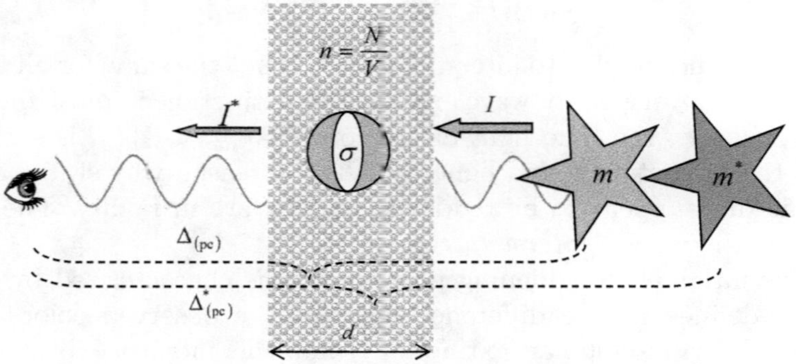


**Fig. T12.6**

$$I^* = I \cdot e^{-\tau}; \tau = n\sigma d;$$

$$\frac{I^*}{I} = e^{-\tau};$$

$$m^* - m = -2.5 \cdot \log \frac{I^*}{I} = -2.5 \cdot \log e^{-\tau};$$

$$m^* - m = 2.5 \cdot \tau \cdot \log e = 1.086 \cdot \tau;$$

$$A_{\text{absorption}} = 1.086 \cdot \tau,$$

representing the extinction of radiation through absorption;

$$m^* - m = A_{\text{abs}};$$

$$m^* = m + A_{\text{abs}}; \; m = m^* - A_{\text{abs}}.$$

Under these conditions, calculating the real distance to the star's location from the observer's position, the result is:

$$|\Delta^*_{(\text{pc})}| = 10^{0.2(m^* - M + 5)}; \quad |\Delta^*_{(\text{pc})}| = 10^{0.2(m + A_{\text{abs}} - M + 5)};$$

$$|\Delta^*_{(\text{pc})}| = \frac{1}{|p^*_{(\text{arcsec})}|};$$

$$|\Delta_{(\mathrm{pc})}| = 10^{0.2(m-M+5)}; \ |\Delta^*_{(\mathrm{pc})}| = |\Delta_{(\mathrm{pc})}| \cdot 10^{0.2 \cdot A_{\mathrm{abs}}};$$

$$|\Delta_{(\mathrm{pc})}| = \frac{|\Delta^*_{(\mathrm{pc})}|}{10^{0.2 \cdot A_{\mathrm{abs}}}} < |\Delta^*_{(\mathrm{pc})}|.$$

**4)** The extinction due to interstellar dust is not the same for all wavelengths. For very short wavelengths, the extinction is most intense. Consequently, the blue light extinction of $\lambda_{\mathrm{Blue}} < \lambda_{\mathrm{Red}}$, is stronger than the extinction of red light. This is the reason why stars behind cosmic dust appear to be redder than they are in reality. The phenomenon is named *interstellar reddening.*

The interstellar reddening phenomenon is characterized by color excess defined as the difference between the observed color index (affected by interstellar extinction) and the intrinsic color index (unaffected by interstellar extinction).

The optical passbands most used by astronomers are those given by the UBVRI filters, named the Johnson–Cousins filter system. For observation precision, an adequate pair of filters is chosen depending on the body color temperature: B–V filters for celestial bodies with medium temperatures, U–V filters for hot celestial bodies, and R–I filters for cold celestial bodies.

Interstellar reddening is inversely proportional to the radiation's wavelength. To determine the reddening degree of a star, the color index (B–V)* is measured under conditions of interstellar extinction. Subsequently, this color index is compared with the real color index of the star (B–V) through the equation

$$E_{\mathrm{B-V}} = (B - V)^* - (B - V) = (B^* - B) - (V^* - V) = A_{\mathrm{B}} - A_{\mathrm{V}},$$

where $E_{\mathrm{B-V}}$ represents the *selective extinction* (the *reddening degree*), and $A_{\mathrm{B}}$ and $A_{\mathrm{V}}$ are the *total extinctions* in the blue and visual bands, respectively.

Since both reddening and interstellar extinction phenomena are the result of light interaction with grains of cosmic dust, they cannot be separated; thus, we expect such phenomena to be stronger along the star's line of sight. Indeed, experiments have proved that

$$A_{\mathrm{V}} = R_{\mathrm{V}} \cdot E_{\mathrm{B-V}} \approx 3.2 \cdot E_{\mathrm{B-V}}.$$

Under these conditions, if the $E_{\mathrm{B-V}}$ reddening is known, we can calculate the $A_{\mathrm{V}}$ extinction, and then we can implement the necessary correction in the magnitude equation to subsequently determine the real distance between the star and the observer:

$$\left|\Delta^*_{(\text{pc})}\right| = 10^{0.2(m^*-M+5)}; \quad \mu = m - M; \quad \left|\Delta^*_{(\text{pc})}\right| = 10^{0.2(m+A_\text{V}-M+5)};$$

$$\left|\Delta^*_{(\text{pc})}\right| = 10^{0.2(\mu+A_\text{V}+5)};$$

$$\log\left|\Delta^*_{(\text{pc})}\right| = 0.2\,(\mu + A_\text{V}+5) = 0.2\mu + 0.2\,(A_\text{V}+5)\,;$$

$$\mu = \frac{\log\left|\Delta^*_{(\text{pc})}\right| - 0.2\,(A_\text{V}+5)}{0.2};$$

$$\mu = 5\cdot\log\left|\Delta^*_{(\text{pc})}\right| - 5 - A_\text{V}; \quad \left|\Delta^*_{(\text{pc})}\right| = \frac{1}{\left|p^*_{(\text{arcsec})}\right|};$$

$$\mu = -5\cdot\log\left|p^*_{(\text{arcsec})}\right| - 5 - A_\text{V};$$

$$M = m + 5 - 5\cdot\log\left|\Delta_{(\text{pc})}\right|; \quad \mu = m - M = 5\cdot\log\left|\Delta_{(\text{pc})}\right| - 5;$$

$$\left|\Delta_{(\text{pc})}\right| = \frac{\left|\Delta^*_{(\text{pc})}\right|}{10^{0.2\cdot A_\text{abs}}} < \left|\Delta^*_{(\text{pc})}\right|.$$

$$\mu = 5\cdot\log\left|\Delta_{(\text{pc})}\right| - 5 = 5\cdot\log\frac{\left|\Delta^*_{(\text{pc})}\right|}{10^{0.2\cdot A_\text{V}}} - 5$$
$$= 5\cdot(\log|\Delta^*_{(\text{pc})}| - \log 10^{0.2\cdot A_\text{V}}) - 5;$$

$$\mu = 5\cdot\left(\log\left|\Delta^*_{(\text{pc})}\right| - 0.2\cdot A_\text{V}\right) - 5;$$

$$\mu = 5\cdot\log\left|\Delta^*_{(\text{pc})}\right| - A_\text{V} - 5;$$

$$m^* = m + A_\text{abs}; \quad m = m^* - A_\text{abs};$$

$$\mu = m - M; \quad M = m - \mu,$$

where $\mu$ is the distance coefficient;

$$M = m + 5\cdot\log\left|p^*_{(\text{arcsec})}\right| + 5 + A_\text{V};$$

$$M = m - 5\cdot\log\left|\Delta^*_{(\text{pc})}\right| + A_\text{V} + 5.$$

**5)** In principle, the effective temperature at the surface of a star can be directly calculated from the star's color index (B–V). For instance, using the Ballesteros formula and considering the star to be a black body, we have

$$T_{\text{eff}} = 4600\left(\frac{1}{0.92(\text{B}-\text{V})+1.7} + \frac{1}{0.92(\text{B}-\text{V})+0.62}\right)\text{ K}.$$

**6)** The bolometric magnitude of a star corresponds to its luminosity, expressed in magnitude units for all the wavelengths of all electromagnetic radiation, considering the atmospheric absorption and the radiation extinction due to interstellar dust, and taking into account the passbands due to the observation instruments.

Typically, the difference between the bolometric magnitudes of the two stars is correlated with their luminosity ratio:

$$M_{\text{bol,Star}} - M_{\text{bol,Sun}} = -2.5\log\frac{L_{\text{Star}}}{L_{\text{Sun}}};$$

$$M_{\text{bol,Star}} = M_{\text{bol,Sun}} - 2.5\cdot\log L_{\text{Star}} + 2.5\cdot\log L_{\text{Sun}};$$

$$L_{\text{Sun}} = 3.828\cdot 10^{26}\,W;\quad M_{\text{bol,Sun}} = 4.74;$$

$$M_{\text{bol,Star}} = -2.5\cdot\log L_{\text{Star}} + 2.5\cdot\log(3.828\cdot 10^{26}) + 4.74;$$

$$M_{\text{bol,Star}} = -2.5\cdot\log L_{\text{Star}} + 71.19.$$

It is more suitable to express the bolometric magnitude of a star according to the Stefan–Boltzmann law, that is:

$$L_{\text{Star}} = 4\pi R^2_{\text{Star}}\sigma T^4_{\text{eff, Star}};$$

$$M_{\text{bol,Star}} = -2.5\cdot\log\left(4\pi R^2_{\text{Star}}\sigma T^4_{\text{eff, Star}}\right) + 71.19;$$

$$M_{\text{bol,Star}} = -2.5\cdot\log\left[(4\pi\sigma)R^2_{\text{Star}}T^4_{\text{eff, Star}}\right] + 71.19;$$

$$M_{\text{bol,Star}} = -2.5\cdot\log(4\pi\sigma) - 2.5\cdot\log R^2_{\text{Star}} - 2.5\cdot\log T^4_{\text{eff, Star}} + 71.19;$$

$$M_{\text{bol,Star}} = -2.5\cdot\log(4\pi\sigma) - 5\cdot\log R_{\text{Star}} - 10\cdot\log T_{\text{eff, Star}} + 71.19;$$

$$\sigma = 5.67\cdot 10^{-8}\,\frac{J}{\text{sm}^2\text{K}^4};$$

$$M_{\text{bol,Star}} = -2.5\cdot\log(4\cdot 3.14\cdot 5.67\cdot 10^{-8}) - 5\cdot\log R_{\text{Star}} - 10\cdot\log T_{\text{eff, Star}} + 71.19;$$

$$M_{\text{bol,Star}} = -5\cdot\log R_{\text{Star}} - 10\cdot\log T_{\text{eff, Star}} + 86.55;$$

$$M_{\text{bol,Star}} = -2.5 \cdot \log L_{\text{Star}} + 71.19;$$

$$\log L_{\text{Star}} = \frac{71.19 - M_{\text{bol,Star}}}{2.5};$$

$$L_{\text{Star}} = 10^{(71.19 - M_{\text{bol,Star}})/2.5}.$$

**7)** The stars' magnitudes are affected by the fact that their light is not monochromatic. The light detector's sensibility varies according to the light wavelength. For this reason, to have a relevant magnitude value, the procedure by which it was determined has to be specified. For this goal, the UBV system is mostly used. In this system, the stars' magnitudes are measured in three spectral bands of the visible light range: the U band, centered on the $\lambda = 350\,\text{nm}$ wavelength, close to the ultraviolet part of the spectrum; the B band, centered on the $\lambda = 435\,\text{nm}$ wavelength in the blue part of the spectrum; and the V band, centered on the $\lambda = 550\,\text{nm}$ wavelength of 140 nm width, where the human eye is best adapted to daylight. When an apparent magnitude is given without any other specifications, we have to assume that it is a magnitude in the V band that can be considered the visual magnitude of the star.

The effective temperature at the surface of a star determines the color of the light emitted by the star. Blue stars are hotter than yellow stars, which are hotter than red stars. A star similar to Sirius, with the effective temperature of 9400 K, emits more blue light than red light; thus, it appears brighter if observed through a blue filter than when it is observed through a red filter. On the contrary, a star similar to Betelgeuse, with the effective temperature of 3400 K, appears brighter if watched through a red filter than through a blue one.

The color index of a star represents the difference between the star's magnitude when observed through two filters of different colors. The most used filters are B – blue; V – green; and R – red. Consequently, the following color indices are defined:

$$\text{B} - \text{V} = m_{\text{B}} - m_{\text{V}}; \quad \text{V} - \text{R} = m_{\text{V}} - m_{\text{R}}.$$

The standard distance in stellar and galactic astronomy is 10 pc. A star located at a 10 pc distance from the observer has a parallax of $0''.1$. Galaxies (and other extended cosmic objects) are further from the observer than 10 pc; thus, their light is emitted over an extended sector of the sky and their total brightness cannot be observed from relatively small distances. Even in such conditions, the absolute magnitude of a galaxy is defined by measurements of the equivalent light emitted by a single celestial body (a single star) located at the standard distance of 10 pc from the observer. The luminosity of the equivalent cosmic body represents the sum of the luminosities of all stars in that galaxy. Consequently, the absolute magnitude of any celestial object (even that of a giant galaxy) is equal to the apparent magnitude of an equivalent celestial body located at a distance of 10 pc from the observer.

The magnitude of a celestial object is measured with an instrument called a bolometer. When we consider the absolute magnitude, the type of electromagnetic radiation used must be specified. Bolometric magnitude refers to the total released energy and it is calculated by adding the bolometric correction to the absolute visual magnitude:

$$M_{\text{bol}} = M_{\text{V}} + \text{BC}.$$

The bolometric correction is necessary since very hot stars mainly emit ultraviolet radiation, while very cold stars mainly emit infrared radiation (according to Planck's law):

$$\text{BC} = M_{\text{bol}} - M_{\text{V}}.$$

**8)** Corresponding to the effective temperature $T_{\text{eff}}$ at its surface, each star is an electromagnetic emitter, generating electromagnetic waves of various wavelengths. The intensity of the radiation emitted by the star (the energy emitted by the star per unit time, per unit surface area, corresponding to one unit of wavelength), according to Planck's law, is:

$$I(\lambda) = \frac{2hc^2}{\lambda^5}(e^{hc/k\lambda T_{\text{eff}}} - 1)^{-1}; \quad \langle I(\lambda;\ T_{\text{eff}})\rangle_{\text{IS}} = \frac{J}{\text{s} \cdot \text{m}^2 \cdot \text{m}};$$

$$e^{hc/k\lambda T_{\text{eff}}} >> 1;$$

$$I(\lambda;\ T_{\text{eff}}) = \frac{2hc^2}{\lambda^5} e^{-hc/k\lambda T_{\text{eff}}}.$$

The graphs of the function for different values of the effective temperature (the black bodies' curves) are represented in Figure T12.7.

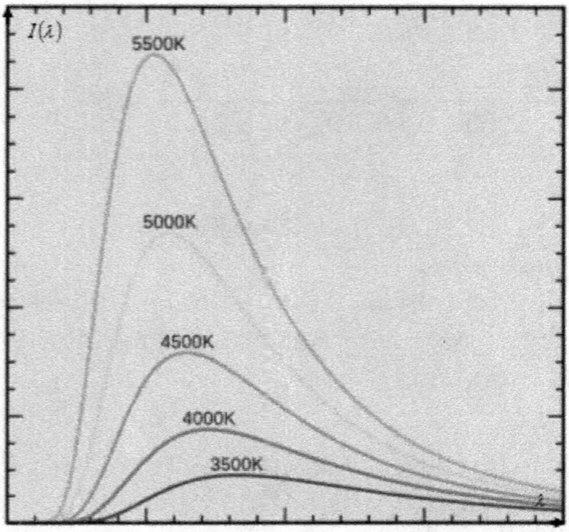


**Fig. T12.7**

Among the electromagnetic radiation (with wavelengths spanning the entire spectrum of electromagnetic waves) emitted by a star whose effective temperature at its surface is $T_{\text{eff}}$, there is one for which the wavelength intensity is maximum.

Under these conditions, the result is:

$$I(\lambda) = \frac{2hc^2}{\lambda^5}\left(e^{hc/k\lambda T_{\text{eff}}} - 1\right)^{-1};$$

$$\frac{dI(\lambda)}{d\lambda} = -\frac{10hc^2}{\lambda^6\left(e^{hc/k\lambda T_{\text{eff}}} - 1\right)} + \frac{2hc^2 e^{hc/k\lambda T_{\text{eff}}}}{\lambda^5\left(e^{hc/k\lambda T_{\text{eff}}} - 1\right)^2} \cdot \frac{hc}{k\lambda^2 T_{\text{eff}}} = 0;$$

$$\frac{e^{hc/k\lambda T_{\text{eff}}}}{\left(e^{hc/k\lambda T_{\text{eff}}} - 1\right)} \cdot \frac{hc}{k\lambda T_{\text{eff}}} = 5; \qquad \frac{hc}{k\lambda T_{\text{eff}}} = x;$$

$$\frac{xe^x}{e^x - 1} = 5.$$

This is a transcendent equation. Solving this equation using the approximation method, it results that:

$$x = 4.965 = \frac{hc}{k\lambda T_{\text{eff}}}; \quad \lambda = \frac{hc}{4.965 \cdot kT_{\text{eff}}} = \lambda_m;$$

$$\lambda_m T_{\text{eff}} = \frac{hc}{4.965 \cdot k};$$

$$h = 6.6249 \cdot 10^{-34}\, Js; \quad k = 1.38 \cdot 10^{-23}\, \mathrm{JK}^{-1}; \quad c = 3 \cdot 10^{8}\, \mathrm{ms}^{-1};$$

$$\lambda_{\mathrm{m}} T_{\mathrm{eff}} = \frac{6.6249 \cdot 10^{-34}\, \mathrm{Js} \cdot 3 \cdot 10^{8}\, \mathrm{ms}^{-1}}{4.965 \cdot 1.38 \cdot 10^{-23}\, \mathrm{JK}^{-1}} \approx 3 \cdot 10^{-3}\, \mathrm{m} \cdot \mathrm{K} = \mathrm{C};$$

$$\lambda_{\mathrm{m}} T_{\mathrm{eff}} = C,$$

representing Wien's displacement law (the law of radiation intensity maximum displacement).

Corresponding to this law, the maximum intensity for the radiation emitted by a star of higher and higher effective temperature moves towards lower and lower wavelengths, as presented in Figure T12.7.

**9)** Neglecting the interstellar extinction of radiation for nearby stars (for instance, stars of the Milky Way), the absolute magnitude of a star can be calculated by knowing its apparent magnitude and the distance between the observer and the star:

$$M = m + 5^{\mathrm{m}} - 5^{\mathrm{m}} \cdot \log \left|\Delta_{(\mathrm{pc})}\right|; \quad \left|\Delta_{(\mathrm{pc})}\right| = 10^{0.2(m-M+5)},$$

where $\Delta_{(\mathrm{pc})}$ is the distance between the star and the observer, expressed in parsecs (1 pc = 206265 AU, or 1 pc = 3.2616 light years). In this case, the radiation observed is not significantly displaced towards the red part of the electromagnetic spectrum.

For stars located very far away (for instance, stars outside the Milky Way), the absolute magnitude can be calculated by knowing the apparent magnitude and the luminosity distance between the observer and the star:

$$M = m + 5 - 5 \cdot \log \left|D_{L(\mathrm{pc})}\right|; \quad D_{L(\mathrm{pc})} = 10^{[(m-M)/5]+1},$$

where $D_{L(\mathrm{pc})} \neq \Delta_{(\mathrm{pc})}$ is the luminosity distance, in parsecs. In this case, the relation between the absolute and the apparent magnitudes is complicated given that the observed radiation moves towards the red part of the spectrum, because, according to the Doppler effect, it is affected by space-time curvature and time expansion.

For nearby cosmic objects (for instance, stars of the Milky Way), the luminosity distance, $D_L$, is approximately identical to the real distance, $\Delta$, between the observer and the star, since the space-time within the Milky Way is almost Euclidian.

The luminosity distance is given by $F = \frac{L}{4\pi D_L^2}$; $D_L = \sqrt{\frac{L}{4\pi F}}$.

# Topic 13

# The Virial Theorem and the Movements of the Planets

The historical formulation of Kepler's third law relating to the movements of the planets around the Sun is written as

$$\frac{R_1^3}{T_1^2} = \frac{R_2^3}{T_2^2},$$

where $T_1$ and $T_2$ are the periods of the movements of two planets, and $R_1$ and $R_2$ are the mean distances between the two planets and the Sun, but without specifying what kind of mean it is.

In a later formulation, given by Newton, Kepler's third law reads as

$$\frac{a_1^3}{T_1^2} = \frac{a_2^3}{T_2^2},$$

where $a_1$ and $a_2$ are the large semi-axes of the two ellipses that the planets move on around the Sun.

Knowing that the temporal mean of the time dependence of a periodic variable $x(t)$ is given by the expression

$$\langle x \rangle_{\mathrm{t}} = \frac{1}{\mathrm{T}} \int_0^{\mathrm{T}} x(t)\mathrm{d}t,$$

which is found by direct integration, then the temporal average of the distance from the ellipse focal point to the points on its outline is:

$$\langle r \rangle_{\mathrm{t}} = \frac{3a^2 - b^2}{2a};$$

$$a > b; \quad \langle r \rangle_{\mathrm{t}} > a,$$

which proves that the mean distance $R = a$, present in the two forms of Kepler's third law, is not the average temporal distance.

Defining the spatial mean of the same variable, $x$, for the points on a curve C as

$$\langle x \rangle_{\mathrm{C}} = \frac{1}{C} \int_0^{\mathrm{C}} x(s) \mathrm{d}s,$$

now that the curve C is an ellipse, by direct integration the spatial mean distance from the ellipse focal point to the points on its outline is

$$\langle r \rangle_{\mathrm{C}} = a = R,$$

which proves that the average distance present in the two forms of Kepler's third law is the average spatial distance.

We will further prove that the previous result can be obtained more intuitively than with the integration path, using elements of the ellipse geometry combined with symmetry arguments.

Thus, it is known that the sum of the distances from a certain point P on the contour of the ellipse to the two focal points F and F′ of the ellipse is equal to the ellipse's large axis:

$$\mathrm{PF} + \mathrm{PF}' = 2a.$$

Let the points P and P′ along the contour of an ellipse be symmetrical with respect to the small axis of the ellipse, as indicated by the drawing in Figure T13.1.

The mean distances from the focus F to all points on the contour of the ellipse can be computed by summing the distances from the focus F to all pairs of symmetrical points, that is,

$$\sum_1^n (\mathrm{FP} + \mathrm{FP}'),$$

where, taking into account the symmetry of the points P and P′ relative to the small axis of the ellipse, FP = PF′, so that the spatial mean distance from the focus F to any point P on the ellipse is

$$\langle \mathrm{FP} \rangle = \frac{\sum_1^n (\mathrm{FP} + \mathrm{FP}')}{2n} = \frac{\sum_1^n (\mathrm{PF} + \mathrm{PF}')}{2n} = \frac{2an}{2n} = a = \langle r \rangle.$$

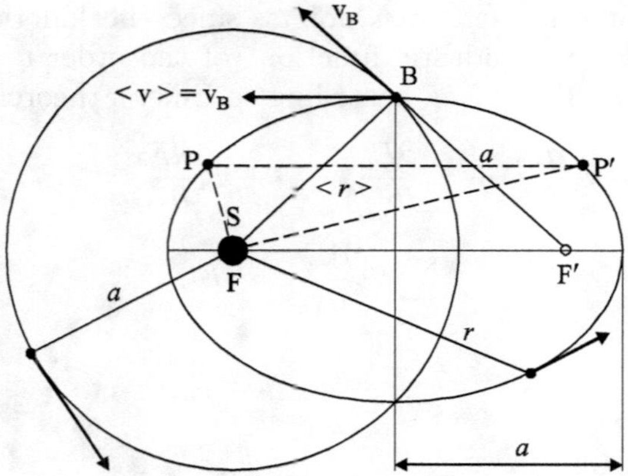


**Fig. T13.1**

With this result, the distance $R$ of Kepler's third law can be considered as an average of the orbit geometry and not as an average of the orbit's dynamics.

Another way of understanding these phenomena is offered by the virial theorem, which correlates the temporal averages of the kinetic and potential energies of a physical system with the magnitude $q$ of the distance on which the potential energy of the system depends.

In order to deduce the relationship between the above-mentioned elements (in order to denote the virial theorem), it should be remembered that mathematical analysis demonstrates that if a function of $n$ variables, $f(x_1, x_2, \ldots, x_n)$, is homogeneous and of order $q$, i.e.,

$$f(\lambda x_1, \lambda x_2, \ldots, \lambda x_n) = \lambda^q \cdot f(x_1, x_2, \ldots, x_n),$$

then the following identity is satisfied:

$$x_1 \frac{\partial f}{\partial x_1} + x_2 \frac{\partial f}{\partial x_2} - \cdots + x_n \frac{\partial f}{\partial x_n} = qf;$$

$$\sum_{k=1}^{n} x_k \frac{\partial f}{\partial x_k} = qf,$$

representing Euler's theorem for homogeneous functions of order $q$.

Indeed, for a system of $n$ points, since the kinetic energy, $E_{\mathrm{c}}$, is a homogeneous quadratic function (of the order $q = 2$), for the components $\vec{\mathrm{v}}_1, \vec{\mathrm{v}}_2, \ldots, \vec{\mathrm{v}}_n$, according to Euler's theorem, we have:

$$\vec{\mathrm{v}}_1 \frac{\partial E_{\mathrm{c}}}{\partial \vec{\mathrm{v}}_1} + \vec{\mathrm{v}}_2 \frac{\partial E_{\mathrm{c}}}{\partial \vec{\mathrm{v}}_2} + \cdots + \vec{\mathrm{v}}_n \frac{\partial E_{\mathrm{c}}}{\partial \vec{\mathrm{v}}_{\mathrm{n}}} = 2E_{\mathrm{c}};$$

$$\sum_{k=1}^{n} \vec{\mathrm{v}}_k \frac{\partial E_{\mathrm{c}}}{\partial \vec{\mathrm{v}}_k} = 2E_{\mathrm{c}};$$

$$\frac{\partial E_{\mathrm{c}}}{\partial \vec{\mathrm{v}}_k} = m_k \vec{\mathrm{v}}_k = \vec{p}_k;$$

$$\sum_{k=1}^{n} \vec{p}_k \vec{\mathrm{v}}_k = 2E_{\mathrm{c}};$$

$$\sum_{k=1}^{n} \vec{p}_k \frac{\mathrm{d}\vec{r}_k}{\mathrm{d}t} = 2E_{\mathrm{c}};$$

$$\frac{\mathrm{d}}{\mathrm{d}t} \sum_{k=1}^{n} \vec{p}_k \vec{r}_k - \sum_{k=1}^{n} \vec{r}_k \frac{\mathrm{d}\vec{p}_k}{\mathrm{d}t} = 2E_{\mathrm{c}};$$

$$\frac{\mathrm{d}\vec{p}_k}{\mathrm{d}t} = \vec{F}_k = -\nabla_k E_{\mathrm{p}} = -\frac{\partial E_{\mathrm{p}}}{\partial \vec{r}_k} = \left( \frac{\partial E_{\mathrm{p}}}{\partial x_k} \vec{i} + \frac{\partial E_{\mathrm{p}}}{\partial y_k} \vec{j} + \frac{\partial E_{\mathrm{p}}}{\partial z_k} \vec{k} \right);$$

$$\sum_{k=1}^{n} \vec{r}_k \frac{\mathrm{d}\vec{p}_k}{\mathrm{d}t} = -\sum_{k=1}^{n} \vec{r}_k \frac{\partial E_{\mathrm{p}}}{\partial \vec{r}_k} = qE_{\mathrm{p}},$$

which is in line with Euler's theorem, if we admit that the potential energy of the system is a homogeneous function of the order $q$;

$$\frac{\mathrm{d}}{\mathrm{d}t} \sum_{k=1}^{n} \vec{p}_k \vec{r}_k + qE_{\mathrm{p}} = 2E_{\mathrm{c}}.$$

In order to calculate the average of the equality in relation to time, we recall that the quantity is called the average value of any function of time, $f(t)$:

$$\bar{f} = \lim_{\tau \to \infty} \frac{1}{\tau} \int_0^{\tau} f(t) \mathrm{d}t.$$

If the function $f(t)$ is derived in relation to the time of a function $F(t)$, i.e., $f(t) = \frac{\mathrm{d}F(t)}{\mathrm{d}t}$, and is bounded (does not have infinite values), then its mean value is null:

$$\bar{f} = \lim_{\tau\to\infty}\frac{1}{\tau}\int_0^{\tau}\frac{\mathrm{d}F}{\mathrm{d}t}\mathrm{d}t = \lim_{\tau\to\infty}\frac{F(\tau)-F(0)}{\tau} = 0,$$

which is true if the function $F(t)$ refers to a limited space domain.

Under these circumstances, we have:

$$\overline{\frac{\mathrm{d}}{\mathrm{d}t}\sum_{k=1}^{n}\vec{p}_k\vec{r}_k} + q\,\langle E_\mathrm{p}\rangle_\mathrm{t} = 2\,\langle E_\mathrm{c}\rangle_\mathrm{t};$$

$$\overline{\frac{\mathrm{d}}{\mathrm{d}t}\sum_{k=1}^{n}\vec{p}_k\vec{r}_k} = \lim_{\tau\to\infty}\frac{1}{\tau}\int_0^{\tau}\frac{\mathrm{d}}{\mathrm{d}t}\left(\sum_{k=1}^{n}\vec{p}_k\vec{r}_k\right)\mathrm{d}t = 0,$$

because each product $\vec{p}_k\vec{r}_k$ remains finite. This gives

$$2\langle E_\mathrm{c}\rangle_\mathrm{t} = q\,\langle E_\mathrm{p}\rangle_t,$$

a relation that represents the virial theorem, highlighting the connection between the temporal environments of the kinetic and potential energies and the homogeneity order of the homogeneous function expressing the potential energy of the system.

For a Sun–planet system, when the kinetic and potential energies of the system are $E_\mathrm{c} = \frac{1}{2}m\mathrm{v}^2$ and $E_\mathrm{p} = -K\frac{mM}{r}$, respectively, and the order of homogeneity of the function $E_\mathrm{p}$ is $q = 1$ (the same as the exponent of $r$ in the homogeneous function $E_\mathrm{p}$), the virial theorem is written as

$$\left\langle \mathrm{v}^2\right\rangle_\mathrm{t} = KM\left\langle\frac{1}{r}\right\rangle_\mathrm{t},$$

this being a relationship between the temporal averages of the square of the velocity and the inverse of the distance.

Let us now define the average Kepler speed of the planet as

$$\langle \mathrm{v}\rangle = \frac{2\pi a}{T},$$

which, according to Kepler's third law, is the same for all elliptical orbits whose large axes are identical, $2a$, and for the confocal circle with radius $a$.

The total energy of the Sun–planet system is

$$E = -K\frac{mM}{2a}.$$

Considering the conservation of total energy when the planet passes through the minor peak B, it follows that:

$$-K\frac{mM}{2a} = \frac{1}{2}m\mathrm{v}_\mathrm{B}^2 - K\frac{mM}{a};$$

$$\mathrm{v}_\mathrm{B}^2 = \frac{KM}{a},$$

which shows that at point B the velocity $\mathrm{v}_\mathrm{B}$ of the planet depends (apart from $M$) on the distance $\mathrm{r}_B = a$ between the focus F and the point B.

Thus, the velocity $\mathrm{v}_\mathrm{B}$ of the planet at the minor peak B of the ellipse must be the same as the speed in a circular orbit whose radius is equal to the ellipse's large semi-axis:

$$\mathrm{v}_\mathrm{B} = \frac{2\pi a}{T} = \langle \mathrm{v} \rangle.$$

From the previous relationships, it follows that

$$\frac{\langle \mathrm{v}^2 \rangle_\mathrm{t}}{\mathrm{v}_\mathrm{B}^2} = \frac{\left\langle \frac{1}{r} \right\rangle_\mathrm{t}}{\frac{1}{R}} = \frac{\langle \mathrm{v}^2 \rangle_\mathrm{t}}{\langle \mathrm{v} \rangle^2} = c,$$

a ratio which, formed for elliptical orbits, must have a constant value, because in the particular case of a circular orbit, where the mean values are determined by the radius of the circle and the orbit speed, $c = 1$.

This result reveals that the Kepler average of the planet's distance from the Sun is identified by the inverse of the temporal mean of the inverse of the planet's distance from the Sun, that is,

$$R = \frac{1}{\left\langle \frac{1}{r} \right\rangle_\mathrm{t}}.$$

The average Kepler velocity of the planet is identified by the square root of the temporal mean square of the orbital velocity, that is,

$$\langle \mathrm{v} \rangle = \sqrt{\langle \mathrm{v}^2 \rangle_\mathrm{t}}.$$

It is demonstrated through direct integration that

$$\langle \mathrm{v} \rangle = \sqrt{\langle \mathrm{v} \rangle_\mathrm{t} \langle \mathrm{v} \rangle_\mathrm{c}}.$$

The Kepler average of the planet's distance from the Sun, $R = a$, is an average over the geometry of the orbit, which is best represented by the oblique focal-peak distance, that is, the distance from the Sun in the focus F to the minor peak B.

The Kepler average orbital velocity, $\langle \mathrm{v} \rangle = \frac{2\pi a}{T} = \mathrm{v}_{\mathrm{B}}$, is the square root of the temporal mean square of the orbital velocity, and it coincides with the instantaneous velocity on the elliptical orbit at the minor peak B.

# Topic 14

# Kepler's Third Law in a New Formulation

In the presentation of Kepler's three laws regarding the movements of the planets around the Sun, there is a certain asymmetry, due to the fact that the first two laws benefit from a graphical presentation (the trajectory of each planet is an ellipse, having the Sun in one of foci (law I); The ray corresponding to each planet sweeps surfaces with equal areas in equal time intervals (law II)), while law III is represented by the formula

$$\frac{a_1^3}{T_1^2} = \frac{a_3^2}{T_2},$$

pointing out that the ratio between the cube of the large ellipse in which a planet is moving and the square of the motion of the same planet is the same for all planets, so that if $a_2 > a_1$, then $T_2 > T_1$.

As a result, the square of the movement period of any planet is directly proportional to the large semi-axis of the ellipse on which the planet evolves ($T^2 = ka^3$).

The comparative study of the orbital movements of two planets, $P_1$ and $P_2$, is made easier by comparing their velocities, $v_1$ and $v_2$, and the distances from them to the Sun, $r_1$ and $r_2$, rather than comparing the periods of their movements, $T_1$ and $T_2$, and the large semi-axes of their elliptic orbits, $a_1$ and $a_2$.

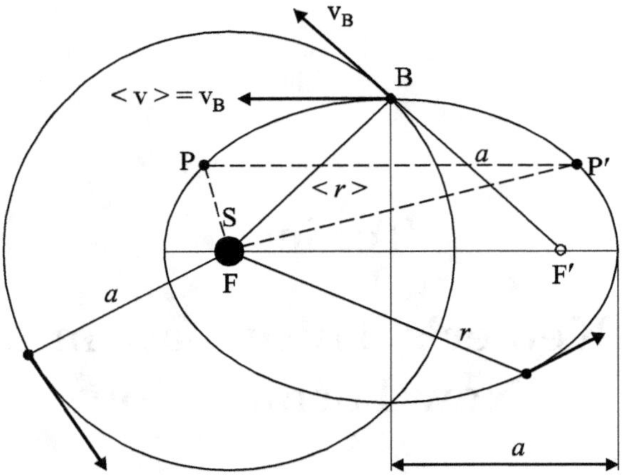


**Fig. T14.1**

But there is a major difficulty in these comparisons: The speeds of the planets and the distances from them to the Sun are variable over the duration of their revolutions around the Sun, in accordance with Kepler's first two laws.

Under these conditions, the average orbital velocities of the two planets, $\langle v_1 \rangle$ and $\langle v_2 \rangle$, must be compared, as well as the average distances of from the planets to the Sun, $\langle r_1 \rangle$ and $\langle r_2 \rangle$.

In the geometry of the ellipse, it is demonstrated that the mean planet–Sun distance during a complete revolution of the planet is equal to the distance from the Sun to one of the extreme points of the small axis of the ellipse:

$$\langle r \rangle = \mathrm{FB} = a,$$

as shown in Figure T14.1.

The previous formula does not allow a conceptual view of Kepler's third law similar to the first two laws.

In order to appreciate the importance of establishing an intuitive presentation of Kepler's third law, let's look at the scenario proposed in Figure T14.2, without using calculations.

Four planets ($P_1$, $P_2$, $P_3$, $P_4$) evolve around the Sun in coplanar, concentric circular orbits with the radii $R$, $2R$, $3R$ and $4R$, respectively, at the moment $t = 0$ in the same direction as the Sun.

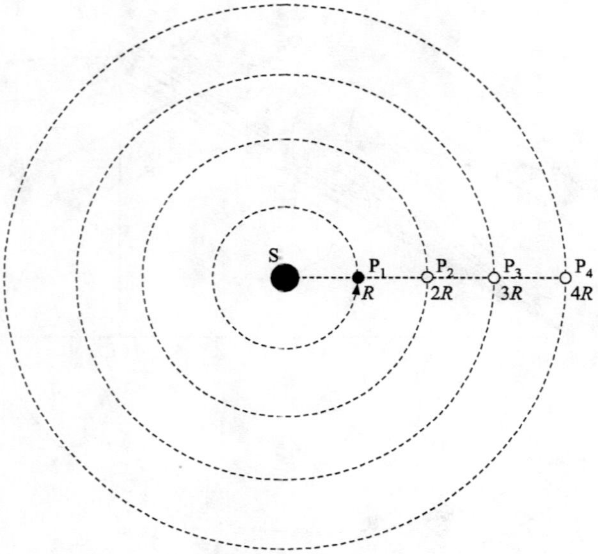


**Fig. T14.2**

Let us mark on the orbits of planets $P_2$, $P_3$, and $P_4$ the arcs indicating their positions at time $t = T_1$, representing the duration of a complete revolution of the planet $P_1$.

The presentation in an intuitive, graphical form of Kepler's third law, proposed by Manfred Bucher of California State University, Fresno, will allow a precise answer to the proposed exercise.

It is also demonstrated that the average orbital velocity of the planet during a complete revolution is equal to the instantaneous velocity of the planet at one of the minor ellipse peaks:

$$\langle \mathrm{v} \rangle = \mathrm{v_B} = \sqrt{KM\left(\frac{2}{FB} - \frac{1}{a}\right)} = \sqrt{\frac{KM}{a}}.$$

*Note*: The mean planet–Sun distance and the average orbital velocity of the planet in its movement on the ellipse in which the Sun is located are the same as the radius of the confocal circle. This radius is equal to the semi-axis of the ellipse, and the velocity of the planet evolving around the Sun on the confocal circle is specified as follows:

$$\langle \mathrm{v} \rangle = \mathrm{v_B} = \frac{2\pi a}{T},$$

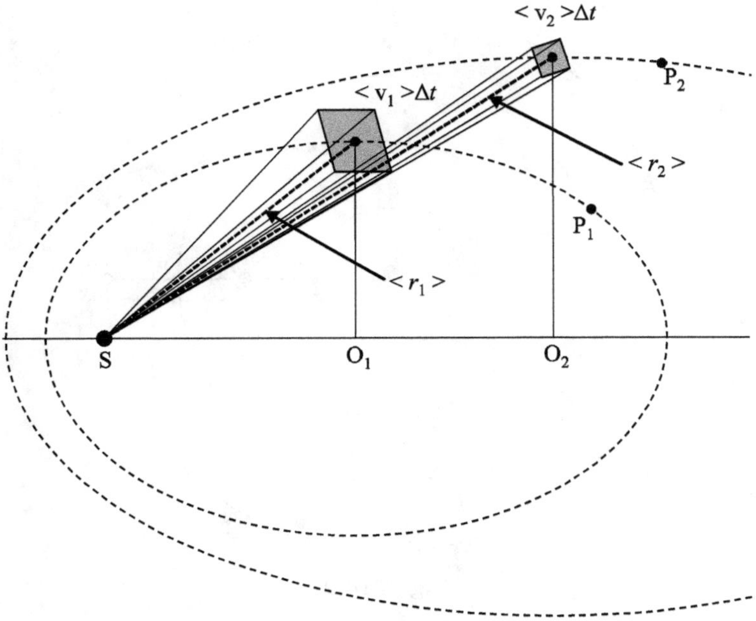


**Fig. T14.3**

where $T$ is the period of motion of the planet on the confocal circle, the same as the period of motion of the planet on the ellipse with semi-axis $a$.

Now, the graphical comparison of the average orbital velocities of the planets $P_1$ and $P_2$ becomes possible with the geometric construction of Figure T14.3, where two pyramids are represented, each having its peak at the center of the Sun and the base centered on the minor peak of each ellipse. Each base is perpendicular to each ellipse minor peak-Sun direction, and the height of each pyramid is equal to the mean distance between the Sun and each planet.

The two pyramids create an oblique link between the ellipse and the minor peaks.

The length of the base of each pyramid is equal to the elemental tangential displacement of each plane, near the minor peak of the corresponding ellipse, in a time $\Delta t << T_1$ and $T_2$, that is,

$$\Delta l = v_B \Delta t = \langle v \rangle \Delta t.$$

As a result, the volume of each link pyramid is

$$\Delta V = \frac{1}{3}(\langle v\rangle \Delta t)^2 \langle r\rangle.$$

Referring to these geometrical constructions, Kepler's third law is reformulated as follows (the oblique link pyramids' volumes, corresponding to the same time interval, are the same for all planets).

Indeed, if:

$$\Delta V_1 = \frac{1}{3}\langle v_1\rangle^2 (\Delta t)^2 \langle r_1\rangle = \frac{1}{3}\frac{4\pi^2 a_1^3}{T_1^2}(\Delta t)^2;$$

$$\Delta V_2 = \frac{1}{3}\langle v_2\rangle^2 (\Delta t)^2 \langle r_2\rangle = \frac{1}{3}\frac{4\pi^2 a_2^3}{T_2^2}(\Delta t)^2;$$

$$\Delta V_1 = \Delta V_2,$$

then it follows that

$$\frac{a_1^3}{T_1^2} = \frac{a_2^3}{T_2^2},$$

representing Kepler's third law in its original form.

*Note*: In any of the proposed formulations, Kepler's third law correlates elements of the motion of a planet with elements of the motion of another planet.

*Caution*: If in the graphical presentation of Kepler's second law, the equal sectors can be constructed anywhere on the surface of the ellipse, in the graphical presentation of Kepler's third law, the oblique linking pyramids of equal volumes can be constructed only with the bases centered on the minor peaks of the ellipses, the planes of these bases being perpendicular to the sloping axes of the minor peak-Sun direction.

The only exceptions to these restrictions are circular orbits whose points are equivalent so that the link pyramids can be oriented with one of the edges of the base tangent to the circle.

Corresponding to the new mode of presentation of Kepler's third law, the average orbital velocities of any two planets have the relationship

$$\frac{\langle v_2\rangle}{\langle v_1\rangle} = \sqrt{\frac{\langle r_1\rangle}{\langle r_2\rangle}}.$$

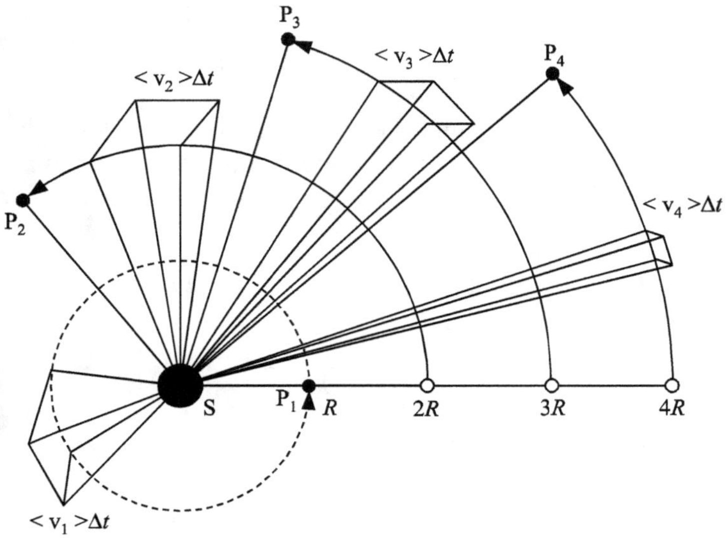


**Fig. T14.4**

We will now provide a graphical representation of Kepler's third law, referring to the initial scenario.

The orbits of the four planets being circular, any points can be used to construct the corresponding connection pyramids, as indicated by the drawing in Figure T14.4, the pyramids being oriented such that the base edge representing the displacement of the respective planet in a time $\Delta t << T_1$ is tangential to the circular orbit.

As a result of the new form of Kepler's third law, if the heights of the $P_2$, $P_3$ and $P_4$ linking pyramids are

$$\langle r_2 \rangle = 2\langle r_1 \rangle; \quad \langle r_3 \rangle = 3\langle r_1 \rangle; \quad \langle r_4 \rangle = 4\langle r_1 \rangle,$$

then the areas of their bases must be

$$\langle \mathrm{v}_2 \rangle^2 (\Delta t)^2 = \frac{1}{2} \langle \mathrm{v}_1 \rangle^2 (\Delta t)^2;$$

$$\langle \mathrm{v}_3 \rangle^2 (\Delta t)^2 = \frac{1}{3} \langle \mathrm{v}_1 \rangle^2 (\Delta t)^2;$$

$$\langle \mathrm{v}_4 \rangle^2 (\Delta t)^2 = \frac{1}{4} \langle \mathrm{v}_1 \rangle^2 (\Delta t)^2,$$

such that

$$\langle v_2 \rangle = \frac{\langle v_1 \rangle}{\sqrt{2}}; \quad \langle v_3 \rangle = \frac{\langle v_1 \rangle}{\sqrt{3}}; \quad \langle v_4 \rangle = \frac{\langle v_1 \rangle}{\sqrt{4}}.$$

It follows that when planet $P_1$ has returned to its initial position (after a time $T_1$), the positions of the planets $P_2$, $P_3$ and $P_4$ in their circular orbits are given by the following angles:

$$\alpha 2 = 2\pi \frac{\langle r_1 \rangle}{\langle r_2 \rangle} \frac{\langle v_2 \rangle}{\langle v_1 \rangle} \approx 127^o;$$

$$\alpha 3 = 2\pi \frac{\langle r_1 \rangle}{\langle r_3 \rangle} \frac{\langle v_3 \rangle}{\langle v_1 \rangle} \approx 69^o;$$

$$\alpha 4 = 2\pi \frac{\langle r_1 \rangle}{\langle r_4 \rangle} \frac{\langle v_4 \rangle}{\langle v_1 \rangle} = 45^\circ.$$

# Topic 15

# Foucault Pendulum

If for a normal gravitational pendulum (small length and small mass) a ground observer states that it retains the vertical plane in which it performs its oscillations, we must accept that for a short time the ground reference system is an inertial reference system.

The same is not true for the unstimulated oscillations of a gravitational pendulum with a large length and mass over a long period. As Foucault observed, the vertical plane in which the oscillations of this pendulum occur is not preserved. This proves that the characteristics of the rotation of the pendulum's oscillation plane are explained by the observer in this system as an effect of the complementary Coriolis force, highlighting not only the rotation of the Earth, but also its influence on the motion of a gravitational pendulum.

On the vertex of a point O$'$, with the geographic latitude $\varphi$, on the surface of the Earth (Figures T15.1 and T15.2), at the point O$''$ and the height O$'$O$'$ = $l$, is suspended a gravitational pendulum with a great length $l$ and mass $m$, which can oscillate around the vertical axis O$'$Z$'$, pointing vertically upwards.

The other axes of the non-inertial system with the origin O$'$S are: O$'$X$'$ – to the east, on the tangent to the geographical parallel passing through O$'$; O$'$Y$'$ – to the north, on the tangent to the geographical meridian that passes through O$'$.

By negating the frictional forces with air and the complementary ground centrifugal force, the vector equation of the gravitational pendulum's motion relative to the non-inertial system X$'$Y$'$Z$'$, fixed in

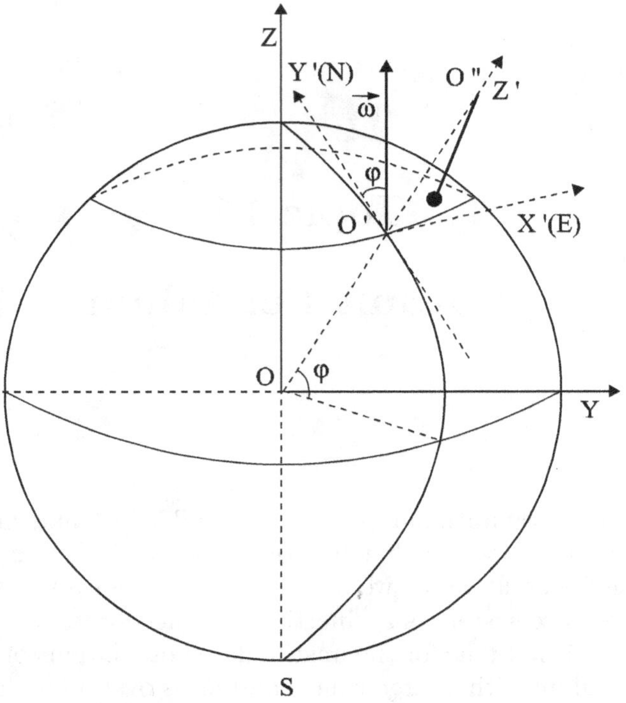


**Fig. T15.1**

relation to the Earth, is:

$$m\vec{a}_{\text{rel}} = \vec{G} + \vec{T} + \vec{F}_{\text{cor}},$$

where $\vec{G}$ – the weight of the pendulum, $\vec{T}$ – the tension of the suspension wire, $\vec{F}_{\text{cor}}$ – the complementary Coriolis force;

$$m\vec{a}_{\text{rel}} = \vec{G} + \vec{T} - 2m\vec{\omega} \times \vec{\text{v}}_{\text{rel}},$$

where $\vec{a}_{\text{rel}}$ and $\vec{\text{v}}_{\text{rel}}$ are the relative acceleration and relative velocity of the pendulum relative to the non-inertial observer O′.

From Figure T15.2, where the forces acting on the pendulum are represented, as well as the other vector sizes characteristic of its movement, it follows that:

$$\vec{r'} = \overrightarrow{\text{O'P}} = x'\vec{i'} + y'\vec{j'} + z'\vec{k'};$$

$$\vec{\omega} = \omega\cos\varphi\vec{j'} + \omega\sin\varphi\vec{k'};$$

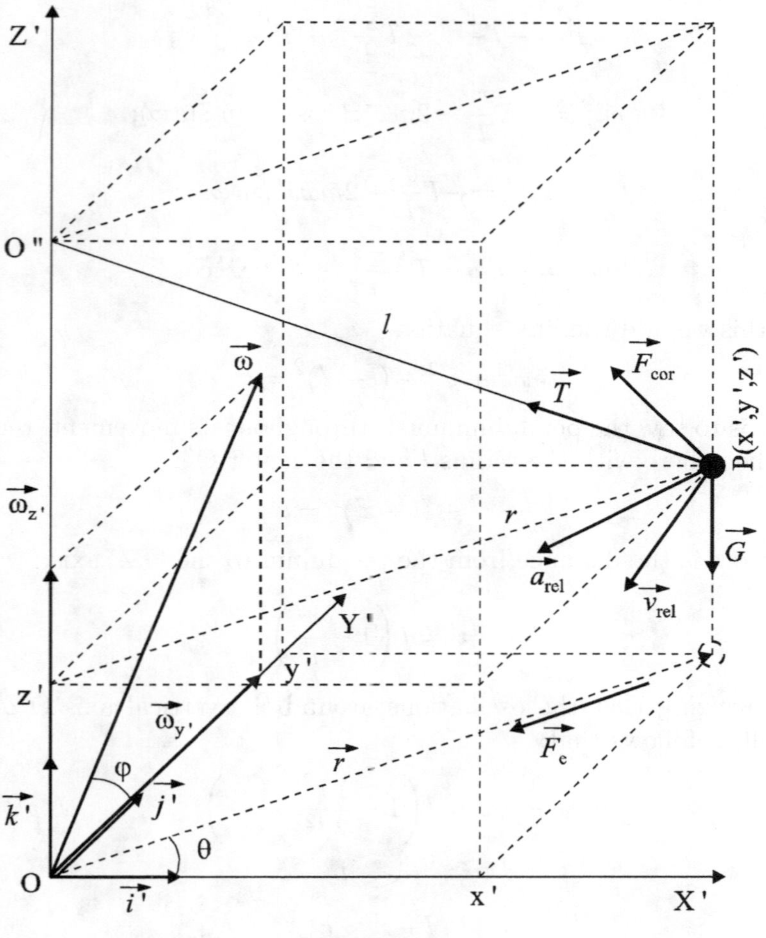


**Fig. T15.2**

$$\vec{\mathrm{v}}_{\mathrm{rel}} = \dot{x}'\vec{i}' + \dot{y}'\vec{j}' + \dot{z}'\vec{k}';$$

$$\vec{a}_{\mathrm{rel}} = \ddot{x}'\vec{i}' + \ddot{y}'\vec{j}' + \ddot{z}'\vec{k}';$$

$$\vec{\omega} \times \vec{\mathrm{v}}_{\mathrm{rel}} = \begin{vmatrix} \vec{i}' & \vec{j}' & \vec{k}' \\ 0 & \omega\cos\varphi & \omega\sin\varphi \\ \dot{x}' & \dot{y}' & \dot{z}' \end{vmatrix}$$

$$= \omega(\dot{z}'\cos\varphi - \dot{y}'\sin\varphi)\vec{i}' + \omega\dot{x}'\sin\varphi\vec{j}' - \omega\dot{x}'\cos\varphi\vec{k}';$$

$$\vec{G} = -mg\vec{k}';$$

$$\vec{T} = -T\frac{x'}{l}\vec{i}' - T\frac{y'}{l}\vec{j}' + T\frac{l-z'}{l}\vec{k}';$$

$$m\ddot{x}' = -\mathrm{T}\frac{x'}{l} - 2m\omega(\dot{z}'\cos\varphi - \dot{y}'\sin\varphi);$$

$$m\ddot{y}' = -T\frac{y'}{l} - 2m\omega\dot{x}'\sin\varphi;$$

$$m\ddot{z}' = -mg + T\frac{l-z'}{l} + 2m\omega\dot{x}'\cos\varphi.$$

To this we add the link equation

$$x'^2 + y'^2 + (l - z')^2 = l^2,$$

that is to say, the pendulum must, throughout its movement, remain in the sphere with the radius $l$ and the center O$''$:

$$r^2 + (l - z')^2 = l^2,$$

where $r$ is the distance from the pendulum to the O'Z' axis;

$$l - z' = l\left(1 - \frac{r^2}{l^2}\right)^{\frac{1}{2}}.$$

Recognizing that the oscillations around the vertical axis O$'$Z$'$ are small, it follows that:

$$l - -z' = l\left(1 - \frac{1}{2}\frac{r^2}{l^2} + \cdots\right);$$

$$r << l;$$

$$l - z' \approx l;$$

$$z' = 0;$$

$$\dot{z}' = 0;$$

$$\ddot{z}' = 0.$$

This means that the small oscillations of the pendulum P occur in the plane $z' = 0$, namely in the plane tangent to the lowest point of the sphere with the center O$''$ and the radius $l$, so that the velocity and acceleration of the pendulum P, the vectors $\vec{v}_{\mathrm{rel}}$ and $\vec{a}_{\mathrm{rel}}$, are contained in the plane $z' = 0$, and their moduli are very small. This is allowed, with a very good approximation, by the equation

$$m\ddot{z}' = -mg + T\left(1 - \frac{z'}{l}\right) + 2m\omega\dot{x}'\cos\varphi,$$

where we admit that the wire tension is constant, $T = mg$.

Under these conditions, the plane motion of the pendulum P is reduced to the movements of its projections on the axes of the plane O′X′Y′, the equations of these movements being:

$$\ddot{x}' = -\frac{g}{l}x' + 2\omega\dot{y}'\sin\varphi; \quad \ddot{y}' = -\frac{g}{l}y' - 2\omega\dot{x}'\sin\varphi.$$

From these, it follows that

$$y'\ddot{x}' - x'\ddot{y}' = 2\omega(x'\dot{x}' + y'\dot{y}')\sin\varphi;$$

$$x'\dot{y}' - y'\dot{x}' + \omega(x'^2 + y'^2)\sin\varphi = C_1,$$

representing the first integral of the angular momentum of the pendulum P.

Indeed, from the definition of absolute angular momentum, it follows that:

$$\vec{L} = \overrightarrow{\mathrm{OP}} \times m\vec{\mathrm{v}}_{\mathrm{abs}} = \overrightarrow{\mathrm{O'P}} \times m\vec{\mathrm{v}}_{\mathrm{abs}},$$

if the origin O of the fixed XYZ inertial system coincides with the origin O′ of the non-inertial system X′Y′Z′;

$$\overrightarrow{\mathrm{O'P}} = \vec{r}'; \quad \vec{L} = \vec{r}' \times m\vec{\mathrm{v}}_{\mathrm{abs}}; \quad \vec{r}' = \vec{r} + z' = \vec{r} + z'\vec{k}';$$

$$z' \approx 0; \quad \vec{r}' \approx \vec{r};$$

$$\vec{\mathrm{v}}_{\mathrm{abs}} = \vec{\mathrm{v}}_{\mathrm{rel}} + \vec{\mathrm{v}}_{\mathrm{transport}};$$

$$\vec{\mathrm{v}}_{\mathrm{transport}} = \vec{\mathrm{v}}_{\mathrm{translation}} + \vec{\omega} \times \vec{r}';$$

$$\vec{\mathrm{v}}_{\mathrm{abs}} = \vec{\mathrm{v}}_{\mathrm{rel}} + \vec{\omega} \times \vec{r};$$

$$\vec{L} = \vec{r} \times m\vec{\mathrm{v}}_{\mathrm{rel}} + m\vec{r} \times (\vec{\omega} \times \vec{r});$$

$$\vec{r} = x'\vec{i}' + y'\vec{j}'; \quad \vec{\mathrm{v}}_{\mathrm{rel}} = \dot{x}'\vec{i}' + \dot{y}'\vec{j}';$$

$$\vec{r} \times \vec{\mathrm{v}}_{\mathrm{rel}} = \begin{vmatrix} \vec{i}' & \vec{j}' & \vec{k}' \\ x' & y' & 0 \\ \dot{x}' & \dot{y}' & 0 \end{vmatrix} = (x'\dot{y}' - y'\dot{x}')\vec{k}';$$

$$\vec{\omega} \times \vec{r} = \begin{vmatrix} \vec{i}' & \vec{j}' & \vec{k}' \\ 0 & \omega_{y'} & \omega_{z'} \\ x' & y' & 0 \end{vmatrix} = y'\omega_{z'}\vec{i}' + x'\omega_z'\vec{j}'x'\omega_{y'}\vec{k}';$$

$$\vec{r} \times (\vec{\omega} \times \vec{r}) = \begin{vmatrix} \vec{i}' & \vec{j}' & \vec{k}' \\ x' & y' & 0 \\ -y'\omega_{z'} & x'\omega_{z'} & -x'\omega_{y'} \end{vmatrix}$$

$$= -x'y'\omega_{y'}\vec{i}' + x'^2\omega_{y'}\vec{j}' + (x'^2 + y'^2)\omega_{z'}\vec{k}';$$

$$\vec{L} = m(-x'y'\omega_{y'}\vec{i}' + x'^2\omega_{y'}\vec{j}') + [(x'\dot{y}' - y'\dot{x}') + (x'^2 + y'^2)\omega_{z'}]\vec{k}'.$$

Since the relative motion of P occurs in the plane X′Y′ and since the plane X′Y′ coincides with the plane XY, it follows that the absolute motion of P occurs in plane XY, so we must have

$$-x'y'\omega_{y'}\vec{i}' + x'^2\omega_{y'}\vec{j}' = \vec{r} \times (\vec{\omega}_{y'} \times \vec{r}) = 0.$$

Thus, the absolute angular momentum of the pendulum P is constant:

$$\vec{L} = m[(x'\dot{y}' - y'\dot{x}') + (x'^2 + y'^2)\omega_{z'}]\vec{k}';$$

$$\vec{k}' = \vec{k}; \quad \omega_{z'} = \omega \sin\varphi;$$

$$L = \text{constant};$$

$$x'\dot{y}' - y'\dot{x}' + \omega(x'^2 + y'^2)\sin\varphi = C_1.$$

Also, from the differential equations of the movements of the projections of P on the axes X′ and Y′, respectively, it results that:

$$\dot{x}'\ddot{x}' + \dot{y}'\ddot{y}' = -\frac{g}{l}(x'\dot{x}' + y'\dot{y}'); \quad \dot{x}'^2 + \dot{y}'^2 + \frac{g}{l}(x'^2 + y'^2) = C_2,$$

representing the prime energy integral of the oscillator P;

$$\frac{m\mathrm{v}_{\mathrm{rel}}^2}{2} + \frac{mgr^2}{2l} = \frac{mC_2}{2};$$

$$k = \frac{mg}{l};$$

$$\frac{m\mathrm{v}_{\mathrm{rel}}^2}{2} + \frac{kr^2}{2} = C,$$

where $\frac{kr^2}{2}$ is the potential energy of the oscillator within the elastic force $\vec{F}_{\mathrm{e}} = -k\vec{r}$.

Indeed, from the vector equation of the spatial motion of the gravitational pendulum P,

$$m\vec{a}_{\text{rel}} = \vec{G} + \vec{T} - 2m\,\vec{\omega} \times \vec{\text{v}}_{\text{rel}}.$$

In the approximation of the small oscillations, when the movement becomes flat and occurs in the plane of the O′X′Y′ system, the $\vec{a}_{\text{rel}}$ and $\vec{\text{v}}_{\text{rel}}$ vectors are contained in this plane, and the vector equation of the plane movement of the oscillator P is:

$$\vec{T} = T\frac{\overrightarrow{\text{PO}''}}{l} = mg\frac{\overrightarrow{\text{O}'\text{O}''} - \vec{r}'}{l};$$

$$\vec{T} = mg\frac{l\vec{k}' - \vec{r}}{l} = mg\vec{k}' - \frac{mg}{l}\vec{r};$$

$$\vec{\omega} \times \vec{\text{v}}_{\text{rel}} = (\vec{\omega}_{y'} + \vec{\omega}_{z'}) \times \vec{\text{v}}_{\text{rel}} = \vec{\omega}_{y'} \times \vec{\text{v}}_{\text{rel}} + \vec{\omega}_{z'} \times \vec{\text{v}}_{\text{rel}};$$

$$m\vec{a}_{\text{rel}} = -\frac{mg}{l}\vec{r} - 2m\vec{\omega}_{y'} \times \vec{\text{v}}_{\text{rel}} 2m\vec{\omega}_{z'} \times \vec{\text{v}}_{\text{rel}};$$

$$\vec{F}_{\text{e}} = -\frac{mg}{l}\vec{r} = -k\vec{r};$$

$$\vec{\omega}_{y'} \times \vec{\text{v}}_{\text{rel}} = 0,$$

because the oscillation occurs in the O′X′Y′ plane;

$$m\vec{a}_{\text{rel}} = -k\vec{r} - 2m\vec{\omega}_{z'} \times \vec{\text{v}}_{\text{rel}}.$$

This represents the vector equation of the plane motion of a material point, attracted by an elastic force $\vec{F}_{\text{e}} = -k\vec{r}$, in the O′X′Y′ system, fixed in relation to the Earth (the horizontal surface above which the pendulum is suspended), when the pendulum rotates around the vertical of that point, in a direct trigonometric sense, with the angular velocity $\vec{\omega}_{z'}$.

In plane polar coordinates ($r$; $\theta$), in the O′X′Y′ plane, the two integral primes of the movement are:

$$r^2(\dot{\theta} + \omega \sin\varphi) = C_1;$$

$$\dot{r}^2 + r^2\left(\dot{\theta}^2 + \frac{g}{l}\right) = C_2.$$

In the horizontal plane of Figure T15.3, where the axes of the O′X′Y′ system are rotated, in a direct trigonometric sense, around the vertical O′Z′ with angular velocity $\vec{\omega}_{z'}$, we represent the system

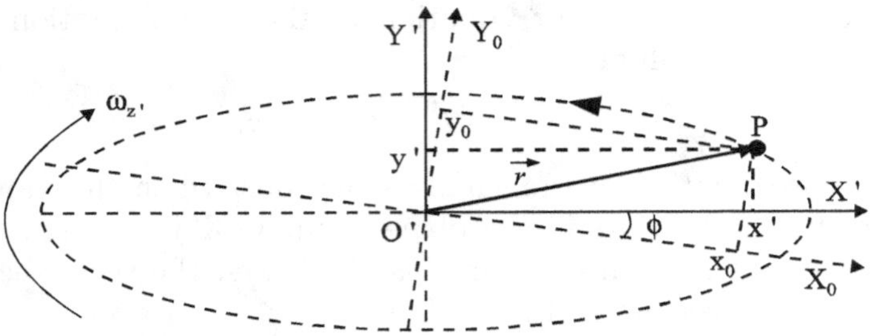


**Fig. T15.3**

of rectangular axes $O'X_0Y_0$, which rotate around the vertical $O'Z'$, in the inverse trigonometric sense, with the angular velocity $-\vec{\omega}_{z'}$ from the $O'X'Y'$ system.

The relationships between the coordinates of oscillator P in the two axes systems are:

$$x' = x_0 \cos\Phi + y_0 \sin\Phi;$$

$$y' = -x_0 \sin\Phi + y_0 \cos\Phi;$$

$$\Phi = \omega_{z'}t = \omega t \sin\varphi.$$

Introducing these into the equations of the projections of P's movements on the two axes of the $O'X'Y'$ system, results in:

$$\ddot{x}_0 + \Omega^2 x_0 = 0;$$

$$\ddot{y}_0 + \Omega^2 y_0 = 0;$$

$$\Omega^2 = \frac{g}{l} + \omega^2 \sin^2\varphi.$$

These represent the differential equations of the projections of oscillator P's on the axes of the system $O'X_0Y_0$, each of them indicating a harmonic oscillatory motion with the same pulse $\Omega$, meaning that under the action of the elastic force $\vec{F}_e = -k\vec{r}$, the trajectory of P in relation to the system $O'X_0Y_0$ is a fixed ellipse whose plane is $z' = 0$.

To determine the semi-axes of this ellipse, we enter the complex variable

$$\xi = x' + iy'.$$

Using the differential equations of the projections of P's movements on the axes of the O′X′Y′ system, this results in:

$$\ddot{\xi} + 2i\omega\dot{\xi}\sin\varphi + \frac{g}{l}\xi = 0,$$

a differential equation which, having a general solution of the form

$$\xi = \xi_0 e^{-i\alpha t},$$

has the characteristic equation

$$\alpha^2 - 2\alpha\omega\sin\varphi - \frac{g}{l} = 0,$$

with roots

$$\alpha_{1,2} = \omega\sin\varphi \pm \sqrt{\frac{g}{l} + \omega^2\sin^2\varphi};$$

$$\alpha_{1,2} = \omega\sin\varphi \pm \Omega.$$

Thus, that the general solution of the differential equation is:

$$\xi = Ae^{-i\alpha_1 t} + Be^{-i\alpha_2 t};$$

$$\xi = Ae^{-i\omega t\sin\varphi}(Ae^{-i\Omega t} + Be^{i\Omega t}).$$

For the determination of constants $A$ and $B$, we consider the following initial conditions:

$$t = 0;$$

$$x' = x'_0;$$

$$y' = 0;$$

$$\dot{x}' = 0;$$

$$\dot{y}' = 0.$$

Thus, we obtain:

$$A = \frac{x'_0}{2}\left(1 - \frac{\omega}{\Omega}\sin\varphi\right); \quad B = \frac{x'_0}{2}\left(1 + \frac{\omega}{\Omega}\sin\varphi\right);$$

$$\cos\Omega t = \frac{e^{i\Omega t} + e^{-i\Omega t}}{2};$$

$$\sin \Omega t = \frac{e^{i\Omega t} - e^{-i\Omega t}}{2};$$

$$\xi(t) = x'_0 \left( \cos \Omega t + i\frac{\omega}{\Omega} \sin \varphi \sin \Omega\, t \right) e^{-i\omega t \sin \varphi},$$

representing the law, in complex form, of the movement of the oscillator P, in relation to the O′X′Y′ system;

$$\xi(t) = \eta(t) e^{-i\omega t \,\sin \varphi},$$

where

$$\eta(t) = x'_0 \left( \cos \Omega\, t + i\frac{\omega}{\Omega} \sin\, \varphi\, \sin \Omega\, t \right),$$

represents the law, in a complex form, of the oscillator P's motion, in relation to the system O′X$_0$Y$_0$, which rotates in relation to O′X′Y′ with the angular velocity $-\vec{\omega}_{z'}$. This indicates that the movement of P occurs on a fixed ellipse in relation to the system O′X$_0$Y$_0$, whose equation and whose semi-axes are obtained as follows:

$$\eta(t) = x_0 + iy_0;$$

$$x_0 = x'_0 \cos \Omega t;$$

$$y_0 = x'_0 \frac{\omega}{\Omega} \sin \varphi \sin \Omega t;$$

$$\frac{x_0^2}{x'^2_0} + \frac{y_0^2}{x'^2_0 \frac{\omega^2}{\Omega^2} \sin^2 \varphi} = 1;$$

$$\frac{x_0^2}{a^2} + \frac{y_0^2}{b^2} = 1;$$

$$a = x'_0;$$

$$b = x'_0 \frac{\omega}{\Omega} \sin \varphi.$$

The ellipse is very elongated, since $b << a$.

The direction of the displacement of P on the ellipse can be easily represented, if we assume that at the moment $t = 0$, the oscillator is at the point ($x_0 = x'_0$; $y_0 = 0$). At the moment $t$, immediately following, for $y_0$ we must have

$$y_0 = x'_0 \frac{\omega}{\Omega} \sin \varphi \sin \Omega\, t > 0,$$

so $x_0$ must vary according to the law

$$x_0 = x_0' \cos \Omega t < x_0.$$

This implies the displacement of P on the ellipse in the direction indicated in the drawing (direct trigonometric sense), the duration of the entire ellipse being

$$\tau = \frac{2\pi}{\Omega} = \frac{2\pi}{\sqrt{\frac{g}{l} + \omega^2 \sin^2 \varphi}},$$

and the duration of a complete rotation performed by the ellipse being

$$T = \frac{2\pi}{\omega_{z'}} = \frac{2\pi}{\omega \sin \varphi}.$$

While the O′X$_0$Y$_0$ system rotates in the O′X′Y′ plane, the two axes of the ellipse describe two concentric circles with the centers O′, whose diameters are equal to the ellipse axes. The oscillator P's path, relative to the system O′X′Y′, is a flat curve between the two circles, alternately touching them, as indicated by the drawing in Figure T15.4, when, as previously stated, at the initial moment the oscillator P is at rest in the deviated position $(x_0'; 0)$, which will cause the oscillator speed to be zero at each "point of contact" with the outer circle.

A non-inertial observer is at rest on the horizontal planar floor O′X′Y′ of the chamber (from the ceiling of which is suspended the gravitational pendulum), rotating around the vertical O′Z′ with the angular velocity $\vec{\omega}_{z'}$ in a direct trigonometric sense (with the period $T = 2\pi/\omega \sin \varphi$). This observer, remaining in the same position, watches the pendulum for a few hours and finds that the plane in which the pendulum oscillate changes over time. The explanation is given in Figure T15.5, where the orientation of the Coriolis force justifies the constant apparent permanent deviation to the right of the oscillator P in relation to the direction of its movement in the O′X′Y′ plane.

For a inertial observer, looking at the "spectacle" of pendulum oscillations, the plane of these oscillations remains the same (preserved), thanks to the conservation of the absolute angular momentum of the system.

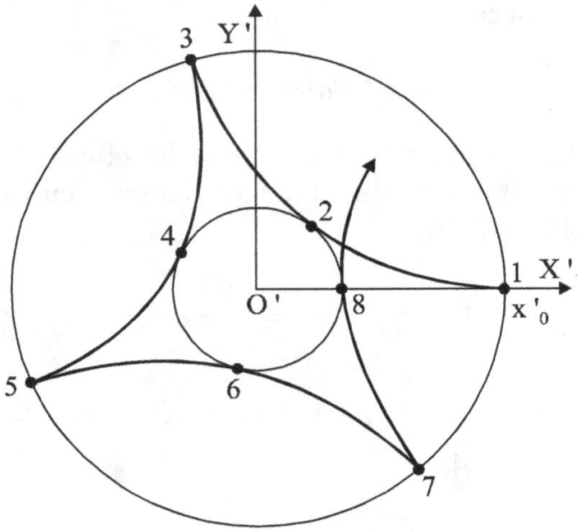


**Fig. T15.4**

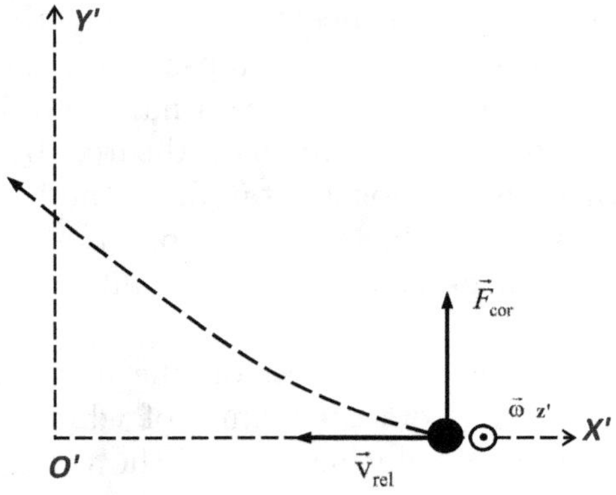


**Fig. T15.5**

The experimental verification of the apparent rotation of the oscillation plane of the gravitational pendulum relative to a non-inertial observer, as well as the conservation of the oscillation plane of the same pendulum relative to an inertial observer, can be achieved with the device represented in Figure T15.6 where, on a horizontal planar platform, a gravitational pendulum is suspended, oscillating in relation to the vertical point of the suspension, while the platform rotates around the axis coinciding with the vertical point of the suspension.

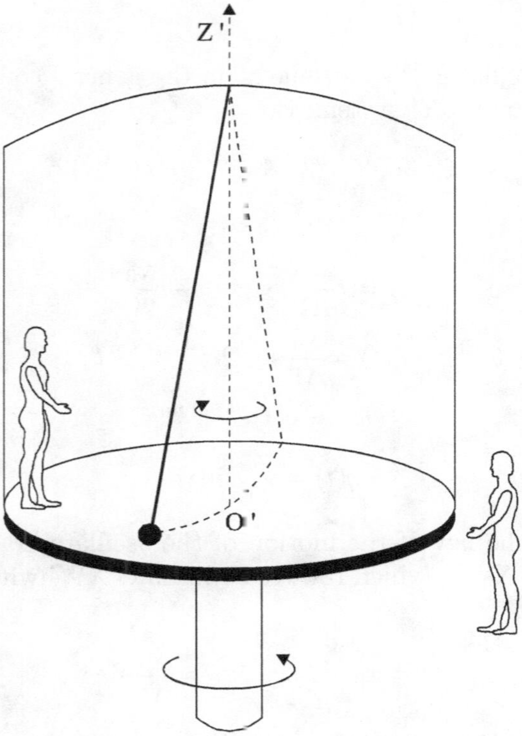


**Fig. T15.6**

The observer on the platform, who is "unaware" that it rotates, finds that the pendulum oscillation plane changes, apparently turning in the direction indicated in the drawing (which is opposite to the direction of rotation of the platform).

The observer outside the platform (inertial observer), who is not interested in the movement of the platform, notes that the plane of the pendulum oscillations does not change.

## Proposed Exercise

Consider, in the study of the Foucault pendulum, that the initial conditions of oscillator P's movement are: $t = 0$; $x' = 0$; $y' = 0$; $\dot{x}' = v_0$; $\dot{y}' = 0$.

## Solution

The law of oscillator P's movement, in the general complex form, in relation to the O′X′Y′ system, is

$$\xi = e^{-i\omega t \sin\varphi} Ae^{-i\Omega t} + Be^{i\Omega t}),$$

resulting in:

$$A = i\frac{\mathrm{v}_0}{2\Omega}; \quad B = -i\frac{\mathrm{v}_0}{2\Omega};$$

$$\xi(t) = \frac{\mathrm{v}_0}{\Omega}\sin\Omega t e^{-i\omega t \sin\varphi};$$

$$\xi(t) = \eta(t)e^{-i\omega t \sin\varphi};$$

$$\eta(t) = \frac{\mathrm{v}_0}{\Omega}\sin\Omega t,$$

representing the law of the motion of the oscillator P in relation to the system $O'X_0Y_0$, which rotates towards O'X'Y' with the angular velocity $-\vec{\omega}_{z'}$;

$$\eta(t) = x_0 + iy_0; \quad x_0 = \frac{\mathrm{v}_0}{\Omega}\sin\Omega t,$$

indicating that the movement of P with respect to the system $O'X_0Y_0$ is a harmonic oscillatory motion along the axis $O'X_0$, with the amplitude $\frac{\mathrm{v}_0}{\Omega}$ and with the pulse $\Omega$.

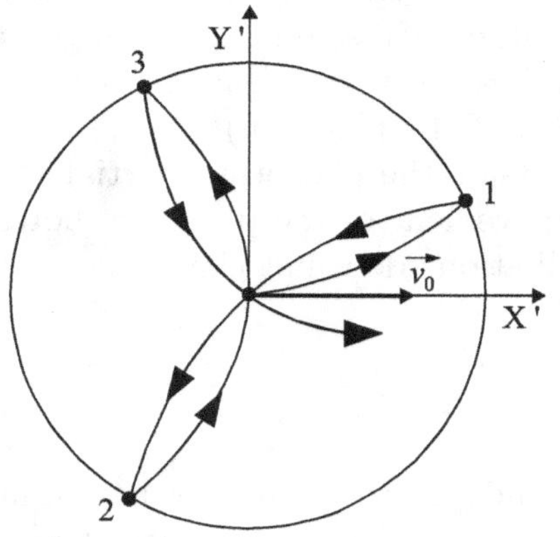


**Fig. T15.7**

While the $O'X_0Y_0$ system rotates in the $O'X'Y'$ plane, the trajectory of P, relative to the $O'X'Y'$ system, is a flat curve coinciding with the circle with the center $O'$ and the radius $\frac{v_0}{\Omega}$, represented in Figure T15.7. The oscillator leaves the center of this circle and returns after each moment of contact with the circle's circumference.

# Topic 16

# The Precession of a Foucault Pendulum and the Action of the Coriolis Force on a Conical Pendulum

The movement of a Foucault pendulum can be interpreted as a "beating phenomenon" resulting from the superposition of two circular movements of a conical pendulum, occuring in opposite directions with slightly different frequencies.

This is a consequence of the fact that the direction of the Coriolis force acting on the ball of a conical pendulum in the direction of the radius of the circle described by it depends on the direction of rotation.

At the origin, point O, on the surface of the Earth, we attach a tri-orthogonal system of axes, so that: The axis OX is towards the east; axis OY is to the north; the OZ axis is to the zenith (Figure T16.1).

Corresponding to the point O, the angular velocity of the Earth's rotation motion around its own axis, the vector $\vec{\Omega}$, is located in the meridian plane (YOZ).

Let us consider a conical pendulum (with the length $l$ and the angular aperture $2\alpha$) in the variants shown in Figure T16.2, when the ball (material point P) moves in the XOY plane, on a circle with its center in the OZ axis and the radius $r << 1$.

Will the relative tangential velocity ($\vec{v}$) of the ball (and thus its angular velocity $\vec{\omega}$) be the same in both variants?

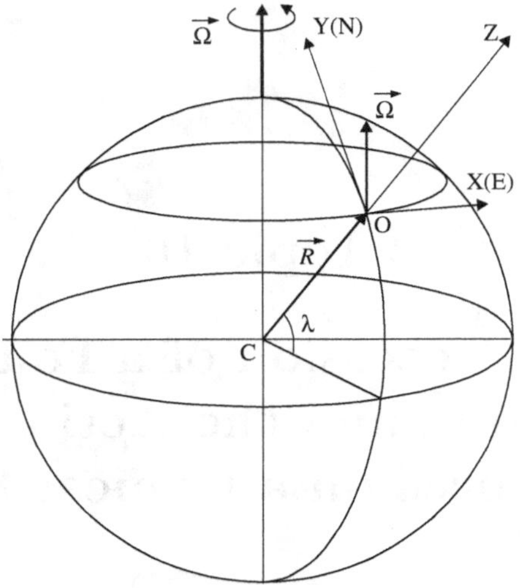


**Fig. T16.1**

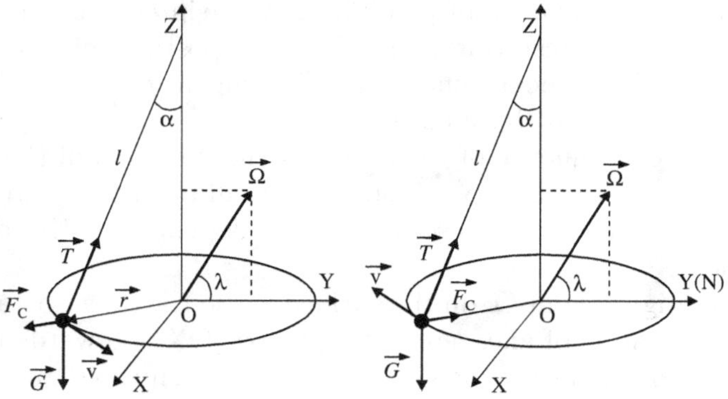


**Fig. T16.2**

Observing that the orientation of the Coriolis force, $\vec{F}_{\text{Coriolis}} = \vec{F}_{\text{C}} = -2m\vec{\Omega} \times \vec{v}$, is not the same in both variants, the answer to the previous question is negative.

Indeed, in accordance with the principle of d'Alembert, for the movement of the material point P in relation to SRNI—OXYZ, we have:

$$\vec{F} + \vec{F}_{\text{c,rel}} + \vec{F}_{\text{c}} = 0,$$

where $\vec{F}$ is the result of the real forces acting on the material point, $\vec{F}_{\text{c,rel}}$ is the relative complementary force acting on the material point, and $\vec{F}_{\text{c}}$ is the result of the complementary forces acting on the material point;

$$\vec{F} = \vec{G} + \vec{T};$$

$$\vec{F}_{\text{c,rel}} = -m\vec{a}_{\text{rel}} = -m\vec{a}_{\text{cp}};$$

$$\vec{F}_{\text{c}} = \vec{F}_{\text{tr}} + \vec{F}_{\text{Coriolis}};$$

$$\vec{F}_{tr} = -m\ddot{\vec{R}} - m\dot{\vec{\Omega}} \times \vec{r} - m\vec{\Omega} \times (\vec{\Omega} \times r);$$

$$\vec{R} = \text{constant}; \quad \vec{\Omega} = \text{constant};$$

$$\vec{F}_{\text{tr}} = -m\vec{\Omega} \times \left(\vec{\Omega} \times r\right) = F_{\text{cf,c}},$$

representing the complementary ground centrifugal force acting on the material point P;

$$\vec{F}_{\text{c}} = \vec{F}_{\text{cf,c}} + \vec{F}_{\text{C}};$$

$$\vec{G} + \vec{T} + \vec{F}_{\text{c,rel}} + \vec{F}_{\text{cf,c}} + \vec{F}_{\text{C}} = 0.$$

In the study of a Foucault pendulum only the influence of the Coriolis force on its movement is to be accepted, as in the study of a conical pendulum.

Under these conditions, the previous equation results in

$$\vec{G} + \vec{T} + \vec{F}_{\text{c,rel}} + \vec{F}_{\text{C}} = 0.$$

For the conical pendulum in the anti-clockwise rotation variant:

$$T \sin\alpha - F_{\text{c,rel}} - F_{\text{C}} = 0;$$

$$T \sin\alpha - ma_{\text{cp}} - 2m\,\Omega \text{v} \sin\lambda;$$

$$T \cos\alpha = mg;$$

$$mg\text{tg}\alpha - m\omega^2 r - 2m\Omega\omega r \sin\lambda;$$

$$r << l; \quad \text{tg}\,\alpha \approx \sin\alpha = \frac{r}{l};$$

$$\omega^2 + 2\Omega \sin\lambda\omega - \frac{g}{l}.$$

This has the acceptable solution:

$$\omega_{\text{anti-clockwise}} = \omega_a = -\Omega \sin\lambda + \sqrt{\Omega^2 \sin^2\lambda + \frac{g}{l}};$$

$$\omega_{\text{a}} = -\omega_1 + \omega_2.$$

For the conical pendulum with clockwise rotation,

$$T \sin\alpha - F_{\text{c,rel}} + F_{\text{c}} = 0;$$

$$\omega^2 - 2\Omega \sin\lambda\omega - \frac{g}{l} = 0.$$

This has the acceptable solution:

$$\omega_{\text{orar}} = \omega_0 = \Omega \sin\lambda + \sqrt{\Omega^2 \sin^2\lambda + \frac{g}{l}};$$

$$\omega_0 = \omega_1 + \omega_2 \neq \omega_a.$$

If the study of the circular motion of the conical pendulum ball in the real XOY plane, in each of the proposed variants, necessitates the study of the rotating vector (real vector function),

$$\vec{r} = \vec{r}(t) = x(t)\vec{i} + y(t)\vec{j},$$

$$r = \sqrt{x^2 + y^2} = \text{constant},$$

then, in the associated complex plane, the study of the circular motion of the pendulum ball involves the study of the following complex functions:

$$\bar{z}_{\text{a}}(t) = r\, e^{i(\omega_{\text{a}} t + \varphi_{\text{a}})},$$

in the variant of anti-clockwise rotation;

$$\bar{z}_0(t) = r\, e^{-i(\omega_0 t + \varphi_0)},$$

in the clockwise rotation variant. Thus, the moduli of the two complex functions are:

$$|\bar{z}_{\text{a}}| = \sqrt{\bar{z}_{\text{a}} \bar{z}_{\text{a}}^*} = r = \text{constant};$$

$$|\bar{z}_0| = \sqrt{\bar{z}_0 \bar{z}_0^*} = r = \text{constant},$$

and the real and imaginary parts of the two complex functions represent harmonic vibrations.

What movement of the material point P could we interpret as resulting from the simultaneous execution of the two circular movements described?

The answer can be based on the superposition principle, so that the study of the resultant movement would involve the study of the complex function

$$\bar{z}(t) = \bar{z}_{\mathrm{a}}(t) + \bar{z}_0(t).$$

Under these circumstances, it follows that:

$$\begin{aligned}
\bar{z} &= r\left(e^{i(\omega_{\mathrm{a}}t+\varphi_{\mathrm{a}})} + e^{-i(\omega_0 t+\varphi_0)}\right)\\
&= r\left[e^{i[(-\omega_1+\omega_2)t+\varphi_{\mathrm{a}}]} + e^{-i[(-\omega_1+\omega_2)t+\varphi_0]}\right]\\
&= r\,e^{-i\omega_1 t}\left[e^{i\omega_2 t}e^{i\varphi_{\mathrm{a}}} + e^{-i\omega_2 t}e^{-i\varphi_0}\right]\\
&= r\,e^{-i\omega_1 t}\left[e^{i\omega_2 t}e^{\frac{i}{2}(\varphi_{\mathrm{a}}-\varphi_0+\varphi_{\mathrm{a}}+\varphi_0)} + e^{-i\omega_2 t}e^{-\frac{i}{2}(\varphi_0-\varphi_{\mathrm{a}}+\varphi_0+\varphi_{\mathrm{a}})}\right]\\
&= re^{-i\omega_1 t}\left[e^{i\omega_2 t}e^{-\frac{i}{2}(\varphi_0-\varphi_{\mathrm{a}})}e^{\frac{i}{2}(\varphi_{\mathrm{a}}-\varphi_0)}\right.\\
&\quad\left.+\,e^{-i\omega_2 t}e^{-\frac{i}{2}(\varphi_0-\varphi_{\mathrm{a}})}e^{-\frac{i}{2}(\varphi_{\mathrm{a}}+\varphi_0)}\right]\\
&= re^{-i[\omega_1 t+\frac{1}{2}(\varphi_0-\varphi_{\mathrm{a}})]}\left[e^{i[\omega_2 t+\frac{1}{2}(\varphi_{\mathrm{a}}+\varphi_0)]} + e^{-i[\omega_2 t+\frac{1}{2}(\varphi_{\mathrm{a}}+\varphi_0)]}\right];
\end{aligned}$$

$$\varphi_1 = \frac{1}{2}(\varphi_0 - \varphi_a); \quad \varphi_2 = \frac{1}{2}(\varphi_a + \varphi_0);$$

$$\bar{z} = re^{-i(\omega_1 t+\varphi_1)}\left[e^{i(\omega_2 t+\varphi_2)} + e^{-i(\omega_2 t+\varphi_2)}\right];$$

$$\bar{z} = e^{-i(\omega_1 t+\varphi_1)}2r\cos\left(\omega_2 t + \varphi_2\right),$$

representing a harmonic oscillatory motion with amplitude $2r$ and pulsation

$$\omega 2 = \sqrt{\Omega^2 \sin^2\lambda + \frac{g}{l}} \approx \sqrt{\frac{g}{l}},$$

so that the plane of these oscillations rotates uniformly in an hourly sense with the angular velocity

$$\omega_1 = \Omega \sin \lambda,$$

a fact highlighted by the term $e^{-i(\omega_1 t + \varphi_1)}$.

*Conclusion*: Under the specified conditions, the conical pendulum can be considered as a Foucault pendulum.

# Problem 1

# Capella Stellar System

Capella ($\alpha$ Aurigae; the brightest star in Auriga constellation) is a stellar system formed of four stars (two pairs of double stars). The first pair of stars are two bright giant stars, $\Sigma_1$ (Ab, the secondary star) and $\Sigma_2$ (Aa, the main star). The second pair of stars consists of two dwarf stars, $\sigma_1$ (Bb, the secondary star) and $\sigma_2$ (Ba, the main star). In Figure 1.1 the orbits of the stars are represented.

You will consider that each star of the system $(\Sigma_1; \Sigma_2)$, is orbiting in concentric circles around their center of mass (CM), located in plane $\Pi$, different from the sky plane $\Pi_c$.

Take into account the following assumptions: the mass center of the system $(\Sigma_1; \Sigma_2)$ is at rest regardless of the observer on Earth, and the plane of the two stars' orbits (centered on the mass center) is not identical to the sky plane, $\Pi \neq \Pi_c$

*Determine*:

**a)** the distance between the stars, $a$;

**b)** the speed of each giant star relative to the CM, $v_{1,CM}$ and $v_{2,CM}$, and the masses of each component, $M_1$ and $M_2$;

**c)** the wavelength $\lambda_0$ of the radiation emitted by each giant star, with the assumption that each star emits radiation with the same wavelength. The maxima of the wavelengths of the radiation emitted by each giant, detected on Earth, are known: $\lambda_{1,max}$ for star $\Sigma_1$ and $\lambda_{2,max} < \lambda_{1,max}$ for star $\Sigma_2$;

**d)** the angle $i$ between the orbit plane $\Pi$ and sky plane $\Pi_c$.

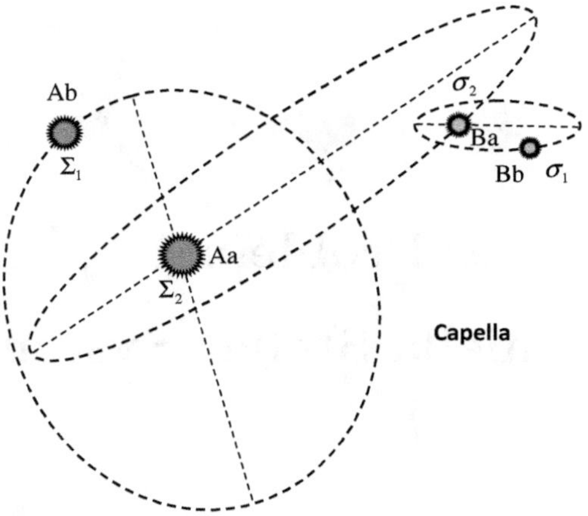


**Fig. 1.1**

The relationship between the luminosity of a star and its mass is known, $L = qM^4$, and the ratio between the luminosities of the two giant stars are

$$\frac{L_{(\mathrm{Aa})}}{L_{(\mathrm{Ab})}} = \frac{L_{(\Sigma_2)}}{L_{(\Sigma_1)}} = \frac{L_2}{L_1} = k > 1.$$

The mass function of the binary visual system is

$$f(M_1; M_2) = \frac{M_2^3 \sin^3 i}{(M_1 + M_2)^2}.$$

*Also known are:* $\beta$ – the angular distance between stars $\Sigma_1$ and $\Sigma_2$; $p$ – the parallax of the main star $\Sigma_2$; $T$ – the rotational time of the two giant stars around their mass center, CM; $K$ – the gravitational constant; $c$ – the speed of light in vacuum.

## Solution

**a)** In order to prove the relation

$$\left|a_{(\mathrm{AU})}\right| = \frac{\left|\beta_{('')}\right|}{\left|p_{('')}\right|},$$

follow the details in Figure 1.2, where: $\Delta$ – Sun–system distance; $a$ – distance between the stars; $\beta$ – angular distance between the stars; $r_{\mathrm{ES}}$ – Earth–Sun distance; $p$ – main star parallax.

Result:

$$a = \beta \cdot \Delta; \quad r_{\mathrm{ES}} = p \cdot \Delta;$$

$$\frac{\left|a_{(\mathrm{AU})}\right|}{\left|r_{\mathrm{ES(AU)}}\right|} = \frac{\left|\beta_{(\mathrm{rad})}\right| \cdot \left|\Delta_{(\mathrm{AU})}\right|}{\left|p_{(\mathrm{rad})}\right| \cdot \left|\Delta_{(\mathrm{AU})}\right|} = \frac{\left|\beta_{(\mathrm{rad})}\right|}{\left|p_{(\mathrm{rad})}\right|} = \frac{\left|\beta_{('')}\right|}{\left|p_{('')}\right|}$$

$$= \frac{\left|a_{(\mathrm{AU})}\right|}{1} = \left|a_{(\mathrm{AU})}\right|;$$

$$\left|a_{(\mathrm{AU})}\right| = \frac{\left|\beta_{('')}\right|}{\left|p_{('')}\right|}.$$

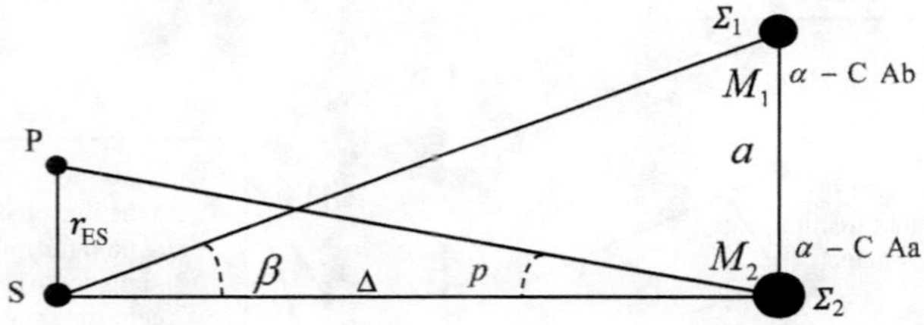


**Fig. 1.2**

**b)** If the two stars are observed as indicated in Figure 1.3 and Figure 1.4, when the angle between the plane of the orbits and the plane perpendicular to the sight seen direction is $i < 90°$, the system's CM is at rest relative to the observer on Earth, $\vec{v}_{\mathrm{CM,Ob}} = 0$, and the radial velocities of each of the two stars relative to the observer (moving away from the observer) are maximum:

$$\vec{H}_{\mathrm{CM,Ob}} = (M_1 + M_2) \cdot \vec{v}_{\mathrm{CM,Ob}} = M_1\vec{v}_{1,\mathrm{CM}} + M_2\vec{v}_{2,\mathrm{CM}} = 0;$$

$$\vec{v}_{\mathrm{CM,Ob}} = \frac{M_1\vec{v}_{1,\mathrm{CM}} + M_2\vec{v}_{2,\mathrm{CM}}}{M_1 + M_2} = 0;$$

$$M_1\vec{v}_{1,\mathrm{CM}} + M_2\vec{v}_{2,\mathrm{CM}} = 0; \quad M_1 v_{1,\mathrm{CM}} = M_2 v_{2,\mathrm{CM}}; \quad \frac{M_1}{M_2} = \frac{v_{2,\mathrm{CM}}}{v_{1,\mathrm{CM}}};$$

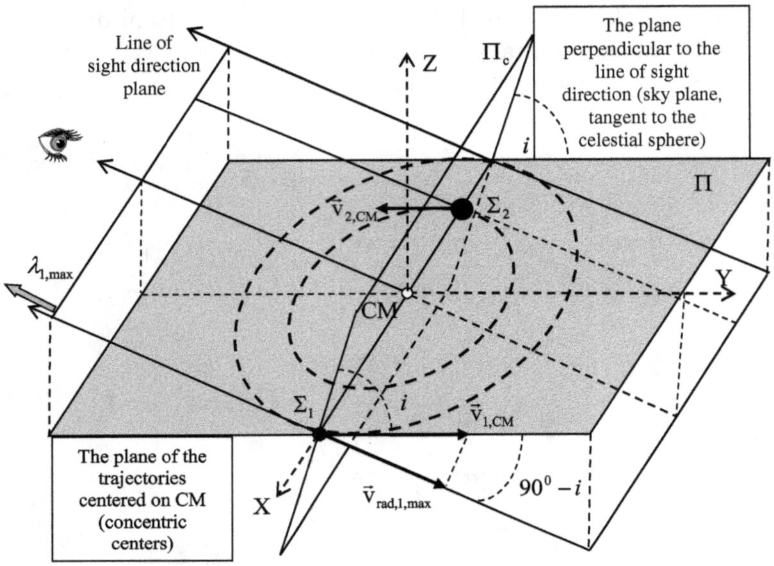

Line of sight direction plane
Z
$\Pi_c$
The plane perpendicular to the line of sight direction (sky plane, tangent to the celestial sphere)
$i$
$\Pi$
$\vec{v}_{2,CM}$
$\Sigma_2$
$\lambda_{1,max}$
Y
CM
$\Sigma_1$
$i$
$\vec{v}_{1,CM}$
The plane of the trajectories centered on CM (concentric centers)
X
$\vec{v}_{rad,1,max}$
$90^0 - i$


**Fig. 1.3**

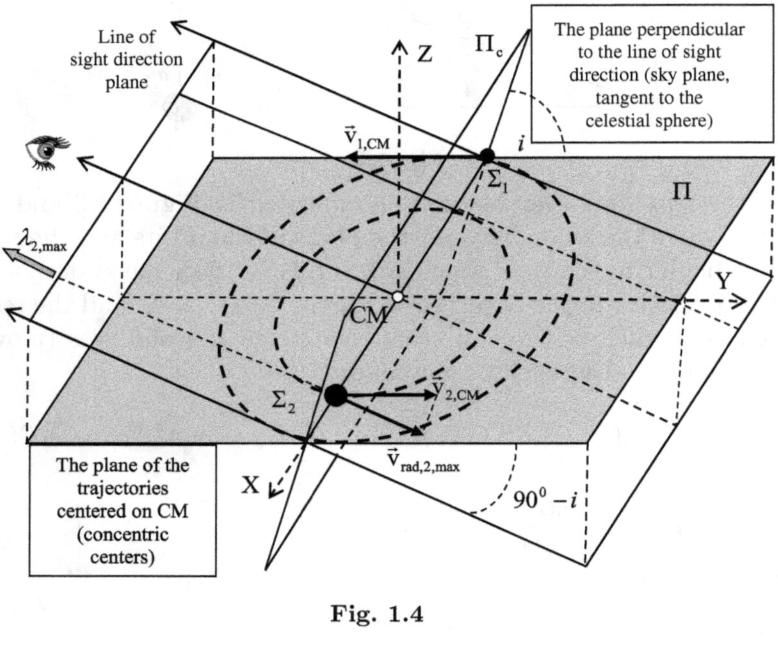

Line of sight direction plane
Z
$\Pi_c$
The plane perpendicular to the line of sight direction (sky plane, tangent to the celestial sphere)
$\vec{v}_{1,CM}$
$i$
$\Sigma_1$
$\Pi$
$\lambda_{2,max}$
Y
CM
$\vec{v}_{2,CM}$
$\Sigma_2$
$\vec{v}_{rad,2,max}$
The plane of the trajectories centered on CM (concentric centers)
X
$90^0 - i$


**Fig. 1.4**

$$\mathrm{v}_{\mathrm{rad},1,\max} = \mathrm{v}_{1,\mathrm{CM}} \cos(90^\circ - i) = \mathrm{v}_{1,\mathrm{CM}} \sin i; \quad \mathrm{v}_{1,\mathrm{CM}} = \frac{\mathrm{v}_{\mathrm{rad},1,\max}}{\sin i};$$

$$\mathrm{v}_{\mathrm{rad},2,\max} = \mathrm{v}_{2,\mathrm{CM}} \cos(90^\circ - i) = \mathrm{v}_{2,\mathrm{CM}} \sin i; \quad \mathrm{v}_{2,\mathrm{CM}} = \frac{\mathrm{v}_{\mathrm{rad},2,\max}}{\sin i};$$

$$\frac{M_1}{M_2} = \frac{\mathrm{v}_{2,\mathrm{CM}}}{\mathrm{v}_{1,\mathrm{CM}}} = \frac{\mathrm{v}_{\mathrm{rad},2,\max}}{\mathrm{v}_{\mathrm{rad},1,\max}}; \quad M_2 > M_1; \quad \mathrm{v}_{\mathrm{rad},1,\max} > \mathrm{v}_{\mathrm{rad},2,\max};$$

$$\mathrm{v}_{1,\mathrm{CM}} = \omega a_1 = \frac{2\pi}{T_1} a_1; \quad \mathrm{v}_{2,\mathrm{CM}} = \omega a_2 = \frac{2\pi}{T_2} a_2;$$

$$a_1 = \frac{\mathrm{v}_{1,\mathrm{CM}} T}{2\pi}; \quad a_2 = \frac{\mathrm{v}_{2,\mathrm{CM}} T}{2\pi};$$

$$a_1 + a_2 = \frac{T}{2\pi} \left(\mathrm{v}_{1,\mathrm{CM}} + \mathrm{v}_{2,\mathrm{CM}}\right) = a;$$

$$M_1 a_1 = M_2 a_2; \quad a_1 + a_2 = a;$$

$$a_1 = a \frac{M_2}{M_1 + M_2}; \quad a_2 = a \frac{M_1}{M_1 + M_2};$$

$$F = K \frac{M_1 M_2}{a^2} = M_1 \frac{4\pi^2}{T^2} a_1 = M_2 \frac{4\pi^2}{T^2} a_2;$$

$$K \frac{M_1 M_2}{a^2} = M_1 \frac{4\pi^2}{T^2} a \frac{M_2}{M_1 + M_2};$$

$$K \frac{1}{a^2} = \frac{4\pi^2}{T^2} a \frac{1}{M_1 + M_2};$$

$$\frac{T^2}{a^3} = \frac{4\pi^2}{K\left(M_1 + M_2\right)}; \quad M_1 + M_2 = \frac{4\pi^2 a^3}{K T^2};$$

$$\frac{T^2}{\left(a_1 + a_2\right)^3} = \frac{4\pi^2}{K\left(M_1 + M_2\right)};$$

$$\frac{T^2}{\frac{T^3}{(2\pi)^3} \left(\mathrm{v}_{1,\mathrm{CM}} + \mathrm{v}_{2,\mathrm{CM}}\right)^3} = \frac{4\pi^2}{K\left(M_1 + M_2\right)};$$

$$M_1 + M_2 = \frac{T}{2\pi K} \left(\mathrm{v}_{1,\mathrm{CM}} + \mathrm{v}_{2,\mathrm{CM}}\right)^3;$$

$$\mathrm{v}_{1,\mathrm{CM}} = \frac{\mathrm{v}_{\mathrm{rad},1,\max}}{\sin i}; \quad \mathrm{v}_{2,\mathrm{CM}} = \frac{\mathrm{v}_{\mathrm{rad},2,\max}}{\sin i};$$

$$M_1 + M_2 = \frac{T}{2\pi K}\left(\frac{\mathrm{v}_{\mathrm{rad,1,max}}}{\sin i} + \frac{\mathrm{v}_{\mathrm{rad,2.\,max}}}{\sin i}\right)^3;$$

$$M_1 + M_2 = \frac{T}{2\pi K \sin^3 i} \cdot (\mathrm{v}_{\mathrm{rad,1,max}} + \mathrm{v}_{\mathrm{rad,2,max}})^3;$$

$$M_1 + M_2 = \frac{T}{2\pi K \sin^3 i} \cdot \mathrm{v}^3_{\mathrm{rad,1,max}}\left(1 + \frac{\mathrm{v}_{\mathrm{rad,2,max}}}{\mathrm{v}_{\mathrm{rad,1,max}}}\right)^3;$$

$$\frac{M_1}{M_2} = \frac{\mathrm{v}_{\mathrm{rad,2,max}}}{\mathrm{v}_{\mathrm{rad,1,max}}};$$

$$M_2 > M_1; \quad \mathrm{v}_{\mathrm{rad,1,max}} > \mathrm{v}_{\mathrm{rad,2,max}};$$

$$M_1 + M_2 = \frac{T}{2\pi K \sin^3 i} \cdot \mathrm{v}^3_{\mathrm{rad,1,max}}\left(1 + \frac{M_1}{M_2}\right)^3;$$

$$M_1 + M_2 = \frac{T}{2\pi K \cdot \sin^3 i} \cdot \mathrm{v}^3_{\mathrm{1,rad,max}} \frac{(M_1 + M_2)^3}{M_2^3};$$

$$1 = \frac{T}{2\pi K \cdot \sin^3 i} \cdot \mathrm{v}^3_{\mathrm{1,rad,max}} \frac{(M_1 + M_2)^2}{M_2^3};$$

$$1 = \frac{T}{2\pi K} \cdot \mathrm{v}^3_{\mathrm{1,rad,max}} \cdot \frac{(M_1 + M_2)^2}{M_2^3 \sin^3 i}.$$

Thus:

$$\frac{M_2^3 \sin^3 i}{(M_1 + M_2)^2} = \frac{T}{2\pi K} \cdot \mathrm{v}^3_{\mathrm{rad,1,max}} = \frac{T}{2\pi K}(\mathrm{v}_{\mathrm{1,CM}} \cdot \sin i)^3$$
$$= f(M_1;\ M_2),$$

representing the mass function of the visual binary system;

$$\frac{M_2^3 \sin^3 i}{(M_1 + M_2)^2} = \frac{T}{2\pi K}(\mathrm{v}_{\mathrm{1,CM}} \cdot \sin i)^3 = \frac{T}{2\pi K} \cdot \mathrm{v}^3_{\mathrm{1,CM}} \cdot \sin^3 i;$$

$$\frac{M_2^3}{(M_1 + M_2)^2} = \frac{T}{2\pi K} \cdot \mathrm{v}^3_{\mathrm{1,CM}},$$

$$\frac{M_2^3}{M_1^2\left(1 + \frac{M_2}{M_1}\right)^2} = \frac{T}{2\pi K} \cdot \mathrm{v}^3_{\mathrm{1,CM}};$$

$$M_2 \cdot \frac{\left(\frac{M_2}{M_1}\right)^2}{\left(1+\frac{M_2}{M_1}\right)^2} = \frac{T}{2\pi K} \cdot \mathrm{v}_{1,\mathrm{CM}}^3;$$

$$L_1 = qM_1^4; \quad L_2 = qM_2^4;$$

$$\frac{L_2}{L_1} = k = \left(\frac{M_2}{M_1}\right)^4; \quad \frac{M_2}{M_1} = \sqrt[4]{k}; \quad M_2 = \sqrt[4]{k} \cdot M_1;$$

$$\sqrt[4]{k} \cdot M_1 \cdot \frac{\left(\sqrt[4]{k}\right)^2}{\left(1+\sqrt[4]{k}\right)^2} = \frac{T}{2\pi K} \cdot \mathrm{v}_{1,\mathrm{CM}}^3;$$

$$\frac{k^{3/4} \cdot M_1}{\left(1+\sqrt[4]{k}\right)^2} = \frac{T}{2\pi K} \cdot \mathrm{v}_{1,\mathrm{CM}}^3;$$

$$M_1 = \frac{T}{2\pi K} \cdot \frac{\left(1+k^{1/4}\right)^2}{k^{3/4}} \cdot \mathrm{v}_{1,\mathrm{CM}}^3;$$

$$M_2 = \sqrt[4]{k} \cdot M_1;$$

$$M_2 = \frac{T}{2\pi K} \cdot \frac{\left(1+k^{1/4}\right)^2}{k^{1/2}} \cdot \mathrm{v}_{1,\mathrm{CM}}^3,$$

representing the masses of the two components of the binary system.

Using Kepler's third law:

$$M_1 + M_2 = \frac{4\pi^2 a^3}{KT^2};$$

$$M_1 + M_2 = \frac{T}{2\pi K}(1+k^{1/4})^2 \left(\frac{1}{k^{3/4}} + \frac{1}{k^{1/2}}\right) \cdot \mathrm{v}_{1,\mathrm{CM}}^3;$$

$$\frac{T}{2\pi K}(1+k^{1/4})^2 \left(\frac{1}{k^{3/4}} + \frac{1}{k^{1/2}}\right) \cdot \mathrm{v}_{1,\mathrm{CM}}^3 = \frac{4\pi^2 a^3}{KT^2};$$

$$\frac{T}{2\pi K}(1+k^{1/4})^2 \cdot \frac{k^{1/2}+k^{3/4}}{k^{5/4}} \cdot \mathrm{v}_{1,\mathrm{CM}}^3 = \frac{4\pi^2 a^3}{KT^2};$$

$$\frac{T}{2\pi K}\left(1+k^{1/4}\right)^2 \cdot \frac{k^{1/2}\left(1+k^{1/4}\right)}{k^{5/4}} \cdot \mathrm{v}_{1,\mathrm{CM}}^3 = \frac{4\pi^2 a^3}{KT^2};$$

$$\frac{T}{2\pi K} \cdot \frac{(1+k^{1/4})^3}{k^{3/4}} \cdot \mathrm{v}_{1,\mathrm{CM}}^3 = \frac{4\pi^2 a^3}{KT^2};$$

$$\mathrm{v}_{1,\mathrm{CM}}^3 = \frac{(2\pi)^3 a^3 k^{3/4}}{T^3(1+k^{1/4})^3};$$

$$\mathrm{v}_{1,\mathrm{CM}} = \frac{2\pi \cdot a \cdot k^{1/4}}{T(1+k^{1/4})}.$$

Thus:

$$M_1 = \frac{T}{2\pi K} \cdot \frac{\left(1+k^{1/4}\right)^2}{k^{3/4}} \cdot \mathrm{v}_{1,\mathrm{CM}}^3;$$

$$M_1 = \frac{T}{2\pi K} \cdot \frac{\left(1+k^{1/4}\right)^2}{k^{3/4}} \cdot \frac{(2\pi)^3 a^3 k^{3/4}}{T^3\left(1+k^{1/4}\right)^3};$$

$$M_1 = \frac{4\pi^2 a^3}{KT^2\left(1+k^{1/4}\right)}; \quad \left|a_{(\mathrm{AU})}\right| = \frac{\left|\beta_{('')}\right|}{\left|p_{('')}\right|}.$$

$$M_2 = \sqrt[4]{k} \cdot M_1;$$

$$M_2 = \frac{4\pi^2 a^3 k^{1/4}}{KT^2\left(1+k^{1/4}\right)};$$

$$\frac{M_1}{M_2} = \frac{\mathrm{v}_{2,\mathrm{CM}}}{\mathrm{v}_{1,\mathrm{CM}}};$$

$$\mathrm{v}_{2,\mathrm{CM}} = \frac{M_1}{M_2} \cdot \mathrm{v}_{1,\mathrm{CM}} = \frac{1}{k^{1/4}} \cdot \sqrt[3]{\frac{(2\pi)^3 a^3 k^{3/4}}{T^3\left(1+k^{1/4}\right)^3}}; \quad \left|a_{(\mathrm{AU})}\right| = \frac{\left|\beta_{('')}\right|}{\left|p_{('')}\right|};$$

$$\mathrm{v}_{2,\mathrm{CM}} = \frac{2\pi \cdot a}{T\left(1+k^{1/4}\right)}.$$

**c)** The maximum velocities of each star are:

$$\mathrm{v}_{\mathrm{rad},1,\mathrm{max}} = \mathrm{v}_{1,\mathrm{CM}} \sin i; \quad \mathrm{v}_{1,\mathrm{CM}} = \frac{2\pi \cdot a \cdot k^{1/4}}{T\left(1+k^{1/4}\right)};$$

$$\mathrm{v}_{\mathrm{rad},2,\max} = \mathrm{v}_{2,\mathrm{CM}} \sin i; \quad \mathrm{v}_{2,\mathrm{CM}} = \frac{2\pi \cdot a}{T\left(1 + k^{1/4}\right)};$$

$$\mathrm{v}_{\mathrm{rad},1,\max} = \frac{2\pi \cdot a \cdot k^{1/4}}{T\left(1 + k^{1/4}\right)} \cdot \sin i;$$

$$\mathrm{v}_{\mathrm{rad},2,\max} = \frac{2\pi \cdot a}{T\left(1 + k^{1/4}\right)} \cdot \sin i,$$

where

$$\left|a_{(\mathrm{AU})}\right| = \frac{\left|\beta_{('')}\right|}{\left|p_{('')}\right|}.$$

According to the longitudinal Doppler effect relationship:

$$\lambda_{1,\max} = \lambda_0 \left(1 + \frac{\mathrm{v}_{\mathrm{rad},1,\max}}{c}\right); \quad \mathrm{v}_{\mathrm{rad},1,\max} = c \cdot \frac{\lambda_{1,\max} - \lambda_0}{\lambda_0};$$

$$\mathrm{v}_{\mathrm{rad},1,\max} = \frac{2\pi \cdot a \cdot k^{1/4}}{T\left(1 + k^{1/4}\right)} \cdot \sin i;$$

$$\sin i = \frac{\mathrm{v}_{\mathrm{rad},1,\max} T\left(1 + k^{1/4}\right)}{2\pi \cdot a \cdot k^{1/4}} = c \cdot \frac{\lambda_{1,\max} - \lambda_0}{\lambda_0} \cdot \frac{T\left(1 + k^{1/4}\right)}{2\pi \cdot a \cdot k^{1/4}};$$

$$\left|a_{(\mathrm{AU})}\right| = \frac{\left|\beta_{('')}\right|}{\left|p_{('')}\right|};$$

$$\lambda_{2,\max} = \lambda_0 \left(1 + \frac{\mathrm{v}_{\mathrm{rad},2,\max}}{c}\right); \quad \mathrm{v}_{\mathrm{rad},2,\max} = c \cdot \frac{\lambda_{2,\max} - \lambda_0}{\lambda_0};$$

$$\mathrm{v}_{\mathrm{rad},2,\max} = \frac{2\pi \cdot a}{T\left(1 + k^{1/4}\right)} \cdot \sin i,$$

$$\sin i = \frac{\mathrm{v}_{\mathrm{rad},2,\max} T\left(1 + k^{1/4}\right)}{2\pi \cdot a} = c \cdot \frac{\lambda_{2,\max} - \lambda_0}{\lambda_0} \cdot \frac{T\left(1 + k^{1/4}\right)}{2\pi \cdot a};$$

$$\left|a_{(\mathrm{AU})}\right| = \frac{\left|\beta_{('')}\right|}{\left|p_{('')}\right|};$$

$$c \cdot \frac{\lambda_{1,\max} - \lambda_0}{\lambda_0} \cdot \frac{T\left(1 + k^{1/4}\right)}{2\pi \cdot a \cdot k^{1/4}} = c \cdot \frac{\lambda_{2,\max} - \lambda_0}{\lambda_0} \cdot \frac{T\left(1 + k^{1/4}\right)}{2\pi \cdot a};$$

$$\frac{\lambda_{1,\max} - \lambda_0}{\lambda_{2,\max} - \lambda_0} = k^{1/4};$$

$$\lambda_0 = \frac{\lambda_{1,\max} - k^{1/4} \cdot \lambda_{2,\max}}{1 - \sqrt[4]{k}}.$$

**d)**

$$\sin i = c \cdot \frac{\lambda_{1,\max} - \lambda_0}{\lambda_0} \cdot \frac{T\left(1 + k^{1/4}\right)}{2\pi \cdot a \cdot k^{1/4}}$$

$$= c \cdot \left(\frac{\lambda_{1,\max}}{\lambda_0} - 1\right) \cdot \frac{T\left(1 + k^{1/4}\right)}{2\pi \cdot a \cdot k^{1/4}};$$

$$\sin i = c \cdot \frac{\lambda_{2,\max} - \lambda_0}{\lambda_0} \cdot \frac{T\left(1 + k^{1/4}\right)}{2\pi \cdot a}$$

$$= c \cdot \left(\frac{\lambda_{2,\max}}{\lambda_0} - 1\right) \cdot \frac{T\left(1 + k^{1/4}\right)}{2\pi \cdot a}.$$

# Problem 2

# Convergent Proper Motion

The components of a cluster may experience convergent movements towards a well-defined point on the celestial sphere, called the *point of convergence,* denoted C. To this point converge all the common parallel movement directions of the cluster's stars. For one of the stars in the cluster, $\sigma$, with equatorial coordinates $\alpha$ and $\delta$, as seen in Figure 2.1, we also indicate the point of intersection C, the star's speed vector $\vec{v}//OC$ ($\vec{v}$ parallel to OC), and its three perpendicular components, two of which are in the plane of the sky and one in the radial direction.

The angle $\eta$ between the arc of the great circle $\sigma$C and the celestial meridian of star $\sigma$ is marked in Figure 2.1.

For each of eight stars from the same cluster, the values of the following are given in Table 2.1:

- $(\alpha; \delta)$, the equatorial coordinates of the star;
- the product $\mu_\alpha \cos\delta$, where $\mu_\alpha$ is the ascension of the proper motion of the star, and $\delta$ is its declination;
- $\mu_\delta$, each star's declination of proper motion.

All the data are extracted from the Hipparcos catalog.

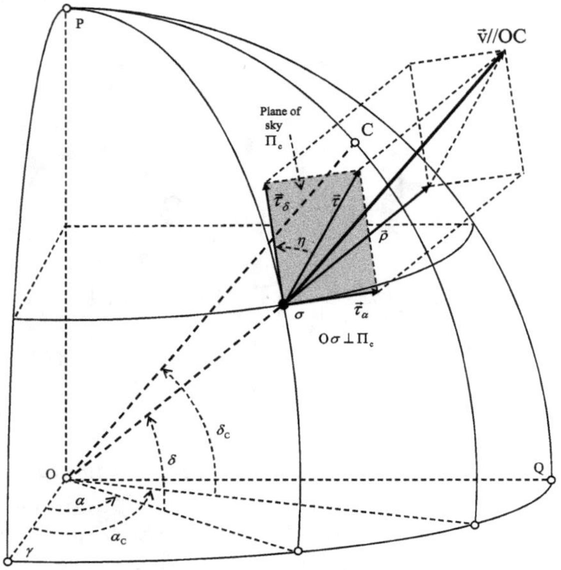


**Fig. 2.1**

**Table 2.1**

| Star | $\alpha$ (hms) | $\delta\,(^{0}\,'\,'')$ | $\mu_\alpha \cos\delta \left(10^{-3}\,\frac{\text{arcsec}}{\text{year}}\right)$ | $\mu_\delta \left(10^{-3}\,\frac{\text{arcsec}}{\text{year}}\right)$ |
|---|---|---|---|---|
| 18170 | 03 53 09.96 | +17 19 37.8 | 143.97 | −29.93 |
| 19554 | 04 11 20.20 | +05 31 22.9 | 146.86 | +5.00 |
| 20261 | 04 20 36.24 | +15 05 43.8 | 108.79 | −20.67 |
| 20901 | 04 28 50.10 | +13 02 51.5 | 105.17 | −15.08 |
| 21589 | 04 38 09.40 | +12 30 39.1 | 101.73 | −14.90 |
| 22157 | 04 46 01.70 | +11 42 20.2 | 67.48 | −7.09 |
| 23479 | 05 03 05.70 | +21 35 24.2 | 68.94 | −40.85 |
| 24019 | 05 09 45.06 | +28 01 50.2 | 55.86 | −60.57 |

**a)** *Calculate* the equatorial position coordinates of the convergence point C for the stars in the cluster ($\alpha_C; \delta_C$), given that the following is known:

$$\vec{v} = \vec{\tau} + \vec{\rho} = \vec{\tau}_\alpha + \vec{\tau}_\delta + \vec{\rho};$$

$$v = \sqrt{\tau_\alpha^2 + \tau_\delta^2 + \rho^2};$$

$$\mathrm{tg}\eta = \frac{\tau_\alpha}{\tau_\delta}; \quad \tau_\alpha = 71.10\frac{\mu_\alpha}{p}\cos\delta; \quad \tau_\delta = 4.74\frac{\mu_\delta}{p};$$

$$\mathrm{tg}\eta = \frac{71.10}{4.74}\cdot\frac{\mu_\alpha\cos\delta}{\mu_\delta};$$

$$\mathrm{tg}\eta = 15\cdot\frac{\mu_\alpha\cos\delta}{\mu_\delta}; \quad \mathrm{ctg}\eta = \frac{1}{15}\cdot\frac{\mu_\delta}{\mu_\alpha\cos\delta}.$$

**b)** *Determine* the angle between each star's line of sight and the line of sight toward the convergence point, $\chi$.

**c)** *Determine* the distance between the observer on Earth and each of the eight stars.

**Solution**

**a)** One of the stars of the considered group, $\sigma$, located by equatorial position coordinates $\alpha$ and $\delta$, is shown in Figure 2.1, where the convergence point C is also indicated, located by its equatorial position coordinates $\alpha_C$ and $\delta_C$. The figure also indicates the speed of the star $\vec{v}$, along with its three perpendicular components. For this star, it is demonstrated that:

$$\vec{v} = \vec{\tau} + \vec{\rho} = \vec{\tau}_\alpha + \vec{\tau}_\delta + \vec{\rho};$$

$$v = \sqrt{\tau_\alpha^2 + \tau_\delta^2 + \rho^2};$$

$$\mathrm{tg}\eta = \frac{\tau_\alpha}{\tau_\delta}; \quad \tau_\alpha = 71.10\frac{\mu_\alpha}{p}\cos\delta; \quad \tau_\delta = 4.74\frac{\mu_\delta}{p};$$

$$\mathrm{tg}\eta = \frac{71.10}{4.74}\cdot\frac{\mu_\alpha\cos\delta}{\mu_\delta};$$

$$\mathrm{tg}\eta = 15\cdot\frac{\mu_\alpha\cos\delta}{\mu_\delta}; \quad \mathrm{ctg}\eta = \frac{1}{15}\cdot\frac{\mu_\delta}{\mu_\alpha\cos\delta}.$$

In the spherical triangle PC$\sigma$, represented in Figures 2.2 and 2.3, considered as a standard spherical triangle ABC, the following

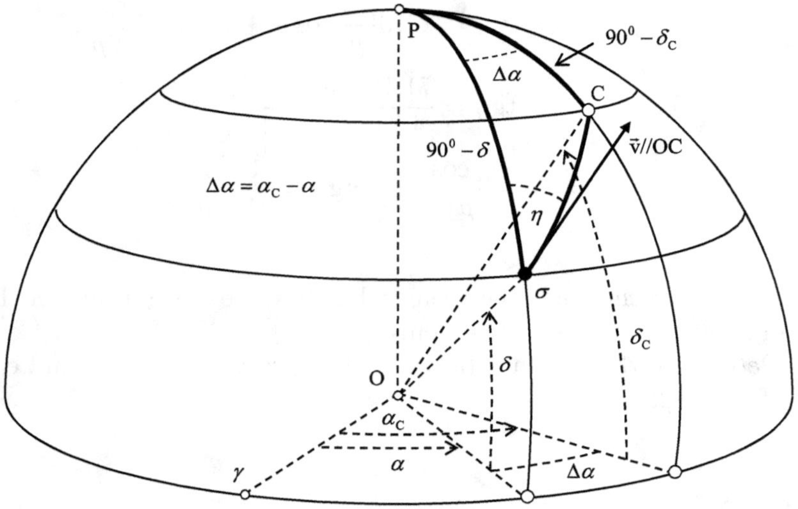


**Fig. 2.2**

relations occur:

$$\sin b \cdot \text{ctg}c = \cos b \cdot \cos A + \sin A \cdot \text{ctg}C;$$

$$\sin(90° - \delta) \cdot \text{ctg}(90° - \delta_C) = \cos(90° - \delta) \cdot \cos(\alpha_C - \alpha) + \sin(\alpha_C - \alpha) \cdot \text{ctg}\eta;$$

$$\cos\delta \cdot \text{tg}\delta_C = \sin\delta \cdot \cos(\alpha_C - \alpha) + \sin(\alpha_C - \alpha) \cdot \text{ctg}\eta;$$

$$\cos\delta \cdot \text{tg}\delta_C = \sin\delta \cdot (\cos\alpha_C \cdot \cos\alpha + \sin\alpha_C \cdot \sin\alpha) + (\sin\alpha_C \cdot \cos\alpha - \cos\alpha_C \cdot \sin\alpha) \cdot \text{ctg}\eta;$$

$$\cos\delta \cdot \text{tg}\delta_C = (\sin\delta \cdot \cos\alpha - \text{ctg}\eta \cdot \sin\alpha) \cdot \cos\alpha_C + (\sin\delta \cdot \sin\alpha + \text{ctg}\eta \cdot \cos\alpha) \cdot \sin\alpha_C.$$

Notation:

$$x = \sin\delta \cdot \cos\alpha - \text{ctg}\eta \cdot \sin\alpha;$$

$$y = \sin\delta \cdot \sin\alpha + \text{ctg}\eta \cdot \cos\alpha.$$

Thus:

$$\cos\delta \cdot \mathrm{tg}\delta_{\mathrm{C}} = x \cdot \cos\alpha_{\mathrm{C}} + y \cdot \sin\alpha_{\mathrm{C}};$$

$$\cos\delta = x \cdot \frac{\cos\alpha_{\mathrm{C}}}{\mathrm{tg}\delta_{\mathrm{C}}} + y \cdot \frac{\sin\alpha_{\mathrm{C}}}{\mathrm{tg}\delta_{\mathrm{C}}};$$

$$a = \frac{\cos\alpha_{\mathrm{C}}}{\mathrm{tg}\delta_{\mathrm{C}}} \qquad b = \frac{\sin\alpha_{\mathrm{C}}}{\mathrm{tg}\delta_{\mathrm{C}}};$$

$$\mathrm{tg}\alpha_{\mathrm{C}} = \frac{b}{a}; \quad \mathrm{tg}\delta_{\mathrm{C}} = \frac{1}{\sqrt{a^2 + b^2}};$$

$$\cos\alpha_{\mathrm{C}} = a \cdot \mathrm{tg}\delta_{\mathrm{C}} \qquad \sin\alpha_{\mathrm{C}} = b \cdot \mathrm{tg}\delta_{\mathrm{C}};$$

$$\cos\delta \cdot \mathrm{tg}\delta_{\mathrm{C}} = x \cdot a \cdot \mathrm{tg}\delta_{\mathrm{C}} + y \cdot b \cdot \mathrm{tg}\delta_{\mathrm{C}};$$

$$\cos\delta = x \cdot a + y \cdot b;$$

$$x \cdot a + y \cdot b = \cos\delta.$$

Hence, for the considered eight stars, the following relationships can be written:

$$\begin{cases} x_1 \cdot a + y_1 \cdot b = \cos\delta_1 = f_1\,(a; b)\,; \\ x_2 \cdot a + y_2 \cdot b = \cos\delta_2 = f_2\,(a; b)\,; \\ \dots\dots\dots\dots\dots\dots\dots\dots\dots\dots \\ x_8 \cdot a + y_8 \cdot b = \cos\delta_8 = f_8(a; b). \end{cases}$$

The solutions of the system of eight equations will be used as eight experimental measurements for the coordinates $(\alpha_{\mathrm{C}};\ \delta_{\mathrm{C}})$ – the equatorial coordinates of the convergence point C.

We suggest that the smallest square method be applied to find out the most probable values of the unknown values.

We use the derived system of equations, i.e., the system of errors equations:

$$\begin{cases} f_1(a; b) - \cos\delta_1 = \varepsilon_1; \\ f_2(a; b) - \cos\delta_2 = \varepsilon_2; \\ \dots\dots\dots\dots\dots\dots\dots\dots \\ f_8(a; b) - \cos\delta_8 = \varepsilon_8, \end{cases}$$

or:

$$\begin{cases} x_1 \cdot a + y_1 \cdot b - \cos\delta_1 = \varepsilon_1; \\ x_2 \cdot a + y_2 \cdot b - \cos\delta_2 = \varepsilon_2; \\ \dots\dots\dots\dots\dots\dots\dots\dots\dots\dots \\ x_8 \cdot a + y_8 \cdot b - \cos\delta_8 = \varepsilon_8. \end{cases}$$

We also apply the condition:

$$S = \varepsilon_1^2 + \varepsilon_2^2 + \cdots\cdots + \varepsilon_8^2;$$

$$\frac{\partial S}{\partial a} = 0; \quad \frac{\partial S}{\partial b} = 0.$$

Thus:

$$\begin{cases} \dfrac{\partial S}{\partial a} = 2\varepsilon_1\dfrac{\partial \varepsilon_1}{\partial a} + 2\varepsilon_2\dfrac{\partial \varepsilon_2}{\partial a} + \cdots\cdots + 2\varepsilon_8\dfrac{\partial \varepsilon_8}{\partial a} = 0; \\ \dfrac{\partial S}{\partial b} = 2\varepsilon_1\dfrac{\partial \varepsilon_1}{\partial b} + 2\varepsilon_2\dfrac{\partial \varepsilon_2}{\partial b} + \cdots\cdots + 2\varepsilon_8\dfrac{\partial \varepsilon_8}{\partial b} = 0; \end{cases}$$

$$\begin{cases} \varepsilon_1\dfrac{\partial \varepsilon_1}{\partial a} + \varepsilon_2\dfrac{\partial \varepsilon_2}{\partial a} + \cdots\cdots + \varepsilon_8\dfrac{\partial \varepsilon_8}{\partial a} = 0; \\ \varepsilon_1\dfrac{\partial \varepsilon_1}{\partial b} + \varepsilon_2\dfrac{\partial \varepsilon_2}{\partial b} + \cdots\cdots + \varepsilon_8\dfrac{\partial \varepsilon_8}{\partial b} = 0; \end{cases}$$

$$\begin{cases} x_1 \cdot a + y_1 \cdot b - \cos\delta_1 = \varepsilon_1; \\ x_2 \cdot a + y_2 \cdot b - \cos\delta_2 = \varepsilon_2; \\ \dots\dots\dots\dots\dots\dots\dots\dots\dots\dots \\ x_8 \cdot a + y_8 \cdot b - \cos\delta_8 = \varepsilon_8; \end{cases}$$

$$\frac{\partial \varepsilon_1}{\partial a} = x_1; \quad \frac{\partial \varepsilon_2}{\partial a} = x_2; \quad \dots\dots\frac{\partial \varepsilon_8}{\partial a} = x_8;$$

$$\frac{\partial \varepsilon_1}{\partial b} = y_1; \quad \frac{\partial \varepsilon_2}{\partial b} = y_2; \quad \dots\dots\frac{\partial \varepsilon_8}{\partial b} = y_8;$$

$$\begin{cases}(x_1a + y_1b - \cos\delta_1)\,x_1 + (x_2a + y_2b - \cos\delta_2)\,x_2\\ \quad + \cdots + (x_8a + y_8b - \cos\delta_8)\,x_8 = 0;\\ (x_1a + y_1b - \cos\delta_1)\,y_1 + (x_2a + y_2b - \cos\delta_2)\,y_2\\ \quad + \cdots + (x_8a + y_8b - \cos\delta_8)\,y_8 = 0;\end{cases}$$

$$\begin{cases}a\sum_{i=1}^{8} x_i^2 + b\sum_{i=1}^{8} x_iy_i = \sum_{i=1}^{8} x_i\cos\delta_i;\\ a\sum_{i=1}^{8} x_iy_i + b\sum_{i=1}^{8} y_i^2 = \sum_{i=1}^{8} y_i\cos\delta_i;\end{cases}$$

$$\begin{cases}a\sum_{i=1}^{8} x_i^2 + b\sum_{i=1}^{8} x_iy_i = \sum_{i=1}^{8} x_i\cos\delta_i; \cdot \sum_{i=1}^{8} y_i^2;\\ a\sum_{i=1}^{8} x_iy_i + b\sum_{i=1}^{8} y_i^2 = \sum_{i=1}^{8} y_i\cos\delta_i; \cdot \left(-\sum_{i=1}^{8} x_iy_i\right)\end{cases};$$

$$\begin{cases}a\cdot\left(\sum_{i=1}^{8} x_i^2\right)\cdot\left(\sum_{i=1}^{8} y_i^2\right) + b\cdot\left(\sum_{i=1}^{8} x_iy_i\right)\cdot\left(\sum_{i=1}^{8} y_i^2\right)\\ \quad = \left(\sum_{i=1}^{8} x_i\cos\delta_i\right)\cdot\left(\sum_{i=1}^{8} y_i^2\right);\\ -a\cdot\left(\sum_{i=1}^{8} x_iy_i\right)^2 - b\cdot\left(\sum_{i=1}^{8} x_iy_i\right)\cdot\left(\sum_{i=1}^{8} y_i^2\right)\\ \quad = -\left(\sum_{i=1}^{8} y_i\cos\delta_i\right)\cdot\left(\sum_{i=1}^{8} x_iy_i\right);\end{cases}$$

$$a = \frac{\left(\sum_{i=1}^{8} x_i\cos\delta_i\right)\cdot\left(\sum_{i=1}^{8} y_i^2\right) - \left(\sum_{i=1}^{8} y_i\cos\delta_i\right)\cdot\left(\sum_{i=1}^{8} x_iy_i\right)}{\left(\sum_{i=1}^{8} x_i^2\right)\cdot\left(\sum_{i=1}^{8} y_i^2\right) - \left(\sum_{i=1}^{8} x_iy_i\right)^2};$$

$$\begin{cases} a\sum_{i=1}^{8} x_i^2 + b\sum_{i=1}^{8} x_i y_i = \sum_{i=1}^{8} x_i \cos\delta_i; \cdot \left(-\sum_{i=1}^{8} x_i y_i\right); \\ a\sum_{i=1}^{8} x_i y_i + b\sum_{i=1}^{8} y_i^2 = \sum_{i=1}^{8} y_i \cos\delta_i; \cdot \sum_{i=1}^{8} x_i^2; \end{cases}$$

$$-a\cdot\left(\sum_{i=1}^{8} x_i^2\right)\cdot\left(\sum_{i=1}^{8} x_i y_i\right) - b\cdot\left(\sum_{i=1}^{8} x_i y_i\right)^2$$

$$= -\left(\sum_{i=1}^{8} x_i \cos\delta_i\right)\cdot\left(\sum_{i=1}^{8} x_i y_i\right);$$

$$a\cdot\left(\sum_{i=1}^{8} x_i^2\right)\cdot\left(\sum_{i=1}^{8} x_i y_i\right) + b\cdot\left(\sum_{i=1}^{8} x_i^2\right)\cdot\left(\sum_{i=1}^{8} y_i^2\right)$$

$$= \left(\sum_{i=1}^{8} y_i \cos\delta_i\right)\cdot\left(\sum_{i=1}^{8} x_i^2\right);$$

$$b = \frac{\left(\sum_{i=1}^{8} y_i \cos\delta_i\right)\cdot\left(\sum_{i=1}^{8} x_i^2\right) - \left(\sum_{i=1}^{8} x_i \cos\delta_i\right)\cdot\left(\sum_{i=1}^{8} x_i y_i\right)}{\left(\sum_{i=1}^{8} x_i^2\right)\cdot\left(\sum_{i=1}^{8} y_i^2\right) - \left(\sum_{i=1}^{8} x_i y_i\right)^2}.$$

Using the information from Table 2.1, presented in the problem statement, we fill in Tables 2.2–2.11.

**Table 2.2**

| Star | $\alpha$ (hms) | $\delta(^{\circ\,\prime\,\prime\prime})$ |
|---|---|---|
| 18170 | 03 53 09.96 | +17 19 37.8 |
| 19554 | 04 11 20.20 | +05 31 22.9 |
| 20261 | 04 20 36.24 | +15 05 43.8 |
| 20901 | 04 28 50.10 | +13 02 51.5 |
| 21589 | 04 38 09.40 | +12 30 39.1 |
| 22157 | 04 46 01.70 | +11 42 20.2 |
| 23479 | 05 03 05.70 | +21 35 24.2 |
| 24019 | 05 09 45.06 | +28 01 50.2 |

**Table 2.3**

| Star | $\alpha$(hms) | $\alpha(^0)$ | $\alpha$(rad) |
|---|---|---|---|
| 18170 | 03 53 09.96 | 58.289 | 1.016 |
| 19554 | 04 11 20.20 | 62.830 | 1.096 |
| 20261 | 04 20 36.24 | 65.144 | 1.136 |
| 20901 | 04 28 50.10 | 67.200 | 1.172 |
| 21589 | 04 38 09.40 | 69.537 | 1.213 |
| 22157 | 04 46 01.70 | 71.506 | 1.247 |
| 23479 | 05 03 05.70 | 75.772 | 1.321 |
| 24019 | 05 09 45.06 | 77.430 | 1.350 |

**Table 2.4**

| Star | $\cos\alpha$ | $\sin\alpha$ |
|---|---|---|
| 18170 | 0.526 | 0.850 |
| 19554 | 0.457 | 0.889 |
| 20261 | 0.421 | 0.906 |
| 20901 | 0.388 | 0.921 |
| 21589 | 0.350 | 0.936 |
| 22157 | 0.318 | 0.948 |
| 23479 | 0.247 | 0.968 |
| 24019 | 0.219 | 0.975 |

**Table 2.5**

| Star | $\delta(^{0\prime\prime\prime})$ | $\delta(^0)$ | $\delta$(rad) |
|---|---|---|---|
| 18170 | +17 19 37.8 | +17.327 | +0.302 |
| 19554 | +05 31 22.9 | +5.523 | +0.096 |
| 20261 | +15 05 43.8 | +15.095 | +0.263 |
| 20901 | +13 02 51.5 | +13.047 | +0.227 |
| 21589 | +12 30 39.1 | +12.510 | +0.218 |
| 22157 | +11 42 20.2 | +11.705 | +0.204 |
| 23479 | +21 35 24.2 | +21.590 | +0.376 |
| 24019 | +28 01 50.2 | +28.030 | +0.488 |

**Table 2.6**

| Star | $\cos\delta$ | $\sin\delta$ |
|---|---|---|
| 18170 | 0.954 | 0.297 |
| 19554 | 0.995 | 0.095 |
| 20261 | 0.965 | 0.062 |
| 20901 | 0.974 | 0.225 |
| 21589 | 0.976 | 0.216 |
| 22157 | 0.979 | 0.202 |
| 23479 | 0.930 | 0.367 |
| 24019 | 0.883 | 0.468 |

To compute the last column in Table 2.7 we use the relation:

$$\text{ctg}\eta = \frac{1}{15} \cdot \frac{\mu_\delta}{\mu_\alpha \cos\delta}.$$

**Table 2.7**

| Star | $\mu_\alpha \cos\delta \left(10^{-3} \frac{\text{arcsec}}{\text{year}}\right)$ | $\mu_\delta \left(10^{-3} \frac{\text{arcsec}}{\text{year}}\right)$ | $\text{ctg}\eta$ |
|---|---|---|---|
| 18170 | 143.97 | −29.93 | -0.01385 |
| 19554 | 146.86 | +5.00 | +0.00226 |
| 20261 | 108.79 | −20.67 | -0.01266 |
| 20901 | 105.17 | −15.08 | -0.00955 |
| 21589 | 101.73 | −14.90 | -0.00976 |
| 22157 | 67.48 | −7.09 | -0.00700 |
| 23479 | 68.94 | −40.85 | -0.03950 |
| 24019 | 55.86 | −60.57 | -0.07228 |

**Table 2.8**

| Star | $\sin\delta \cdot \cos\alpha$ | $\text{ctg}\eta \cdot \sin\alpha$ | $x$ |
|---|---|---|---|
| 18170 | 0.01562 | − 0.01177 | 0.02739 |
| 19554 | 0.04341 | 0.00200 | 0.04141 |
| 20261 | 0.02610 | − 0.01146 | 0.03756 |
| 20901 | 0.08730 | − 0.00879 | 0.09609 |
| 21589 | 0.07560 | − 0.00913 | 0.08473 |
| 22157 | 0.06423 | − 0.00663 | 0.07708 |
| 23479 | 0.09064 | − 0.03823 | 0.12887 |
| 24019 | 0.10249 | − 0.07047 | 0.17296 |

**Table 2.9**

| Star | $\sin\delta\cdot\sin\alpha$ | $\mathrm{ctg}\eta\cdot\cos\alpha$ | $y$ |
|---|---|---|---|
| 18170 | 0.25245 | − 0.00728 | 0.24517 |
| 19554 | 0.08445 | +0.00103 | 0.08548 |
| 20261 | 0.05617 | −0.00532 | 0.05085 |
| 20901 | 0.20722 | −0.00370 | 0.20352 |
| 21589 | 0.20217 | −0.00341 | 0.19876 |
| 22157 | 0.19149 | −0.00222 | 0.18927 |
| 23479 | 0.35525 | −0.00975 | 0.34550 |
| 24019 | 0.45630 | −0.01582 | 0.44048 |

**Table 2.10**

| Star | $x_i$ | $x_i^2$ | $x_i\cos\delta_i$ |
|---|---|---|---|
| 18170 | 0.02739 | 0.00075 | 0.02613 |
| 19554 | 0.04141 | 0.00171 | 0.41202 |
| 20261 | 0.03756 | 0.00141 | 0.03624 |
| 20901 | 0.09609 | 0.00923 | 0.09359 |
| 21589 | 0.08473 | 0.00717 | 0.08269 |
| 22157 | 0.07708 | 0.00594 | 0.07546 |
| 23479 | 0.12887 | 0.01660 | 0.11984 |
| 24019 | 0.17296 | 0.02991 | 0.15272 |

**Table 2.11**

| Star | $y_i$ | $y_i^2$ | $y_i\cos\delta_i$ | $x_iy_i$ |
|---|---|---|---|---|
| 18170 | 0.24517 | 0.06010 | 0.23389 | 0.00671 |
| 19554 | 0.08548 | 0.00730 | 0.08505 | 0.00353 |
| 20261 | 0.05085 | 0.00258 | 0.04907 | 0.00190 |
| 20901 | 0.20352 | 0.04142 | 0.19822 | 0.01955 |
| 21589 | 0.19876 | 0.03950 | 0.19398 | 0.01684 |
| 22157 | 0.18927 | 0.03582 | 0.18529 | 0.01458 |
| 23479 | 0.34550 | 0.11937 | 0.32131 | 0.04452 |
| 24019 | 0.44048 | 0.19402 | 0.38894 | 0.07618 |

Finally, results that:

$$\sum_{i=1}^{8} x_i^2 = 0.07272; \quad \sum_{i=1}^{8} x_i \cos\delta_i = 0.99869;$$

$$\sum_{i=1}^{8} y_i^2 = 0.50011; \quad \sum_{i=1}^{8} y_i \cos\delta_i = 1.65575; \quad \sum_{i=1}^{8} x_i y_i = 0.18381;$$

$$\left(\sum_{i=1}^{8} x_i y_i\right)^2 = 0.03378;$$

$$a = \frac{\left(\sum_{i=1}^{8} x_i \cos\delta_i\right) \cdot \left(\sum_{i=1}^{8} y_i^2\right) - \left(\sum_{i=1}^{8} y_i \cos\delta_i\right) \cdot \left(\sum_{i=1}^{8} x_i y_i\right)}{\left(\sum_{i=1}^{8} x_i^2\right) \cdot \left(\sum_{i=1}^{8} y_i^2\right) - \left(\sum_{i=1}^{8} x_i y_i\right)^2};$$

$$a = \frac{0.99869 \cdot 0.50011 - 1.65575 \cdot 0.18381}{0.7272 \cdot 0.50011 - 0.03378} = \frac{0.19511}{0.00258} = 75.62403;$$

$$b = \frac{\left(\sum_{i=1}^{8} y_i \cos\delta_i\right) \cdot \left(\sum_{i=1}^{8} x_i^2\right) - \left(\sum_{i=1}^{8} x_i \cos\delta_i\right) \cdot \left(\sum_{i=1}^{8} x_i y_i\right)}{\left(\sum_{i=1}^{8} x_i^2\right) \cdot \left(\sum_{i=1}^{8} y_i^2\right) - \left(\sum_{i=1}^{8} x_i y_i\right)^2};$$

$$b = \frac{1.65575 \cdot 0.07272 - 0.99869 \cdot 0.18381}{0.7272 \cdot 0.50011 - 0.03378} = \frac{-0.06316}{0.00258}$$

$$= -24.48062;$$

$$\mathrm{tg}\alpha_{\mathrm{C}} = \frac{b}{a}; \quad \mathrm{tg}\delta_{\mathrm{C}} = \frac{1}{\sqrt{a^2 + b^2}};$$

$$\mathrm{tg}\alpha_{\mathrm{C}} = \frac{-24.48062}{75.62403}; \quad \mathrm{tg}\alpha_{\mathrm{C}} = -0.32371;$$

$$\mathrm{tg}\delta_{\mathrm{C}} = \frac{1}{\sqrt{(75.62403)^2 + (-24.48062)^2}} = \frac{1}{\sqrt{6318.29466}} = \frac{1}{79.48770};$$

$$\mathrm{tg}\delta_{\mathrm{C}} = 0.01258; \quad \mathrm{tg}\delta_{\mathrm{C}} \approx \delta_{\mathrm{C}} = 0.01258;$$

$$\mathrm{tg}\alpha_{\mathrm{C}} = -0.32371; \quad \mathrm{tg}\delta_{\mathrm{C}} = 0.01258;$$

$$\alpha_{\mathrm{C}} = 2.826\,\mathrm{rad} = 162°;$$

$$\delta_{\mathrm{C}} \approx 0.01258\,\mathrm{rad} = 0.72° = 43'\,12''.$$

**b)** From the same spherical triangle, PC$\sigma$, represented in the drawing in Figure 2.3, where $\chi = \angle\sigma$OC is the angle between the line of sight of the star and the line of sight toward the convergence point, we obtain:

$$\cos\chi = \cos(90^\circ - \delta)\cdot\cos(90^\circ - \delta_C)$$
$$+\sin(90^\circ - \delta)\cdot\sin(90^\circ - \delta_C)\cdot\cos(\alpha_C - \alpha);$$
$$\cos\chi = \sin\delta\cdot\sin\delta_C + \cos\delta\cdot\cos\delta_C\cdot\cos(\alpha_C - \alpha);$$

where $(\alpha_C;\ \delta_C)$ is determined by the smallest square method, and $(\alpha;\ \delta)$ are known;

$$\mathrm{tg}\delta_C = 0.01258;$$
$$\sin\delta_C = \frac{\mathrm{tg}\delta_C}{\sqrt{1+\mathrm{tg}^2\delta_C}} = 0.01257;$$
$$\cos\delta_C = \sqrt{1-\sin^2\delta_C} = 0.99992;$$
$$\mathrm{tg}\alpha_C = -0.32371;$$
$$\sin\alpha_C = \frac{\mathrm{tg}\alpha_C}{\sqrt{1+\mathrm{tg}^2\alpha_C}} = 0.30797;$$
$$\cos\alpha_C = -\sqrt{1-\sin^2\alpha_C} = -0.95139;$$
$$\cos(\alpha_C - \alpha) = \cos\alpha_C\cos\alpha + \sin\alpha_C\sin\alpha;$$
$$\cos\chi = \sin\delta\cdot\sin\delta_C + \cos\delta\cdot\cos\delta_C\cdot\cos(\alpha_C - \alpha);$$

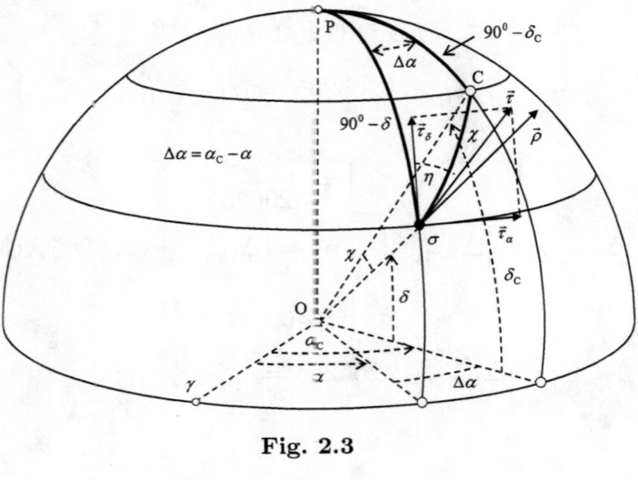


**Fig. 2.3**

**c)** The annual parallax of a star $\sigma$, located outside our solar system, is the angle $p_{\text{an}}$, under which the average radius of the Earth's orbit around the Sun, viewed from the center of the star, would be seen at that time of year when the Earth–star (E$\sigma$) direction is perpendicular to the Sun–Earth direction (SE), as indicated by the drawing in Figure 2.4. This results in:

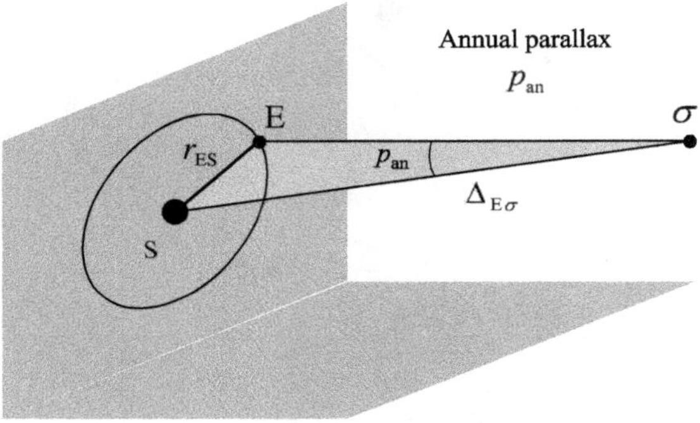


**Fig. 2.4**

$$\sin p_{\text{an}} = \frac{r_{\text{ES}}}{\Delta_{\text{E}\sigma}} \approx p_{\text{an}}; \quad \frac{r_{\text{ES}}}{\Delta_{\text{E}\sigma}} \approx p_{\text{an}};$$

$$\frac{r_{\text{ES(AU)}}}{\Delta_{\text{E}\sigma\text{(AU)}}} \approx p_{\text{an(rad)}}; \quad \frac{r_{\text{ES(pc)}}}{\Delta_{\text{E}\sigma\text{(pc)}}} \approx p_{\text{an(rad)}};$$

$$r_{\text{ES(pc)}} = \left|r_{\text{ES(pc)}}\right| \cdot 1\,\text{pc} = \left|r_{\text{ES(pc)}}\right| \cdot 206265\,\text{AU}$$

$$= \left|r_{\text{ES(AU)}}\right| \cdot 1\,\text{AU};$$

$$\left|r_{\text{ES(pc)}}\right| \cdot 206265 = \left|r_{\text{ES(AU)}}\right|;$$

$$\left|r_{\text{ES(pc)}}\right| = \frac{\left|r_{\text{ES(AU)}}\right|}{206265};$$

$$\Delta_{\text{E}\sigma\text{(pc)}} = \left|\Delta_{\text{E}\sigma\text{(pc)}}\right| \cdot 1\,\text{pc} = \left|\Delta_{\text{E}\sigma\text{(pc)}}\right| \cdot 206265\,\text{AU}$$

$$= \left|\Delta_{\text{E}\sigma\text{(AU)}}\right| \cdot 1\,\text{AU};$$

$$\left|\Delta_{\text{E}\sigma\text{(pc)}}\right| \cdot 206265 = \left|\Delta_{\text{E}\sigma\text{(AU)}}\right|;$$

$$\left|\Delta_{\mathrm{E}\sigma(\mathrm{pc})}\right| = \frac{\left|\Delta_{\mathrm{E}\sigma(\mathrm{AU})}\right|}{206265};$$

$$\frac{r_{\mathrm{ES(pc)}}}{\Delta_{\mathrm{E}\sigma(\mathrm{pc})}} = \frac{\left|r_{\mathrm{ES(pc)}}\right| \mathrm{pc}}{\left|\Delta_{\mathrm{E}\sigma(\mathrm{pc})}\right| \mathrm{pc}} = \frac{\left|r_{\mathrm{ES(pc)}}\right|}{\left|\Delta_{\mathrm{E}\sigma(\mathrm{pc})}\right|};$$

$$\frac{r_{\mathrm{ES(pc)}}}{\Delta_{\mathrm{E}\sigma(\mathrm{pc})}} = \frac{\left|r_{\mathrm{ES(pc)}}\right|}{\left|\Delta_{\mathrm{E}\sigma(\mathrm{pc})}\right|};$$

$$\left|r_{\mathrm{ES(pc)}}\right| = \frac{\left|r_{\mathrm{ES(AU)}}\right|}{206265};$$

$$\frac{r_{\mathrm{ES(pc)}}}{\Delta_{\mathrm{E}\sigma(\mathrm{pc})}} = \frac{\frac{\left|r_{\mathrm{ES(AU)}}\right|}{206265}}{\left|\Delta_{\mathrm{E}\sigma(\mathrm{pc})}\right|};$$

$$\frac{r_{\mathrm{ES(pc)}}}{\Delta_{\mathrm{E}\sigma(\mathrm{pc})}} = \frac{\left|r_{\mathrm{ES(AU)}}\right|}{206265 \cdot \left|\Delta_{\mathrm{E}\sigma(\mathrm{pc})}\right|};$$

$$\left|r_{\mathrm{ES(AU)}}\right| = 1;$$

$$\frac{r_{\mathrm{ES(pc)}}}{\Delta_{\mathrm{E}\sigma(\mathrm{pc})}} = \frac{1}{206265 \cdot \left|\Delta_{\mathrm{E}\sigma(\mathrm{pc})}\right|};$$

$$\frac{r_{\mathrm{ES(pc)}}}{\Delta_{\mathrm{E}\sigma(\mathrm{pc})}} = p_{\mathrm{an(rad)}};$$

$$p_{\mathrm{an(rad)}} = \left|p_{\mathrm{an(rad)}}\right| \cdot 1\,\mathrm{rad};$$

$$p_{\mathrm{an(arcsec)}} = \left|p_{\mathrm{an(arcsec)}}\right| \cdot 1\,\mathrm{arcsec};$$

$$\begin{aligned} p_{\mathrm{an(rad)}} = \left|p_{\mathrm{an(rad)}}\right| \cdot 1\,\mathrm{rad} &= \left|p_{\mathrm{an(rad)}}\right| \cdot 206265\,\mathrm{arcsec} \\ &= \left|p_{\mathrm{an(arcsec)}}\right| \cdot 1\,\mathrm{arcsec}; \end{aligned}$$

$$\left|p_{\mathrm{an(rad)}}\right| \cdot 206265 = \left|p_{\mathrm{an(arcsec)}}\right|;$$

$$\left|p_{\mathrm{an(rad)}}\right| = \frac{\left|p_{\mathrm{an(arcsec)}}\right|}{206265};$$

$$\frac{r_{\mathrm{ES(pc)}}}{\Delta_{\mathrm{E}\sigma\mathrm{(pc)}}} = p_{\mathrm{an(rad)}};$$

$$\frac{r_{\mathrm{ES(pc)}}}{\Delta_{\mathrm{E}\sigma\mathrm{(pc)}}} = \left|p_{\mathrm{an(rad)}}\right| \cdot 1\,\mathrm{rad} = \left|p_{\mathrm{an(rad)}}\right|,$$

$$\frac{r_{\mathrm{ES(pc)}}}{\Delta_{\mathrm{E}\sigma\mathrm{(pc)}}} = \left|p_{\mathrm{an(rad)}}\right|;$$

$$\left|p_{\mathrm{an(rad)}}\right| = \frac{\left|p_{\mathrm{an(arcsec)}}\right|}{206265};$$

$$\frac{r_{\mathrm{ES(pc)}}}{\Delta_{\mathrm{E}\sigma\mathrm{(pc)}}} = \frac{\left|p_{\mathrm{an(arcsec)}}\right|}{206265};$$

$$\frac{r_{\mathrm{ES(pc)}}}{\Delta_{\mathrm{E}\sigma\mathrm{(pc)}}} = \frac{1}{206265 \cdot \left|\Delta_{\mathrm{E}\sigma\mathrm{(pc)}}\right|};$$

$$\frac{1}{206265 \cdot \left|\Delta_{\mathrm{E}\sigma\mathrm{(pc)}}\right|} = \frac{\left|p_{\mathrm{an(arcsec)}}\right|}{206265};$$

$$\left|\Delta_{\mathrm{E}\sigma\mathrm{(pc)}}\right| = \frac{1}{\left|p_{\mathrm{an(arcsec)}}\right|}.$$

| Star | $p\,(10^{-3}$ arcsec) | $\Delta$ (pc) | Order of distances |
|---|---|---|---|
| 18170 | 24.14 | 41.425 | 2 |
| 19554 | 25.89 | 38.624 | 1 |
| 20261 | 21.20 | 47.169 | 4 |
| 20901 | 20.33 | 49.188 | 5 |
| 21589 | 21.79 | 45.892 | 3 |
| 22157 | 12.24 | 81.699 | 8 |
| 23479 | 20.01 | 49.975 | 6 |
| 24019 | 18.28 | 54.704 | 7 |

# Problem 3

# Exoplanet and Host Star

In Figure 3.1 the star S and the exoplanet P have been represented in plane Π. The two celestial bodies move on circular orbits around their center of mass. The distance between their centers is $a$.

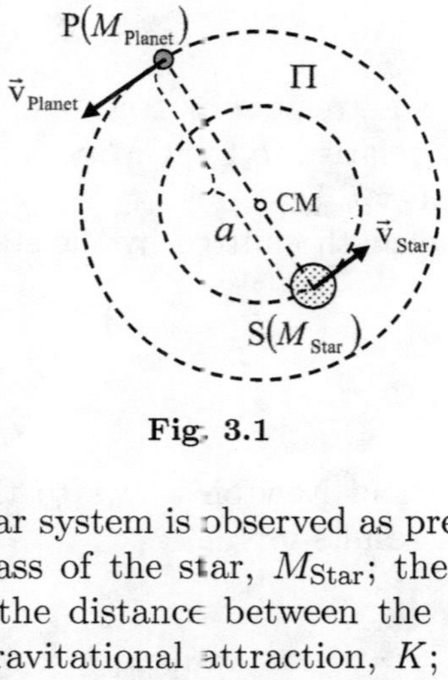


**Fig. 3.1**

The exoplanet–star system is observed as presented in Figure 3.2.

We know: the mass of the star, $M_{Star}$; the mass of the planet, $M_{Planet} << M_{Star}$; the distance between the star and the planet, $a$; the constant of gravitational attraction, $K$; the speed of light in vacuum, $c$; the minimum and maximum values of the wavelengths of the radiation emitted by the star and recorded by the observer on Earth, $\lambda_{min,Star}$ and $\lambda_{max,Star}$.

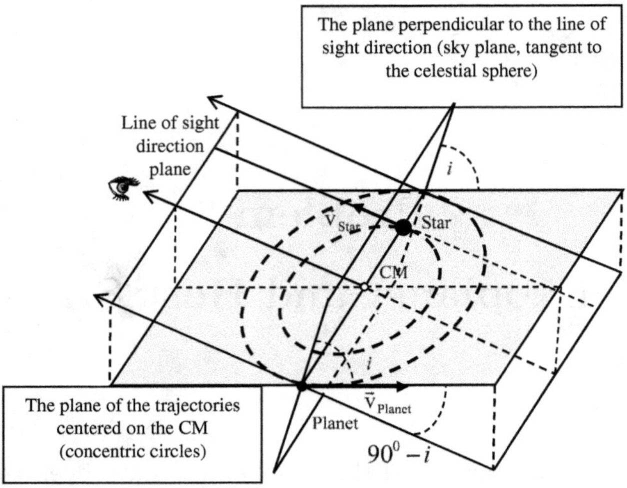


**Fig. 3.2**

*Determine*:

**a)** the speed of the star relative to the planet, $v_{\text{relative,Star}-\text{Planet}}$; the star's velocity relative to the CM, $v_{\text{Star}}$; the planet's velocity relative to the CM, $v_{\text{Planet}}$;
**b)** the radiation wavelength emitted by the star, $\lambda_0$.

## Solution

**a)** Applying Kepler's and Newton's laws to these celestial bodies, and using Figure 3.3, results in:

$$v_{\text{Star}} = \frac{2\pi a_{\text{Star}}}{T}; \quad v_{\text{Planet}} = \frac{2\pi a_{\text{Planet}}}{T}; \quad a_{\text{Star}} + a_{\text{Planet}} = a;$$

$$M_{\text{Star}} v_{\text{Star}} = M_{\text{Planet}} v_{\text{Planet}}; \quad M_{\text{Star}} a_{\text{Star}} = M_{\text{Planet}} a_{\text{Planet}};$$

$$a_{\text{Planet}} = \frac{a M_{\text{Star}}}{M_{\text{Planet}} + M_{\text{Star}}}; \quad a_{\text{Star}} = \frac{a M_{\text{Planet}}}{M_{\text{Planet}} + M_{\text{Star}}};$$

$$v_{\text{Star}} = \frac{2\pi a_{\text{Star}}}{T} = \frac{2\pi}{T} \frac{M_{\text{Planet}}}{M_{\text{Planet}} + M_{\text{Star}}} a;$$

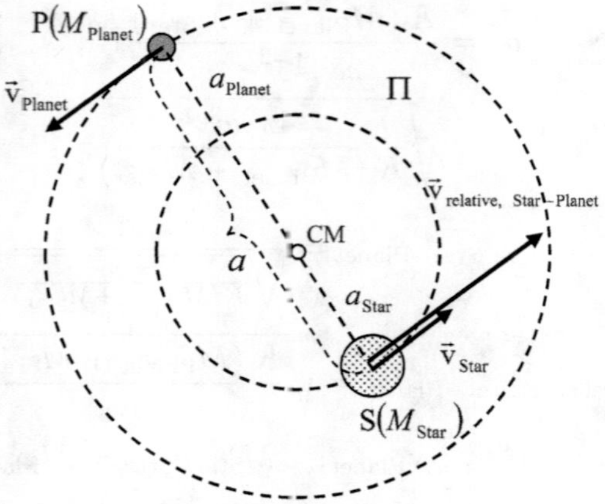


**Fig. 3.3**

$$a^3 = \frac{K\left(M_{\text{Planet}} + M_{\text{Star}}\right)}{4\pi^2} T^2;$$

$$a = \sqrt[3]{\frac{K\left(M_{\text{Planet}} + M_{\text{Star}}\right)T^2}{4\pi^2}};$$

$$\text{v}_{\text{Star}} = \frac{2\pi}{T}\frac{M_{\text{Planet}}}{M_{\text{Planet}} + M_{\text{Star}}}\sqrt[3]{\frac{K\left(M_{\text{Planet}} + M_{\text{Star}}\right)T^2}{4\pi^2}};$$

$$\text{v}_{\text{Star}} = M_{\text{Planet}} \cdot \sqrt[3]{\frac{(2\pi)^3 K\left(M_{\text{Planet}} + M_{\text{Star}}\right)T^2}{\left(M_{\text{Planet}} + M_{\text{Star}}\right)^3 T^3 (2\pi)^2}};$$

$$\text{v}_{\text{Star}} = M_{\text{Planet}} \cdot \sqrt[3]{\frac{2\pi K}{\left(M_{\text{Planet}} + M_{\text{Star}}\right)^2 T}};$$

$$\vec{\text{v}}_{\text{relative, Star}-\text{Planet}} = \vec{\text{v}}_{\text{Star}} - \vec{\text{v}}_{\text{Planet}};$$

$$\text{v}_{\text{relative, Star}-\text{Planet}} = \text{v}_{\text{Star}} + \text{v}_{\text{Planet}} = \frac{2\pi a_{\text{Star}}}{T} + \frac{2\pi a_{\text{Planet}}}{T}$$

$$= \frac{2\pi}{T}\left(a_{\text{Star}} + a_{\text{Planet}}\right);$$

$$\text{v}_{\text{relative, Star}-\text{Planet}} = \frac{2\pi}{T}a;$$

$$a^3 = \frac{K\left(M_{\text{Planet}} + M_{\text{Star}}\right)}{4\pi^2}T^2;$$

$$T = \sqrt{\frac{4\pi^2 a^3}{K\left(M_{\text{Planet}} + M_{\text{Star}}\right)}};$$

$$\text{v}_{\text{relative, Star-Planet}} = \frac{2\pi a}{\sqrt{\frac{4\pi^2 a^3}{K(M_{\text{Planet}}+M_{\text{Star}})}}};$$

$$\text{v}_{\text{relative, Star-Planet}} = \sqrt{\frac{K\left(M_{\text{Planet}} + M_{\text{Star}}\right)}{a}};$$

$$M_{\text{Star}}\text{v}_{\text{Star}} = M_{\text{Planet}}\text{v}_{\text{Planet}}; \quad M_{\text{Star}}a_{\text{Star}} = M_{\text{Planet}}a_{\text{Planet}};$$

$$\frac{\text{v}_{\text{Star}}}{a_{\text{Star}}} = \frac{\text{v}_{\text{Planet}}}{a_{\text{Planet}}};$$

$$\text{v}_{\text{Planet}} = \frac{a_{\text{Planet}}}{a_{\text{Star}}}\text{v}_{\text{Star}};$$

$$\text{v}_{\text{relative, Star-Planet}} = \text{v}_{\text{Star}} + \text{v}_{\text{Planet}} = \text{v}_{\text{Star}} + \frac{a_{\text{Planet}}}{a_{\text{Star}}}\text{v}_{\text{Star}};$$

$$\text{v}_{\text{relative, Star-Planet}} = \text{v}_{\text{Star}}\left(1 + \frac{a_{\text{Planet}}}{a_{\text{Star}}}\right)$$

$$= \frac{a_{\text{Star}} + a_{\text{Planet}}}{a_{\text{Star}}} \cdot \text{v}_{\text{Star}} = \frac{a}{a_{\text{Star}}}\text{v}_{\text{Star}};$$

$$\text{v}_{\text{Star}} = \frac{a_{\text{Star}}}{a}\text{v}_{\text{relative, Star-Planet}};$$

$$\text{v}_{\text{relative, Star-Planet}} = \sqrt{\frac{K\left(M_{\text{Planet}} + M_{\text{Star}}\right)}{a}};$$

$$\text{v}_{\text{Star}} = \frac{a_{\text{Star}}}{a}\sqrt{\frac{K\left(M_{\text{Planet}} + M_{\text{Star}}\right)}{a}};$$

$$a_{\text{Star}} = \frac{aM_{\text{Planet}}}{M_{\text{Planet}} + M_{\text{Star}}}; \quad \frac{a_{\text{Star}}}{a} = \frac{M_{\text{Planet}}}{M_{\text{Planet}} + M_{\text{Star}}};$$

$$\text{v}_{\text{Star}} = \frac{M_{\text{Planet}}}{M_{\text{Planet}} + M_{\text{Star}}}\sqrt{\frac{K\left(M_{\text{Planet}} + M_{\text{Star}}\right)}{a}};$$

$$\text{v}_{\text{Star}} = M_{\text{Planet}} \cdot \sqrt{\frac{K\left(M_{\text{Planet}} + M_{\text{Star}}\right)}{a\left(M_{\text{Planet}} + M_{\text{Star}}\right)^2}};$$

$$\mathrm{v}_{\mathrm{Star}} = M_{\mathrm{Planet}} \cdot \sqrt{\frac{K}{a\left(M_{\mathrm{Planet}} + M_{\mathrm{Star}}\right)}}.$$

Or:

$$\frac{M_{\mathrm{Star}}\mathrm{v}_{\mathrm{Star}}^2}{a_{\mathrm{Star}}} = K\frac{M_{\mathrm{Star}}M_{\mathrm{Planet}}}{a^2};$$

$$\frac{\mathrm{v}_{\mathrm{Star}}^2}{a_{\mathrm{Star}}} = K\frac{M_{\mathrm{Planet}}}{a^2};$$

$$\mathrm{v}_{\mathrm{Star}} = \sqrt{\frac{Ka_{\mathrm{Star}}M_{\mathrm{Planet}}}{a^2}}; \quad a_{\mathrm{Star}} = \frac{aM_{\mathrm{Planet}}}{M_{\mathrm{Planet}} + M_{\mathrm{Star}}} \approx \frac{aM_{\mathrm{Planet}}}{M_{\mathrm{Star}}};$$

$$\mathrm{v}_{\mathrm{Star}} = M_{\mathrm{Planet}} \cdot \sqrt{\frac{Ka}{aM_{\mathrm{Star}}}}.$$

Or:

$$\mathrm{v}_{\mathrm{Star}} = M_{\mathrm{Planet}} \cdot \sqrt[3]{\frac{2\pi K}{\left(M_{\mathrm{Planet}} + M_{\mathrm{Star}}\right)^2 T}};$$

$$\mathrm{v}_{\mathrm{Star}} = M_{\mathrm{Planet}} \cdot \sqrt[3]{\frac{2\pi K\left(M_{\mathrm{Planet}} + M_{\mathrm{Star}}\right)}{\left(M_{\mathrm{Planet}} + M_{\mathrm{Star}}\right)^3 T}};$$

$$\mathrm{v}_{\mathrm{Star}} = \frac{M_{\mathrm{Planet}}}{M_{\mathrm{Planet}} + M_{\mathrm{Star}}} \cdot \sqrt[3]{\frac{2\pi K\left(M_{\mathrm{Planet}} + M_{\mathrm{Star}}\right)}{T}};$$

$$a^3 = \frac{K\left(M_{\mathrm{Planet}} + M_{\mathrm{Star}}\right)}{4\pi^2}T^2 \quad T = \sqrt{\frac{4\pi^2 a^3}{K\left(M_{\mathrm{Planet}} + M_{\mathrm{Star}}\right)}};$$

$$\mathrm{v}_{\mathrm{Star}} = \frac{M_{\mathrm{Planet}}}{M_{\mathrm{Planet}} + M_{\mathrm{Star}}} \sqrt[3]{\frac{2\pi K\left(M_{\mathrm{Planet}} + M_{\mathrm{Star}}\right)}{\sqrt{\frac{4\pi^2 a^3}{K(M_{\mathrm{Planet}} + M_{\mathrm{Star}})}}}};$$

$$\mathrm{v}_{\mathrm{Star}} = \frac{M_{\mathrm{Planet}}}{M_{\mathrm{Planet}} + M_{\mathrm{Star}}} \cdot \sqrt[3]{\frac{2\pi K\left(M_{\mathrm{Planet}} + M_{\mathrm{Star}}\right)}{2\pi a \cdot \sqrt{\frac{a}{K(M_{\mathrm{Planet}} + M_{\mathrm{Star}})}}}};$$

$$\mathrm{v}_{\mathrm{Star}} = \frac{M_{\mathrm{Planet}}}{M_{\mathrm{Planet}} + M_{\mathrm{Star}}} \cdot \sqrt[3]{\frac{K\left(M_{\mathrm{Planet}} + M_{\mathrm{Star}}\right)}{a \cdot \sqrt{\frac{a}{K(M_{\mathrm{Planet}} + M_{\mathrm{Star}})}}}};$$

$$\mathrm{v}_{\text{Star}} = \frac{M_{\text{Planet}}}{M_{\text{Planet}} + M_{\text{Star}}} \cdot \sqrt[3]{\frac{K\left(M_{\text{Planet}} + M_{\text{Star}}\right)\sqrt{K\left(M_{\text{Planet}} + M_{\text{Star}}\right)}}{a\sqrt{a}}};$$

$$\mathrm{v}_{\text{Star}} = \frac{M_{\text{Planet}}}{M_{\text{Planet}} + M_{\text{Star}}} \cdot \sqrt[3]{\frac{\left[K\left(M_{\text{Planet}} + M_{\text{Star}}\right)\right]^{3/2}}{a^{3/2}}};$$

$$\mathrm{v}_{\text{Star}} = \frac{M_{\text{Planet}}}{M_{\text{Planet}} + M_{\text{Star}}} \cdot \sqrt[3]{\left[\frac{K\left(M_{\text{Planet}} + M_{\text{Star}}\right)}{a}\right]^{3/2}};$$

$$\mathrm{v}_{\text{Star}} = \frac{M_{\text{Planet}}}{M_{\text{Planet}} + M_{\text{Star}}} \left[\left(\frac{K\left(M_{\text{Planet}} + M_{\text{Star}}\right)}{a}\right)^{3/2}\right]^{1/3};$$

$$\mathrm{v}_{\text{Star}} = \frac{M_{\text{Planet}}}{M_{\text{Planet}} + M_{\text{Star}}} \sqrt{\frac{K\left(M_{\text{Planet}} + M_{\text{Star}}\right)}{a}};$$

$$M_{\text{Planet}} << M_{\text{Star}};$$

$$\mathrm{v}_{\text{Star}} \approx \frac{M_{\text{Planet}}}{M_{\text{Star}}} \sqrt{\frac{K M_{\text{Star}}}{a}};$$

$$\mathrm{v}_{\text{Star,CM}} = M_{\text{Planet}} \sqrt{\frac{K}{a M_{\text{Star}}}},$$

representing the velocity of the star S relative to the CM;

$$M_{\text{Star}} \mathrm{v}_{\text{Star}} = M_{\text{Planet}} \mathrm{v}_{\text{Planet}};$$

$$\mathrm{v}_{\text{Planet,CM}} = \sqrt{\frac{K M_{\text{Star}}}{a}},$$

representing the velocity of the exoplanet P relative to the CM.

**b)** If the exoplanet–star system is observed as presented in Figure 3.4, according to the Doppler effect, the results is:

$$\mathrm{v}_{\text{rad,max,Star}} = \mathrm{v}_{\text{obs,max,Star}} = \mathrm{v}_{\text{Star}} \cos\left(90^\circ - i\right) = \mathrm{v}_{\text{Star}} \sin i;$$

$$\mathrm{v}_{\text{Star}} = M_{\text{Planet}} \sqrt{\frac{K}{a M_{\text{Star}}}};$$

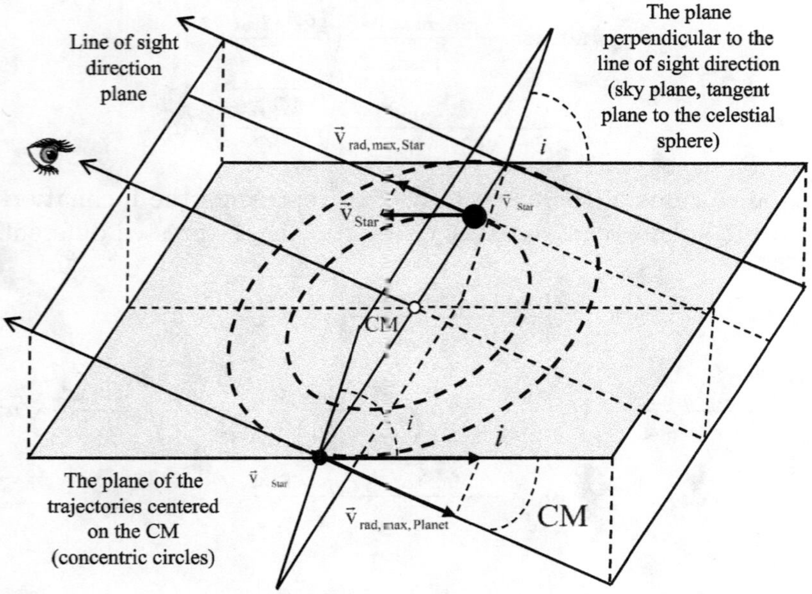


**Fig. 3.4**

$$\mathrm{v}_{\mathrm{rad,max,Star}} = M_{\mathrm{Planet}}\sqrt{\frac{K}{aM_{\mathrm{Star}}}} \cdot \sin i;$$

$$\sin i = \frac{\mathrm{v}_{\mathrm{rad,max,Star}}}{\mathrm{v}_{\mathrm{Star}}};$$

$$\sin i = \frac{\mathrm{v}_{\mathrm{rad,max,Star}}}{M_{\mathrm{Planet}}}\sqrt{\frac{aM_{\mathrm{Star}}}{K}};$$

$$\sin i = \frac{\mathrm{v}_{\mathrm{rad,max,Star}}}{M_{\mathrm{Planet}}}\sqrt{\frac{M_{\mathrm{Star}}}{K}} \cdot \sqrt{a};$$

$$\lambda_{\mathrm{min,Star}} = \lambda_0\left(1 - \frac{\mathrm{v}_{\mathrm{rad,max,Star}}}{c}\right);$$

$$\frac{\lambda_0 - \lambda_{\mathrm{min,Star}}}{\lambda_0} = \frac{\mathrm{v}_{\mathrm{rad,max,Star}}}{c};$$

$$\mathrm{v}_{\mathrm{rad,max,Star}} = \frac{c}{\lambda_0}\left(\lambda_0 - \lambda_{\mathrm{min,Star}}\right);$$

$$\sin i = \frac{\mathrm{v}_{\text{rad,max,Star}}}{M_{\text{Planet}}}\sqrt{\frac{aM_{\text{Star}}}{K}};$$

$$\sin i = \frac{c\left(\lambda_0 - \lambda_{\text{min,Star}}\right)}{\lambda_0 M_{\text{Planet}}}\sqrt{\frac{M_{\text{Star}}}{K}} \cdot \sqrt{a},$$

for the calculus of the angle $i$, where $i$ represents the inclination of the orbits' plane relative to the celestial plane. Expressed differently:

$$\sin i = \frac{c\left(\lambda_{\text{max,Star}} - \lambda_0\right)}{\lambda_0 M_{\text{Planet}}}\sqrt{\frac{M_{\text{Star}}}{K}} \cdot \sqrt{a};$$

$$\frac{c\left(\lambda_0 - \lambda_{\text{min,Star}}\right)}{\lambda_0 M_{\text{Planet}}}\sqrt{\frac{M_{\text{Star}}}{K}} \cdot \sqrt{a} = \frac{c\left(\lambda_{\text{max,Star}} - \lambda_0\right)}{\lambda_0 M_{\text{Planet}}}\sqrt{\frac{M_{\text{Star}}}{K}} \cdot \sqrt{a};$$

$$\lambda_0 = \frac{\lambda_{\text{min,Star}} + \lambda_{\text{max,Star}}}{2}.$$

# Problem 4

# Intergalactic Cloud

At the time of its formation, an intergalactic, spherical, and homogenous cloud rotates around its own axis with the angular velocity $\omega_{\text{cloud}}$. The cloud is made of rarefied gas and cosmic dust, and it is of radius $R$ and of mass $m$.

Due to internal gravitational effects, the cloud substance has accumulated in two massive spheres of different radii. A binary stellar system is thus created, and its components rotate rapidly around their common center of mass.

**a)** *Determine* the rotation period ($T_{\text{rot}}$) of the two stars formed in the initial cloud, around the common center of mass, if the stars' masses are $m_1$ and $m_2 < m_1$, respectively. The gravitational attraction constant, $K$, is considered known.

**b)** *Demonstrate* that the two stars can not only rotate around the center of mass, but also oscillate along the line of their centers. *Determine* the period ($T_{\text{osc}}$) of the "small" oscillations of the two stars.

**c)** The astronomical observations made by an interstellar cosmic laboratory on this binary stellar system have proved that the oscillation period of its components uniformly decreases over time. *Specify* the physical meaning of these observations and *determine* the minimum value of the system's oscillation period. *Estimate* the evolution of the system after the moment when the minimum rotation period is reached.

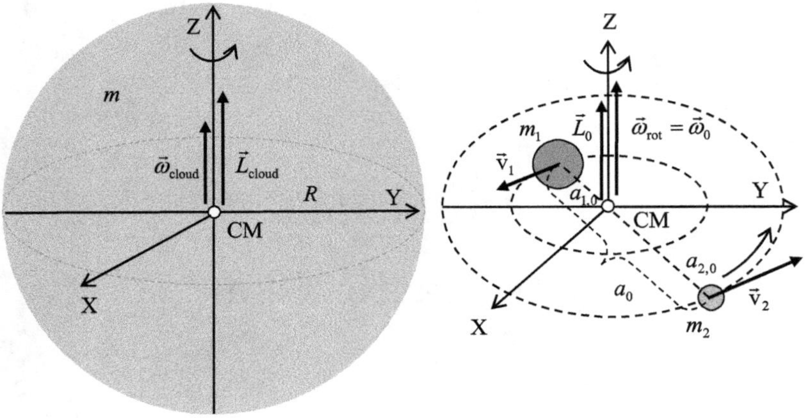


**Fig. 4.1**

## Solution

**a)** According to the notation in Figure 4.1, if $\vec{L}_{cloud}$ is the initial angular moment of the cosmic cloud, and $\vec{L}$ is the total angular moment of the binary stellar system, the entire evolution of the system complies with the angular momentum conservation law. Thus, the result is:

$$L_{cloud} = I_{cloud}\omega_{cloud} = \frac{2}{5}mR^2\omega_{cloud};$$

$$L_0 = m_1 v_1 a_{1,0} + m_2 v_2 a_{2,0} = m_1\omega_{rot}a_{1,0}^2$$
$$+ m_2\omega_{rot}a_{2,0}^2 = \omega_{rot}\left(m_1 a_{1,0}^2 + m_2 a_{2,0}^2\right);$$

$$m_1 a_{1,0} = m_2 a_{2,0}; \quad a_{1,0} + a_{2,0} = a_0; \quad m_1 + m_2 = m;$$

$$a_{1,0} = \frac{m_2 a_0}{m_1 + m_2}; \quad a_{2,0} = \frac{m_1 a_0}{m_1 + m_2}; \quad a_{1,0} = \frac{m_2}{m_1}a_{2,0};$$

$$L_0 = \omega_{rot}\left(m_1 a_{1,0}^2 + m_2 a_{2,0}^2\right);$$

$$L_0 = \omega_{rot}\left(m_1\frac{m_2^2}{m_1^2}a_{2,0}^2 + m_2 a_{2,0}^2\right) = \omega_{rot}m_2\left(1 + \frac{m_2}{m_1}\right)a_{2,0}^2;$$

$$L_0 = L_{cloud};$$

$$\omega_{rot} = \omega_0 = \frac{L_{cloud}}{m_2\left(1 + \frac{m_2}{m_1}\right)a_{2,0}^2};$$

$$F_{\mathrm{cp},2} = m_2\omega_{\mathrm{rot}}^2 a_{2,0} = m_2 \frac{L_{\mathrm{cloud}}^2}{m_2^2\left(1+\frac{m_2}{m_1}\right)^2 a_{2,0}^4} a_{2,0} = \frac{L_{\mathrm{cloud}}^2}{m_2\left(1+\frac{m_2}{m_1}\right)^2 a_{2,0}^3};$$

$$F_{\mathrm{g},0} = K\frac{m_1 m_2}{a_0^2}; \quad a_0 = \frac{a_{2,0}\left(m_1+m_2\right)}{m_1};$$

$$F_{\mathrm{g},0} = K\frac{m_1 m_2}{\frac{a_{2,0}^2\left(m_1+m_2\right)^2}{m_1^2}} = K\frac{m_1^3 m_2}{\left(m_1+m_2\right)^2 a_{2,0}^2} = K\frac{m_1^3 m_2}{m_1^2\left(1+\frac{m_2}{m_1}\right)^2 a_{2,0}^2};$$

$$F_{\mathrm{g},0} = K\frac{m_1 m_2}{\left(1+\frac{m_2}{m_1}\right)^2 a_{2,0}^2};$$

$$F_{\mathrm{cp},2} = F_{\mathrm{g},0};$$

$$\frac{L_{\mathrm{cloud}}^2}{m_2\left(1+\frac{m_2}{m_1}\right)^2 a_{2,0}^3} = K\frac{m_1 m_2}{\left(1+\frac{m_2}{m_1}\right)^2 a_{2,0}^2};$$

$$\frac{L_{\mathrm{cloud}}^2}{m_2 a_{2,0}} = K m_1 m_2;$$

$$a_{2,0} = \frac{L_{\mathrm{cloud}}^2}{K m_1 m_2^2}; \quad m_1 a_{1,0} = m_2 a_{2,0}; \quad a_{2,0} = \frac{m_1}{m_2} a_{1,0};$$

$$a_{1,0} = \frac{L_{\mathrm{cloud}}^2}{K m_1^2 m_2}; \quad a_{1,0} + a_{2,0} = a_0;$$

$$a_0 = \frac{L_{\mathrm{cloud}}^2}{K m_1^2 m_2} + \frac{L_{\mathrm{cloud}}^2}{K m_1 m_2^2} = \frac{L_{\mathrm{cloud}}^2}{K m_1 m_2}\left(\frac{1}{m_1} + \frac{1}{m_2}\right);$$

$$a_0 = \frac{L_{\mathrm{cloud}}^2\left(m_1+m_2\right)}{K m_1^2 m_2^2};$$

$$L_{\mathrm{cloud}} = \frac{2}{5} m R^2 \omega_{\mathrm{cloud}} = \frac{2}{5}\left(m_1+m_2\right) R^2 \omega_{\mathrm{cloud}};$$

$$\omega_{\mathrm{rot}} = \omega_0 = \frac{L_{\mathrm{cloud}}}{m_2\left(1+\frac{m_2}{m_1}\right) a_{2,0}^2}; \quad a_{2,0} = \frac{m_1 a_0}{m_1+m_2};$$

$$\omega_{\mathrm{rot}} = \omega_0 = \frac{L_{\mathrm{cloud}}}{m_2\left(\frac{m_1+m_2}{m_1}\right)\frac{m_1^2 a_0^2}{\left(m_1+m_2\right)^2}} = \frac{L_{\mathrm{cloud}}\left(m_1+m_2\right)}{m_1 m_2 a_0^2} = \frac{2\pi}{T_{\mathrm{rot}}};$$

$$a_0 = \frac{L_{\text{cloud}}^2 (m_1 + m_2)}{K m_1^2 m_2^2};$$

$$T_{\text{rot}} = \frac{2\pi m_1 m_2}{L_{\text{cloud}} (m_1 + m_2)} a_0^2 = \frac{2\pi m_1 m_2}{L_{\text{cloud}} (m_1 + m_2)} \frac{L_{\text{cloud}}^4 (m_1 + m_2)^2}{K^2 m_1^4 m_2^4};$$

$$T_{\text{rot}} = \frac{2\pi (m_1 + m_2) L_{\text{cloud}}^3}{K^2 m_1^3 m_2^3}; \quad L_{\text{cloud}} = \frac{2}{5} m R^2 \omega_{\text{cloud}}.$$

$$L_0 = m_1 \mathrm{v}_1 a_{1,0} + m_2 \mathrm{v}_2 a_{2,0} = m_1 \omega_{\text{rot}} a_{1,0}^2 + m_2 \omega_{\text{rot}} a_{2,0}^2$$

$$= \omega_{\text{rot}} \left( m_1 a_{1,0}^2 + m_2 a_{2,0}^2 \right);$$

$$m_1 a_{1,0} = m_2 a_{2,0}; \quad a_{1,0} + a_{2,0} = a_0; \quad m_1 + m_2 = m;$$

$$a_{1,0} = \frac{m_2 a_0}{m_1 + m_2}; \quad a_{2,0} = \frac{m_1 a_0}{m_1 + m_2}; \quad a_{1,0} = \frac{m_2}{m_1} a_{2,0};$$

$$a_{2,0} = \frac{m_1}{m_2} a_{1,0};$$

$$L_0 = \omega_{\text{rot}} \left( m_1 a_{1,0}^2 + m_2 a_{2,0}^2 \right);$$

$$L_0 = \omega_{\text{rot}} \left( m_1 a_{1,0}^2 + m_2 \frac{m_1^2}{m_2^2} a_{1,0}^2 \right) = \omega_{\text{rot}} m_1 \left( 1 + \frac{m_1}{m_2} \right) a_{1,0}^2;$$

$$L_0 = L_{\text{cloud}};$$

$$\omega_{\text{rot}} = \omega_0 = \frac{L_{\text{cloud}}}{m_1 \left( 1 + \frac{m_1}{m_2} \right) a_{1,0}^2};$$

$$F_{\text{cp},1} = m_1 \omega_{\text{rot}}^2 a_{1,0} = m_1 \frac{L_{\text{cloud}}^2}{m_1^2 \left( 1 + \frac{m_1}{m_2} \right)^2 a_{1,0}^4} a_{1,0} = \frac{L_{\text{cloud}}^2}{m_1 \left( 1 + \frac{m_1}{m_2} \right)^2 a_{1,0}^3};$$

$$F_{\text{g},0} = K \frac{m_1 m_2}{a_0^2}; \quad a_0 = \frac{a_{2,0} (m_1 + m_2)}{m_1}; \quad a_0 = \frac{a_{1,0} (m_1 + m_2)}{m_2};$$

$$F_{\text{g},0} = K \frac{m_1 m_2}{\frac{a_{1,0}^2 (m_1 + m_2)^2}{m_2^2}} = K \frac{m_1 m_2^3}{(m_1 + m_2)^2 a_{1,0}^2} = K \frac{m_1 m_2^3}{m_2^2 \left( 1 + \frac{m_1}{m_2} \right)^2 a_{1,0}^2};$$

$$F_{\text{g},0} = K \frac{m_1 m_2}{\left( 1 + \frac{m_1}{m_2} \right)^2 a_{1,0}^2};$$

$$F_{\text{cp},1} = F_{\text{g},0};$$

$$\frac{L_{\text{cloud}}^2}{m_1\left(1+\frac{m_1}{m_2}\right)^2 a_{1,0}^3} = K\frac{m_1 m_2}{\left(1+\frac{m_1}{m_2}\right)^2 a_{1,0}^2};$$

$$\frac{L_{\text{cloud}}^2}{m_1 a_{1,0}} = K m_1 m_2 \qquad \frac{L_{\text{cloud}}^2}{m_2 a_{2,0}} = K m_1 m_2;$$

$$a_{1,0} = \frac{L_{\text{cloud}}^2}{K m_1^2 m_2}; \quad m_1 a_{1,0} = m_2 a_{2,0}; \quad a_{2,0} = \frac{m_1}{m_2} a_{1,0};$$

$$a_{2,0} = \frac{L_{\text{cloud}}^2}{K m_1 m_2^2}; \quad a_{1,0} + a_{2,0} = a_0;$$

$$a_0 = \frac{L_{\text{cloud}}^2}{K m_1^2 m_2} + \frac{L_{\text{cloud}}^2}{K m_1 m_2^2} = \frac{L_{\text{cloud}}^2}{K m_1 m_2}\left(\frac{1}{m_1} + \frac{1}{m_2}\right);$$

$$a_0 = \frac{L_{\text{cloud}}^2 (m_1 + m_2)}{K m_1^2 m_2^2};$$

$$L_{\text{cloud}} = \frac{2}{5} m R^2 \omega_{\text{cloud}} = \frac{2}{5}(m_1 + m_2) R^2 \omega_{\text{cloud}};$$

$$\omega_{\text{rot}} = \omega_0 = \frac{L_{\text{cloud}}}{m_1\left(1+\frac{m_1}{m_2}\right) a_{1,0}^2};$$

$$a_{1,0} = \frac{m_2 a_0}{m_1 + m_2};$$

$$\omega_{\text{rot}} = \omega_0 = \frac{L_{\text{cloud}}}{m_1\left(\frac{m_1+m_2}{m_2}\right)\frac{m_2^2 a_0^2}{(m_1+m_2)^2}} = \frac{L_{\text{cloud}}(m_1 + m_2)}{m_1 m_2 a_0^2} = \frac{2\pi}{T_{\text{rot}}};$$

$$a_0 = \frac{L_{\text{cloud}}^2 (m_1 + m_2)}{K m_1^2 m_2^2};$$

$$T_{\text{rot}} = \frac{2\pi m_1 m_2}{L_{\text{cloud}}(m_1 + m_2)} a_0^2 = \frac{2\pi m_1 m_2}{L_{\text{cloud}}(m_1 + m_2)} \frac{L_{\text{cloud}}^4 (m_1 + m_2)^2}{K^2 m_1^4 m_2^4};$$

$$T_{\text{rot}} = \frac{2\pi (m_1 + m_2) L_{\text{cloud}}^3}{K^2 m_1^3 m_2^3}; \quad L_{\text{cloud}} = \frac{2}{5} m R^2 \omega_{\text{cloud}};$$

$$m = m_1 + m_2.$$

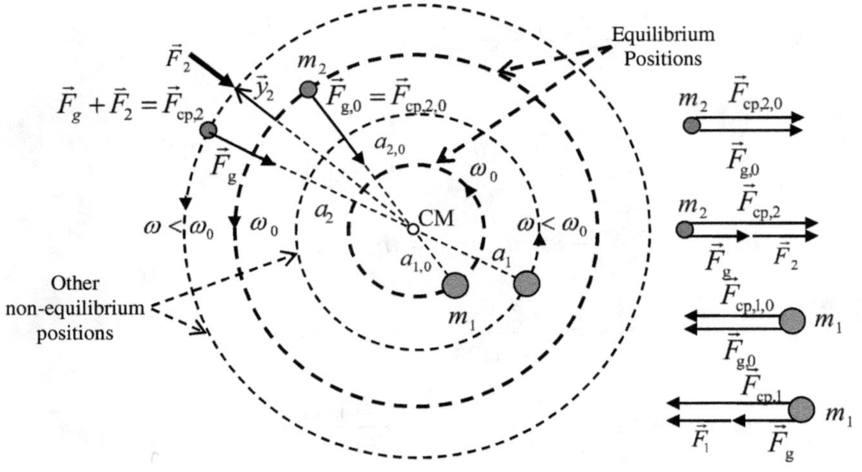


**Fig. 4.2**

**b)** According to the notation in from Figure 4.2, for the equilibrium position of the star with mass $m_2$, the result is:

$$\vec{F}_{\text{g},0} = \vec{F}_{\text{cp},2,0}; \quad F_{\text{g},0} = F_{\text{cp},2,0};$$

$$F_{\text{g},0} = K\frac{m_1 m_2}{a_0^2}; \quad a_0 = \frac{a_{2,0}\left(m_1 + m_2\right)}{m_1};$$

$$F_{\text{g},0} = K\frac{m_1 m_2}{\left(1 + \frac{m_2}{m_1}\right)^2 a_{2,0}^2};$$

$$F_{\text{cp},2,0} = m_2 \omega_0^2 a_{2,0};$$

$$F_{\text{cp},2,0} = F_{\text{g},0};$$

$$m_2 \omega_0^2 a_{2,0} = K\frac{m_1 m_2}{\left(1 + \frac{m_2}{m_1}\right)^2 a_{2,0}^2}; \quad \omega_0^2 a_{2,0} = K\frac{m_1}{\left(1 + \frac{m_2}{m_1}\right)^2 a_{2,0}^2};$$

$$\omega_0^2 = K\frac{m_1}{\left(1 + \frac{m_2}{m_1}\right)^2 a_{2,0}^3};$$

$$\omega_0^2 = \frac{Km_1m_2^2a_{2,0}}{m_2^2 \cdot \left(1+\frac{m_2}{m_1}\right)^2 a_{2,0}^4};$$

$$\frac{L_{\text{cloud}}^2}{m_2a_{2,0}} = Km_1m_2; \quad L_{\text{cloud}}^2 = Km_1m_2^2a_{2,0};$$

$$\omega_0^2 = \frac{L_{\text{cloud}}^2}{m_2^2\left(1+\frac{m_2}{m_1}\right)^2 a_{2,0}^4};$$

$$\omega_0 = \frac{L_{\text{cloud}}}{m_2\left(1+\frac{m_2}{m_1}\right) \cdot a_{2,0}^2};$$

$$F_{\text{cp},2,0} = m_2\omega_0^2a_{2,0};$$

$$F_{\text{cp},2,0} = m_2\frac{L_{\text{cloud}}^2}{m_2^2\left(1+\frac{m_2}{m_1}\right)^2 a_{2,0}^4} \cdot a_{2,0};$$

$$F_{\text{cp},2,0} = \frac{L_{\text{cloud}}^2}{m_2\left(1+\frac{m_2}{m_1}\right)^2 a_{2,0}^3};$$

$$F_{\text{g},0} = K\frac{m_1m_2}{\left(1+\frac{m_2}{m_1}\right)^2 a_{2,0}^2};$$

$$F_{\text{cp},2,0} = F_{\text{g},0};$$

$$\frac{L_{\text{cloud}}^2}{m_2\left(1+\frac{m_2}{m_1}\right)^2 a_{2,0}^3} = K\frac{m_1m_2}{\left(1+\frac{m_2}{m_1}\right)^2 a_{2,0}^2};$$

$$m_1a_{1,0} = m_2a_{2,0};$$

$$a_{2,0} = \frac{m_1}{m_2}a_{1,0};$$

$$\frac{L_{\text{cloud}}^2}{m_2\left(1+\frac{m_2}{m_1}\right)^2 \frac{m_1^3}{m_2^3}a_{1,0}^3} = K\frac{m_1m_2}{\left(1+\frac{m_2}{m_1}\right)^2 \frac{m_1^2}{m_2^2}a_{1,0}^2};$$

$$\frac{L_{\text{cloud}}^2}{m_1\left(1+\frac{m_2}{m_1}\right)^2 a_{1,0}^3} = K\frac{m_1m_2}{\left(1+\frac{m_2}{m_1}\right)^2 a_{1,0}^2}.$$

For some arbitrary position, according to the notation in Figure 4.2, for the star with the mass $m_2$, the result is:

$$\vec{F}_g + \vec{F}_2 = \vec{F}_{\mathrm{cp},2}; \quad F_g + F_2 = F_{\mathrm{cp},2}; \quad F_2 = F_{\mathrm{cp},2} - F_g;$$

$$F_g = K\frac{m_1 m_2}{a^2}; \quad a = \frac{a_2\left(m_1 + m_2\right)}{m_1}; \quad a = \left(1 + \frac{m_2}{m_1}\right) \cdot a_2;$$

$$F_g = K\frac{m_1 m_2}{\left(1 + \frac{m_2}{m_1}\right)^2 a_2^2};$$

$$F_{\mathrm{cp},2} = m_2 \omega^2 a_2;$$

$$\omega_{\mathrm{rot}} = \frac{L_{\mathrm{cloud}}}{m_2\left(1 + \frac{m_2}{m_1}\right) a_2^2}; \quad \omega = \frac{L_{\mathrm{cloud}}}{m_2\left(1 + \frac{m_2}{m_1}\right) a_2^2};$$

$$F_{\mathrm{cp},2} = m_2 \cdot \frac{L_{\mathrm{cloud}}^2}{m_2^2\left(1 + \frac{m_2}{m_1}\right)^2 a_2^4} a_2;$$

$$F_{\mathrm{cp},2} = \frac{L_{\mathrm{cloud}}^2}{m_2\left(1 + \frac{m_2}{m_1}\right)^2 a_2^3};$$

$$L_0 = L,$$

representing the law of conservation of angular momentum;

$$I_0\omega_0 = I\omega; \quad \omega = \frac{I_0}{I}\omega_0 = \frac{m_1 a_{1,0}^2 + m_2 a_{2,0}^2}{m_1 a_1^2 + m_2 a_2^2}\omega_0;$$

$$a_{1,0} = \frac{m_2 a_0}{m_1 + m_2}; \quad a_{2,0} = \frac{m_1 a_0}{m_1 + m_2};$$

$$a_1 = \frac{m_2 a}{m_1 + m_2}; \quad a_2 = \frac{m_1 a}{m_1 + m_2};$$

$$\omega = \frac{m_1\frac{m_2^2 a_0^2}{(m_1+m_2)^2} + m_2\frac{m_1^2 a_0^2}{(m_1+m_2)^2}}{m_1\frac{m_2^2 a^2}{(m_1+m_2)^2} + m_2\frac{m_1^2 a^2}{(m_1+m_2)^2}}\omega_0 = \left(\frac{a_0}{a}\right)^2 \omega_0;$$

$$a > a_0; \ \rightarrow \omega < \omega_0;$$

$$F_{\text{cp},2,0} = \frac{L_{\text{cloud}}^2}{m_2\left(1+\frac{m_2}{m_1}\right)^2 a_{2,0}^3}; \quad F_{\text{cp},2} = \frac{L_{\text{cloud}}^2}{m_2\left(1+\frac{m_2}{m_1}\right)^2 a_2^3};$$

$$a_2 > a_{2,0}; \rightarrow F_{\text{cp},2} < F_{\text{cp},2,0};$$

$$F_{\text{g},0} = K\frac{m_1 m_2}{\left(1+\frac{m_2}{m_1}\right)^2 a_{2,0}^2}; \quad F_g = K\frac{m_1 m_2}{\left(1+\frac{m_2}{m_1}\right)^2 a_2^2};$$

$$F_g < F_{\text{g},0};$$

$$F_2 = F_g - F_{\text{cp},2} = K\frac{m_1 m_2}{\left(1+\frac{m_2}{m_1}\right)^2 a_2^2} - \frac{L_{\text{cloud}}^2}{m_2\left(1+\frac{m_2}{m_1}\right)^2 a_2^3};$$

$$a_2 = a_{2,0} + y_2; \quad y_2 << a_{2.0};$$

$$F_2 = K\frac{m_1 m_2}{\left(1+\frac{m_2}{m_1}\right)^2 (a_{2,0}+y_2)^2} - \frac{L_{\text{cloud}}^2}{m_2\left(1+\frac{m_2}{m_1}\right)^2 (a_{2,0}+y_2)^3};$$

$$F_2 = K\frac{m_1 m_2}{\left(1+\frac{m_2}{m_1}\right)^2 a_{2,0}^2}\left(1+\frac{y_2}{a_{2,0}}\right)^{-2} - \frac{L_{\text{cloud}}^2}{m_2\left(1+\frac{m_2}{m_1}\right)^2 a_{2,0}^3}\left(1+\frac{y_2}{a_{2,0}}\right)^{-3};$$

$$F_2 = K\frac{m_1 m_2}{\left(1+\frac{m_2}{m_1}\right)^2 a_{2,0}^2}\left(1-2\frac{y_2}{a_{2,0}}\right) - \frac{L_{\text{cloud}}^2}{m_2\left(1+\frac{m_2}{m_1}\right)^2 a_{2,0}^3}\left(1-3\frac{y_2}{a_{2,0}}\right);$$

$$F_2 = K\frac{m_1 m_2}{\left(1+\frac{m_2}{m_1}\right)^2 a_{2,0}^2} - 2K\frac{m_1 m_2}{\left(1+\frac{m_2}{m_1}\right)^2 a_{2,0}^3}y_2 - \frac{L_{\text{cloud}}^2}{m_2\left(1+\frac{m_2}{m_1}\right)^2 a_{2,0}^3} + \frac{3L_{\text{cloud}}^2}{m_2\left(1+\frac{m_2}{m_1}\right)^2 a_{2,0}^4}y_2;$$

$$F_{\text{g},0} = K\frac{m_1 m_2}{\left(1+\frac{m_2}{m_1}\right)^2 a_{2,0}^2}; \quad F_{\text{cp},2,0} = \frac{L_{\text{cloud}}^2}{m_2\left(1+\frac{m_2}{m_1}\right)^2 a_{2,0}^3};$$

$$F_{\text{cp},2,0} = F_{\text{g},0};$$

$$\frac{L_{\text{cloud}}^2}{m_2\left(1+\frac{m_2}{m_1}\right)^2 a_{2,0}^3} = K\frac{m_1 m_2}{\left(1+\frac{m_2}{m_1}\right)^2 a_{2,0}^2};$$

$$F_2 = -2K\frac{m_1 m_2}{\left(1+\frac{m_2}{m_1}\right)^2 a_{2,0}^3} y_2 + \frac{3L_{\text{cloud}}^2}{m_2\left(1+\frac{m_2}{m_1}\right)^2 a_{2,0}^4} y_2;$$

$$F_2 = \frac{1}{\left(1+\frac{m_2}{m_1}\right)^2 a_{2,0}^3}\left(\frac{3L_{\text{cloud}}^2}{m_2 a_{2,0}} - 2Km_1m_2\right) y_2;$$

$$\frac{L_{\text{cloud}}^2}{m_2 a_{2,0}} = Km_1m_2;$$

$$F_2 = \frac{1}{\left(1+\frac{m_2}{m_1}\right)^2 a_{2,0}^3}\left(3Km_1m_2 - 2Km_1m_2\right) y_2;$$

$$F_2 = \frac{Km_1m_2}{\left(1+\frac{m_2}{m_1}\right)^2 a_{2,0}^3} y_2; \quad k_2 = \frac{Km_1m_2}{\left(1+\frac{m_2}{m_1}\right)^2 a_{2,0}^3};$$

$$F_2 = k_2 y_2; \quad \vec{F}_2 = -k_2\vec{y}_2,$$

which justifies the possibility of harmonic oscillatory radial motion;

$$a_{2,0} = \frac{m_1 a_0}{m_1+m_2}; \quad a_0 = \frac{L_{\text{cloud}}^2 (m_1+m_2)}{Km_1^2m_2^2};$$

$$k_2 = \frac{Km_1m_2}{\left(1+\frac{m_2}{m_1}\right)^2 \frac{m_1^3 a_0^3}{(m_1+m_2)^3}} = \frac{Km_1m_2}{\frac{(m_1+m_2)^2}{m_1^2}\frac{m_1^3}{(m_1+m_2)^3}\frac{L_{\text{cloud}}^6(m_1+m_2)^3}{K^3m_1^6m_2^6}};$$

$$k_2 = \frac{K^4 m_1^6 m_2^7}{L_{\text{cloud}}^6 (m_1+m_2)^2} = m_2\omega_{\text{osc}}^2 = m_2\frac{4\pi^2}{T_{\text{osc}}^2};$$

$$F_2 = k_2 y_2; \quad \vec{F}_2 = -k_2\vec{y}_2;$$

$$T_{\text{osc}} = 2\pi\frac{L_{\text{cloud}}^3 (m_1+m_2)}{K^2m_1^3m_2^3},$$

representing the period of harmonic oscillatory radial motion.

We obtain the same result by studying the motion of the star with the mass $m_1$:

$$\vec{F}_{1,0} = \vec{F}_{\text{cp},1,0} + \vec{F}_{\text{g},0} = 0; \quad F_{\text{cp},1,0} = F_{\text{g},0};$$

$$F_{\text{g},0} = K\frac{m_1 m_2}{a_0^2}; \quad a_0 = \frac{a_{1,0}\left(m_1 + m_2\right)}{m_2}; \quad F_{\text{g},0} = K\frac{m_1 m_2}{\left(1 + \frac{m_1}{m_2}\right)^2 a_{1,0}^2};$$

$$F_{\text{cp},1,0} = m_1 \omega_0^2 a_{1,0};$$

$$m_1 \omega_0^2 a_{1,0} = K\frac{m_1 m_2}{\left(1 + \frac{m_1}{m_2}\right)^2 a_{1,0}^2}; \quad \omega_0^2 = K\frac{m_2}{\left(1 + \frac{m_1}{m_2}\right)^2 a_{1,0}^3};$$

$$\frac{L_{\text{cloud}}^2}{m_2 a_{2,0}} = K m_1 m_2;$$

$$L_{\text{cloud}}^2 = K m_1 m_2^2 a_{2,0}; \quad m_1 a_{1,0} = m_2 a_{2,0};$$

$$L_{\text{cloud}}^2 = K m_1 m_2 m_2 a_{2,0} = K m_1 m_2 m_1 a_{1,0};$$

$$L_{\text{cloud}}^2 = K m_1^2 m_2 a_{1,0};$$

$$L_{\text{cloud}}^2 = K m_2 m_1^2 a_{1,0}; \quad \frac{L_{\text{cloud}}^2}{m_2 a_{2,0}} = K m_1 m_2; \quad L_{\text{cloud}}^2 = K m_1 m_2^2 a_{2,0};$$

$$\omega_0^2 = K\frac{m_2 m_1^2 a_{1,0}}{m_1^2 \left(1 + \frac{m_1}{m_2}\right)^2 a_{1,0}^4}; \quad \omega_0^2 = \frac{L_{\text{cloud}}^2}{m_1^2 \left(1 + \frac{m_1}{m_2}\right)^2 a_{1,0}^4};$$

$$\omega_0 = \frac{L_{\text{cloud}}}{m_1 \left(1 + \frac{m_1}{m_2}\right) a_{1,0}^2};$$

$$F_{\text{cp},1,0} = m_1 \omega_0^2 a_{1,0};$$

$$F_{\text{cp},1,0} = m_1 \frac{L_{\text{cloud}}^2}{m_1^2 \left(1 + \frac{m_1}{m_2}\right)^2 a_{1,0}^4} \cdot a_{1,0};$$

$$F_{\text{cp},1,0} = \frac{L_{\text{cloud}}^2}{m_1 \left(1 + \frac{m_1}{m_2}\right)^2 a_{1,0}^3};$$

$$F_{\text{g},0} = K\frac{m_1 m_2}{\left(1 + \frac{m_1}{m_2}\right)^2 a_{1,0}^2};$$

$$F_{\text{cp},1,0} = F_{\text{g},0};$$

$$\frac{L_{\text{cloud}}^2}{m_1\left(1+\frac{m_1}{m_2}\right)^2 a_{1,0}^3} = K\frac{m_1 m_2}{\left(1+\frac{m_1}{m_2}\right)^2 a_{1,0}^2};$$

$$L_{\text{cloud}}^2 = K m_2 m_1^2 a_{1,0};$$

$$\vec{F}_g + \vec{F}_1 = \vec{F}_{\text{cp},1}; \quad F_g + F_1 = F_{\text{cp},1}; \quad F_1 = F_{\text{cp},1} - F_g;$$

$$F_g = K\frac{m_1 m_2}{a^2}; \quad a = \frac{a_1(m_1+m_2)}{m_2}; \quad F_g = K\frac{m_1 m_2}{\left(1+\frac{m_1}{m_2}\right)^2 a_1^2};$$

$$F_{\text{cp},1} = m_1\omega^2 a_1;$$

$$\omega_{\text{rot}} = \frac{L_{\text{cloud}}}{m_2\left(1+\frac{m_2}{m_1}\right)a_2^2} = \omega; \quad m_1 a_1 = m_2 a_2;$$

$$\omega = \frac{L_{\text{cloud}}}{m_2\left(1+\frac{m_2}{m_1}\right)\frac{m_1^2}{m_2^2}a_1^2} = \frac{L_{\text{cloud}}}{m_2\frac{m_1}{m_2}\left(1+\frac{m_2}{m_1}\right)\frac{m_1}{m_2}a_1^2};$$

$$\omega = \frac{L_{\text{cloud}}}{m_1\left(1+\frac{m_1}{m_2}\right)a_1^2};$$

$$F_{\text{cp},1} = m_1 \cdot \frac{L_{\text{cloud}}^2}{m_1^2\left(1+\frac{m_1}{m_2}\right)^2 a_1^4} a_1;$$

$$F_{\text{cp},1} = \frac{L_{\text{cloud}}^2}{m_1\left(1+\frac{m_1}{m_2}\right)^2 a_1^3};$$

$$L_0 = L;$$

$$I_0\omega_0 = I\omega; \quad \omega = \frac{I_0}{I}\omega_0 = \frac{m_1 a_{1,0}^2 + m_2 a_{2,0}^2}{m_1 a_1^2 + m_2 a_2^2}\omega_0;$$

$$a_{1,0} = \frac{m_2 a_0}{m_1+m_2}; \quad a_{2,0} = \frac{m_1 a_0}{m_1+m_2};$$

$$a_1 = \frac{m_2 a}{m_1+m_2}; \quad a_2 = \frac{m_1 a}{m_1+m_2};$$

$$\omega = \frac{m_1 \frac{m_2^2 a_0^2}{(m_1+m_2)^2} + m_2 \frac{m_1^2 a_0^2}{(m_1+m_2)^2}}{m_1 \frac{m_2^2 a^2}{(m_1+m_2)^2} + m_2 \frac{m_1^2 a^2}{(m_1+m_2)^2}} \omega_0 = \left(\frac{a_0}{a}\right)^2 \omega_0;$$

$$a > a_0; \rightarrow \omega < \omega_0;$$

$$F_{\text{cp},1,0} = \frac{L_{\text{cloud}}^2}{m_1 \left(1 + \frac{m_1}{m_2}\right)^2 a_{1,0}^3}; \quad F_{\text{cp},1} = \frac{L_{\text{cloud}}^2}{m_1 \left(1 + \frac{m_1}{m_2}\right)^2 a_1^3};$$

$$a_1 > a_{1,0}; \rightarrow F_{\text{cp},1} < F_{\text{cp},1,0};$$

$$F_{\text{g},0} = K \frac{m_1 m_2}{\left(1 + \frac{m_1}{m_2}\right)^2 a_{1,0}^2}; \quad F_g = K \frac{m_1 m_2}{\left(1 + \frac{m_1}{m_2}\right)^2 a_1^2};$$

$$F_g < F_{\text{g},0};$$

$$F_1 = F_g - F_{\text{cp},1} = K \frac{m_1 m_2}{\left(1 + \frac{m_1}{m_2}\right)^2 a_1^2} - \frac{L_{\text{cloud}}^2}{m_1 \left(1 + \frac{m_1}{m_2}\right)^2 a_1^3};$$

$$a_1 = a_{1,0} + y_1; \quad y_1 << a_{1.0};$$

$$F_1 = K \frac{m_1 m_2}{\left(1 + \frac{m_1}{m_2}\right)^2 (a_{1,0} + y_1)^2} - \frac{L_{\text{cloud}}^2}{m_1 \left(1 + \frac{m_1}{m_2}\right)^2 (a_{1,0} + y_1)^3};$$

$$F_1 = K \frac{m_1 m_2}{\left(1 + \frac{m_1}{m_2}\right)^2 a_{1,0}^2} \left(1 + \frac{y_1}{a_{1,0}}\right)^{-2} - \frac{L_{\text{cloud}}^2}{m_1 \left(1 + \frac{m_1}{m_2}\right)^2 a_{1,0}^3} \left(1 + \frac{y_1}{a_{1,0}}\right)^{-3};$$

$$F_1 = K \frac{m_1 m_2}{\left(1 + \frac{m_1}{m_2}\right)^2 a_{1,0}^2} \left(1 - 2\frac{y_1}{a_{1,0}}\right) - \frac{L_{\text{cloud}}^2}{m_1 \left(1 + \frac{m_1}{m_2}\right)^2 a_{1,0}^3} \left(1 - 3\frac{y_1}{a_{1,0}}\right);$$

$$F_1 = K \frac{m_1 m_2}{\left(1 + \frac{m_1}{m_2}\right)^2 a_{1,0}^2} - 2K \frac{m_1 m_2}{\left(1 + \frac{m_1}{m_2}\right)^2 a_{1,0}^3} y_1 - \frac{L_{\text{cloud}}^2}{m_1 \left(1 + \frac{m_1}{m_2}\right)^2 a_{1,0}^3} + \frac{3L_{\text{cloud}}^2}{m_1 \left(1 + \frac{m_1}{m_2}\right)^2 a_{1,0}^4} y_1;$$

$$F_{\text{g},0} = K\frac{m_1 m_2}{\left(1+\frac{m_1}{m_2}\right)^2 a_{1,0}^2}; \quad F_{\text{cp},1,0} = \frac{L_{\text{cloud}}^2}{m_1\left(1+\frac{m_1}{m_2}\right)^2 a_{1,0}^3};$$

$$F_{\text{cp},1,0} = F_{\text{g},0};$$

$$F_1 = -2K\frac{m_1 m_2}{\left(1+\frac{m_1}{m_2}\right)^2 a_{1,0}^3} y_1 + \frac{3L_{\text{cloud}}^2}{m_1\left(1+\frac{m_1}{m_2}\right)^2 a_{1,0}^4} y_1;$$

$$F_1 = \frac{1}{\left(1+\frac{m_1}{m_2}\right)^2 a_{1,0}^3}\left(\frac{3L_{\text{cloud}}^2}{m_1 a_{1,0}} - 2Km_1m_2\right) y_1;$$

$$\frac{L_{\text{cloud}}^2}{m_2 a_{2,0}} = Km_1m_2; \quad m_1 a_{1,0} = m_2 a_{2,0};$$

$$\frac{L_{\text{cloud}}^2}{m_1 a_{1,0}} = Km_1m_2;$$

$$F_1 = \frac{1}{\left(1+\frac{m_1}{m_2}\right)^2 a_{1,0}^3}\left(3Km_1m_2 - 2Km_1m_2\right) y_1;$$

$$F_1 = \frac{Km_1m_2}{\left(1+\frac{m_1}{m_2}\right)^2 a_{1,0}^3} y_1; \quad k_1 = \frac{Km_1m_2}{\left(1+\frac{m_1}{m_2}\right)^2 a_{1,0}^3};$$

$$F_1 = k_1 y_1; \quad \vec{F_1} = -k_1\vec{y_1};$$

$$a_{1,0} = \frac{m_2 a_0}{m_1+m_2}; \quad a_0 = \frac{L_{\text{cloud}}^2 (m_1+m_2)}{Km_1^2 m_2^2};$$

$$k = \frac{Km_1m_2}{\left(1+\frac{m_1}{m_2}\right)^2 \frac{m_2^3 a_0^3}{(m_1+m_2)^3}} = \frac{Km_1m_2}{\frac{(m_1+m_2)^2}{m_2^2}\frac{m_2^3}{(m_1+m_2)^3}\frac{L_{\text{cloud}}^6 (m_1+m_2)^3}{K^3 m_1^6 m_2^6}};$$

$$k = \frac{K^4 m_1^7 m_2^6}{L_{\text{cloud}}^6\ (m_1+m_2)^2} = m_1\omega_{\text{osc}}^2 = m_1\frac{4\pi^2}{T_{\text{osc}}^2};$$

$$F_2 = ky_1; \quad \vec{F_1} = -k\vec{y_1};$$

$$T_{\text{osc}} = 2\pi\frac{L_{\text{cloud}}^3 (m_1+m_2)}{K^2 m_1^3 m_2^3}.$$

**c)**

$$\frac{K^4 m_1^6 m_2^6}{L_{\text{cloud}}^6 (m_1 + m_2)^2} = \omega_{\text{osc}}^2; \quad T_{\text{osc}} = 2\pi \frac{L_{\text{cloud}}^3 (m_1 + m_2)}{K^2 m_1^3 m_2^3};$$

$$\omega_{\text{osc}} = \frac{K^2 m_1^3 m_2^3}{L_{\text{cloud}}^3 (m_1 + m_2)} = \frac{2\pi}{T_{\text{osc}}};$$

$$T_{\text{osc}} \downarrow \Rightarrow \omega_{\text{osc}} \uparrow \Rightarrow \omega_{\text{osc,max}};$$

$$m_1 + m_2 = \text{constant};$$

$$\omega_{\text{osc}} = \omega_{\text{osc,max}}, \text{ when } m_1 = m_2 = \frac{m}{2};$$

$$\omega_{\text{osc,max}} = \frac{K^2 m^5}{64 L_{\text{cloud}}^3} = \frac{4\pi^2}{T_{\text{osc,min}}^2}; \quad T_{\text{osc,min}} = 16\pi \frac{L_{\text{cloud}}}{K m^2} \cdot \sqrt{\frac{L_{\text{cloud}}}{m}}.$$

# Problem 5
# A Star's Image Contrast

Even the brightest stars cannot be seen in the sky with the naked eye during daytime. However, using a telescope, not only the stars that are very bright but also those that are less bright can be seen during the day!

*Determine* the increase in a star's image contrast when observed through a telescope relative to the contrast of the same star's image when oberved with the naked eye. The following are considered known: $d$ – the diameter of the eye's pupil; $D$ – the diameter of the telescope's lens.

### Solution

If we observe the sky with the naked eye during the day, the stars cannot be seen against the bright background. The reason is that eye's sensitivity cannot perceive the very low contrast between the star and the sky. For this reason, the use of a telescope that increases the contrast between the star's and the sky's brightness is needed.

The observer's eye estimates the star's brightness relative to its illumination on the retina. The brighter the star is, the higher its image's illumination. A small portion of the sky can be assimilated with a star during the day.

The measure of the contrast between the star's image and the image of the sky background around the star on the retina of the eye is the ratio between the illumination of these two images on the retina, that is,

$$C = \frac{E_{\text{star}}}{E_{\text{sky background}}}.$$

This contrast (ratio) depends both on the physical parameters of the two sources (star, sky background) and on the parameters of the optical instrument (eye, telescope).

The illumination of an image is the ratio between the light flux received and the image surface:

$$E = \frac{F}{S}.$$

Since the star observed with the telescope is far away, the light beams received by the telescope lens are practically parallel. Consequently, the image of the star formed in the telescope lens' focus is the diffraction pattern presented in Figure 5.1. This image coincides with the diffraction image in the case of the diffraction of a parallel light beam when passing through a circular hole (slit) of a very small diameter in an opaque barrier, as presented in Figure 5.2. This diffraction image of the star is subsequently analyzed through the telescope's lens. The circular slit that limits the parallel light beam producing diffraction is the aperture of the telescope lens mounting.

The diffraction pattern of light corresponding to a circular slit has a central diffraction maximum (the Airy disk, or the zero-order

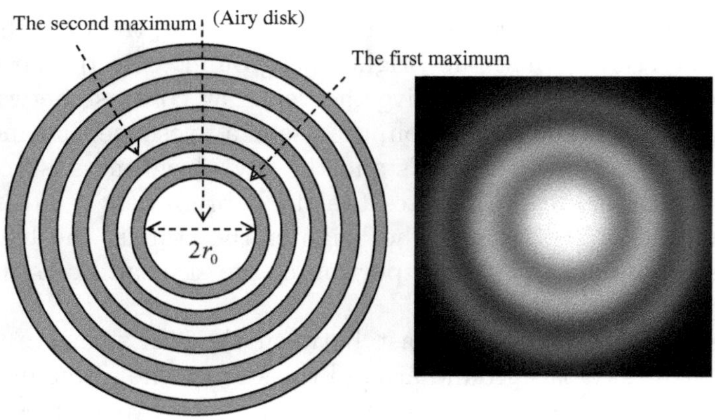


**Fig. 5.1**

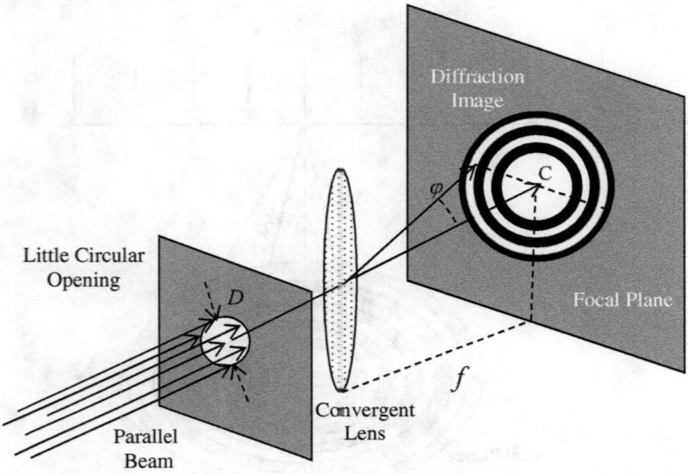


**Fig. 5.2**

maximum) whose linear diameter is demonstrated to be

$$2r_0 = f\Delta\varphi_0 = 2.44 \cdot \frac{\lambda}{D} \cdot f,$$

where: $\Delta\varphi_0$ is the angular diameter of the central maximum seen from the telescope lens' optical center; $\lambda$ is the wavelength of the respective radiation; $D$ is the diameter of the circular slit (in this particular case, the telescope diameter); $f$ is the focal length of the lens in whose focal plane the diffraction pattern is formed (surrounded by secondary maxima and minima, as presented in Figures 5.3, 5.4, 5.5, and 5.6). The diameter of the central maximum (the zero-order maximum) becomes larger as the light wavelength increases and the diameter of the circular slit through which the telescope incident parallel beam passes decreases. Around the central maximum there is a pattern of alternating dark and bright concentric rings.

The angular radii of the first two dark rings are:

$$\sin\varphi_1 \approx \varphi_1 = 0.61\frac{\lambda}{D}; \quad \sin\varphi_2 \approx \varphi_2 = 1.116\frac{\lambda}{D}.$$

Thus, the angular diameters of the first two dark rings are:

$$2\varphi_1 = 1.22\frac{\lambda}{D}; \quad 2\varphi_2 = 2.232\frac{\lambda}{D}.$$

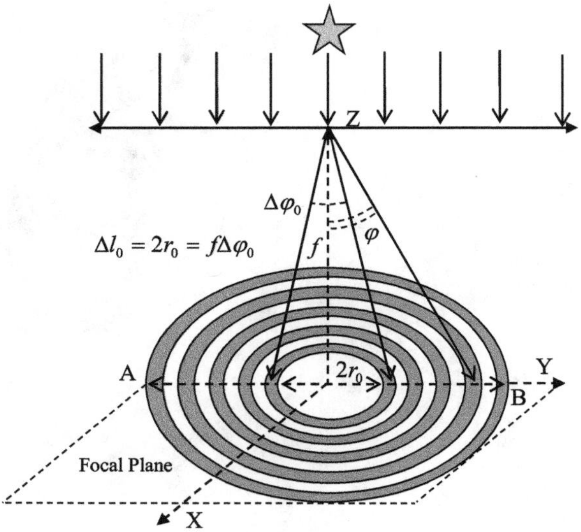
Z
$\Delta\varphi_0$
$\varphi$
$\Delta l_0 = 2r_0 = f\Delta\varphi_0$
$f$
A
$2r_0$
Y
B
Focal Plane
X

**Fig. 5.3**

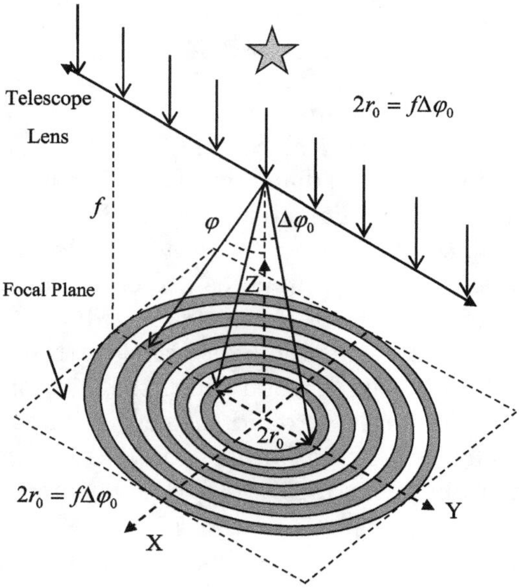
Telescope
Lens
$2r_0 = f\Delta\varphi_0$
$f$
$\varphi$
$\Delta\varphi_0$
Z
Focal Plane
$2r_0$
$2r_0 = f\Delta\varphi_0$
Y
X

**Fig. 5.4**

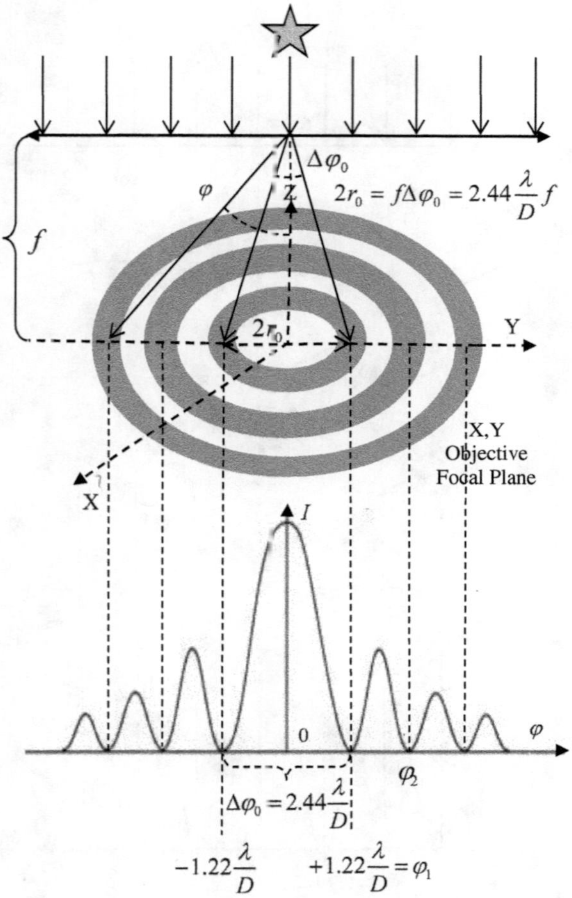


**Fig. 5.5**

The distribution of the light intensity inside the star's diffraction pattern formed in the telescope lens focal plane is presented in Figures 5.5 and 5.6. The existence of the central maximum surrounded by alternating dark and bright rings of decreasing luminosities is shown in Figures 5.5 and 5.6. Approximately 84% of the intensity of the light crossing the telescope lens is concentrated in the central maximum. If the illumination of the central maximum is $I_0$, the illumination of the first (bright) ring (the first-order maximum) is $0.0174I_0$, and the illumination of the

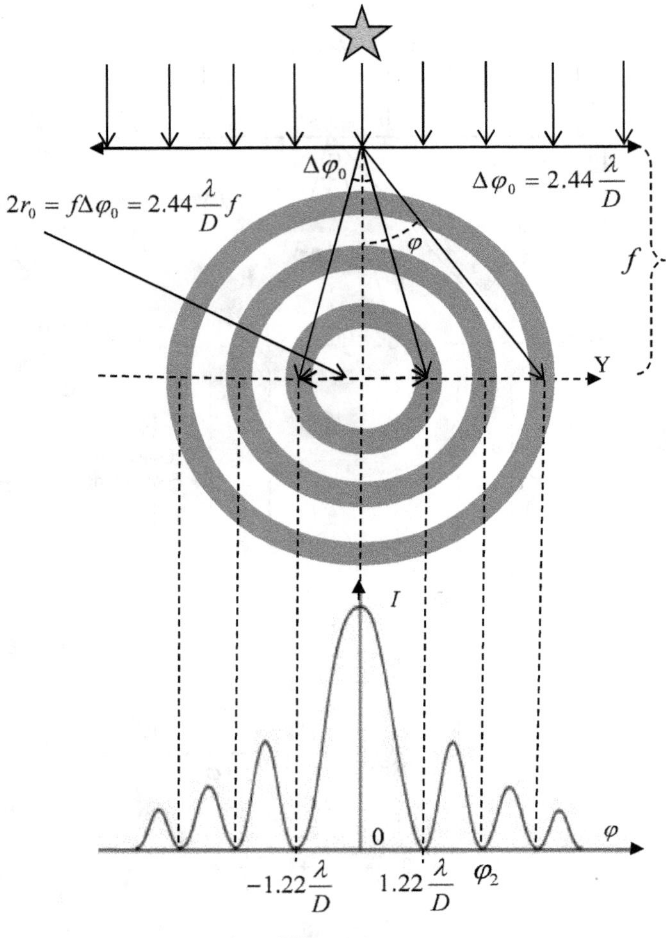


**Fig. 5.6**

second (bright) ring (the second-order maximum) is $0.0041I_0$. The illumination of the dark rings is zero.

The characteristics of the diffraction pattern were determined by Fresnel. He divided the surface of the wave front reaching the circular opening in the barrier into concentric zones (Fresnel zones). These zones are built in such a manner that the difference between the distance from two neighboring zones to the central point C is $\lambda/2$. Thus, the electromagnetic vibrations arriving at point C from two neighboring zones have opposed phases.

The diffraction image is different from a regular image. It does not resemble the real object. The diffraction image consists of alternating (concentric) bright and dark rings with a circular maximum in the center. About 84% of the light that crosses the circular opening is in the central maximum. Thus, the star's image formed by the telescope can be identified with the central maximum of the diffraction pattern.

Consequently, no matter the star's size, when observed with the same telescope, the diameter of the diffraction image will be identical and equal to the diameter of the central maximum, whose value depends exclusively on $\lambda$, $D$ and $f_{\text{lens}}$, as previously demonstrated.

$$(2r_0)_{\text{telescope}} = 2.44 \cdot \frac{\lambda}{D} \cdot f_{\text{lens}}.$$

For stars of different brightnesses, the brightness of their central maxima (the stars' image brightness) also differs. This brightness depends on the light flux received by the telescope lens from each star.

We will analyze now the image obtained by the naked eye retina placed in the focal plane of the lens. We consider to be known: $f_{\text{eye lens}}$ – the focal length of the eye's lens; $d$ – the pupil's diameter (Figure 5.7).

Since the star is very far away, the light rays received by the observer's eye represent a parallel beam. The image formed on the retina is not identical to the star, but a diffraction pattern. The circular central maximum of this pattern represents the star's diffraction image. The linear dimensions of such an image depend only on the eye's characteristics ($d$ – the pupil diameter; $f$ – the focal length of the lens; $\lambda$ – the wavelength of the incident radiation reaching the

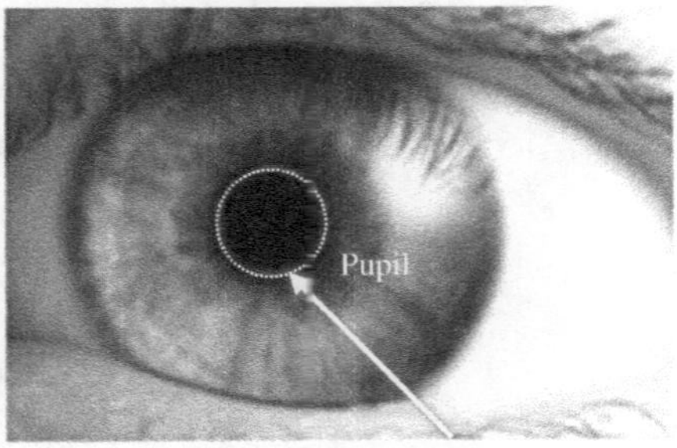


**Fig. 5.7**

eye's retina):

$$(2r_0)_{\text{retina}} = 2.44 \cdot \frac{\lambda}{d} f_{\text{eye lens}}.$$

For a star of luminosity $L$ located at the distance $r$ from the Earth, the energy flux density (the energy that crosses one unit surface area per unit time) at distance $r$ (at the observer) is

$$F_{\text{star}} = \frac{L_{\text{star}}}{4\pi r^2}.$$

The radiation flux (the energy of the incident radiation per unit time) received at the entrance to the telescope mounting through its entire transversal cross-section is

$$\varphi_{\text{star, telescope}} = F_{\text{star}} \cdot \Delta S_{\text{telescope}} = F_{\text{star}} \cdot \pi \left(\frac{D}{2}\right)^2$$
$$= \frac{L_{\text{star}}}{4\pi r^2} \cdot \frac{\pi D^2}{4} = \frac{L_{\text{star}} D^2}{16 r^2}.$$

The density of the radiation flux received in the central maximum represents the energy arriving per unit time per unit surface area of the central maximum (the Airy disk).

In the lens' focal plane where the image is formed, the illumination of the central diffraction maximum (the Airy disk) is:

$$E_{\text{star, Airy, telescope}} = \frac{\varphi_{\text{star, telescope}}}{S_{\text{star, Airy, telescope}}} = \frac{\frac{L_{\text{star}} D^2}{16 r^2}}{\pi r^2_{0,\text{ star, Airy, telescope}}}$$
$$= \frac{L_{\text{star}} D^2}{16\pi r^2 r^2_{0,\text{ star, Airy, telescope}}};$$

$$r_{0,\text{star, Airy, telescope}} = 1.22 \cdot \frac{\lambda}{D} \cdot f_{\text{lens}};$$

$$E_{\text{star, Airy, telescope}} = \frac{L_{\text{star}} D^2}{16\pi r^2 (1.22)^2 \frac{\lambda^2}{D^2} f^2_{\text{lens}}};$$

$$E_{\text{star, Airy, telescope}} = \frac{L_{\text{star}}}{16 (1.22)^2 \pi r^2} \frac{D^4}{\lambda^2 f^2_{\text{lens}}},$$

showing that the illumination of the central maximum of the star's diffraction pattern (the Airy disk) in the telescope lens focal plane is $E_{\text{star, Airy, telescope}} \sim D^4$.

For a portion of the daytime sky of luminosity $L_{\text{sky}}$, considered an extended light source and localized (as with the star) at the same distance, $r$, from the observer on the Earth, the density of the energy flux at distance $r$ (at the observer) is

$$F_{\text{sky}} = \frac{L_{\text{sky}}}{4\pi r^2}.$$

The density of the energy flux represents the energy that crosses one unit surface area in one time unit.

Thus, the flux of received radiation (the energy of the radiation received in one time unit) at the entrance of the telescope mounting, through the surface of its entire transversal cross-section, is

$$\begin{aligned}\varphi_{\text{sky, telescope}} &= F_{\text{sky}} \cdot \Delta S_{\text{telescope}} = F_{\text{sky}} \cdot \pi \left(\frac{D}{2}\right)^2 \\ &= \frac{L_{\text{sky}}}{4\pi r^2} \cdot \frac{\pi D^2}{4} = \frac{L_{\text{sky}} D^2}{16 r^2}.\end{aligned}$$

Consequently, the illumination corresponding to the respective portion of the sky in the focal plane of the telescope's lens (the density of the radiation flux in the focal plane of the lens, that is, the energy received in one time unit by one unit surface area in the focal plane of the objective lens) is

$$\begin{aligned}E_{\text{sky, telescope}} &= \frac{\varphi_{\text{sky, telescope}}}{4\pi r^2} = \frac{L_{\text{sky}} D^2}{16 r^2 4\pi f^2_{\text{lens, telescope}}} \\ &= \frac{L_{\text{sky}}}{4 \cdot 16\pi r^2} \frac{D^2}{f^2_{\text{lens, telescope}}},\end{aligned}$$

showing that the illumination of the image of the sky portion in the focal plane of the telescope lens is $E_{\text{sky,telescope}} \sim D^2$. We specify that the image of the sky sector formed in the focal plane of the telescope's lens is not a diffraction image, in contrast to the star's image in the same plane.

Let us define the contrast of the star when observed through the telescope during the daytime:

$$C_{\text{star, sky, telescope}} = \frac{E_{\text{sky, telescope}}}{E_{\text{sky, telescope}}} = \frac{\frac{L_{\text{star}}}{16\cdot(1{,}22)^2\pi r^2}\cdot\frac{D^4}{\lambda^2 f^2_{\text{lens, telescope}}}}{\frac{L_{\text{star}}}{4\cdot 16\pi r^2}\cdot\frac{D^2}{f^2_{\text{lens, telescope}}}};$$

$$C_{\text{star, sky, telescope}} = \frac{4L_{\text{star}}}{(1,22)^2 L_{\text{sky}}}\cdot\frac{D^2}{\lambda^2}.$$

Let us consider that the same star and the same portion of the daytime sky are observed with the naked eye. The density of the radiation flux received by the eye's pupil from a star located at a distance $r$ is

$$F_{\text{star}} = \frac{L_{\text{star}}}{4\pi r^2}.$$

The pupil is considered to be a circular aperture of diameter $d$, as shown in Figure 5.7.

The energetic flux (that is, the energy crossing a surface in one time unit) at distance $r$, where the observer's pupil is located, across the entire surface of the pupil, is

$$\varphi_{\text{star, eye}} = F_{\text{star}}\cdot\Delta S_{\text{pupil}} = F_{\text{star}}\cdot\pi\left(\frac{d}{2}\right)^2$$

$$= \frac{L_{\text{star}}}{4\pi r^2}\cdot\frac{\pi d^2}{4} = \frac{L_{\text{star}} d^2}{16 r^2}.$$

Consequently, the illumination of central diffraction maximum (the Airy disk) in the focal plane of the eye lens where the star's image forms is:

$$E_{\text{star, Airy, eye}} = \frac{\varphi_{\text{star, eye}}}{S_{\text{star, Airy, eye}}} = \frac{\frac{L_{\text{star}} d^2}{16 r^2}}{\pi r^2_{0,\text{star, Airy,retina}}}$$

$$= \frac{L_{\text{star}} d^2}{16\pi r^2 r^2_{0,\text{star, Airy,retina}}};$$

$$r_{0,\text{star, Airy,retina}} = 1.22\cdot\frac{\lambda}{d}\cdot f_{\text{eye lens}};$$

$$E_{\text{star, Airy, eye}} = \frac{L_{\text{star}} d^2}{16\pi r^2 (1.22)^2 \frac{\lambda^2}{d^2} f_{\text{eye lens}}^2};$$

$$E_{\text{star, Airy, eye}} = \frac{L_{\text{star}}}{16 (1.22)^2 \pi r^2} \frac{d^4}{\lambda^2 f_{\text{eye lens}}^2}.$$

The flux density of the radiation received at the central maximum represents the energy received in one time unit by one unit surface area of the central Airy maximum.

The above formula shows that the illumination of the central maximum of the star's diffraction image (the Airy disk) in the focal plane of the eye's lens (on the retina) is $E_{\text{star, Airy, eye}} \sim d^4$.

Let us consider a portion of the daytime sky considered to be an extended light source located at the same distance $r$ from the observer on the Earth as the star. The luminosity of this portion of the daytime sky is $L_{\text{sky}}$. The density of the energetic flux (that is, the energy that crosses one unit surface area in one time unit) at distance $r$ from the observer, corresponding to the same portion of the sky, is

$$F_{\text{sky}} = \frac{L_{\text{sky}}}{4\pi r^2}.$$

Thus, the flux of the radiation (that is, the energy of the radiation received in one time unit) at the pupil level, across the entire pupil surface, is

$$\varphi_{\text{sky, eye}} = F_{\text{sky}} \cdot \Delta S_{\text{pupil}} = F_{\text{sky}} \cdot \pi \left(\frac{d}{2}\right)^2 = \frac{L_{\text{sky}}}{4\pi r^2} \cdot \frac{\pi d^2}{4} = \frac{L_{\text{sky}} d^2}{16 r^2}.$$

Consequently, the illumination of the sky portion in the focal plane of the eye lens, on the eye's retina (the density of the radiation flux received in the focal plane of the lens, that is, the energy received in one time unit by one unit surface area of the lens in its focal plane, on the retina) is

$$E_{\text{sky, eye}} = \frac{\varphi_{\text{sky, eye}}}{4\pi r^2} = \frac{L_{\text{sky}} d^2}{16 r^2 4\pi f_{\text{eye lense}}^2} = \frac{L_{\text{sky}}}{4 \cdot 16\pi r^2} \frac{d^2}{f_{\text{eye lens}}^2}.$$

This shows that the illumination of the sky sector's image in the focal plane of the eye lens is $E_{\text{sky, eye}} \sim d^2$. We specify that the image of the sky portion in the focal plane of the telescope lens is not a diffraction image, in contrast to the image of the star in the same plane.

We define the contrast between the star and the daytime sky observed with the naked eye as:

$$C_{\text{star, sky, eye}} = \frac{E_{\text{star, eye}}}{E_{\text{sky, eye}}} = \frac{\frac{L_{\text{star}}}{16\cdot(1{,}22)^2\pi r^2} \cdot \frac{d^4}{\lambda^2 f_{\text{eye lens}}^2}}{\frac{L_{\text{sky}}}{4\cdot 16\pi r^2} \cdot \frac{d^2}{f_{\text{eye lens}}^2}};$$

$$C_{\text{star, sky, eye}} = \frac{4L_{\text{star}}}{(1.22)^2 L_{\text{sky}}} \cdot \frac{d^2}{\lambda^2}.$$

Under these conditions, the following results:

$$\frac{C_{\text{star, sky, telescope}}}{C_{\text{star, sky, eye}}} = \frac{\frac{4L_{\text{star}}}{(1.22)^2 L_{\text{sky}}} \cdot \frac{D^2}{\lambda^2}}{\frac{4L_{\text{star}}}{(1.22)^2 L_{\text{sky}}} \cdot \frac{d^2}{\lambda^2}};$$

$$\frac{C_{\text{star, sky, telescope}}}{C_{\text{star, sky, eye}}} = \frac{D^2}{d^2};$$

$$C_{\text{star, sky, telescope}} = \left(\frac{D}{d}\right)^2 C_{\text{star, sky, eye}};$$

$$D >> d; \quad C_{\text{star, sky, telescope}} >> C_{\text{star, sky, eye}}.$$

In this case, the use of the telescope increases by $(D/d)^2$ times the contrast between the image of the star and the sky background during the day. Consequently, with a telescope, less bright stars can be seen even during the day.

# Problem 6

# The Alpha Centauri Star System

The triple star system Alpha Centauri is formed of: the star Alpha Centauri A (the brightest star in the system); the star Alpha Centauri B, which orbits around the star Alpha Centauri A; and Alpha Centauri C, the closest star to our solar system which is also called Proxima Centauri. Alpha Centauri C orbits around the double star system Alpha Centauri AB.

At the time of the epoch J2000.0, we know

- the equatorial coordinates of the star Alpha Centauri A:

$$\alpha_{\mathrm{A}} = 14^{\mathrm{h}}39^{\mathrm{m}}36.50^{\mathrm{s}}; \quad \delta_{\mathrm{A}} = -60^{0}50'\,02.3'';$$

- the equatorial coordinates of the star Proxima Centauri (Alpha Centauri C):

$$\alpha_{\mathrm{P}} = 14^{\mathrm{h}}29^{\mathrm{m}}42.95^{\mathrm{s}}; \quad \delta_{\mathrm{P}} = -62^{0}40'\,46.1''.$$

**a)** *Derive* the approximate angular distance, $\Delta\theta$, between the stars Alpha Centauri A and Proxima Centauri, observed from the Earth.

**b)** If the distance between the Earth and the star Proxima Centauri is $D = 4$ light years, *derive* the distance $d$ between the stars Alpha Centauri A and Proxima Centauri.

**c)** *Derive* the angle $\phi$ between the celestial meridian of the star Proxima Centauri and the great circle on the celestial sphere containing the star Proxima Centauri and the star Alpha Centauri A.

**Solution**

**a)** Using the notation in Figure 6.1, where $\sigma_A$ is the star Alpha Centauri A and $\sigma_P$ is the star Proxima Centauri (Alpha Centauri C), it results that:

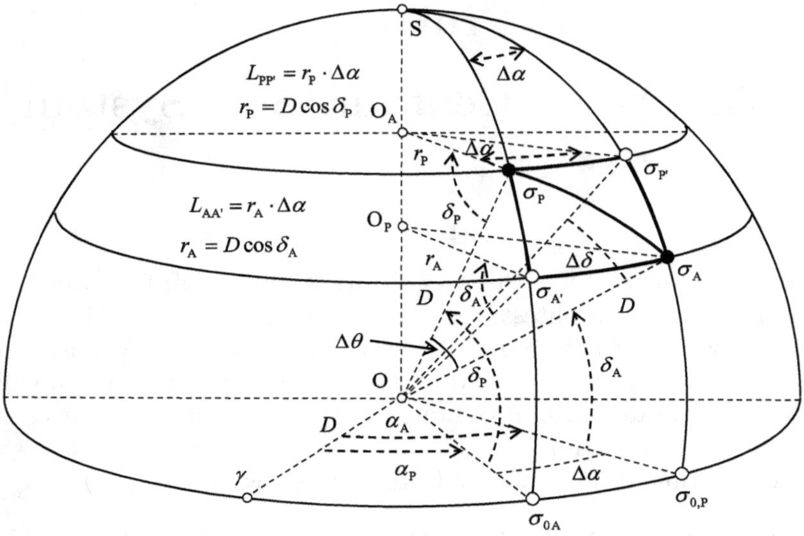


**Fig. 6.1**

$$\sigma_A\sigma_P = D \cdot \Delta\theta,$$

where $\Delta\theta$ is the angular distance between the two stars;

$$\sigma_A\sigma_{P'} = \sigma_P\sigma_{A'} = D \cdot \Delta\delta; \Delta\delta = |\delta_P| - |\delta_A|;$$

$$\sigma_A\sigma_{A'} = r_A \cdot \Delta\alpha = D \cdot \cos\delta_A \cdot \Delta\alpha; \quad \Delta\alpha = \alpha_A - \alpha_P;$$

$$\sigma_P\sigma_{P'} = r_P \cdot \Delta\alpha = D \cdot \cos\delta_P \cdot \Delta\alpha; \quad \Delta\alpha = \alpha_A - \alpha_P;$$

$$\Delta(\sigma_P\sigma_A\sigma_{A'});$$

$$\sigma_P\sigma_A = \sqrt{(\sigma_P\sigma_{A'})^2 + (\sigma_A\sigma_{A'})^2};$$

$$\Delta\theta = \sqrt{(\Delta\delta)^2 + (\cos\delta_A \cdot \Delta\alpha)^2};$$

$$\Delta\theta = \sqrt{(\Delta\delta)^2 + (\cos\delta_P \cdot \Delta\alpha)^2};$$

$$\Delta\delta = |\delta_P| - |\delta_A| = 62^0 40'\ 46.1'' - 60^0 50'\ 02.3'' = 1^0 50'\ 43.77'';$$

$$\Delta\alpha = \alpha_{\rm A} - \alpha_{\rm P} = 14^{\rm h}39^{\rm m}36.50^{\rm s} - 14^{\rm h}29^{\rm m}42.95^{\rm s} = 9^{\rm m}53.55^{\rm s}$$
$$= 2.4731^0;$$
$$\Delta\theta = 2.435^0.$$

**b)**

$$d = D \cdot \Delta\theta = 1.7 \cdot 10^{15} \text{ m}.$$

**c)** According to the law of sines for the spherical triangle $S\sigma_P\sigma_A$, outlined in Figure 6.2, the result is:

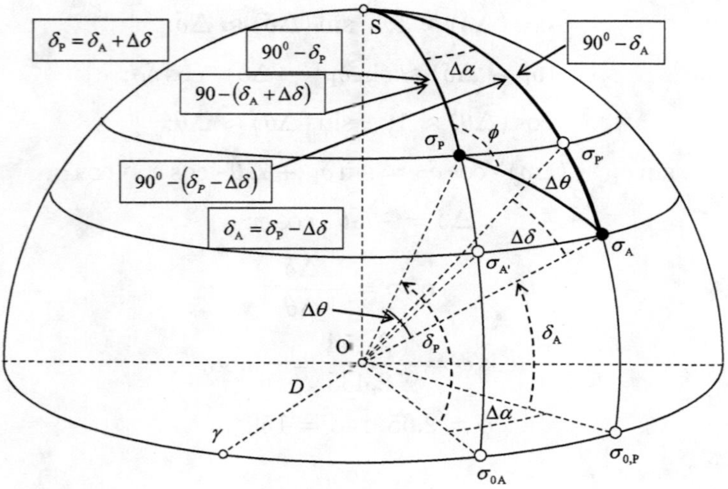


**Fig. 6.2**

$$\frac{\sin a}{\sin A} = \frac{\sin b}{\sin B} = \frac{\sin c}{\sin C};$$
$$\frac{\sin(\Delta\theta)}{\sin(\Delta\alpha)} = \frac{\sin\left[90^0 - (\delta_{\rm P} - \Delta\delta)\right]}{\sin\phi};$$
$$\frac{\sin(\Delta\theta)}{\sin(\Delta\alpha)} = \frac{\cos(\delta_{\rm P} - \Delta\delta)}{\sin\phi};$$

$$\sin(\Delta\theta) \approx \Delta\theta; \quad \sin(\Delta\alpha \approx \Delta\alpha); \quad \cos(\delta_P - \Delta\delta) \approx \cos\delta_P;$$

$$\sin\phi = \frac{\Delta\alpha}{\Delta\theta} \cdot \cos\delta_P.$$

From the law of cosines applied to the same spherical triangle, it results that:

$$\cos a = \cos b \cdot \cos c + \sin b \cdot \sin c \cdot \cos A;$$

$$\cos[90^\circ - (\delta_P - \Delta\delta)] = \cos(\Delta\theta) \cdot \cos(90^\circ - \delta_P) + \sin(\Delta\theta) \cdot \sin(90^\circ - \delta_P) \cdot \cos\phi;$$

$$\sin(\delta_P - \Delta\delta) = \cos(\Delta\theta) \cdot \sin\delta_P + \sin(\Delta\theta) \cdot \cos\delta_P \cdot \cos\phi;$$

$$\sin(\delta_P - \Delta\delta) = \sin\delta_P \cdot \cos(\Delta\delta) - \cos\delta_P \cdot \sin(\Delta\delta);$$

$$\cos(\Delta\delta) \approx 1; \quad \sin(\Delta\delta) \approx \Delta\delta;$$

$$\sin(\delta_P - \Delta\delta) \approx \sin\delta_P - (\Delta\delta) \cdot \cos\delta_P;$$

$$\cos(\Delta\theta) \approx 1; \quad \sin(\Delta\theta) \approx \Delta\theta;$$

$$\sin\delta_P - (\Delta\delta) \cdot \cos\delta_P = \sin\delta_P + \Delta\theta \cdot \cos\delta_P \cdot \cos\phi;$$

$$\Delta\delta = -\Delta\theta \cdot \cos\phi;$$

$$\cos\phi = -\frac{\Delta\delta}{\Delta\theta};$$

$$\cos\phi = -\frac{2.154}{2.435} = -0{,}88;$$

$$\phi = 2.65 \ \text{rad} = 152^\circ;$$

$$\sin\phi = \frac{\Delta\alpha}{\Delta\theta} \cdot \cos\delta_P;$$

$$\sin^2\phi + \cos^2\phi = 1;$$

$$(\Delta\theta)^2 = (\Delta\alpha \cdot \cos\delta_P)^2 + (\Delta\delta)^2;$$

$$\Delta\theta = \sqrt{(\Delta\delta)^2 + (\cos\delta_P \cdot \Delta\alpha)^2}.$$

# Problem 7

# Binary Star System in Eclipse

In Figure 7.1 is represented the light curve (the intensity of the light at the observer as a function of time) $I = f(t)$ for a binary star in eclipse ($\sigma_1$; $\sigma_2$), The notation is: $m_0 = 10.4$ – the apparent magnitude of the binary star when the two stars are not in eclipse; $m_1 = 10.68$ – the apparent magnitude of the binary star system when the star $\sigma_2$ is behind the star $\sigma_1$; $m_{a.e} = 10.78$ – the apparent magnitude of the binary star during the annular eclipse. It is known that $R_{\sigma_1} > R_{\sigma_2}$ and $T_{\sigma_1} > T_{\sigma_2}$.

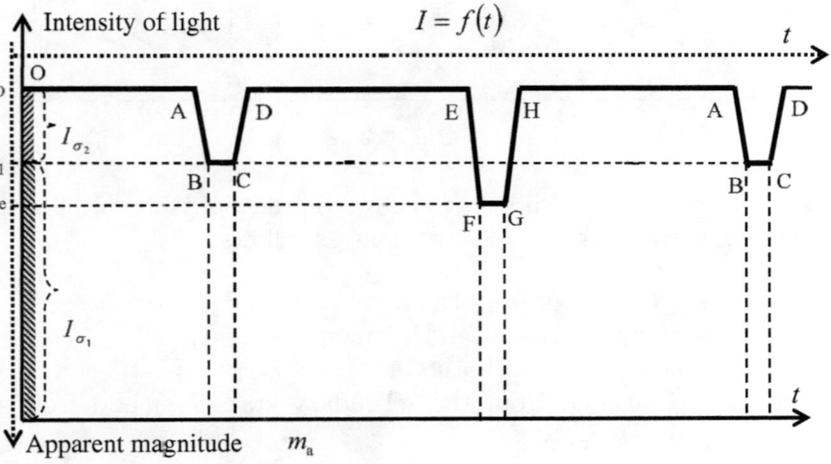


**Fig. 7.1**

*Derive* the ratio of the effective temperatures of the two stars' surfaces, $T_2/T_1$.

## Solution

Figure 7.2 shows the concentric circular orbits of the two stars with respect to the center of mass. If the observer of the binary star is in the plane of the orbits of the two stars, when $i = 90°$, as indicated in Figure 7.2, then the observer sees only the oscillatory motions of the projections of the two stars on a common diameter (MN), the two stars eclipsing each other periodically.

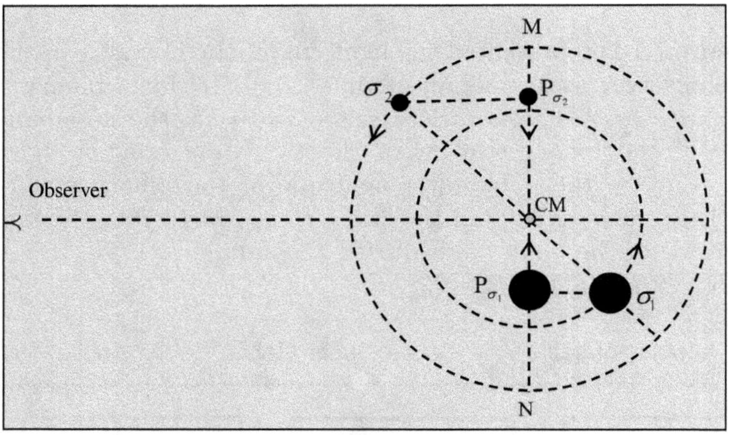


**Fig. 7.2**

Corresponding to different sectors of the light curve, shown in Figure 7.3, the observer receives light as follows:

- on the sector OA, from both stars ($I_{\sigma 1}$; $I_{\sigma 2}$);
- on the sector BC, only from the main star ($I_{\sigma 1}$);
- on the sector DE, from both stars ($I_{\sigma 1}$; $I_{\sigma 2}$);
- on the sector FG, from the secondary star ($I_{\sigma 2}$) and from the primary star ($\eta I_{\sigma 1} < I_{\sigma 1}$);
- on the sector HA, from both stars ($I_{\sigma 1}$; $I_{\sigma 2}$).

Corresponding to the positions I, II, and IV represented in Figure 7.3, when the magnitudes of the binary star system are $m_0$,

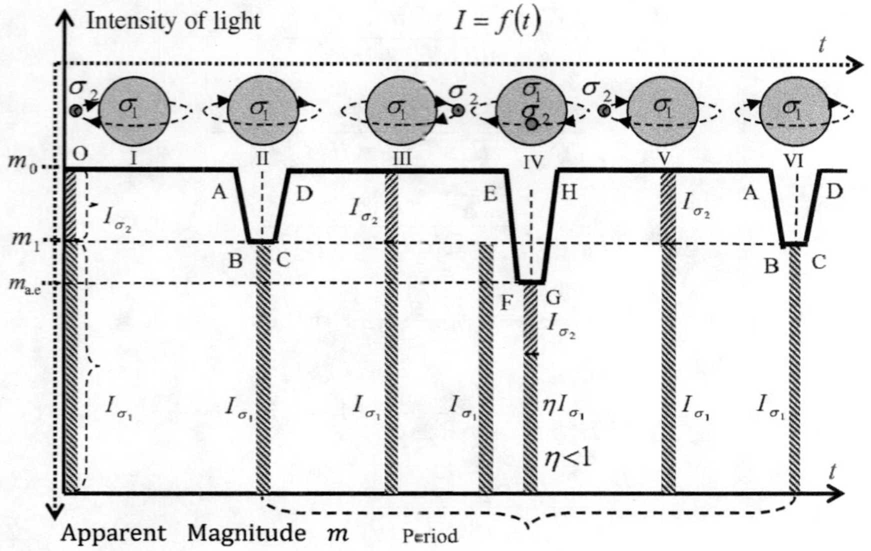


**Fig. 7.3**

$m_1$ and $m_{\text{a.e}}$, respectively, their luminosities are calculated as:

$$L_0 = \pi R_1^2 \sigma T_1^4 + \pi R_2^2 \sigma T_2^4;$$

$$L_1 = \pi R_1^2 \sigma T_1^4;$$

$$L_{\text{a.e}} = \pi \left(R_1^2 - R_2^2\right) \sigma T_1^4 + \pi R_2^2 \sigma T_2^4.$$

Thus, according to the Pogson formula, the following results occur:

$$\log \frac{L_1}{L_0} = -0.4\,(m_1 - m_0);$$

$$m_1 = 10.68 \qquad m_0 = 10.04;$$

$$\log \frac{L_1}{L_0} = -0.4\,(m_1 - m_0); \quad \log \frac{L_1}{L_0} = -0.256;$$

$$\log \frac{L_0}{L_1} = 0.256; \quad \frac{L_0}{L_1} = 10^{0.256};$$

$$\frac{L_0}{L_1} = 1.8; \quad \frac{L_1}{L_0} = 0.55;$$

$$\frac{L_1}{L_0} = \frac{\pi R_1^2 \sigma T_1^4}{\pi R_1^2 \sigma T_1^4 + \pi R_2^2 T_2^4};$$

$$\frac{L_1}{L_0} = \frac{\pi R_1^2 \sigma T_1^4 + \pi R_2^2 \sigma T_2^4 - \pi R_2^2 \sigma T_2^4}{\pi R_1^2 \sigma T_1^4 + \pi R_2^2 T_2^4};$$

$$\frac{L_1}{L_0} = 1 - \frac{\pi R_2^2 \sigma T_2^4}{\pi R_1^2 \sigma T_1^4 + \pi R_2^2 T_2^4};$$

$$1 - \frac{\pi R_2^2 \sigma T_2^4}{\pi R_1^2 \sigma T_1^4 + \pi R_2^2 T_2^4} = 0.55;$$

$$\frac{\pi R_2^2 \sigma T_2^4}{\pi R_1^2 \sigma T_1^4 + \pi R_2^2 T_2^4} = 1 - 0.55;$$

$$\frac{\pi R_2^2 \sigma T_2^4}{\pi R_1^2 \sigma T_1^4 + \pi R_2^2 T_2^4} = 0.45;$$

$$\log \frac{L_{\text{a.e}}}{L_0} = -0.4\,(m_{\text{a.e}} - m_0);$$

$$m_{\text{a.e}} = 10.78; \quad m_0 = 10.04;$$

$$\log \frac{L_{\text{a.e}}}{L_0} = -0.4\,(m_{\text{a.e}} - m_0); \quad \log \frac{L_{\text{a.e}}}{L_0} = -0.296;$$

$$\log \frac{L_0}{L_{\text{a.e}}} = 0.296; \quad \frac{L_0}{L_{\text{a.e}}} = 10^{0.296};$$

$$\frac{L_0}{L_{\text{a.e}}} = 1.95; \quad \frac{L_{\text{a.e}}}{L_0} = 0.51;$$

$$L_{\text{a.e}} = \pi \left(R_1^2 - R_2^2\right) \sigma T_1^4 + \pi R_2^2 \sigma T_2^4,$$

$$L_0 = \pi R_1^2 \sigma T_1^4 + \pi R_2^2 \sigma T_2^4;$$

$$\frac{L_{\text{a.e}}}{L_0} = \frac{\pi R_1^2 \sigma T_1^4 + \pi R_2^2 \sigma T_2^4 - \pi R_2^2 T_1^4}{\pi R_1^2 \sigma T_1^4 + \pi R_2^2 T_2^4};$$

$$\frac{L_{\text{a.e}}}{L_0} = 1 - \frac{\pi R_2^2 T_1^4}{\pi R_1^2 \sigma T_1^4 + \pi R_2^2 T_2^4}; \quad \frac{L_{\text{a.e}}}{L_0} = 0.51;$$

$$1 - \frac{\pi R_2^2 T_1^4}{\pi R_1^2 \sigma T_1^4 + \pi R_2^2 T_2^4} = 0.51;$$

$$\frac{\pi R_2^2 T_1^4}{\pi R_1^2 \sigma T_1^4 + \pi R_2^2 T_2^4} = 1 - 0.51;$$

$$\frac{\pi R_2^2 T_1^4}{\pi R_1^2 \sigma T_1^4 + \pi R_2^2 T_2^4} = 0.49;$$

$$\frac{\pi R_2^2 \sigma T_2^4}{\pi R_1^2 \sigma T_1^4 + \pi R_2^2 T_2^4} = 0.45;$$

$$\frac{T_2^4}{T_1^4} = \frac{0.45}{0.49} = \frac{45}{49};$$

$$\frac{T_1^4}{T_2^4} = \frac{49}{45}; \quad \left(\frac{T_1}{T_2}\right)^4 = \frac{49}{45};$$

$$4 \log \frac{T_1}{T_2} = \log \frac{49}{45}; \quad \log \frac{T_1}{T_2} = \frac{1}{4} \log \frac{49}{45};$$

$$\log \frac{T_1}{T_2} = \frac{1}{4} \log \frac{49}{45}; \quad \frac{T_1}{T_2} = 1.021;$$

$$\frac{T_2}{T_1} = 0.98,$$

represents the ratio of the absolute effective temperatures of the surfaces of the two stars.

# Problem 8

# The Horizontal Diurnal Parallax of the Sun

The following quantities are known: the semi-major axis of the elliptical orbit of Mars around the Sun, $a_{\mathrm{M}} = 227.93 \cdot 10^6$ km; the eccentricity of Mars, elliptical orbit, $e_{\mathrm{M}} = 0.0934$; the radius of the Earth's circular orbit around the Sun, $a_{\mathrm{E}} = 149.59 \cdot 10^6$ km; the horizontal diurnal parallax of Mars during opposition, $p_{0,\mathrm{M,opposition}} = 23.04$ arcsec; the horizontal diurnal parallax of Mars during conjunction, $p_{0,\mathrm{M,conjunction}} = 3.29$ arcsec.

*Derive* the horizontal diurnal parallax of the Sun, $p_{0,\mathrm{S}}$.

### Solution

### 1) Mars in opposition

To start with, the horizontal diurnal parallax of the planet Mars is considered known (as a planet close to the Earth at the moment of its "opposition"), when, as shown in Figure 8.1, the planet Mars is at the perihelion of its elliptical orbit around the Sun ($a_{\mathrm{M}}$ – semi-major axis of Mars' elliptical orbit), on the same side as the Earth, which has a circular orbit around the Sun ($r_{\mathrm{ES}} = a_{\mathrm{E}}$).

From the study of the motion of a material point under the action of the central gravitational force, it is known that when, in its evolution on an ellipse with the Sun in one of its foci, the planet passes through the perihelion of the orbit, the planet is at its minimum distance in relation to the Sun:

$$r_{\min,\mathrm{M}} = r_{\mathrm{MS},\min} = a_{\mathrm{M}}\,(1 - e_{\mathrm{M}}),$$

where $e_{\mathrm{M}}$ is the numerical eccentricity of Mars' elliptical orbit.

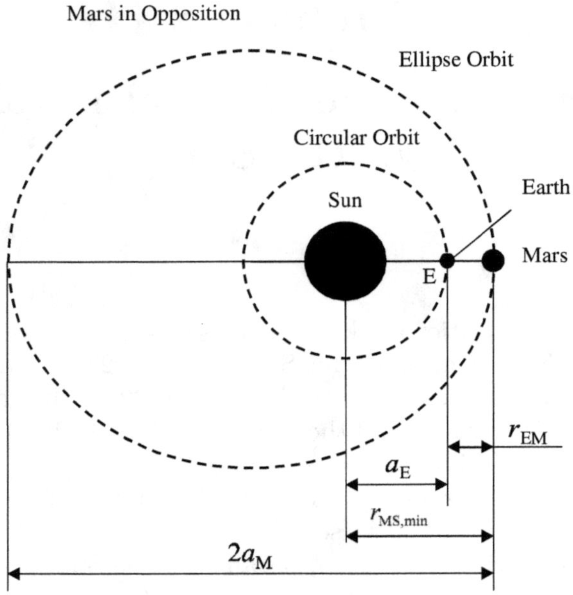


**Fig. 8.1**

This condition results in:

$$r_{\mathrm{EM}} = r_{\mathrm{MS},\min} - r_{\mathrm{ES}};$$

$$r_{\mathrm{EM}} = a_{\mathrm{M}}\,(1 - e_{\mathrm{M}}) - a_{\mathrm{E}}.$$

Using Figure 8.2 and the definition of the horizontal diurnal parallax of a star, the result is:

$$\sin p_{0,\mathrm{S}} \approx p_{0,\mathrm{S}} = \frac{R}{r_{\mathrm{ES}}} = \frac{R}{a_{\mathrm{E}}};$$

$$\sin p_{0,\mathrm{M}} \approx p_{0,\mathrm{M}} = \frac{R}{r_{\mathrm{EM}}},$$

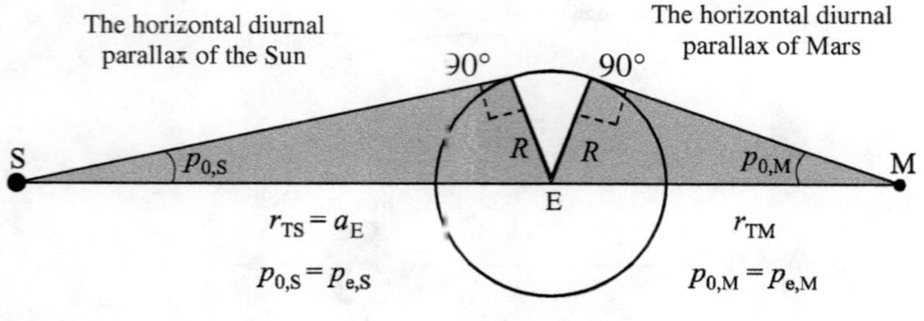


**Fig. 8.2**

where $p_{0,S}$ is the horizontal diurnal parallax of the Sun, $p_{0,M}$ is the horizontal diurnal parallax of Mars, and $R$ is the radius of the Earth, considered to be spherical;

$$R = a_E \cdot p_{0,S} = r_{EM} \cdot p_{0,M};$$

$$a_E \cdot p_{0,S} = r_{EM} \cdot p_{0,M};$$

$$r_{EM} = a_M (1 - e_M) - a_E;$$

$$a_E \cdot p_{0,S} = (a_M (1 - e_M) - a_E) \cdot p_{0,M};$$

$$p_{0,S} = \left[\frac{a_M}{a_E}(1 - e_M) - 1\right] p_{0,M};$$

$$a_M = 227.93 \cdot 10^6 \text{ km}; \quad e_M = 0.0934; \quad a_E = 149.59 \cdot 10^6 \text{ km};$$

$$p_{0,M,\text{opposition}} = 23.04 \text{ arcsec};$$

$$p_{0,S} = \left[\frac{227.93 \cdot 10^6 \text{ km}}{149.59 \cdot 10^6 \text{ km}}(1 - 0.0934) - 1\right] \cdot 23.04 \text{ arcsec};$$

$$p_{0,S} = \left[\frac{227.93}{149.59} \cdot 0.9066 - 1\right] \cdot 23.04 \text{ arcsec};$$

$$p_{0,S} = 8.78 \text{ arcsec}.$$

## 2) Mars in conjunction

This time, we take the horizontal diurnal parallax of the planet Mars (which is close to the Earth at the moment of its solar "conjunction") when, as seen from Figure 8.3, the planet Mars is at the aphelion of its elliptical orbit with respect to the Sun ($a_M$ is the semi-major axis of the elliptical orbit of Mars), on the other side compared

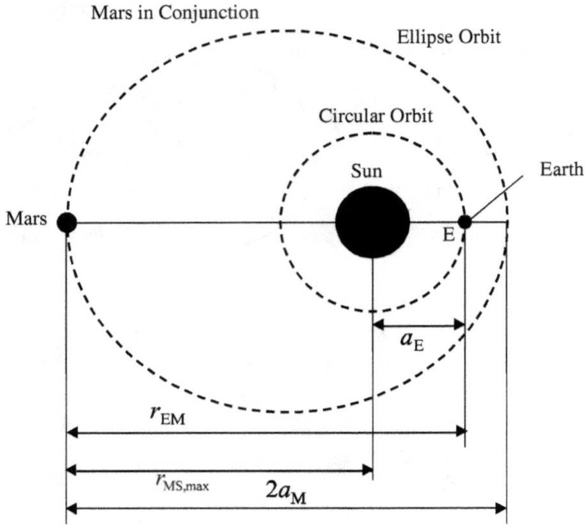


**Fig. 8.3**

with the Earth, which moves on a circular orbit around the Sun ($r_{ES} = a_E$).

In these conditions, the result is:

$$r_{EM} = r_{MS,max} + r_{ES};$$
$$r_{EM} = a_M (1 + e_M) + a_E.$$

By using Figure 8.2 and the definition of the horizontal diurnal parallax, the result is:

$$\sin p_{0,S} \approx p_{0,S} = \frac{R}{r_{ES}} = \frac{R}{a_E};$$

$$\sin p_{0,M} \approx p_{0,M} = \frac{R}{r_{EM}},$$

where $p_{0,S}$ is the horizontal diurnal parallax of the Sun, $p_{0,M}$ is the horizontal diurnal parallax of Mars, and $R$ is the Earth's radius, considered spherical;

$$R = a_E \cdot p_{0,S} = r_{EM} \cdot p_{0,M}; a_E \cdot p_{0,S} = r_{EM} \cdot p_{0,M};$$
$$r_{EM} = a_M(1 + e_M) + a_E;$$
$$a_E \cdot p_{0,S} = (a_M (1 + e_M) + a_E) \cdot p_{0,M};$$

$$p_{0,\mathrm{S}} = \left[\frac{a_\mathrm{M}}{a_\mathrm{E}}(1 - e_\mathrm{M}) + 1\right] p_{0,\mathrm{M}};$$

$$a_\mathrm{M} = 227.93 \cdot 10^6 \text{ km}; \ e_\mathrm{M} = 0.0934; \ a_\mathrm{E} = 149.59 \cdot 10^6 \text{ km};$$

$$p_{0,\mathrm{M},\,\text{conjunction}} = 3.29 \text{ arcsec};$$

$$p_{0,\mathrm{S}} = \left[\frac{227.93 \cdot 10^6 \text{ km}}{149.59 \cdot 10^6 \text{ km}}(1 + 0.0934) + 1\right] \cdot 3.29 \text{ arcsec};$$

$$p_{0,\mathrm{S}} = \left[\frac{227.93}{149.59} \cdot 1.0934 + 1\right] \cdot 3.29 \text{ arcsec}; \quad p_{0,\mathrm{S}} = 8.77 \text{ arcsec}.$$

# Problem 9

# The Equatorial Horizontal Diurnal Parallax of the Moon

Two observers, $O_1$ and $O_2$, situated in two locations on the Earth's surface, on the same meridian, one in the Northern Hemisphere and one in the Southern Hemisphere, measure, at the same diurnal time, the topocentric zenith distances $z_1$ and $z_2$ of the Moon.

*Derive* the angular distance, $\Delta\varphi$, between the two observation locations, knowing that the equatorial horizontal parallax of the Moon is $p_{e.M} = 57'\,02.7''$.

## Solution

In Figure 9.1, O represents a given observation point on the Earth's surface, $z$ is the topocentric zenith distance of the Moon, and $p$ is the diurnal parallax of the Moon, i.e., the angle under which the radius of the Earth at the given observation point is seen from the center of the Moon.

In the same figure, $O_0$ represents a given observation point on the Earth's surface when the topocentric zenith distance of the Moon is $z_0 = 90°$, and $p_{0,M}$ is the *horizontal diurnal parallax* of the Moon, when the Moon is on the horizon of the observation point, such that

$$p_{0,M} = p_{max},$$

that is, the horizontal diurnal parallax of the Moon represents the maximum value of the Moon's diurnal parallax.

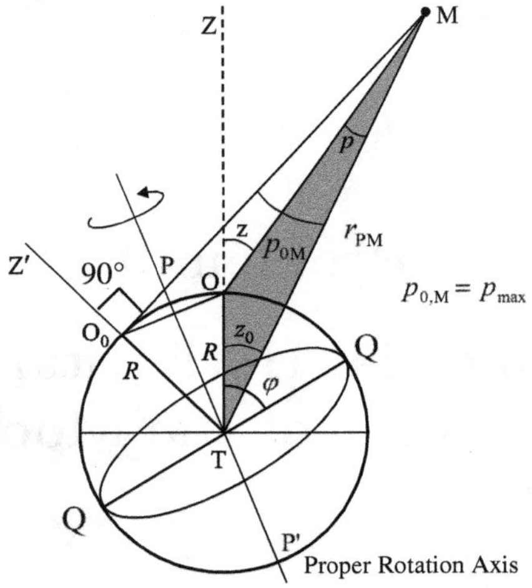


**Fig. 9.1**

In these conditions, the result is

$$\sin p_{OM} = \frac{R}{r_{PM}},$$

such that, using also the law of sines for the triangle ΔOTM, we obtain:

$$\frac{\sin p}{R} = \frac{\sin(180° - z)}{r_{PM}}; \quad \frac{\sin p}{R} = \frac{\sin z}{r_{PM}};$$

$$\sin p = \frac{R}{r_{PM}} \sin z; \quad \sin p = \sin p_{OM} \cdot \sin z;$$

$$\sin p \approx p; \quad \sin p_{OM} \approx p_{OM};$$

$$p = p_{OM} \cdot \sin z.$$

If $z_1$ and $z_2$ are the topocentric angular distances of the Moon, and $p_1$ and $p_2$ are the diurnal height parallaxes of the Moon in relation to the two observation sites, as shown in Figure 9.2, then between the angles of the quadrilateral $TO_1MO_2$, which is formed of the triangles $TO_1M$ and $TO_2M$, the following relation exists:

$$(180° - z_1 + (\varphi_1 - x) + p_1) + (180° - z_2 + (|\varphi_2| + x) + p_2) = 360°;$$
$$p_1 + p_2 = z_1 + z_2 - (\varphi_1 + |\varphi_2|).$$

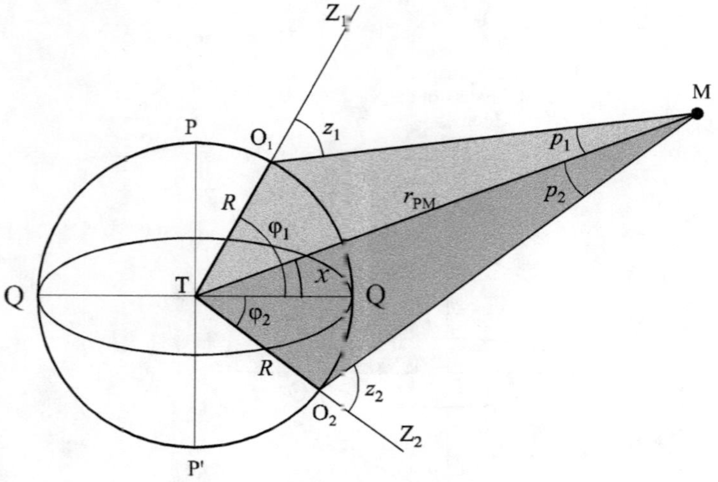


**Fig 9.2**

From the previous formula,

$$p = p_{0,M} \cdot \sin z,$$

for the two observation points, as outlined in Figure 9.2, we obtain:

$$p_1 = p_{0,M} \sin z_1; \quad p_2 = p_{0,M} \sin z_2;$$

$$p_1 + p_2 = z_1 + z_2 - (\varphi_1 + |\varphi_2|);$$

$$p_{0,M} \sin z_1 + p_{0,M} \sin z_2 = z_1 + z_2 - (\varphi_1 + |\varphi_2|);$$

$$p_{0,M} = \frac{z_1 + z_2 - (\varphi_1 + |\varphi_2|)}{\sin z_1 + \sin z_2},$$

representing the horizontal diurnal parallax of the Moon.

Assuming that the Earth is spherical, as seen from Figure 9.3, it results that the equatorial horizontal diurnal parallax of the Moon, $p_{e.M}$, is equal to the horizontal diurnal parallax of the Moon, $p_{0,M}$, such that we have:

- the diurnal height parallax of the Moon, $p$;
- the horizontal diurnal parallax of the Moon, $p_{0,M} = p_{max}$;
- the equatorial horizontal diurnal parallax of the Moon, $p_{e.M} = p_{0,M}$.

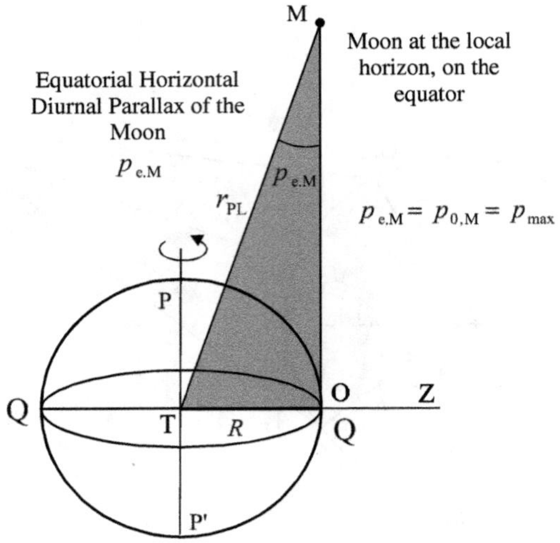


**Fig. 9.3**

Thus:

$$\sin p_{\text{e.M}} = \frac{R}{r_{\text{PM}}} = p_{0,\text{M}};$$

$$p_{0,\text{M}} = p_{\text{e.M}} = \frac{z_1 + z_2 - (\varphi_1 + |\varphi_2|)}{\sin z_1 + \sin z_2};$$

$$\varphi_1 + |\varphi_2| = \Delta\varphi;$$

$$p_{\text{e.M}} = \frac{z_1 + z_2 - \Delta\varphi}{\sin z_1 + \sin z_2};$$

$$z_1 + z_2 - \Delta\varphi = p_{\text{e.M}}(\sin z_1 + \sin z_2);$$

$$\Delta\varphi = z_1 + z_2 + p_{\text{e.M}}(\sin z_1 + \sin z_2);$$

$$p_{\text{e.M}} = 57'02'',7;$$

$$z_1 = 30^\circ; \quad z_2 = 45^\circ; \quad \sin z_1 = 0.5; \sin z_2 = 0.7;$$

$$\Delta\varphi = 75^\circ + 57'\,02''.7 \cdot (0.5 + 0.7)\,;$$

$$\Delta\varphi = 75^\circ + 57'\,02''.7 \cdot 1.2; \quad \Delta\varphi = 75^\circ + 3422''.7 \cdot 1.2;$$

$$\Delta\varphi = 75^\circ + 4107''.24; \quad \Delta\varphi = 75^\circ + 1^\circ.1409;$$

$$\Delta\varphi = 76^\circ + 0^\circ.1409; \quad \Delta\varphi = 76^\circ + 8'.454;$$

$$\Delta\varphi = 76^\circ + 8'\,27''.\,24; \quad \Delta\varphi = 76^\circ\ 8'27''.24.$$

## Annex – The Diurnal Parallax of a Star

An observer situated at a point O on the Earth's surface does not observe the absolute diurnal rotation of the Earth around its axis, with respect to a fixed star, $\sigma$, situated at a distance $r$ from the Sun's center, as indicated in Figure 9.4, but can observe the relative diurnal rotation of the star around the axis of the Earth, such that the star stays, for one day, at the same distance from the Earth's center.

In Figure 9.4 the star $\sigma$ is represented at the diurnal time of passing through the local meridian, when its topocentric zenith distance is $z = \angle \mathrm{ZO}\sigma$, and the geocentric zenith distance is $z_0 = \angle \mathrm{ZT}\sigma$.

The diurnal height parallax of a star $\sigma$ is the angle $p = \angle \mathrm{O}\sigma\mathrm{T}$ under which one can see the radius of the Earth (corresponding to the observation point) from the center of the star.

From the law of sines of the triangle $\Delta\,\mathrm{OT}\sigma$, the result is:

$$\frac{\sin p}{R} = \frac{\sin (180^\circ - z)}{r}; \quad \frac{\sin p}{R} = \frac{\sin z}{r};$$

$$\sin p = \frac{R}{r} \sin z,$$

where $R$ is the radius of the Earth (considered to be spherical).

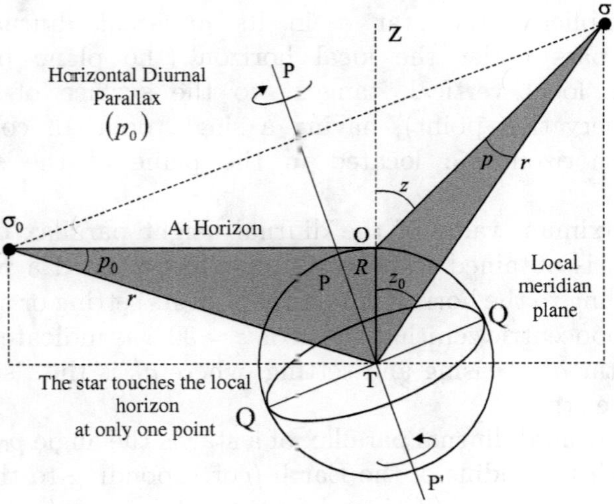


**Fig. 9.4**

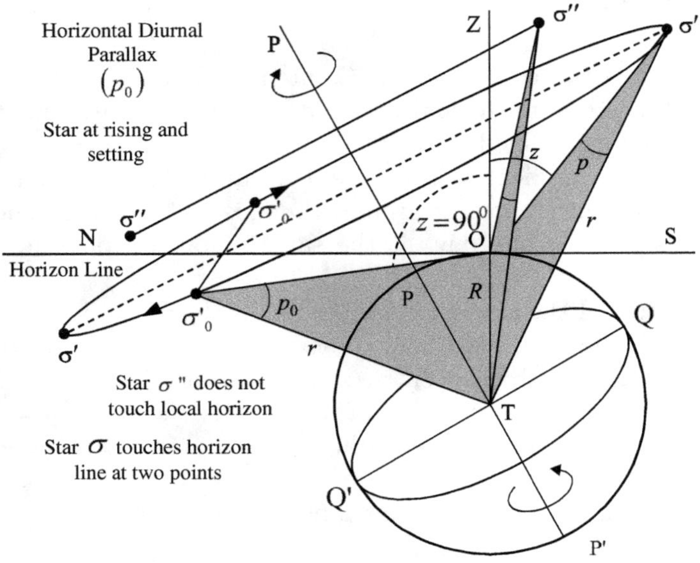


**Fig. 9.5**

The diurnal height parallax of a star depends on the distance between the center of the star and the center of the Earth and on the topocentric zenith distance.

For simplicity, the star $\sigma$ in its apparent diurnal motion, does not pass under the local horizon (the plane perpendicular to the local vertical, tangent to the surface of the Earth at the observation point), having a single point of contact with the local horizon, $\sigma_0$, located in the plane of the same local meridian.

The maximum value of the diurnal height parallax of the star, $p_{\max} = p_0$, is obtained when the star $\sigma$ has reached a position $\sigma_0$, corresponding to the horizon line, that is, at its setting or at its rising, when its topocentric zenith distance is $z = 90°$, as indicated in Figure 9.5 for a star $\sigma'$ at rising and setting, where $\sigma'_0$ is the rising/setting point of the star.

The horizontal diurnal parallax of a star is the angle $p_0 = \angle \mathrm{O}\sigma_0\mathrm{T}$ under which the radius of the Earth (corresponding to the observation site) would be seen if viewed from the center of the star when it is at the horizon.

When the star is in the relative position $\sigma_0$ with respect to the Earth (at the diurnal moment of reaching the horizon plane, the positions $\sigma_0$ and $\sigma$ being symmetrical with respect to the Earth's axis), the distance from the center of the star to the center of the Earth is also $r$, such that from the right triangle $\Delta O_0 \mathrm{T}\sigma$, with right angle at $O_0$, as shown in Figures 9.4 and 9.5, we obtain:

$$\sin p_0 = \frac{R}{r}.$$

By analyzing the absolute diurnal rotation of the Earth around its own axis (which coincides with the direction of the Earth's axis) in relation to the fixed star (Figure 9.6), it is obvious that the distance between the center of the Earth and the center of the star is constant ($r$). This actually changes (due to the Earth's rotation) the orientation of the local vertical observation site, so that both the topocentric zenith distance of the star and the distance from the observer to the center of the star are variable.

Under these conditions, the diurnal height parallax of the star (the angle under which the radius of the Earth is seen, corresponding to the observation point at the center of the star) is variable, having the maximum value when the observer is in the position $\mathrm{O}_0$ and sees the

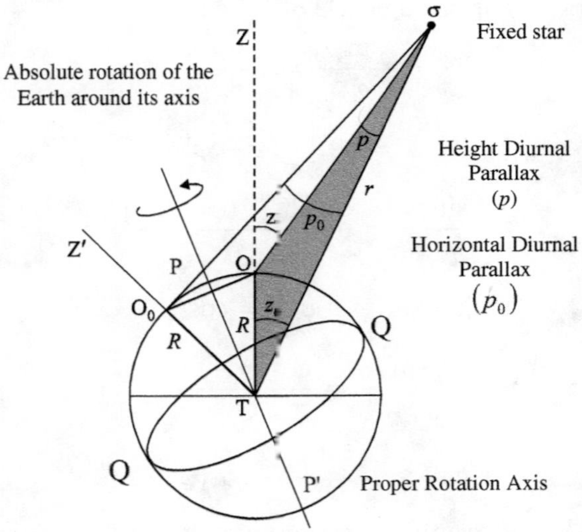


**Fig. 9.6**

star at the local horizon ($p_0 = p_{\max}$). The horizontal diurnal parallax of a star is equal to the maximum value of the diurnal height parallax of the same star.

Taking into account the relations that allow the determination of each diurnal parallax of the same star results in:

$$\sin p = \frac{R}{r}\sin z; \quad \sin p_0 = \frac{R}{r};$$

$$\sin p = \sin p_0 \sin z;$$

$$\sin p \approx p; \quad \sin p_0 \approx p_0.$$

From the astronomical observations, it is shown that the angles which define the two parallaxes are very small, such that:

$$p = p_0 \sin z; \quad p_0 = \frac{R}{r}.$$

In measurements of high precision, one must take into account that the Earth is not spherical, so that when determining the parallax, the value $R$ must be replaced by $\rho_{\text{geo}}$, representing the geocentric radius corresponding to the observation site.

As a result, for a star situated at the local observation horizon, its horizontal diurnal parallax is a function of $\rho_{\text{geo}}$ (corresponding to the observation site), such that by using Figure 9.7 and the sine law written for the right triangle $\mathrm{OT}\sigma_0$, the result is:

$$\frac{\sin p_0}{\rho_{\text{geo}}} = \frac{\sin x}{r};$$

$$x = 90^\circ - (\varphi - \varphi');$$

$$\frac{\sin p_0}{\rho_{\text{geo}}} = \frac{\sin[90 - (\varphi - \varphi')]}{r};$$

$$\sin[90^\circ - (\varphi - \varphi')] = \cos(\varphi - \varphi');$$

$$\frac{\sin p_0}{\rho_{\text{geo}}} = \frac{\cos(\varphi - \varphi')}{r};$$

$$\sin p_0 \approx p_0 = \frac{\rho_{\text{geo}}}{r}\cos(\varphi - \varphi\prime),$$

where $\varphi$ is the geographic (astronomic) latitude of the observation site, and $\varphi'$ is the geocentric latitude of the observation site.

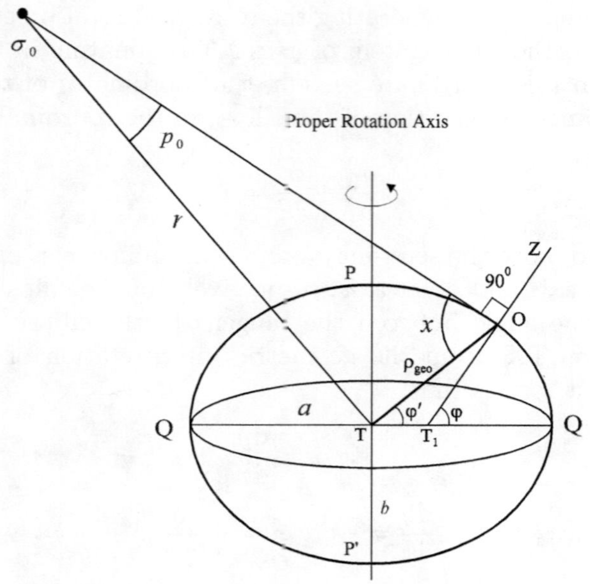


**Fig. 9.7**

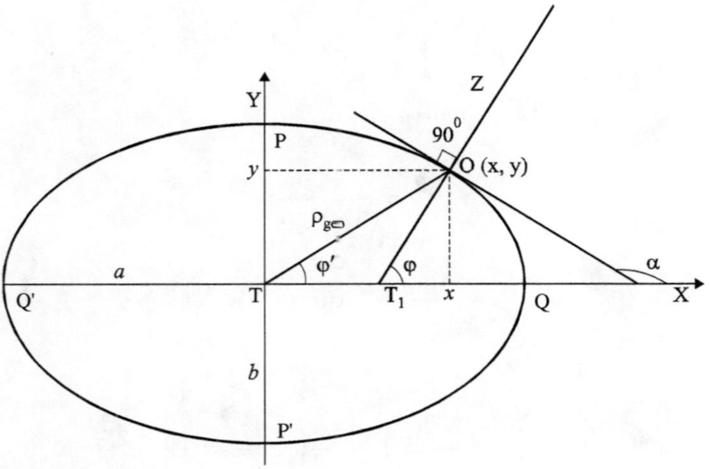


**Fig. 9.8**

In order to establish the relationship between the geographic latitude ($\varphi$) and the geocentric latitude ($\varphi'$) of the location O on the surface of the Earth, in Figure 9.8 is represented the meridian ellipse of the point O, generating the terrestrial rotation ellipsoid relative to an orthogonal system of axes XY originating in the Earth's center T. In this coordinate system, the coordinates of the point O are $(x,\ y)$, and the equation of the ellipse in the coordinates $(x,\ y)$ is

$$\frac{x^2}{a^2} + \frac{y^2}{b^2} = 1,$$

where $a$ and $b$ are the semi-major and semi-minor axes of the ellipse (equatorial axis and polar axis, respectively, of the ellipsoid).

If $\alpha$ is the angle between the tangent to the ellipse at point O and the axis TX, from the geometric interpretation of a function derivative, it results that:

$$\operatorname{tg} \alpha = \frac{\mathrm{d}y}{\mathrm{d}x};$$

$$\alpha = \varphi + 90°; \quad \frac{\mathrm{d}y}{\mathrm{d}x} = -\operatorname{ctg} \varphi = -\frac{1}{\operatorname{tg} \varphi}; \quad \frac{\mathrm{d}x}{\mathrm{d}y} = -\operatorname{tg} \varphi;$$

$$y^2 = b^2 \left(1 - \frac{x^2}{a^2}\right); \quad \operatorname{tg}\ \varphi' = \frac{y}{x};$$

$$2y \cdot \mathrm{d}y = -\frac{b^2}{a^2} \cdot 2x \cdot \mathrm{d}x;$$

$$y \,\mathrm{d}y = -\frac{b^2}{a^2} x \,\mathrm{d}x;$$

$$\frac{y}{x} = -\frac{b^2}{a^2} \frac{\mathrm{d}x}{\mathrm{d}y};$$

$$\frac{y}{x} = \operatorname{tg} \varphi'; \quad \frac{\mathrm{d}x}{\mathrm{d}y} = -\operatorname{tg} \varphi;$$

$$\operatorname{tg} \varphi' = \frac{b^2}{a^2} \operatorname{tg} \varphi;$$

$$e^2 = \frac{a^2 - b^2}{a^2} = 1 - \frac{b^2}{a^2}; \quad \frac{b^2}{a^2} = 1 - e^2;$$

$$\operatorname{tg} \varphi' = (1 - e^2) \operatorname{tg} \varphi,$$

where $e$ is the numerical eccentricity of an ellipse.

As a consequence, the maximum value of $p_0$ is obtained when the star is observed from point O on the Earth's Equator (Figure 9.9), a point where $\rho_{\text{geo}} = a_{\text{e}}$ (the equatorial radius of the Earth).

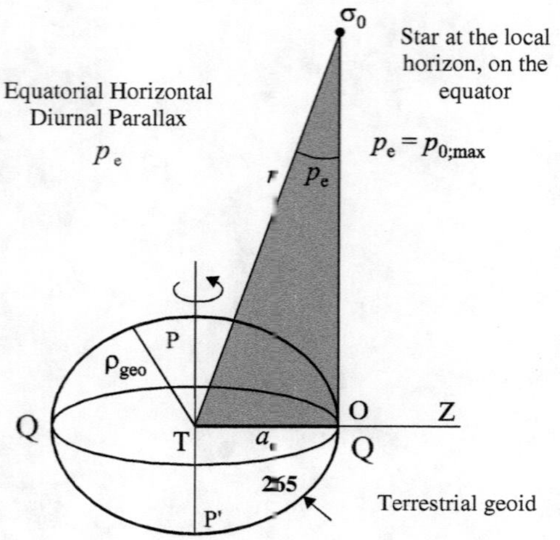


**Fig. 9.9**

The *equatorial horizontal diurnal parallax* is the angle $p_e$ under which the equatorial radius of the terrestrial geoid would be seen from the center of a star located at the horizon of an observation spot on the terrestrial Equator.

The *equatorial horizontal diurnal parallax* is equal to the maximum value of the horizontal diurnal parallax of a star observed from different points of the Earth's geoid:

$$p_e = p_{0,\max} = \frac{a_e}{r},$$

a relation which permits the derivation of the distance between the center of the Earth and the center of the star if the equatorial horizontal diurnal parallax of the star is known,

$$r = \frac{a_e}{p_e}.$$

If the Earth is considered spheric, then the *equatorial horizontal diurnal parallax* of a star is equal to the *horizontal diurnal parallax* of the same star.

# Problem 10

# Maximum Radial Velocities

The elliptical orbit of star $\sigma$ around star $\Sigma$ is shown in Figure 10.1, where the observation line of the system is also indicated.

**a)** *Calculate* the maximum radial speed of star $\sigma$. Known variables: the ellipse semi-axes $a$ and $b$; $K$ is the gravitational attraction constant; $M$ is the mass of star $\Sigma$. The mass of star $\sigma$ is $m \ll M$.

**b)** *Calculate* the duration $\tau_1$ during which the radial component of the speed of star $\sigma$ grows from zero to its maximal value, and the duration $\tau_2$ during which the same component decreases from its maximal value to zero, if $\tau_1/\tau_2 = n$.

**c)** *Identify* the two interpretations of durations $\tau_1$ and $\tau_2$.

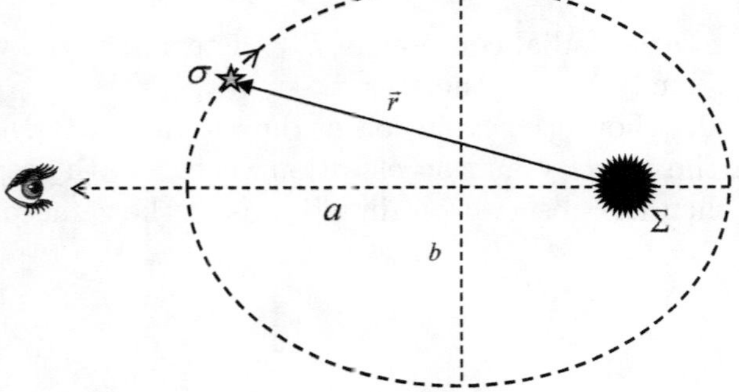


**Fig. 10.1**

## Solution

**a)** For a star $\sigma$, whose velocity is $\vec{v}$ with respect to an observer O, as shown in Figure 10.2, let us define its radial velocity, $\vec{v}_{rad}$, as the velocity component along the direction of observation, and its tangential velocity, $\vec{v}_{tang}$, as the velocity component perpendicular to the direction of observation.

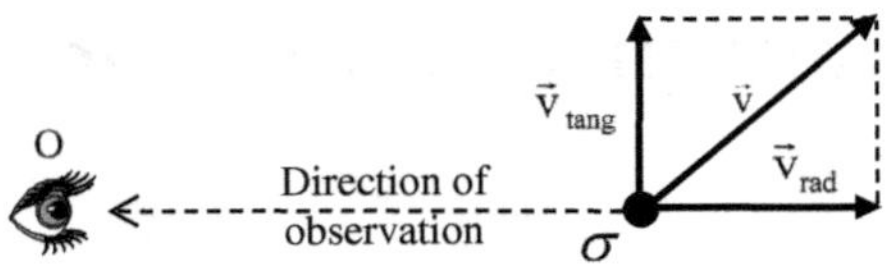


**Fig. 10.2**

Under these conditions, as Figure 10.2 shows, we have:

$$v_1 = v_{max} = v_{tang.\,max}; \quad v_2 = v_{min} = v_{tang.\,min};$$

$$v_{rad,1} = v_{rad,2} = 0;$$

$$v_5 = v_6 = v = v_{rad}.$$

We can do the same for the acceleration of the star $\sigma$, which is $\vec{a} = \frac{\vec{F}}{m}$, due to the central gravitational force from the star $\Sigma$, so we can deconstruct it into a tangential and radial component, as Figure 10.3 shows:

$$\vec{a} = \vec{a}_{rad} + \vec{a}_{tang}.$$

However, only the radial component $\vec{a}_{rad}$ determines the variation of the radial velocity $\vec{v}_{rad}$ of the star $\sigma$.

Figure 10.4 shows the evolution of the radial and tangential components of the velocity and acceleration vectors with respect to the observer, when the observation direction is in the same plane as the orbit.

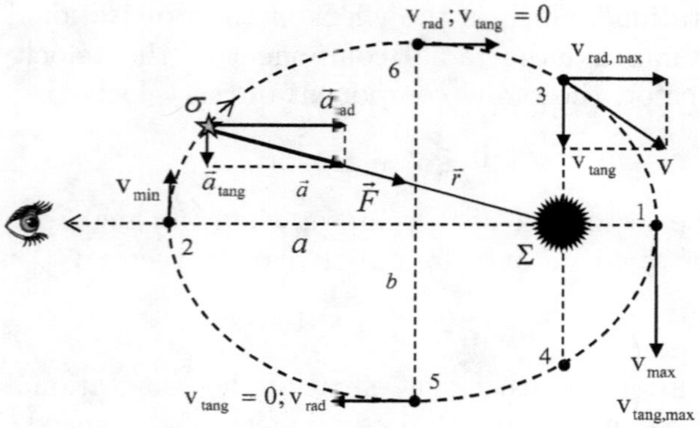


**Fig. 10.3**

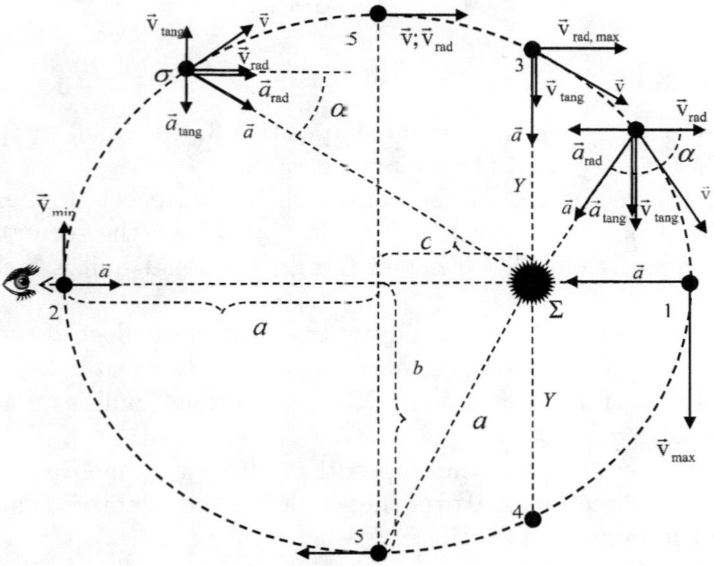


**Fig. 10.4**

On the sector 2-Σ-3 of the ellipse, when the angle $\alpha$, between the acceleration vector $\vec{a}$ and the radial velocity vector $\vec{\mathrm{v}}_{\mathrm{rad}}$, is

$$0 \leq \alpha \leq 90^{\circ},$$

the acceleration (which is the effect of the gravitational attraction force) will increase the radial component of the velocity. As such, over this sector, the radial component of the velocity is

$$0 \leq \mathrm{v}_{\mathrm{rad}} \leq \mathrm{v}_{\mathrm{rad,max}}.$$

Over the sector 3–1 of the ellipse, when the angle $\alpha$ between the acceleration vector $\vec{a}$ and the radial velocity vector $\vec{\mathrm{v}}_{\mathrm{rad}}$ is

$$90 \leq \alpha \leq 180^\circ,$$

the acceleration (which is the effect of the gravitational attraction force) will decrease the radial component of the speed. Thus, over this sector, the radial component of the velocity will be

$$0 \leq \mathrm{v}_{\mathrm{rad}} \leq \mathrm{v}_{\mathrm{rad,max}}.$$

**Conclusions:**

- for $\alpha = 90^\circ$, when the star $\sigma$ is in position 3, the radial component of the velocity reaches its maximal value;
- over the sector 2–3 of the ellipse, the radial effect of the gravitational pull is an accelerating effect, and over the sector 3–1 of the ellipse, the radial effect of the gravitational pull is a slowing effect;
- over the sector 2–3 of the ellipse, the tangential effect of the gravitational pull is a slowing effect, and over the sector 3–1 of the ellipse, the tangential effect of the gravitational pull is an accelerating effect;
- over the sector 2–3 of the ellipse, the vectors $\vec{\mathrm{v}}_{\mathrm{rad}}$ and $\vec{a}_{\mathrm{rad}}$ point in the same direction, and over the sector 3–1 the vectors $\vec{\mathrm{v}}_{\mathrm{rad}}$ and $\vec{a}_{\mathrm{rad}}$ point in opposite directions;
- in position 3, where the direction of the vector $\vec{a}_{\mathrm{rad}}$ is changing, the vector $\vec{\mathrm{v}}_{\mathrm{rad}}$ is at its maximum.

In a random position on the ellipse, the angular momentum of the star $\sigma$ is:

$$\vec{L} = \vec{r} \times m\vec{\mathrm{v}}; \quad L = rm\mathrm{v} \cdot \sin(\vec{r}; \vec{\mathrm{v}}).$$

Thus, in accordance with the angular momentum conservation law, we have:

$$\vec{L} = \text{constant}; \quad L = rm\text{v} \cdot \sin(\vec{r}; \vec{v}) = r_{\text{min}} m\text{v}_{\text{max}} = r_{\text{max}} m\text{v}_{\text{min}};$$

$$r = \frac{p}{1 + e\cos\theta}; \quad \text{v} = \sqrt{KM\left(\frac{2}{r} - \frac{1}{a}\right)};$$

$$r_{\text{min}} = \frac{p}{1+e}; \quad \text{v}_{\text{max}} = \sqrt{\frac{KM\,(1+e)}{1-e}};$$

$$r_{\text{min}} = \frac{p}{1-e}; \quad \text{v}_{\text{min}} = \sqrt{\frac{KM\,(1-e)}{1+e}};$$

$$p = a\left(1 - e^2\right); \quad p = b\sqrt{1-e^2};$$

$$L = m\sqrt{\frac{KMa^2\,(1-e)^2\,(1+e)}{a\,(1-e)}} = mb\sqrt{\frac{KM}{a}}.$$

In position 3 of star $\sigma$, its angular momentum is

$$L = Ym\text{v}_{\text{rad,max}}.$$

Thus, we have:

$$Ym\,\text{v}_{\text{rad,max}} = mb\sqrt{\frac{KM}{a}}; \quad \text{v}_{\text{rad,max}} = \frac{b}{Y} \cdot \sqrt{\frac{KM}{a}};$$

$$\frac{x^2}{a^2} + \frac{y^2}{b^2} = 1;$$

$$x = c; \quad y = Y; \quad \frac{c^2}{a^2} + \frac{Y^2}{b^2} = 1; \quad c^2 = a^2 - b^2; \quad Y = \frac{b^2}{a};$$

$$\text{v}_{\text{rad,max}} = \frac{a}{b} \cdot \sqrt{\frac{KM}{a}}.$$

**b)**

$$\Delta\text{v}_{\text{rad},23} = \text{v}_{\text{rad,max}} - 0 = \text{v}_{\text{rad,max}}; \quad \Delta t_{23} = \tau_1;$$

$$\Delta\text{v}_{\text{rad},31} = 0 - \text{v}_{\text{rad,max}} = -\text{v}_{\text{rad,max}}; \quad \Delta t_{31} = \tau_2;$$

$$\frac{\Delta S_1}{\tau_1} = \frac{\Delta S_2}{\tau_2} = \frac{S_{\text{ellipse}}}{T} = \frac{\pi ab}{T}; \quad \Delta S_1 = \pi ab \cdot \frac{\tau_1}{T}; \quad \Delta S_2 = \pi ab \cdot \frac{\tau_2}{T};$$

$$\Delta S_1 + \Delta S_2 = \frac{1}{2} \cdot S_{\text{ellipse}}; \quad \pi ab \cdot \frac{\tau_1}{T} + \pi ab \cdot \frac{\tau_2}{T} = \frac{1}{2} \cdot \pi ab;$$

$$\tau_1 + \tau_2 = \frac{1}{2} T; \quad \frac{\tau_1}{\tau_2} = n;$$

$$\tau_1 = \frac{nT}{2(n+1)}; \quad \tau_2 = \frac{T}{2(n+1)}; \quad T = 2\pi \sqrt{\frac{a^3}{KM}}.$$

**c)** The interval $\tau_2$ is the duration in which the radial component of the velocity of star $\sigma$ increases from zero (position 1) to its maximum (position 4); the interval $\tau_1$ is the duration in which the radial component of the velocity of star $\sigma$ decreases from its maximum (position 4) to zero (position 2); $\tau_1/\tau_2 = n$.

# Problem 11
# Radial Velocity

Figure 11.1 represents the movements of the two stars $\sigma_1$ and $\sigma_2$ relative to the center of mass of the system. CM, on concentric circular trajectories in the plane $\Pi \perp \Pi_c$, where $\Pi_c$ is the sky plane, and $\sigma_{1,0}$ and $\sigma_{2,0}$ are the initial positions of the stars. We consider that the system's CM is stationary relative to the observer.

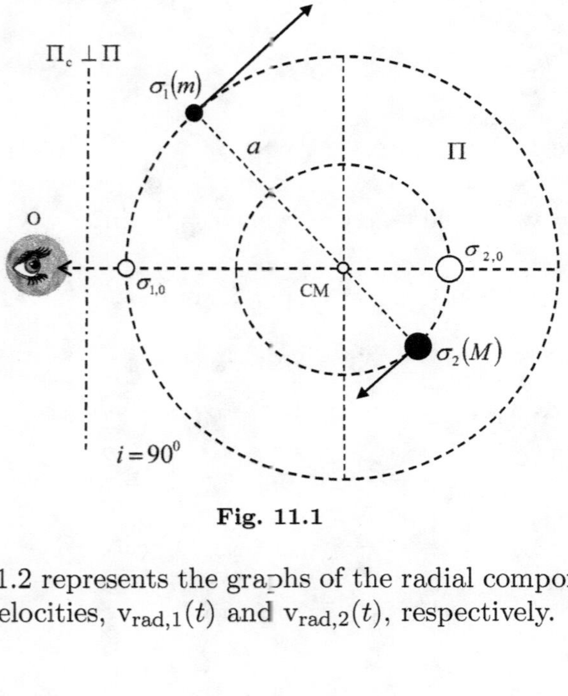


**Fig. 11.1**

Figure 11.2 represents the graphs of the radial components of the two stars' velocities, $v_{\text{rad},1}(t)$ and $v_{\text{rad},2}(t)$, respectively.

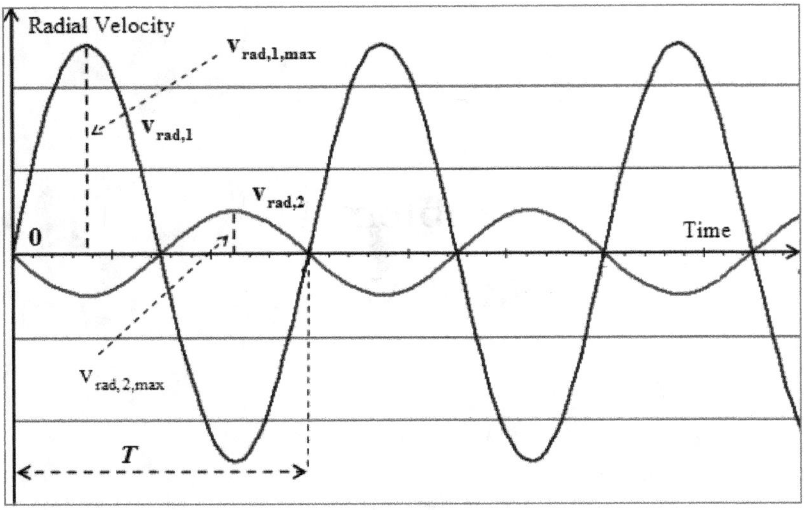


**Fig. 11.2**

*Determine* the masses of the two stars, $M$ and $m$, if $a$ is the distance between the stars and $K$ is the gravitational constant.

## Solution

From Figure 11.3, we have:

$$\mathrm{v}_{\mathrm{rad},1} = \mathrm{v}_1 \cos\left(90^0 - \alpha\right) = \mathrm{v}_1 \sin\alpha = \mathrm{v}_1 \sin\omega t = \mathrm{v}_1 \sin\frac{2\pi}{T}t$$

$$= \mathrm{v}_{\mathrm{rad},1,\mathrm{max}} \sin\frac{2\pi}{T}t;$$

$$\mathrm{v}_1 = \mathrm{v}_{\mathrm{rad},1,\mathrm{max}};$$

$$\mathrm{v}_{\mathrm{rad},2} = -\mathrm{v}_2 \cos\left(90^0 - \alpha\right) = -\mathrm{v}_2 \sin\alpha$$

$$= -\mathrm{v}_2 \sin\omega t = -\mathrm{v}_2 \sin\frac{2\pi}{T}t$$

$$= -\mathrm{v}_{\mathrm{rad},2,\mathrm{max}} \sin\frac{2\pi}{T}t;$$

$$\mathrm{v}_2 = \mathrm{v}_{\mathrm{rad},2,\mathrm{max}};$$

$$m\vec{v}_1 + M\vec{v}_2 = 0; \quad mv_1 - Mv_2 = 0;$$

$$mv_1 = Mv_2; \quad \frac{m}{M} = \frac{v_2}{v_1} = \frac{v_{rad,2,max}}{v_{rad,1,max}}.$$

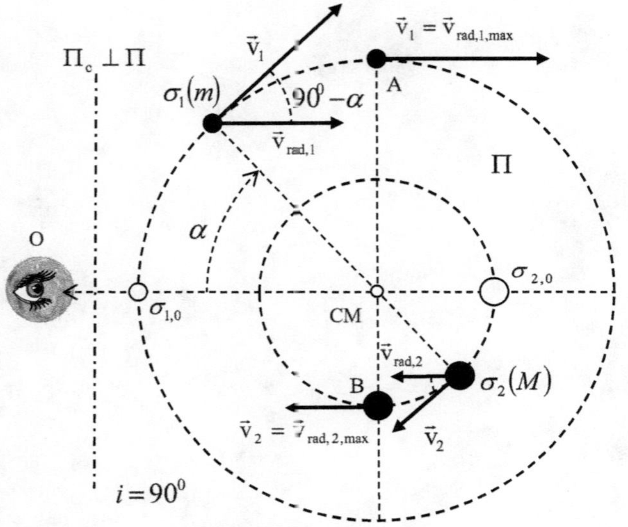


**Fig. 11.3**

From Kepler's third law:

$$(m + M)\,T^2 = \frac{4\pi^2}{K}a^3;$$

$$\frac{m}{M} = \frac{v_{rad,2,max}}{v_{rad,1,max}}; \quad m + M = \frac{4\pi^2}{KT^2}a^3;$$

$$m = \frac{4\pi^2 a^3}{KT^2} \cdot \frac{v_{rad,2,max}}{v_{rad,1,max} + v_{rad,2,max}};$$

$$M = \frac{4\pi^2 a^3}{KT^2} \cdot \frac{v_{rad,1,max}}{v_{rad,1,max} + v_{rad,2,max}}.$$

# Problem 12

# Ocean Tides Caused by the Moon

For the study of the ocean tides produced by the Moon, in the middle of the Earth's oceans (far from the shore), we can make the following simplifying remarks: 1) the Earth and the Moon are an isolated mechanical system; 2) the distance between the center of the Earth and the center of the Moon is constant; 3) the Earth is completely covered in water; 4) the dynamic effects caused by the Earth's rotation around its axis are negligible; 5) with respect to a reference system at rest in relation to the centers of the Earth and the Moon, the surface of the Earth's oceans is static.

In the plane that contains the center of the Earth (E) and the center of the Moon (M), in a random position $Q(r;\varphi)$ on the surface of the ocean, we can consider a liquid particle of mass $m$. The quantities $r$ and $\varphi$ are the polar coordinates of the liquid particle: $\varphi$ – the angle between EQ and EM; $r$ – the distance between the liquid particle at point Q and the center of the Earth E, under equilibrium (this is the radius of the circle centered at E, for the height $h$ of the tide at point Q). Thus, we have:

$$r(\varphi) = \mathrm{EQ} = R_{\mathrm{E}} + h(\varphi),$$

where $R_{\mathrm{E}}$ is the radius of the Earth, and $h(\varphi)$ is the height of the tide at a random point Q on the ocean.

**a)** *Determine* the angular speed $\omega$ at which the Earth–Moon system is rotating around its center of mass CM.

**b)** *Calculate* the approximate expression of the total mechanical energy $E(r;\varphi)$ of the interaction of the liquid particle at point Q with the Earth and the Moon.

**c)** *Calculate* the approximate expression of the height of the ocean tide $h(\varphi)$.

**d)** *Calculate* the approximate value of the difference between the maximum tide height and the minimum tide height:

$$\Delta h = h_{\text{max}} - h_{\text{min}}.$$

*The following are known*: the mass of the Earth, $M_{\text{E}} = 5.98 \cdot 10^{24}$ kg; the mass of the Moon, $M_{\text{M}} = 7.3 \cdot 10^{22}$ kg; the distance between the center of the Earth and the center of the Moon, $d_{\text{EM}} = 3.84 \cdot 10^{8}$ m; the radius of the Earth, $R_{\text{E}} = 6.37 \cdot 10^{6}$ m; the gravitational attraction constant $K = 6.67 \cdot 10^{-11}\ \frac{\text{Nm}^2}{\text{kg}^2}$.

*We know that*:

$$a \ll 1;$$

$$\frac{1}{\sqrt{1 + a^2 - 2a\cos\varphi}} \approx 1 + a\cos\varphi + \frac{1}{2}a^2\left(3\cos^2\varphi - 1\right).$$

## Solution

**a)** The result of the gravitational interaction between the Earth and the Moon (as an isolated system) is the uniform circular rotation of the center of the Earth and the center of the Moon in the plane Π, around their common center of mass CM, with the same angular speed $\omega$ (see Figure 12.1).

Under these conditions, the centripetal force responsible for the circular motion of both bodies around the CM is equal to the gravitational attraction force between the Earth and the Moon, so we have:

$$F_{\text{EM}} = F_{\text{cp}};$$

$$M_{\text{E}}\omega^2 d_{\text{E}} = K\frac{M_{\text{E}}M_{\text{M}}}{d_{\text{EM}}^2}; \quad \omega^2 d_{\text{E}} = K\frac{M_{\text{M}}}{d_{\text{EM}}^2};$$

$$M_{\text{M}}\omega^2 d_{\text{M}} = K\frac{M_{\text{E}}M_{\text{M}}}{d_{\text{EM}}^2}; \quad \omega^2 d_{\text{M}} = K\frac{M_{\text{E}}}{d_{\text{EM}}^2};$$

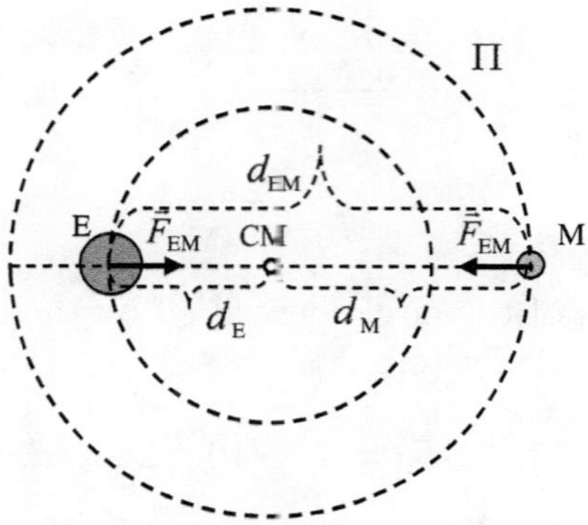


**Fig. 12.1**

$$\omega^2 d_E + \omega^2 d_M = K\frac{M_M}{d_{EM}^2} + K\frac{M_E}{d_{EM}^2};$$

$$\omega^2 (d_E + d_M) = \frac{K}{d_{EM}^2}(M_E + M_M);$$

$$d_M = d_{EM} - d_E;$$

$$\omega = \sqrt{\frac{K(M_E + M_M)}{d_{EM}^3}},$$

which is the common angular speed of the center of the Earth and the center of the Moon, in their uniform circular motion around the CM.

$$M_E = 5.98 \cdot 10^{24}\ \text{kg}; \quad M_M = 7.3 \cdot 10^{22}\ \text{kg}; \quad d_{EM} = 3.84 \cdot 10^8\ \text{m};$$

$$K = 6.67 \cdot 10^{-11}\ \frac{\text{Nm}^2}{\text{kg}^2};$$

$$\omega \approx 2.65 \cdot 10^{-6}\ \frac{1}{\text{s}},$$

which gives a period of $T = \frac{2\pi}{\omega} \approx 27.2$ days.

$$\omega^2 d_E = K\frac{M_M}{d_{EM}^2}; \quad d_E = K\frac{M_M}{\omega^2 d_{EM}^2};$$

$$d_{\mathrm{E}} = \frac{KM_{\mathrm{M}}}{\frac{K(M_{\mathrm{E}}+M_{\mathrm{M}})}{d_{\mathrm{EM}}^3} \cdot d_{\mathrm{EM}}^2};$$

$$d_{\mathrm{E}} = \frac{M_{\mathrm{M}}}{M_{\mathrm{E}} + M_{\mathrm{M}}} d_{\mathrm{EM}},$$

which is the radius of the circle described by the center of the Earth around the CM of the system.

$$M_{\mathrm{E}} = 5.98 \cdot 10^{24}\ \mathrm{kg}; \quad M_{\mathrm{M}} = 7.3 \cdot 10^{22}\ \mathrm{kg}; \quad d_{\mathrm{EM}} = 3.84 \cdot 10^{8}\ \mathrm{m};$$

$$d_{\mathrm{E}} \approx 4630\ \mathrm{km}; \quad R_{\mathrm{E}} = 6.37 \cdot 10^{6}\ \mathrm{m};$$

$$d_{\mathrm{E}} < R_{\mathrm{E}},$$

which means that the CM of the Earth–Moon system is inside the Earth, as Figure 12.2 shows, at the distance $d_{\mathrm{E}} = 4630$ km from the center of the Earth.

Any other point belonging to the Earth, particularly the point N at the surface of the Earth, is in motion around the CM on a circle of radius $r_{\mathrm{N}}$, as shown in Figure 12.3, with the same angular speed $\omega$, as the center E of the Earth.

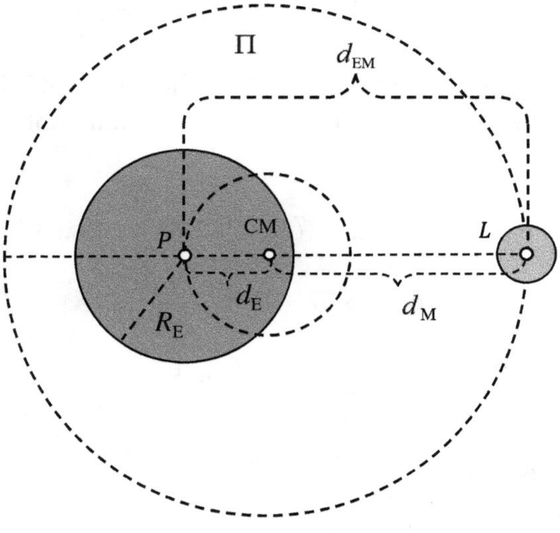


**Fig. 12.2**

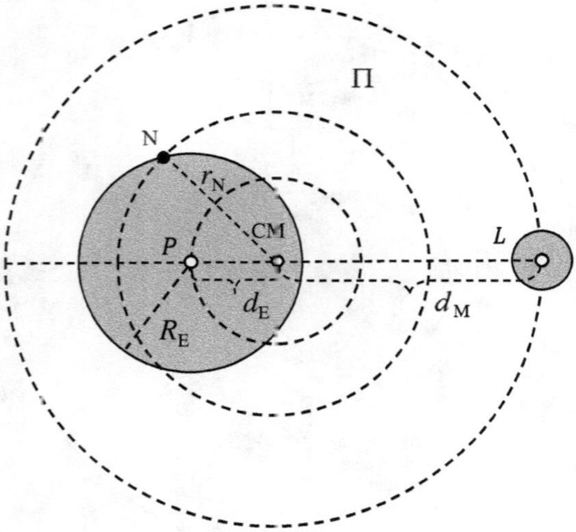


**Fig. 12.3**

**b)** A liquid particle of mass $m$, in plane Π, at the surface of the planetary ocean in position Q is subject to the gravitational attractions of the Earth and Moon. It is located (as shown in Figure 12.4) with respect to the center E of the Earth at the polar coordinates $r$ and $\varphi$, where: $\varphi$ – the angle between EQ and EM; $r$ – the distance between the liquid particle and the center of the Earth, under equilibrium, which is the radius of the circle centered at E, for the height of the ocean tide at Q. Thus, $r(\varphi) = \mathrm{EQ} = R_\mathrm{E} + h(\varphi)$, where $R_\mathrm{E}$ is the radius of the Earth and $h(\varphi)$ is the height of the ocean tide at a random point Q of the planetary ocean's surface.

The surface of the oceans is considered to be static, as though the water were frozen. As such, the liquid particle in position Q is rotating around the CM on a circle of radius $r_\mathrm{Q}$, with the angular speed $\omega$.

The forces acting on the liquid particle at a random point Q on the surface of the ocean are shown in Figure 12.5 as: $\vec{F}_\mathrm{E}$ – the gravitational attraction of the Earth over the particle in position Q; $\vec{F}_\mathrm{M}$ – the gravitational attraction of the Moon over the particle in position Q; $\vec{N}$ – the perpendicular reaction of the planetary ocean over the particle in position Q.

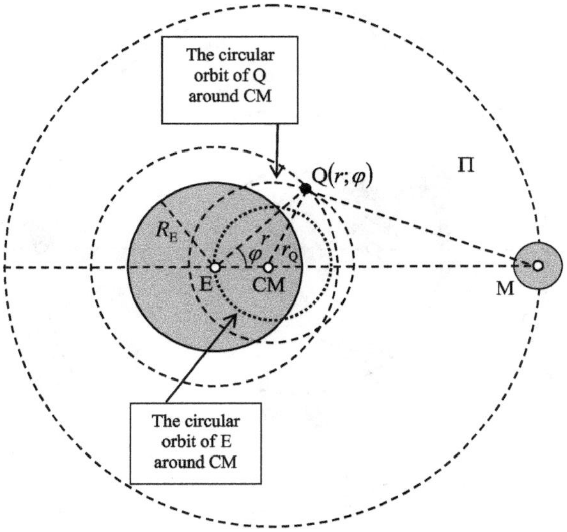


**Fig. 12.4**

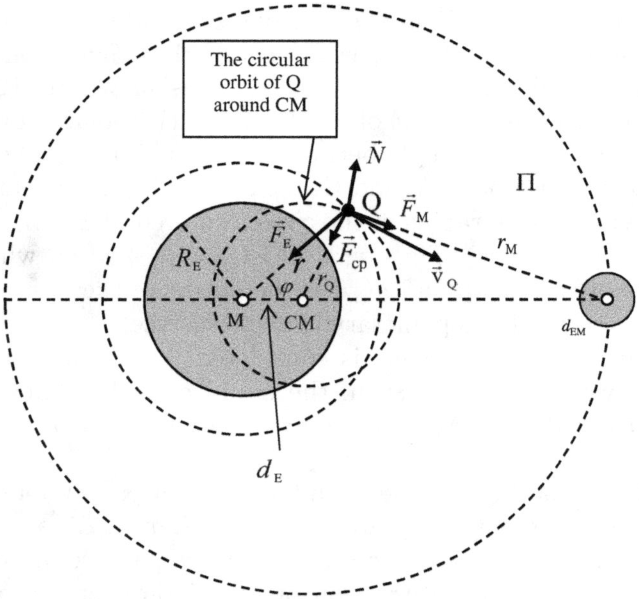


**Fig. 12.5**

As a result of these three forces over the liquid particle at Q, the particle will move around the CM on a circle of radius $r_Q$, due to the resulting centripetal force:

$$\vec{F}_{cp} = \vec{F}_E + \vec{F}_M + \vec{N};$$

$$F_{cp} = m\omega^2 r_Q.$$

The total mechanical energy $E$ of the interaction of the liquid particle in position Q with the Earth and the Moon is:

$$E = E_c + E_{p,E} + E_{p,M};$$

$$E = \frac{mv_Q^2}{2} - K\frac{mM_E}{r} - K\frac{mM_M}{r_M};$$

$$v_Q = \omega \cdot r_Q;$$

$$E = \frac{m\omega^2}{2} r_Q^2 - K\frac{mM_E}{r} - K\frac{mM_M}{r_M};$$

$$r_Q^2 = r^2 + d_E^2 - 2rd_E \cos\varphi;$$

$$r_M^2 = r^2 + d_{EM}^2 - 2rd_{EM} \cos\varphi;$$

$$r_M = \sqrt{d_{EM}^2 + r^2 - 2rd_{EM} \cos\varphi};$$

$$r_M = d_{EM} \cdot \sqrt{1 + \left(\frac{r}{d_{EM}}\right)^2 - 2\frac{r}{d_{EM}} \cos\varphi};$$

$$\frac{r}{d_{EM}} = a \ll 1;$$

$$r_M = d_{EM} \cdot \sqrt{1 + a^2 - 2a\cos\varphi};$$

$$E = \frac{m\omega^2}{2}\left(r^2 + d_E^2 - 2rd_E\cos\varphi\right) - K\frac{mM_E}{r} - K\frac{mM_M}{d_{EM} \cdot \sqrt{1 + a^2 - 2a\cos\varphi}};$$

$$E = \frac{m\omega^2}{2}\left(r^2 + d_E^2 - 2rd_E\cos\varphi\right) - K\frac{mM_E}{r} - K\frac{mM_M}{d_{EM}} \cdot \frac{1}{\sqrt{1 + a^2 - 2a\cos\varphi}};$$

$$a \ll 1;$$

$$\frac{1}{\sqrt{1 + a^2 - 2a\cos\varphi}} \approx 1 + a\cos\varphi + \frac{1}{2}a^2\left(3\cos^2\varphi - 1\right);$$

$$E = \frac{m\omega^2}{2}\left(r^2 + d_{\mathrm{E}}^2 - 2rd_{\mathrm{E}}\cos\phi\right)$$

$$- K\frac{mM_{\mathrm{E}}}{r} - K\frac{mM_{\mathrm{M}}}{d_{\mathrm{EM}}} \cdot \left(1 + a\cos\phi + \frac{1}{2}a^2\left(3\cos^2\phi - 1\right)\right);$$

$$\frac{r}{d_{\mathrm{EM}}} = a;$$

$$E = \frac{m\omega^2}{2}\left(r^2 + d_{\mathrm{E}}^2 - 2rd_{\mathrm{E}}\cos\phi\right) - K\frac{mM_{\mathrm{E}}}{r}$$

$$- K\frac{mM_{\mathrm{M}}}{d_{\mathrm{EM}}} \cdot \left(1 + \frac{r}{d_{\mathrm{EM}}}\cos\phi + \frac{1}{2}\frac{r^2}{d_{\mathrm{EM}}^2}\left(3\cos^2\phi - 1\right)\right);$$

$$E = \frac{m\omega^2 r^2}{2} - K\frac{mM_{\mathrm{E}}}{r} - K\frac{mM_{\mathrm{M}}r^2}{2d_{\mathrm{EM}}^3}\left(3\cos^2\phi - 1\right)$$

$$+ mr\omega^2 d_{\mathrm{E}}\cos\phi - K\frac{mM_{\mathrm{M}}r}{d_{\mathrm{EM}}^2}\cos\phi + \frac{m\omega^2 d_{\mathrm{E}}^2}{2} - K\frac{mM_{\mathrm{M}}}{d_{\mathrm{EM}}};$$

$$E = \frac{m\omega^2 r^2}{2} - K\frac{mM_{\mathrm{E}}}{r} - K\frac{mM_{\mathrm{M}}r^2}{2d_{\mathrm{EM}}^3}\left(3\cos^2\phi - 1\right)$$

$$+ mr\cos\phi\left(\omega^2 d_{\mathrm{E}} - K\frac{M_{\mathrm{M}}}{d_{\mathrm{EM}}^2}\right) + \frac{m\omega^2 d_{\mathrm{E}}^2}{2} - K\frac{mM_{\mathrm{M}}}{d_{\mathrm{EM}}};$$

$$M_{\mathrm{E}}\omega^2 d_{\mathrm{E}} = K\frac{M_{\mathrm{E}}M_{\mathrm{M}}}{d_{\mathrm{EM}}^2}; \quad \omega^2 d_{\mathrm{E}} = K\frac{M_{\mathrm{M}}}{d_{\mathrm{EM}}^2};$$

$$\omega^2 d_{\mathrm{E}} - K\frac{M_{\mathrm{M}}}{d_{\mathrm{EM}}^2} = 0;$$

$$E = \frac{m\omega^2 r^2}{2} - K\frac{mM_{\mathrm{E}}}{r} - K\frac{mM_{\mathrm{M}}r^2}{2d_{\mathrm{EM}}^3}\left(3\cos^2\varphi - 1\right)$$

$$+ \frac{m\omega^2 d_{\mathrm{E}}^2}{2} - K\frac{mM_{\mathrm{M}}}{d_{\mathrm{EM}}};$$

$$\frac{m\omega^2 d_{\mathrm{E}}^2}{2} - K\frac{mM_{\mathrm{M}}}{d_{\mathrm{EM}}} = C',$$

as this is a combination of constants;

$$E = \frac{m\omega^2 r^2}{2} - K\frac{mM_{\mathrm{E}}}{r} - K\frac{mM_{\mathrm{M}}r^2}{2d_{\mathrm{EM}}^3}\left(3\cos^2\varphi - 1\right) + C';$$

$$r = R_{\mathrm{E}} + h; \quad h = r - R_{\mathrm{E}} \ll R_{\mathrm{E}};$$

$$r^2 = (R_{\mathrm{E}} + h)^2 = R_{\mathrm{E}}^2 + 2R_{\mathrm{E}}h + h^2;$$

$$h = r - R_{\mathrm{E}} \ll R_{\mathrm{E}};$$

$$r^2 \approx R_{\mathrm{E}}^2 + 2R_{\mathrm{E}}h;$$

$$\frac{1}{r} = \frac{1}{R_{\mathrm{E}} + h} = \frac{1}{R_{\mathrm{E}}\left(1 + \frac{h}{R_{\mathrm{E}}}\right)} = \frac{1}{R_{\mathrm{E}}}\left(1 + \frac{h}{R_{\mathrm{E}}}\right)^{-1} \approx \frac{1}{R_{\mathrm{E}}}\left(1 - \frac{h}{R_{\mathrm{E}}}\right);$$

$$E = \frac{m\omega^2}{2}\left(R_{\mathrm{E}}^2 + 2R_{\mathrm{E}}h\right) - K\frac{mM_{\mathrm{E}}}{R_{\mathrm{E}}}\left(1 - \frac{h}{R_{\mathrm{E}}}\right) - K\frac{mM_{\mathrm{M}}r^2}{2d_{\mathrm{EM}}^3}\left(3\cos^2\varphi - 1\right) + C';$$

$$\omega = \sqrt{\frac{K(M_{\mathrm{E}} + M_{\mathrm{M}})}{d_{\mathrm{EM}}^3}};$$

$$E = \frac{m}{2}K\frac{M_{\mathrm{E}} + M_{\mathrm{M}}}{d_{\mathrm{EM}}^3}\left(R_{\mathrm{E}}^2 + 2R_{\mathrm{E}}h\right) - K\frac{mM_{\mathrm{E}}}{R_{\mathrm{E}}}\left(1 - \frac{h}{R_{\mathrm{E}}}\right) - K\frac{mM_{\mathrm{M}}r^2}{2d_{\mathrm{EM}}^3}\left(3\cos^2\varphi - 1\right) + C';$$

$$E = \frac{m}{2}K\frac{M_{\mathrm{E}} + M_{\mathrm{M}}}{d_{\mathrm{EM}}^3}R_{\mathrm{E}}^2 + Km\frac{M_{\mathrm{E}} + M_{\mathrm{M}}}{d_{\mathrm{EM}}^3}R_{\mathrm{E}}h - K\frac{mM_{\mathrm{E}}}{R_{\mathrm{E}}} + K\frac{mM_{\mathrm{E}}}{R_{\mathrm{E}}^2}h - K\frac{mM_{\mathrm{M}}r^2}{2d_{\mathrm{EM}}^3}\left(3\cos^2\phi - 1\right) + C';$$

$$E = \frac{m}{2}K\frac{M_{\mathrm{E}} + M_{\mathrm{M}}}{d_{\mathrm{EM}}^3}R_{\mathrm{E}}^2 - K\frac{mM_{\mathrm{E}}}{R_{\mathrm{E}}} + Km\frac{M_{\mathrm{E}} + M_{\mathrm{M}}}{d_{\mathrm{EM}}^3}R_{\mathrm{E}}h + K\frac{mM_{\mathrm{E}}}{R_{\mathrm{E}}^2}h - K\frac{mM_{\mathrm{M}}r^2}{2d_{\mathrm{EM}}^3}\left(3\cos^2\phi - 1\right) + C';$$

$$\frac{m}{2}K\frac{M_{\mathrm{E}} + M_{\mathrm{M}}}{d_{\mathrm{EM}}^3}R_{\mathrm{E}}^2 - K\frac{mM_{\mathrm{E}}}{R_{\mathrm{E}}} = C'',$$

as this is a combination of constants;

$$E = Km\frac{M_{\rm E}+M_{\rm M}}{d_{\rm EM}^3}R_{\rm E}h + K\frac{mM_{\rm E}}{R_{\rm E}^2}h$$
$$- K\frac{mM_{\rm M}r^2}{2d_{\rm EM}^3}\left(3\cos^2\varphi - 1\right) + C' + C'';$$

$$E = K\frac{mM_{\rm E}}{R_{\rm E}^2}\left(\frac{\left(M_{\rm E}+M_{\rm M}\right)R_{\rm E}h}{d_{\rm EM}^3}\cdot\frac{R_{\rm E}^2}{M_{\rm E}}\right.$$
$$\left. + h - \frac{M_{\rm M}r^2}{2d_{\rm EM}^3}\cdot\frac{R_{\rm E}^2}{M_{\rm E}}\left(3\cos^2\varphi - 1\right)\right) + C' + C'';$$

$$E = K\frac{mM_{\rm E}}{R_{\rm E}^2}\left(\left(1+\frac{M_{\rm M}}{M_{\rm E}}\right)\cdot\left(\frac{R_{\rm E}}{d_{\rm EM}}\right)^3 h\right.$$
$$\left. + h - \frac{M_{\rm M}r^2}{2d_{\rm EM}^3}\cdot\frac{R_{\rm E}^2}{M_{\rm E}}\left(3\cos^2\varphi - 1\right)\right) + C' + C'';$$

$$M_{\rm E} = 5.98\cdot 10^{24}\,\text{kg};\quad M_{\rm M} = 7.3\cdot 10^{22}\,\text{kg};\quad d_{\rm EM} = 3.84\cdot 10^{8}\,\text{m};$$
$$R_{\rm E} = 6.37\cdot 10^{6}\,\text{m};$$

$$\left(1+\frac{M_{\rm M}}{M_{\rm E}}\right)\cdot\left(\frac{R_{\rm E}}{d_{\rm EM}}\right)^3 \approx 10^{-5} \ll 1;$$

$$E\left(r;\varphi\right) = K\frac{mM_{\rm E}}{R_{\rm E}^2}\left(h - \frac{M_{\rm M}r^2}{2d_{\rm EM}^3}\cdot\frac{R_{\rm E}^2}{M_{\rm E}}\left(3\cos^2\varphi - 1\right)\right) + C' + C''.$$

**c)** The value of $E$ must be constant regardless of the values of $r$ and $\varphi$, so that

$$E = \text{constant},$$

which means that

$$h - \frac{M_{\rm M}R_{\rm E}^2}{2d_{\rm EM}^3M_{\rm E}}r^2\left(3\cos^2\varphi - 1\right) = C_0;$$

$$h = \frac{M_{\rm M}R_{\rm E}^2}{2d_{\rm EM}^3M_{\rm E}}r^2\left(3\cos^2\varphi - 1\right) + C_0;\quad r \approx R_{\rm E};$$

$$h = \frac{M_M R_E^4}{2d_{EM}^3 M_E} \cdot (3\cos^2\varphi - 1) + C_0.$$

**d)**

$$\varphi = 0; \quad \varphi = \pi;$$

$$h = h_{max} = \frac{M_M R_E^4}{d_{EM}^3 M_E} + C_0;$$

$$\varphi = 90^\circ; \quad \varphi = 270^\circ;$$

$$h = h_{min} = C_0 - \frac{M_M R_E^4}{2d_{EM}^3 M_E}.$$

# Problem 13
# Venus's Rotation

We know that in our solar system, the current directions of the rotation of Earth and Venus around their own axes are opposite, and the directions of their revolution around the Sun are identical. Their orbits are considered to be in the same plane.

Let us assume that, when the solar system's planets were formed, the direction of the rotation of Venus around its own axis was the same as for the Earth, as Figure 13.1 indicates.

Notation: $\vec{\omega}_{0,\mathrm{E}}$ – the initial angular velocity of the Earth's rotation; $\vec{\omega}_{0,\mathrm{V}}$ – the initial angular velocity of Venus's rotation; $\vec{Q}_{0,\mathrm{E}}$ – the initial angular momentum for the Earth's rotation; $\vec{Q}_{0,\mathrm{V}}$ – the initial angular momentum, for Venus's rotation; $\vec{\Omega}_{0,\mathrm{V}}$ – the initial angular velocity of Venus's revolution around the Sun; $\vec{L}_{0,\mathrm{V}}$ – the initial angular momentum of Venus's revolution around the Sun; $D_0$ – the initial distance between the centers of Venus and the Sun.

In the same hypothetical situation, tens of millions of years ago, Venus had an enormous water-based ocean, a thick layer of clouds and a very dense atmosphere. The orbits of Venus and the Earth are in the same plane.

Currently, the rotation of Venus around its own axis and the Earth's rotation around its own axis are in opposite directions, as Figure 13.2 indicates.

Notation: $\vec{\omega}_{\mathrm{E}}$ – the current angular velocity of the Earth's rotation; $\vec{\omega}_{\mathrm{V}}$ – the current angular velocity of Venus's rotation; $\vec{Q}_{\mathrm{E}}$ – the current angular momentum for the Earth's rotation; $\vec{Q}_{\mathrm{V}}$ – the current angular velocity of Venus's revolution around the Sun; $\vec{\Omega}_{\mathrm{V}}$ – the current angular velocity of Venus's revolution around the Sun; $\vec{L}_V$ – the current angular momentum of Venus's revolution around the Sun; $D$ – the current distance between the centers of Venus and the Sun.

The change in direction of Venus's rotation around its own axis can be explained as an effect of the tides created by the Sun in Venus's ocean, modeled by Figure 13.3.

In this model, the maximal tidal deformations caused by the Sun in Venus's ocean can be considered as two identical bodies, of small size, each having a mass $m = 3.6 \cdot 10^{16}$ kg, and placed in diametrically

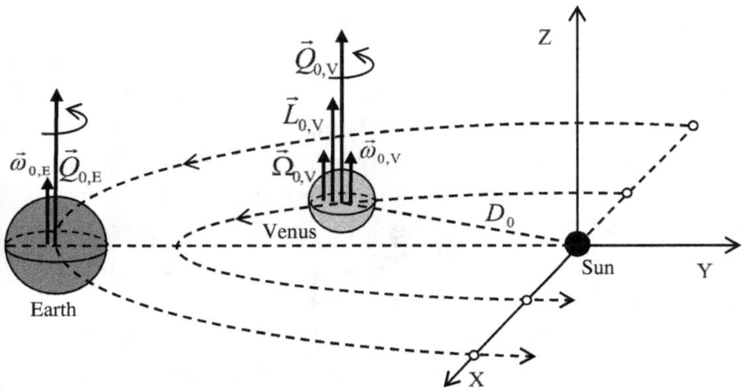


**Fig. 13.1**

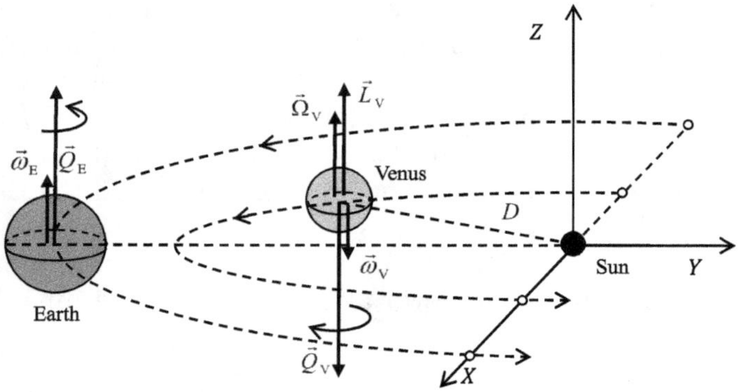


**Fig. 13.2**

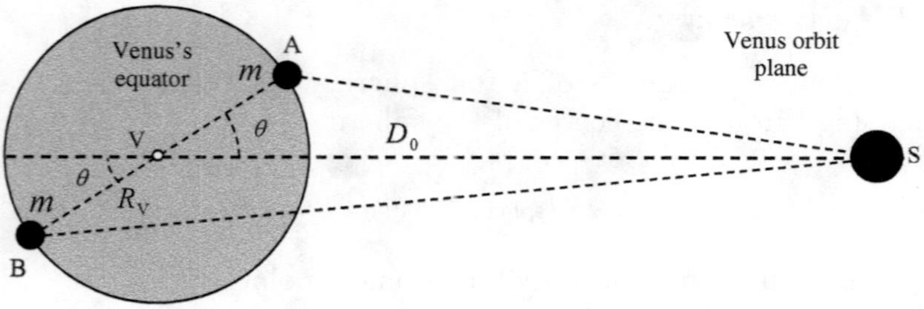


**Fig. 13.3**

opposite positions on Venus's equator in the same plane as Venus's orbit around the Sun. Their diameter AB makes a very small angle $\theta = 3°$ with the direction described by the centers of Venus and the Sun, SV, as Figure 13.3 indicates, where $D_0$ is the initial distance (unknown) between the center of Venus and the center of the Sun.

**a)** *Explain* the possibility of the change in direction of Venus's rotation around its own axis, as an effect of the tides created by the Sun in Venus's ocean, based on the model above.

*We know*: $R_V$ – Venus's radius; $m_V$ – Venus's mass; $m_S$ – the mass of the Sun; $K$ – the gravitational attraction constant; $D$ – the current distance between the centers of Venus and the Sun; $\omega_{0,V}$ – the initial angular velocity of Venus's rotation; $\omega_V$ – the current angular velocity of Venus's rotation, $\omega_V = \omega_{0,V}$; $\Delta t$ – the duration in which the direction of Venus's rotation changed. Compared to the Sun, the two planets' dimensions are negligible.

**b)** *Determine* the initial and current angular velocities of Venus's revolution around the Sun, before and after the change in direction of Venus's rotation. These are $\Omega_{0,V}$ and $\Omega_V$.

**c)** *Determine* the initial distance $D_0$ between the centers of Venus and the Sun.

*We know that*:

$$(1+x)^n \approx 1 + nx, \quad if x << 1;$$

$$\frac{R_V}{D_0} << 1; \quad \frac{R_V}{D_0}\left(\frac{R_V}{D_0} - 2\cos\theta\right) << 1; \quad \frac{R_V}{D_0}\left(\frac{R_V}{D_0} + 2\cos\theta\right) << 1.$$

*We also know*:

- the moment of inertia of a full sphere, with respect to an axis passing through the center of the sphere:

$$I_{\text{sphere}} = \frac{2}{5}mR^2;$$

- the moment of inertia of a dimensionless point;
- the theorem of the variation in angular momentum:

$$\frac{\Delta\vec{J}}{\Delta t} = \vec{M}_{\text{resultant}},$$

that is, the variation of the angular momentum of a body (considered dimensionless) is equal to the total torque of the forces acting on the body.

## Solution

Let us assume that the angular momentum of Venus rotating around its own axis, immediately after the formation of the solar system, was $\vec{Q}_{0,\text{V}}$, as Figure 13.4 shows; its orientation is the same as the angular momentum of the Earth's rotation $\vec{Q}_{0,\text{E}}$, while the orbits of the two planets are considered to be in the same plane.

The torque of the gravitational forces from the Sun acting on Venus, $\vec{M}_{\text{S,V}}$, caused a variation in the angular momentum of Venus, $(\Delta\vec{J})_{\text{Venus}}$, so that, in accordance with the angular momentum variation theorem, we have

$$\vec{M}_{\text{S,V}} = \frac{\left(\Delta\vec{J}\right)_{\text{Venus}}}{\Delta t} = \frac{\vec{J}_{\text{V}} - \vec{J}_{0,\text{V}}}{\Delta t},$$

where the final angular momentum points in the opposite direction to the initial angular momentum, $\vec{Q}_{0,\text{V}}$, as Figure 13.5 shows.

The maximal tidal deformations, shown in Figure 13.3 of the problem statement, can be modeled as two identical dimensionless bodies of mass $m$, which we also show in Figure 13.6.

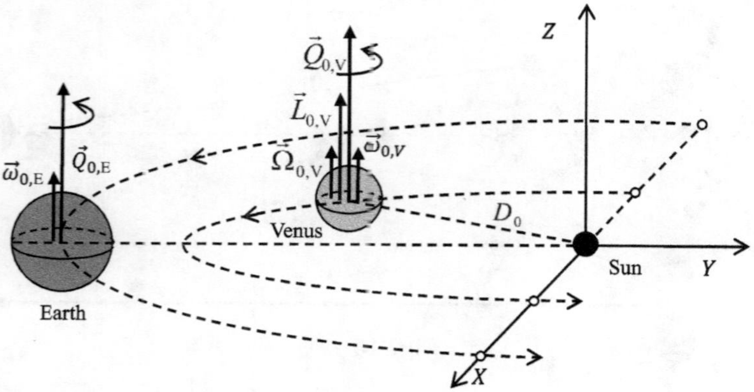


**Fig. 13.4**

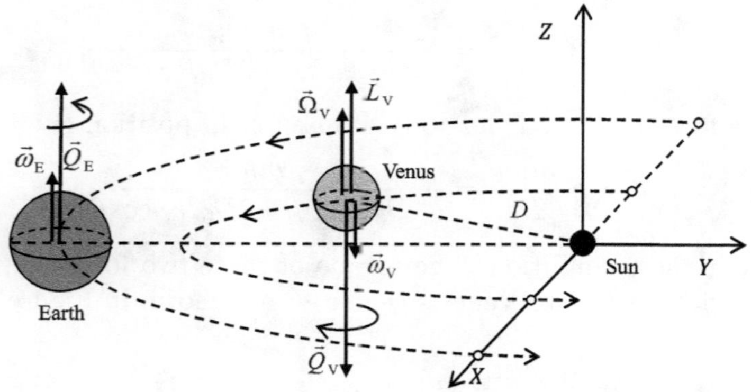


**Fig. 13.5**

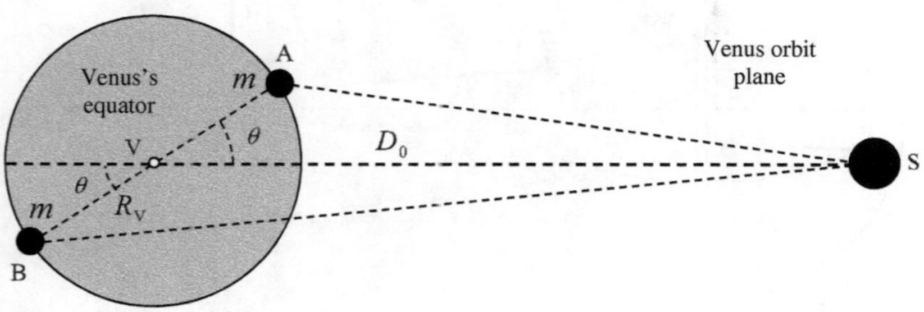


**Fig. 13.6**

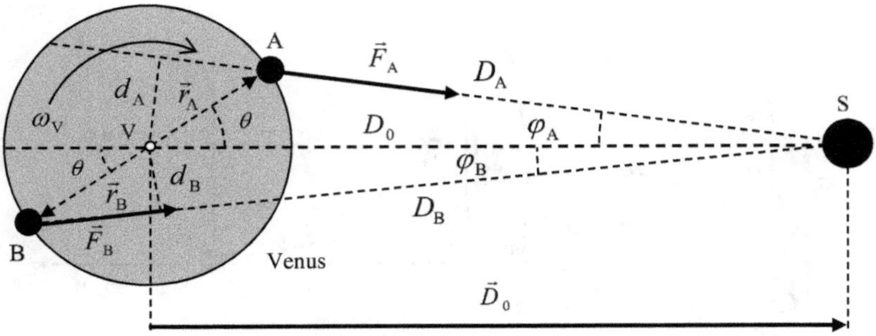


**Fig. 13.7**

In accordance with the notation in Figure 13.7, the gravitational pull of the Sun on the body of mass $m$ in position A is

$$F_A = K\frac{mm_S}{D_A^2} = K\frac{mm_S}{D_0^2 + R_V - 2D_0R_V\cos\theta},$$

and the force acting on the body of mass $m$ in position B is

$$F_B = K\frac{mm_S}{D_B^2} = K\frac{mm_S}{D_0^2 + R_V + 2D_0R_V\cos\theta}.$$

Under these conditions, the torque of these two forces acting on Venus, with respect to Venus's center V, are shown in Figure 13.8:

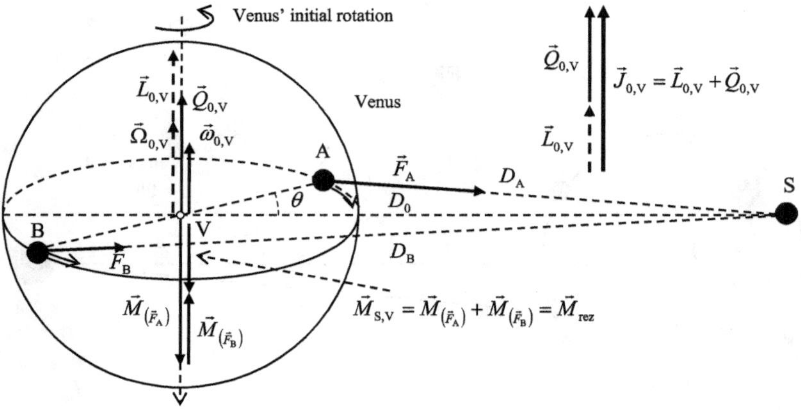


**Fig. 13.8**

$$\vec{M}_{(\tilde{F}_A)} = \vec{D}_0 \; x \; \vec{F}_A;$$

$$M_{(\tilde{F}_A)} = F_A D_0 \sin\varphi_A = F_A d_A;$$

$$d_A = D_0 \sin\varphi_A;$$

$$M_{(\tilde{F}_A)} = F_A d_A = F_A D_0 \sin\varphi_A;$$

$$\frac{\sin\theta}{D_A} = \frac{\sin\varphi_A}{R_V}; \quad \sin\varphi_A = \frac{R_V}{D_A}\sin\theta;$$

$$M_{(\tilde{F}_A)} = K\frac{mm_S}{D_A^2} D_0 \frac{R_V}{D_A}\sin\theta;$$

$$M_{(\tilde{F}_A)} = K\frac{mm_S}{D_A^3} D_0 R_V \sin\theta;$$

$$D_A = \sqrt{D_0^2 + R_V^2 - 2D_0 R_V \sin\theta};$$

$$M_{(\tilde{F}_A)} = K\frac{mm_S}{\left(D_0^2 + R_V^2 - 2D_0 R_V \cos\theta\right)^{3/2}} D_0 R_V \sin\theta;$$

$$M_{(\tilde{F}_A)} = K\frac{mm_S R_V \sin\theta}{D_0^2}\frac{1}{\left(1 + \frac{R_V^2}{D_0^2} - 2\frac{R_V}{D_0}\cos\theta\right)^{3/2}};$$

$$M_{(\tilde{F}_A)} = K\frac{mm_S R_V \sin\theta}{D_0^2}\frac{1}{\left(1 + \frac{R_V}{D_0}\left(\frac{R_V}{D_0} - 2\cos\theta\right)\right)^{3/2}};$$

$$M_{(\tilde{F}_A)} = K\frac{mm_S R_V \sin\theta}{D_0^2}\left(1 + \frac{R_V}{D_0}\left(\frac{R_V}{D_0} - 2\cos\theta\right)\right)^{-3/2};$$

$$\frac{R_V}{D_0} << 1; \quad \frac{R_V}{D_0}\left(\frac{R_V}{D_0} - 2\cos\theta\right) << 1;$$

$$\left(1 + \frac{R_V}{D_0}\left(\frac{R_V}{D_0} - 2\cos\theta\right)\right)^{-3/2} \approx 1 - \frac{3}{2}\frac{R_V}{D_0}\left(\frac{R_V}{D_0} - 2\cos\theta\right);$$

$$M_{(\tilde{F}_A)} = K\frac{mm_S R_V \sin\theta}{D_0^2}\left(1 - \frac{3}{2}\frac{R_V}{D_0}\left(\frac{R_V}{D_0} - 2\cos\theta\right)\right);$$

$$\vec{M}_{(\tilde{F}_B)} = \vec{D}_0 \; x \; \vec{F}_B;$$

$$M_{(\tilde{F}_B)} = F_B D_0 \sin \varphi_B = F_B d_B;$$

$$d_B = D_0 \sin \varphi_B;$$

$$M_{(\tilde{F}_B)} = F_B d_B = F_B D_0 \sin \varphi_B;$$

$$\frac{\sin (180^\circ - \theta)}{D_B} = \frac{\sin \varphi_B}{R_V} = \frac{\sin \theta}{D_B}; \quad \sin \varphi_B = \frac{R_V}{D_B} \sin \theta;$$

$$M_{(\tilde{F}_B)} = K \frac{m m_L}{D_B^2} D_0 \frac{R_P}{D_B} \sin \theta;$$

$$M_{(\tilde{F}_B)} = K \frac{m m_S}{D_B^3} D_0 R_V \sin \theta;$$

$$D_B = \sqrt{D_0^2 + R_V^2 + 2 D_0 R_V \sin \theta};$$

$$M_{(\tilde{F}_B)} = K \frac{m m_S}{\left(D_0^2 + R_V^2 + 2 D_0 R_V \cos \theta\right)^{3/2}} D_0 R_V \sin \theta;$$

$$M_{(\tilde{F}_B)} = K \frac{m m_S R_V \sin \theta}{D_0^2} \frac{1}{\left(1 + \frac{R_V^2}{D_0^2} + 2 \frac{R_V}{D_0} \cos \theta\right)^{3/2}};$$

$$M_{(\tilde{F}_B)} = K \frac{m m_S R_V \sin \theta}{D_0^2} \frac{1}{\left(1 + \frac{R_V}{D_0} \left(\frac{R_V}{D_0} + 2 \cos \theta\right)\right)^{3/2}};$$

$$M_{(\tilde{F}_B)} = K \frac{m m_S R_V \sin \theta}{D_0^2} \left(1 + \frac{3}{2} \frac{R_V}{D_0} \left(\frac{R_V}{D_0} + 2 \cos \theta\right)\right);$$

$$\frac{R_V}{D_0} << 1; \quad \frac{R_V}{D_0} \left(\frac{R_V}{D_0} + 2 \cos \theta\right) << 1;$$

$$\left(1 + \frac{R_V}{D_0} \left(\frac{R_V}{D_0} + 2 \cos \theta\right)\right)^{-3/2} \approx 1 - \frac{3}{2} \frac{R_V}{D_0} \left(\frac{R_V}{D_0} + 2 \cos \theta\right);$$

$$M_{(\tilde{F}_B)} = K \frac{m m_S R_V \sin \theta}{D_0^2} \left(1 - \frac{3}{2} \frac{R_V}{D_0} \left(\frac{R_V}{D_0} + 2 \cos \theta\right)\right).$$

Thus, the total torque will be:

$$\vec{M}_{(\tilde{F}_A)} + \vec{M}_{(\tilde{F}_B)} = \vec{M}_{\text{res}};$$

$$M_{(\tilde{F}_A)} - M_{(\tilde{F}_B)} = M_{\text{res}};$$

$$M_{\text{res}} = K\frac{mm_{\text{S}}R_{\text{V}}\sin\theta}{D_0^2}\left(1 - \frac{3}{2}\frac{R_{\text{V}}}{D_0}\left(\frac{R_{\text{V}}}{D_0} - 2\cos\theta\right)\right)$$

$$-K\frac{mm_{\text{S}}R_{\text{V}}\sin\theta}{D_0^2}\left(1 - \frac{3}{2}\frac{R_{\text{V}}}{D_0}\left(\frac{R_{\text{V}}}{D_0} + 2\cos\theta\right)\right);$$

$$M_{\text{res}} = K\frac{mm_{\text{S}}R_{\text{V}}\sin\theta}{D_0^2}\left(1 - \frac{3}{2}\frac{R_{\text{V}}}{D_0}\left(\frac{R_{\text{V}}}{D_0} - 2\cos\theta\right) - 1\right.$$

$$\left. + \frac{3}{2}\frac{R_{\text{V}}}{D_0}\left(\frac{R_{\text{V}}}{D_0} + 2\cos\theta\right)\right);$$

$$M_{\text{res}} = K\frac{mm_{\text{S}}R_{\text{V}}\sin\theta}{D_0^2}\left(3\frac{R_{\text{V}}}{D_0}\cos\theta + 3\frac{R_{\text{V}}}{D_0}\cos\theta\right);$$

$$M_{\text{res}} = 6K\frac{mm_{\text{S}}R_{\text{V}}^2\sin\theta\cos\theta}{D_0^3}.$$

In the initial state, shown in Figure 13.8, when the Venus–Sun distance is $D_0$, Venus's angular momentum is:

$$\vec{J}_{0,\text{V}} = \vec{Q}_{0,\text{V}} + \vec{L}_{0,\text{V}},$$

where $\vec{Q}_{0,\text{V}}$ is the rotational angular momentum of Venus around its axis and $\vec{L}_{0,\text{V}}$ is the angular momentum of Venus's revolution around the Sun;

$$J_{0,\text{V}} = L_{0,\text{V}} + Q_{0,\text{V}};$$

$$L_{0,\text{V}} = I_{0,\text{V,pm}}\Omega_{0,\text{V}}; \quad Q_{0,\text{V}} = I_{0,\text{V,sphere}}\omega_{0,\text{V}},$$

where $I_{0,\text{V,pm}}$ is Venus's moment of inertia in the initial state (where Venus's dimensions are negligible) for Venus's revolution around the Sun, $\Omega_{0,\text{V}}$ is the initial angular velocity of Venus (again as a dimensionless body) for Venus's revolution around the Sun, and $I_{0,\text{V,sphere}}$ is the moment of inertia of Venus as a sphere for its rotation around its own axis with angular speed $\omega_{0,\text{V}}$;

$$J_{0,\text{V}} = I_{0,\text{V,pm}}\Omega_{0,\text{V}} + I_{0,\text{V,sphere}}\omega_{0,\text{V}};$$

$$I_{0,\text{V,pm}} = m_{\text{V}}D_0^2; \quad I_{0,\text{V,sphere}} = \frac{2}{5}m_{\text{V}}R_{\text{V}}^2;$$

$$m_{\text{V}}\Omega_{0,\text{V}}^2 D_0 = K\frac{m_{\text{S}}m_{\text{V}}}{D_0^2};$$

$$\Omega_{0,\text{V}}^2 D_0^3 = Km_\text{S};$$

$$\Omega_{0,\text{V}} = \sqrt{\frac{Km_\text{S}}{D_0^3}};$$

$$L_{0,\text{V}} = I_{0,\text{V,pm}}\Omega_{0,\text{V}}; \quad L_{0,\text{V}} = m_\text{V}\sqrt{KD_0 m_\text{S}};$$

$$J_{0,\text{V}} = m_\text{V} D_0^2 \sqrt{\frac{Km_\text{S}}{D_0^3}} + I_{0,\text{V,sphere}}\omega_{0,\text{V}};$$

$$J_{0,\text{V}} = m_\text{V}\sqrt{KD_0 m_\text{S}} + I_{0,\text{V,sphere}}\omega_{0,\text{V}},$$

which is the total angular momentum of Venus with respect to the center of the Sun.

The calculation is similar for the total *current* angular momentum of Venus, after an interval $\Delta t$, when Venus's rotation has changed and the Sun–Venus distance has also changed (shown in Figure 13.9):

$$\vec{J}_\text{V} = \vec{Q}_\text{V} + \vec{L}_\text{V},$$

where $\vec{Q}_\text{V}$ is the current angular momentum of Venus's rotation and $\vec{L}_\text{V}$ is the current angular momentum of Venus's revolution around the Sun (whose direction has not changed);

$$J_\text{V} = L_\text{V} - Q_\text{V};$$

$$L_\text{V} = I_{\text{V,pm}}\Omega_\text{V}; \quad Q_\text{V} = I_{\text{V,sphere}}\omega_\text{V},$$

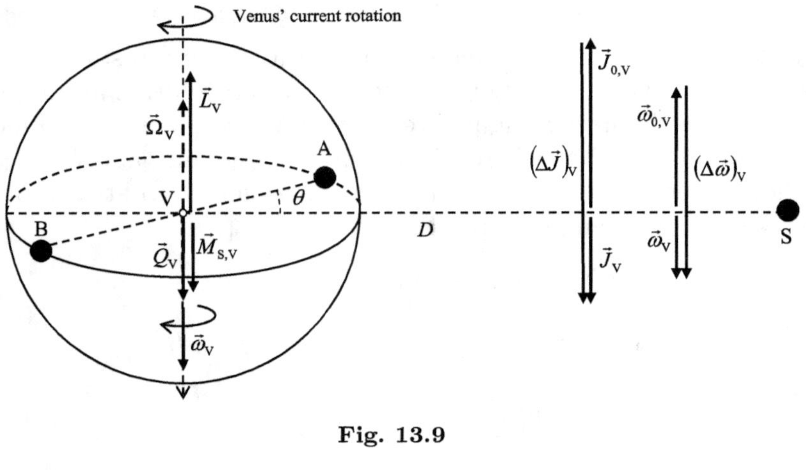


**Fig. 13.9**

where $I_{V,pm}$ is the moment of inertia for Venus as a dimensionless body in its revolution around the Sun, $\Omega_V$ is the angular velocity of Venus as a dimensionless body in its revolution around the Sun, and $I_{V,sphere}$ is the moment of inertia for Venus as a sphere rotating around its axis with the angular velocity $\omega_V$;

$$J_V = I_{V,pm}\Omega_V - I_{V,sphere}\omega_V;$$

$$I_{V,pm} = m_V D^2; \quad I_{V,sphere} = \frac{2}{5} m_V R_V^2 = I_{0,V,sphere};$$

$$m_V \Omega_V^2 D = K \frac{m_S m_V}{D^2};$$

$$\Omega_V^2 D^3 = K m_S;$$

$$\Omega_V = \sqrt{\frac{K m_S}{D^3}};$$

$$L_V = I_{V,pm}\Omega_V; \quad L_V = m_V \sqrt{K D m_S};$$

$$J_V = m_V D^2 \sqrt{\frac{K m_S}{D^3}} - I_{V,sphere}\omega_V;$$

$$J_V = m_V \sqrt{K D m_S} - I_{V,sphere}\omega_V,$$

which is the total current angular momentum of Venus with respect to the center of the Sun;

$$D = D_0 + \Delta D;$$

$$L_V = m_V \sqrt{K m_S D} = m_V \sqrt{K m_S (D_0 + \Delta D)}$$

$$= m_V \sqrt{K m_S D_0 \left(1 + \frac{\Delta D}{D_0}\right)};$$

$$L_V = m_V \sqrt{K m_S D_0} \cdot \sqrt{1 + \frac{\Delta D}{D_0}};$$

$$L_V = m_V \sqrt{K m_S D_0} \cdot \left(1 + \frac{\Delta D}{D_0}\right)^{1/2};$$

$$\Delta D << D_0;$$

$$L_V = m_V\sqrt{Km_S D_0}\cdot\left(1+\frac{1}{2}\frac{\Delta D}{D_0}\right);$$

$$J_V = m_V\sqrt{KD_0 m_S}\left(1+\frac{1}{2}\frac{\Delta D}{D_0}\right) - I_{V,\text{sphere}}\omega_V;$$

$$I_{V,\text{sphere}} = \frac{2}{5}m_V R_V^2 = I_{0,V,\text{sphere}};$$

$$J_V = m_V\sqrt{KD_0 m_S}\left(1+\frac{1}{2}\frac{\Delta D}{D_0}\right) - I_{V,\text{sphere}}\omega_V.$$

In accordance with the angular momentum variation theorem:

$$\vec{M}_{\text{res}} = \frac{\left(\Delta\vec{J}\right)_{\text{Venus}}}{\Delta t};\quad M_{\text{res}} = \frac{J_V - J_{0,V}}{\Delta t};$$

$$M_{\text{res}} = 6K\frac{mm_S R_V^2\sin\theta\cos\theta}{D_0^3}.$$

$$J_{0,V} = m_V\sqrt{KD_0 m_S} + I_{0,V,\text{sphere}}\omega_{0,V};$$

$$J_V = m_V\sqrt{KD_0 m_S}\left(1+\frac{1}{2}\frac{\Delta D}{D_0}\right) - I_{V,\text{sphere}}\omega_V;$$

$$(\Delta J)_V = J_V - J_{0,V} = m_V\sqrt{KD_0 m_S}\left(1+\frac{1}{2}\frac{\Delta D}{D_0}\right)$$
$$-I_{V,\text{sphere}}\omega_V - m_V\sqrt{KD_0 m_S} - I_{0,V,\text{sphere}}\omega_{0,V};$$

$$(\Delta J)_V = m_V\sqrt{KD_0 m_S}\left(\frac{1}{2}\frac{\Delta D}{D_0}\right) - I_{V,\text{sphere}}\omega_V - I_{0,V,\text{sphere}}\omega_{0,V};$$

$$\omega_{0,V} = \omega_V;\quad I_{0,V,\text{sphere}} = \frac{2}{5}m_V R_V^2 = I_{V,\text{sphere}};$$

$$(\Delta J)_V = m_V\sqrt{KD_0 m_S}\left(\frac{1}{2}\frac{\Delta D}{D_0}\right) - I_{V,\text{sphere}}\omega_V - I_{V,\text{sphere}}\omega_V;$$

$$(\Delta J)_V = m_V\sqrt{KD_0 m_S}\left(\frac{1}{2}\frac{\Delta D}{D_0}\right) - 2I_{V,\text{sphere}}\omega_V;$$

$$(\Delta J)_V = m_V\sqrt{\frac{Km_S}{D_0}}\left(\frac{\Delta D}{2}\right) - 2I_{V,\text{sphere}}\omega_V;$$

$$(\Delta J)_{\mathrm{V}} = m_{\mathrm{V}}\sqrt{\frac{Km_{\mathrm{S}}}{D-\Delta D}}\left(\frac{\Delta D}{2}\right) - 2I_{\mathrm{V,sphere}}\omega_{\mathrm{V}};$$

$$(\Delta J)_{\mathrm{V}} = m_{\mathrm{V}}\sqrt{\frac{Km_{\mathrm{S}}}{D\left(1-\frac{\Delta D}{D}\right)}}\left(\frac{\Delta D}{2}\right) - 2I_{\mathrm{V,sphere}}\omega_{\mathrm{V}};$$

$$(\Delta J)_{\mathrm{V}} = m_{\mathrm{V}}\sqrt{\frac{Km_{\mathrm{S}}}{D}}\cdot\left(1-\frac{\Delta D}{D}\right)^{-1/2}\cdot\left(\frac{\Delta D}{2}\right) - 2I_{\mathrm{V,sphere}}\omega_{\mathrm{V}};$$

$$\Delta D << D;$$

$$(\Delta J)_{\mathrm{V}} = m_{\mathrm{V}}\sqrt{\frac{Km_{\mathrm{S}}}{D}}\cdot\left(1+\frac{1}{2}\frac{\Delta D}{D}\right)\cdot\left(\frac{\Delta D}{2}\right) - 2I_{\mathrm{V,sphere}}\omega_{\mathrm{V}};$$

$$M_{\mathrm{res}} = 6K\frac{mm_{\mathrm{S}}R_{\mathrm{V}}^2\sin\theta\cos\theta}{D_0^3};$$

$$M_{\mathrm{res}} = 6K\frac{mm_{\mathrm{S}}R_{\mathrm{V}}^2\sin\theta\cos\theta}{(D-\Delta D)^3} = 6K\frac{mm_{\mathrm{S}}R_{\mathrm{V}}^2\sin\theta\cos\theta}{D^3\left(1-\frac{\Delta D}{D}\right)^3}$$

$$= 6K\frac{mm_{\mathrm{S}}R_{\mathrm{V}}^2\sin\theta\cos\theta}{D^3}\left(1-\frac{\Delta D}{D}\right)^{-3};$$

$$\Delta D << D;$$

$$M_{\mathrm{res}} = 6K\frac{mm_{\mathrm{S}}R_{\mathrm{V}}^2\sin\theta\cos\theta}{D^3}\left(1+3\frac{\Delta D}{D}\right);$$

$$M_{\mathrm{res}} = \frac{(\Delta J)_{\mathrm{V}}}{\Delta t};$$

$$M_{\mathrm{res}}\Delta t = (\Delta J)_{\mathrm{V}};$$

$$6K\frac{mm_{\mathrm{S}}R_{\mathrm{V}}^2\sin\theta\cos\theta}{D^3}\left(1-3\frac{\Delta D}{D}\right)\cdot\Delta t$$

$$= m_{\mathrm{V}}\sqrt{\frac{Km_{\mathrm{S}}}{D}}\cdot\left(1+\frac{1}{2}\frac{\Delta D}{D}\right)\cdot\left(\frac{\Delta D}{2}\right) - 2I_{\mathrm{V,sphere}}\omega_{\mathrm{V}};$$

$$6K\frac{mm_{\mathrm{S}}R_{\mathrm{V}}^2\sin\theta\cos\theta}{D^3}\cdot\Delta t + 18K\frac{mm_{\mathrm{S}}R_{\mathrm{V}}^2\sin\theta\cos\theta}{D^4}\cdot\Delta t\cdot\Delta D$$

$$= \frac{m_{\mathrm{V}}}{2}\cdot\sqrt{\frac{Km_{\mathrm{S}}}{D}}\cdot\Delta D + \frac{m_{\mathrm{V}}}{4D}\cdot\sqrt{\frac{Km_{\mathrm{S}}}{D}}\cdot(\Delta D)^2 - 2I_{\mathrm{V,sphere}}\omega_{\mathrm{V}};$$

$$\frac{m_{\mathrm{V}}}{4D}\cdot\sqrt{\frac{Km_{\mathrm{S}}}{D}}\cdot(\Delta D)^2+\frac{m_{\mathrm{V}}}{2}\cdot\sqrt{\frac{Km_{\mathrm{S}}}{D}}\cdot\Delta D$$
$$-18K\frac{mm_{\mathrm{S}}R_{\mathrm{V}}^2\sin\theta\cos\theta}{D^4}\cdot\Delta t\cdot\Delta D$$
$$-6K\frac{mm_{\mathrm{S}}R_{\mathrm{V}}^2\sin\theta\cos\theta}{D^3}\cdot\Delta t-2I_{\mathrm{V,sphere}}\omega_{\mathrm{V}}=0;$$

$$\frac{m_{\mathrm{V}}}{4D}\cdot\sqrt{\frac{Km_{\mathrm{S}}}{D}}\cdot(\Delta D)^2$$
$$+\left(\frac{m_{\mathrm{V}}}{2}\cdot\sqrt{\frac{Km_{\mathrm{S}}}{D}}-18K\frac{mm_{\mathrm{S}}R_{\mathrm{V}}^2\sin\theta\cos\theta}{D^4}\cdot\Delta t\right)\cdot(\Delta D)$$
$$-6K\frac{mm_{\mathrm{S}}R_{\mathrm{V}}^2\sin\theta\cos\theta}{D^3}\cdot\Delta t-2I_{\mathrm{V,sphere}}\omega_{\mathrm{V}}=0;$$

$$\frac{m_{\mathrm{V}}}{4D}\cdot\sqrt{\frac{Km_{\mathrm{S}}}{D}}=a;$$
$$\left(\frac{m_{\mathrm{V}}}{2}\cdot\sqrt{\frac{Km_{\mathrm{S}}}{D}}-18K\frac{mm_{\mathrm{S}}R_{\mathrm{V}}^2\sin\theta\cos\theta}{D^4}\cdot\Delta t\right)=b;$$
$$6K\frac{mm_{\mathrm{S}}R_{\mathrm{V}}^2\sin\theta\cos\theta}{D^3}\cdot\Delta t+2I_{\mathrm{V,sphere}}\omega_{\mathrm{V}}=c;$$
$$a\cdot(\Delta D)^2+b\cdot(\Delta D)-c=0;$$
$$\Delta D=\frac{\sqrt{b^2+4ac}-b}{2a};$$
$$\Delta D=D-D_0;$$
$$D_0=D-\Delta D;$$
$$\Omega_{0,\mathrm{V}}=\sqrt{\frac{Km_{\mathrm{S}}}{D_0^3}};\quad \Omega_{\mathrm{V}}=\sqrt{\frac{Km_{\mathrm{S}}}{D^3}}.$$

# Problem 14

# And a Star Was Born!

Let us take as a fact that stars form from gas and dust, which represent the diffuse interstellar medium. If the mass of the diffuse interstellar medium making up an interstellar cloud of a given volume is larger than a critical value, then the mass in the volume will start contracting under the action of gravitational force.

Let us say that at a given moment in its evolution, through this mechanism, a homogeneous gas sphere has formed, of radius $r$ and mass $m$, as indicated in the drawing in Figure 14.1, and the subsequent evolution of the star occurred through the addition of successive very thin concentric shells.

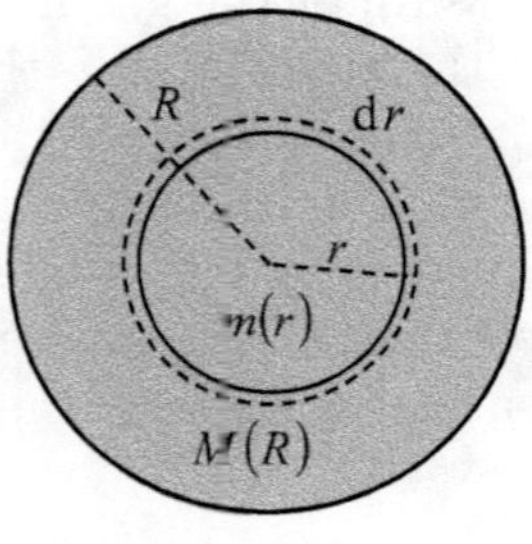


**Fig. 14.1**

In order for the star to be spherical, we assume that the star has no rotation around its own axis (or that such rotation has a negligible speed), that the star has no magnetic field, and that on the surface of the star there are no tidal effects when the star is in a binary or multiple star system.

**a)** *Determine* the binding gravitational potential energy of the star, $E_{pg}$, at a moment when the gas star, in a state of hydrostatic equilibrium, has radius $R$ and mass $M$. You should assume that the gravitational constant $K$ is known.

The star formed through the gravitational attraction of particles that make up the interstellar medium in a cloud with an infinite spherical distribution of matter, where there is no gravitational interaction between the individual particles.

**b)** The hydrostatic equilibrium of a star requires that the force produced by the pressure of the gas of the star (pressure from the thermal motion of the particles in the stellar gas), together with the force produced by the radiation emitted by the particles of the plasma of the interstellar gas, both pushing towards the outside of the star, applied on a volume element of the star (elementary radial cylinder), $\mathrm{d}V$, with height $\mathrm{d}r$, mass $\mathrm{d}m$ and density $\rho$, positioned at a distance $r$ from the center of the star, be equal to the gravitational force acting on the same volume element from the nucleus of the star of radius $r$, towards the center of the star.

*Deduce* the equation of hydrostatic equilibrium of the star given

$$\frac{\mathrm{d}p(r)}{\mathrm{d}r} + K\frac{m(r)}{r^2}\rho = 0,$$

where: $p(r)$ – the pressure of the gas inside the star with radius $r$ from the center of the star; $m(r)$ – the mass of the spherical nucleus of radius $r$; $\rho$ – the density of the star, considered to be a homogeneous sphere. *Determine* the pressure of the gas as a function of the distance away from the center of the star, $p(r)$, knowing that the pressure at the surface of the star is $p(R) = 0$. *Determine* the pressure of the gas at the center of the star.

It is known that:

$$f(x + \mathrm{d}x) \approx f(x) + \frac{\mathrm{d}f(x)}{\mathrm{d}x} \cdot \mathrm{d}x; \quad \mathrm{d}x << x.$$

**c)** *Determine* the internal energy of the star, made of an ideal monatomic gas, $U(R)$.

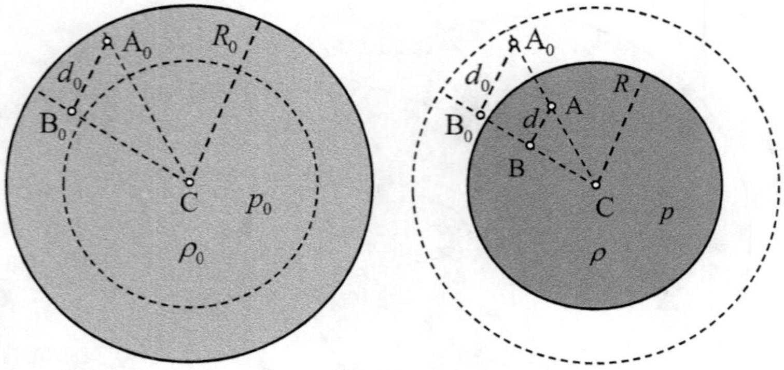


**Fig. 14.2**

**d)** *Determine* the mean temperature of the star, $T$, assuming the star is made of hydrogen and helium atoms that are completely ionized, and knowing: $\alpha$ – the relative proportion of hydrogen in the mass of the star; $\mu_{\mathrm{H}}$ – the molecular mass of hydrogen; $\mu_{\mathrm{He}}$ – the molecular mass of helium; $R_0$ – the ideal gas constant.

**e)** *Determine* the Kelvin–Helmholtz thermal time for a spherical star, $t_{KH}$, which is defined as the time required for a star configuration to contract from the initial state of an infinite interstellar cloud to the state of hydrostatic equilibrium when the radius and mass of the star are $R$ and $M$.

*Determine* the Kelvin–Helmholtz thermal time for the Sun, $t_{\mathrm{KH,S}}$, knowing the radius of the Sun $R_{\mathrm{S}} = 6.96 \cdot 10^5\,\mathrm{km}$; the mass of the Sun $M_{\mathrm{S}} = 1.99 \cdot 10^{30}\,\mathrm{kg}$; the luminosity of the Sun $L_{\mathrm{S}} = 3.86 \cdot 10^{26}\,\mathrm{W}$; the gravitational constant $K = 6.67 \cdot 10^{-11}$, $\mathrm{Nm^2kg^{-2}}$.

**f)** Assume that, during the contraction of a star, shown in Figure 14.2, the distance between any two points of the star changes by the same ratio as the radius of the star: $\mathrm{d} = y\mathrm{d}_0$; $R = yR_0$; $y < 1$. In this case, the contraction of the star is called a *homological contraction.*

*Prove* that in the process of the homological contraction, the pressure of the stellar gas ($p$) and its density ($\rho$) vary such that

$$\frac{p_0}{\rho_0^{4/3}} = \frac{p}{\rho^{4/3}} = \text{constant}.$$

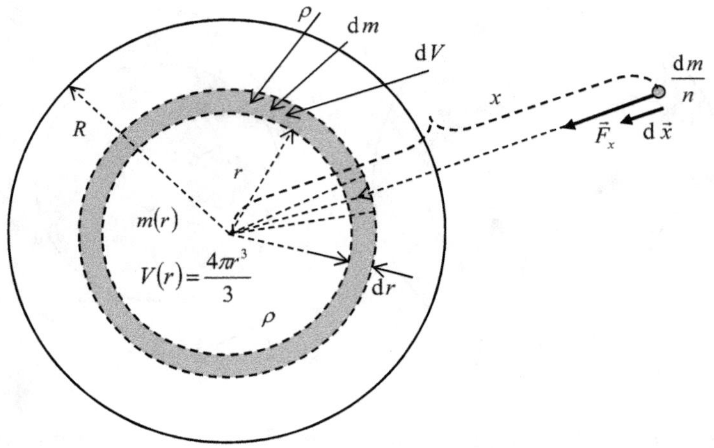


**Fig. 14.3**

## Solution

**a)** The gravitational potential energy for a spherical star is defined as being equal to the mechanical work done by the gravitational force to bring the material from the state in which it was infinitely dispersed to the current spherical state.

Consider that, at a given time during the evolution of the star through this mechanism, a homogeneous sphere has formed, with radius $r$ and mass $m$, as shown in Figure 14.3, and in the infinitesimal time after that, through extra gravitational contraction, the next concentrically spherical shell was added, of width d$r$, volume d$V$, mass d$m$ and density $\rho$, by bringing $n$ different material points from infinity, each with mass $\frac{\mathrm{d}m}{n}$, such that when they are distributed on the sphere of radius $r$, they form a spherical shell of mass $n \cdot \frac{\mathrm{d}m}{n} = dm$, width d$r$, volume $\mathrm{d}V = 4\pi r^2 \mathrm{d}r$ and density $\rho$.

In these conditions, the mechanical work done by the gravitational force, $\vec{F}_x$, created by the sphere of radius r for the elementary displacement $\mathrm{d}\vec{x}$ of the material point of mass $\frac{\mathrm{d}m}{n}$ is

$$\mathrm{d}L_x = \vec{F}_x \cdot \mathrm{d}\vec{x} = F_x \cdot \mathrm{d}x = K\frac{m(r) \cdot \frac{\mathrm{d}m}{n}}{x^2} \cdot \mathrm{d}x,$$

such that the mechanical work done to bring the material point of mass $\frac{\mathrm{d}m}{n}$ from infinity to distance $r$ from the center of the sphere is

$$L_1 = \int_{\infty}^{r} \mathrm{d}L_x = K \cdot m(r) \cdot \frac{\mathrm{d}m}{n} \cdot \int_{\infty}^{r} \frac{\mathrm{d}x}{x^2} = -K \frac{m(r) \cdot \frac{\mathrm{d}m}{n}}{r}.$$

As a result, the mechanical work done to create the entire spherical shell of width $\mathrm{d}r$, volume $\mathrm{d}V = 4\pi r^2 \mathrm{d}r$ and mass $\mathrm{d}m = \rho \cdot \mathrm{d}V$, by bringing from infinity the $n$ material points, each with mass $\frac{\mathrm{d}m}{n}$, is

$$\mathrm{d}L = n \cdot L_1 = -K \frac{m(r) \cdot \mathrm{d}m}{r},$$

such that the total mechanical work done by the gravitational forces to form a spherical star of radius $R$ and mass $M$, point by point, spherical shell after spherical shell, bringing from infinity the matter of an interstellar cloud, is

$$L = \int_0^R \mathrm{d}L = -K \int_0^R \frac{m(r) \cdot \mathrm{d}m}{r}.$$

This mechanical work equals the binding gravitational potential energy of the star:

$$L = -K \int_0^R \frac{m(r) \cdot \mathrm{d}m}{r} = E_{\mathrm{pg}};$$

$$m(r) = \rho \cdot V(r) = \rho \frac{4\pi r^3}{3};$$

$$\mathrm{d}m = \rho \cdot \mathrm{d}V = \rho \cdot \frac{4\pi}{3} \cdot 3r^2 \cdot \mathrm{d}r = 4\pi\rho \cdot r^2 \cdot \mathrm{d}r;$$

$$E_{\mathrm{pg}} = -K \int_0^R \rho \frac{4\pi r^3}{3} \cdot \frac{1}{r} \cdot 4\pi\rho \cdot r^2 \cdot \mathrm{d}r;$$

$$E_{\mathrm{pg}} = -K \frac{(4\pi\rho)^2}{3} \int_0^R r^4 \cdot \mathrm{d}r;$$

$$E_{\mathrm{pg}} = -K \frac{(4\pi\rho)^2}{3} \cdot \frac{R^5}{5};$$

$$E_{\mathrm{pg}} = -K \cdot \left(\frac{4\pi\rho}{3}\right)^2 \cdot \frac{3R^6}{5R};$$

$$E_{\text{pg}} = -K \cdot \frac{3}{5R}\left(\rho\frac{4\pi R^3}{3}\right)^2;$$

$$\rho\frac{4\pi R^3}{3} = M;$$

$$E_{\text{pg}} = -K \cdot \frac{3}{5R} \cdot M^2;$$

$$E_{\text{pg}} = -\frac{3}{5} \cdot \frac{KM^2}{R},$$

which represents the binding gravitational potential energy of the homogenous star of mass $M$ and radius $R$.

**b)**

*Solution I*

The hydrostatic equilibrium in the interior of the star implies that at each point inside the star the gravitational forces and the pressure forces cancel each other, as the drawing in Figure 14.4 indicates, such that the star does not blow up in space under the action of the pressure forces, nor does it contract towards its center under the influence of the gravitational force. The hydrostatic equilibrium is maintained globally inside the star for a prolonged time. The equilibrium may be locally perturbed in some areas and temporarily perturbed in some stages during the stellar evolution. The equation of hydrostatic equilibrium must explain the hydrostatic equilibrium present at each point in the interior of the star.

A star whose structure is gaseous is in hydrostatic equilibrium when it is neither collapsing nor exploding. In Figure 14.5, an elementary sector inside the star is in hydrostatic equilibrium under the action of gravitational forces (oriented towards the center) and pressure forces (oriented towards the exterior of the star) if the resulting radial force acting on the elementary sector is zero, such that

$$\vec{F}_{\text{pr}(r)} = -\vec{F}_{\text{gr}(r)}.$$

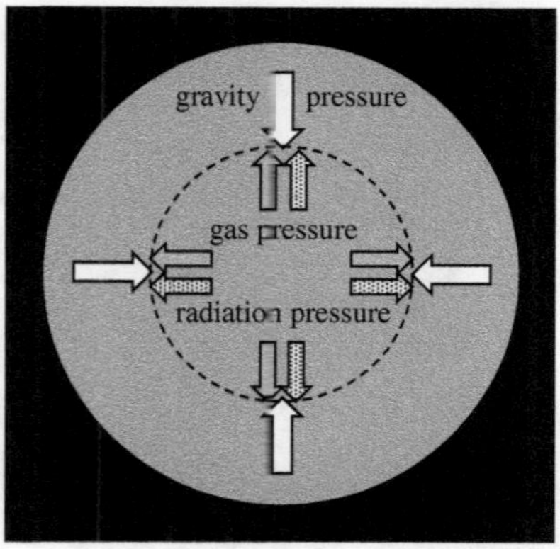


**Fig. 14.4**

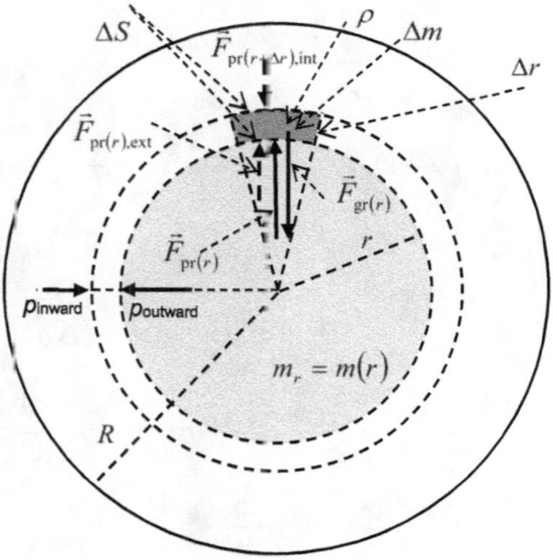


**Fig. 14.5**

In these conditions, we have:

$$F_{\mathrm{gr}(r)} = K\frac{m_{(r)} \cdot \Delta m}{r^2} = K\frac{m_{(r)}}{r^2} \cdot \rho \cdot \Delta V = K\frac{m_{(r)}}{r^2} \cdot \rho \cdot \Delta S \cdot \Delta r,$$

where $\rho$ = constant, because we considered a homogeneous sphere;

$$p_{\text{outward}(r)} > p_{\text{inward}(r+\Delta r)}; \quad p_{\text{outward}(r)} - p_{\text{inward}(r+\Delta r)} > 0;$$

$$\left(p_{\text{outward}(r)} - p_{\text{inward}(r+\Delta r)}\right)_{(r)} > 0; \quad (\Delta p)_{(r)} > 0;$$

$$-\left(p_{\text{inward}(r+\Delta r)} - p_{\text{outward}(r)}\right)_{(r)} > 0;$$

$$\left(p_{\text{inward}(r+\Delta r)} - p_{\text{outward}(r)}\right)_{(r)} = (\Delta p)_{(r)} < 0;$$

$$F_{\text{pr}(r)} = F_{\text{pr}(r),\text{ext}} - F_{\text{pr}(r+\Delta r),\text{int}};$$

$$F_{\text{pr}(r)} = \left(p_{\text{ext}(r)} - p_{\text{int}(r+\Delta r)}\right)_{(r)} \cdot \Delta S = (\Delta p)_{(r)} \cdot \Delta S;$$

$$F_{\text{pr}(r)} = -\left(p_{\text{int}(r+\Delta r)} - p_{\text{ext}(r)}\right)_{(r)} \cdot \Delta S = -(\Delta p)_{(r)} \cdot \Delta S;$$

$$\vec{F}_{\text{pr}(r)} = -\vec{F}_{\text{weight}(r)};$$

$$F_{\text{pr}(r)} = F_{\text{weight}(r)};$$

$$F_{\text{pr}(r)} = -(\Delta p)_{(r)} \cdot \Delta S; \quad F_{\text{gr}(r)} = K\frac{m_{(r)}}{r^2} \cdot \rho \cdot \Delta S \cdot \Delta r;$$

$$-(\Delta p)_{(r)} \cdot \Delta S = K\frac{m_{(r)}}{r^2} \cdot \rho \cdot \Delta S \cdot \Delta r; \quad (\Delta p)_{(r)} < 0;$$

$$(\Delta p)_{(r)} = -\rho\frac{Km_{(r)}}{r^2}\Delta r; \quad \Delta r > 0; \quad (\Delta p)_{(r)} < 0;$$

$$\frac{(\Delta p)_{(r)}}{\Delta r} = -\rho\frac{Km_{(r)}}{r^2}; \quad m_{(r)} = \rho\frac{4\pi r^3}{3};$$

$$\frac{(\Delta p)_{(r)}}{\Delta r} = -\rho\frac{K}{r^2} \cdot \rho\frac{4\pi r^3}{3};$$

$$\frac{(\Delta p)_{(r)}}{\Delta r} = -K\frac{4\pi r}{3}\rho^2;$$

$$\frac{(\Delta p)_{(r)}}{\Delta r} + K\frac{4\pi r}{3}\rho^2 = 0;$$

$$\Delta r \to dr; \quad (\Delta p)_{(r)} \to dp;$$

$$\frac{\mathrm{d}p}{dr} + K\frac{4\pi r}{3}\rho^2.$$

This represents the equation of hydrostatic equilibrium for the considered star, from which we have:

$$\mathrm{d}p = -K\frac{4\pi}{3}\rho^2 r dr;$$

$$\int_{p(r)}^{p(r)} \mathrm{d}p = -\frac{4\pi K}{3}\rho^2 \int_r^R r\mathrm{d}r;$$

$$p(R) - p(r) = -\frac{4\pi K}{3}\rho^2 \left(\frac{r^2}{2}\right)_r^R = -\frac{4\pi K}{6}\rho^2 \left(R^2 - r^2\right).$$

Thus, knowing that at the surface of the star, the pressure of the gas is

$$p(r) = 0,$$

we have

$$p(r) = \frac{2\pi K}{3}\rho^2(R^2 - r^2),$$

representing the pressure of the gas at distance $r$ from the center of the star;

$$p(r = R) = 0; \quad p(r = 0) = \frac{2\pi K}{3}\rho^2 R^2 = p_{\max};$$

$$\rho = \frac{M}{V} = \frac{3M}{4\pi R^3}; \quad p_{\max} = \frac{3}{8}\frac{KM^2}{R^4}.$$

*Solution II*

In order that the volume element d$V$, shown in Figure 14.6, be in hydrostatic equilibrium, we need to have the pressures acting on it, shown in the drawing, fulfill the condition

$$p(r + \mathrm{d}r) + p_{\mathrm{gr}(r)} = p(r),$$

from which we have:

$$-p(r + \mathrm{d}r) + p(r) = p_{\mathrm{gr}(r)};$$

$$f(x + \mathrm{d}x) \approx f(x) + \frac{\mathrm{d}f(x)}{\mathrm{d}x} \cdot \mathrm{d}x; \quad \mathrm{d}x << x;$$

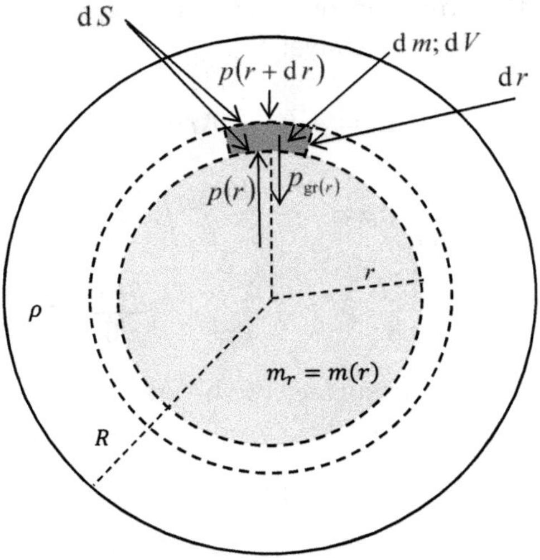


**Fig. 14.6**

$$-p(r) - \frac{\mathrm{d}p(r)}{\mathrm{d}r} \cdot \mathrm{d}r + p(r) = p_{\mathrm{gr}(r)};$$

$$\frac{\mathrm{d}p(r)}{\mathrm{d}r} \cdot \mathrm{d}r = -p_{\mathrm{gr}(r)}; \quad \mathrm{d}p(r) = -p_{\mathrm{gr}(r)};$$

$$p_{\mathrm{gr}(r)} = \frac{\mathrm{d}m \cdot g_{(r)}}{\mathrm{d}S} = \frac{\rho \cdot \mathrm{d}V \cdot g_{(r)}}{\mathrm{d}S} = \frac{\rho \cdot \mathrm{d}r \cdot \mathrm{d}S \cdot g_{(r)}}{\mathrm{d}S};$$

$$p_{\mathrm{gr}(r)} = \rho \cdot g_{(r)}. \cdot \mathrm{d}r; \quad \mathrm{d}p(r) = -\rho \cdot g_{(r)}. \cdot \mathrm{d}r;$$

$$g_{(r)} = K\frac{m_{(r)}}{r^2};$$

$$\mathrm{d}p(r) = -\rho \cdot \frac{Km_{(r)}}{r^2} \cdot \mathrm{d}r.$$

This represents the equation of hydrostatic equilibrium of the star, from which, through integration, we have:

$$p(r) - p(r) = -\frac{4\pi K}{6}\rho^2\left(R^2 - r^2\right); \quad p(r) = 0;$$

$$p(r) = \frac{2\pi K}{3}\rho^2\left(R^2 - r^2\right),$$

representing the pressure of the gas at a distance r from the center of the star.

**c)**

*Solution I*

The binding gravitational potential energy of the homogeneous star of mass $M$ and radius $R$ is

$$E_{pg} = -\frac{3}{5} \cdot \frac{KM^2}{R}.$$

Then, using the virial theorem, we have the internal energy of the star U given by:

$$2U + E_{pg} = 0; \quad U = -\frac{1}{2}E_{pg}; \quad U = \frac{3}{10} \cdot \frac{KM^2}{R}.$$

*Solution II*

For an ideal monatomic gas, for a star of radius $R$, volume $V$ and mass $M$, we know the internal energy of the gas is:

$$U(r) = \frac{3}{2}\upsilon R_0 T = \frac{3}{2}\frac{N}{N_A}R_0 T = \frac{3}{2}\frac{R_0}{N_A}NT,$$

where $R_0$ is the ideal gas constant;

$$p = nkT = \frac{N}{V}kT = \frac{k}{V}NT; \quad NT = \frac{pV}{k};$$

$$U(r) = \frac{3}{2}\frac{R_0}{N_A}\frac{pV}{k}; \quad N_A k = R_0; \quad \frac{R_0}{N_A} = k;$$

$$U(r) = \frac{3}{2}pV; \quad V = \frac{M}{\rho}; \quad U(R) = \frac{3}{2}p\frac{M}{\rho};$$

$$u = \frac{U(R)}{M} = \frac{3}{2}\frac{p}{\rho},$$

representing the internal energy per unit mass of an ideal monatomic gas.

If the internal energy of the central spherical nucleus of radius r and mass $m(r)$ is $U(r)$, then, using the previous results, the internal energy per unit mass of the central spherical nucleus is

$$u(r) = \frac{U(r)}{m(r)},$$

such that:

$$U(r) = u(r) \cdot m(r);$$
$$\mathrm{d}U = u(r) \cdot \mathrm{d}m = u(r)\rho \mathrm{d}V;$$
$$\int_0^R \mathrm{d}U = U(R) = \int_0^R u(r) \cdot \rho \cdot \mathrm{d}V; \quad \mathrm{d}V = 4\pi r^2 \mathrm{d}r,$$

where $U(R)$ is the internal energy of the entire sphere;

$$U(R) = \int_0^R u(r) \cdot \rho \cdot 4\pi \cdot r^2 \mathrm{d}r; \quad u(r) = \frac{3}{2}\frac{p(r)}{\rho};$$
$$U(R) = \int_0^R \frac{3}{2}\frac{p(r)}{\rho} \cdot \rho \cdot 4\pi \cdot r^2 \mathrm{d}r;$$
$$U(R) = 6\pi \cdot \int_0^R p(r) \cdot r^2 \mathrm{d}r;$$
$$p(r) = \frac{2\pi K}{3}\rho^2 \left(R^2 - r^2\right);$$
$$U(R) = 6\pi \cdot \frac{2\pi K}{3} \cdot \rho^2 \int_0^R \left(R^2 - r^2\right) \cdot r^2 \mathrm{d}r;$$
$$U(R) = 4\pi^2 K \cdot \rho^2 \int_0^R \left(R^2 - r^2\right) \cdot r^2 \mathrm{d}r;$$
$$U(R) = 4\pi^2 K \cdot \rho^2 \left(R^2 \int_0^R r^2 \mathrm{d}r - \int_0^R r^4 \mathrm{d}r\right);$$
$$U(R) = 4\pi^2 K \cdot \rho^2 \left(R^2 \frac{R^3}{3} - \frac{R^5}{5}\right);$$
$$U(R) = 4\pi^2 K \cdot \rho^2 \frac{2R^5}{15}; \quad U(R) = \frac{8}{15}\pi^2 K \cdot \rho^2 \frac{R^6}{R};$$

$$\rho = \frac{3M}{4\pi R^3};$$

$$U(R) = \frac{8}{15}\pi^2 K \cdot \frac{9M^2}{16\pi^2 R^6}\frac{R^6}{R};$$

$$U(R) = \frac{1}{2}\cdot\frac{3}{5}\cdot\frac{KM^2}{R};$$

$$U(R) = \frac{3}{10}\cdot\frac{KM^2}{R},$$

representing the internal energy of the star.

According to the virial theorem:

$$E_{\text{pg}} = -\frac{3}{5}\cdot\frac{KM^2}{R}; \quad U(R) = \frac{1}{2}\cdot\frac{3}{5}\frac{KM^2}{R};$$

$$2U + E_{\text{pg}} = 0.$$

**d)** Given the fact that the star is made of hydrogen and helium atoms, for a mean temperature of the star $T$, the internal energy of the star is:

$$U = U_{\text{H}} + U_{\text{He}} = N_{\text{H}}E_{\text{c m,H}} + N_{\text{He}}E_{\text{c m,He}},$$

where $N_{\text{H}}$ is number of hydrogen atoms in the structure of the star, $E_{\text{c m,H}}$ is the mean kinetic energy of a hydrogen atom, $N_{\text{He}}$ is the number of helium atoms in the structure of the star, and $E_{\text{c m,He}}$ is the mean kinetic energy of a helium atom;

$$E_{\text{c m,H}} = \frac{m_{\text{H}}\text{v}_{T,\text{H}}^2}{2}; \quad E_{\text{c m,He}} = \frac{m_{He}\text{v}_{T,\text{He}}^2}{2};$$

where $m_{\text{H}}$ is the mass of a hydrogen atom, $\text{v}_{T,\text{H}}$ is the thermal velocity of the hydrogen atoms, $m_{\text{He}}$ is the mass of a helium atom, and $\text{v}_{T,\text{He}}$ is the thermal velocity of the helium atoms;

$$\text{v}_{T,\text{H}} = \sqrt{\frac{3kT}{m_{\text{H.}}}}; \quad \text{v}_{T,\text{He}} = \sqrt{\frac{3kT}{m_{\text{He.}}}},$$

where $k$ is Boltzmann's constant;

$$E_{\mathrm{c\,m,H}} = \frac{3}{2}kT; \quad E_{\mathrm{c\,m,He}} = \frac{3}{2}kT,$$

such that, at the same temperature, $T$, the mean kinetic energy of the hydrogen atoms and helium atoms are

$$E_{\mathrm{c\,m,H}} = E_{\mathrm{c\,m,He}};$$

$$U = N_{\mathrm{H}}\frac{3}{2}kT + N_{\mathrm{He}}\frac{3}{2}kT;$$

$$N_{\mathrm{H}} = \frac{\mu_{\mathrm{H}}}{N_{\mathrm{A}}}; \quad N_{\mathrm{He}} = \frac{\mu_{\mathrm{He}}}{N_{\mathrm{A}}},$$

where $\mu_{\mathrm{H}}$ is the molar mass of the hydrogen, $\mu_{\mathrm{He}}$ is the molar mass of helium, and $N_{\mathrm{A}}$ is Avogadro's number;

$$U = \frac{\mu_{\mathrm{H}}}{N_{\mathrm{A}}}\frac{3}{2}kT + \frac{\mu_{\mathrm{He}}}{N_{\mathrm{A}}}\frac{3}{2}kT;$$

$$N_{\mathrm{H}} = \frac{M_{\mathrm{H}}}{m_{\mathrm{H}}}; \quad N_{\mathrm{He}} = \frac{M_{\mathrm{He}}}{m_{\mathrm{He}}};$$

$$U = \frac{M_{\mathrm{H}}}{m_{\mathrm{H}}}\frac{3}{2}kT + \frac{M_{\mathrm{He}}}{m_{\mathrm{He}}}\frac{3}{2}kT,$$

where $M_{\mathrm{H}}$ is the total mass of hydrogen in the star and $M_{\mathrm{He}}$ is the total mass of helium in the star;

$$m_{\mathrm{H}} = \frac{\mu_{\mathrm{H}}}{N_{\mathrm{A}}}; \quad m_{\mathrm{He}} = \frac{\mu_{\mathrm{He}}}{N_{\mathrm{A}}};$$

$$U = \frac{M_{\mathrm{H}}}{\frac{\mu_{\mathrm{H}}}{N_{\mathrm{A}}}}\frac{3}{2}kT + \frac{M_{\mathrm{He}}}{\frac{\mu_{\mathrm{He}}}{N_{\mathrm{A}}}}\frac{3}{2}kT;$$

$$U = \frac{M_{\mathrm{H}}}{\mu_{\mathrm{H}}}\frac{3}{2}N_{\mathrm{A}}kT + \frac{M_{\mathrm{He}}}{\mu_{\mathrm{He}}}\frac{3}{2}N_{\mathrm{A}}kT;$$

$$N_{\mathrm{A}}k = R_0,$$

where $R_0$ is the ideal gas constant;

$$U = \frac{M_{\mathrm{H}}}{\mu_{\mathrm{H}}}\frac{3}{2}R_0T + \frac{M_{\mathrm{He}}}{\mu_{\mathrm{He}}}\frac{3}{2}R_0T;$$

$$U = \frac{3}{2}R_0T\left(\frac{M_{\mathrm{H}}}{\mu_{\mathrm{H}}} + \frac{M_{\mathrm{He}}}{\mu_{\mathrm{He}}}\right);$$

$$M_{\mathrm{H}} = \alpha M; \quad M_{\mathrm{He}} = (1-\alpha)M,$$

where $M$ is the mass of the star;

$$U = \frac{3}{2} R_0 T \left( \frac{\alpha}{\mu_{\mathrm{H}}} + \frac{1-\alpha}{\mu_{\mathrm{He}}} \right) M.$$

As a result, under these conditions, we have:

$$U = \frac{3}{10}\frac{KM^2}{R};$$

$$U = \frac{3}{2} R_0 T \left( \frac{\alpha}{\mu_{\mathrm{H}}} + \frac{1-\alpha}{\mu_{\mathrm{He}}} \right) M;$$

$$\frac{3}{2} R_0 T \left( \frac{\alpha}{\mu_{\mathrm{H}}} + \frac{1-\alpha}{\mu_{\mathrm{He}}} \right) M = \frac{3}{10}\frac{KM^2}{R};$$

$$R_0 T \left( \frac{\alpha}{\mu_{\mathrm{H}}} + \frac{1-\alpha}{\mu_{\mathrm{He}}} \right) = \frac{1}{5}\frac{KM}{R};$$

$$T = \frac{K u_{\mathrm{H}} \mu_{\mathrm{He}} M}{5 R_0 R \left( \alpha \mu_{\mathrm{He}} + (1-\alpha)\, \mu_{\mathrm{H}} \right)}.$$

**e)** Knowing that

$$E_{\mathrm{pg}} = -\frac{3}{5}\frac{KM^2}{R}; \quad U = \frac{3}{10} \cdot \frac{KM^2}{R} = -\frac{1}{2} E_{\mathrm{pg}},$$

the total energy of the star is:

$$E = E_{\mathrm{pg}} + U = E_{\mathrm{pg}} - \frac{1}{2} E_{\mathrm{pg}}; \quad E = \frac{1}{2} \cdot E_{\mathrm{pg}}; \quad E = -\frac{3}{10} \cdot \frac{KM^2}{R}.$$

During gravitational contraction, the total energy of the star decreases when the radius of the star decreases. The energy thus released, radiated into space, is equal to half of the gravitational potential energy.

The time in which the star contracted from the original infinite distance until the radius corresponded to the hydrostatic equilibrium, during which the luminosity of the star stayed constant, represents the Kelvin–Helmholtz thermal time of the star, $t_{\mathrm{KH}}$.

If $R_0 \to \infty$ is the initial radius of the cloud from which, through gravitational contraction, the star was formed, and which now, in conditions of hydrostatic equilibrium, has radius $R$, then the change in total energy of the star as a result of its gravitational contraction is:

$$\Delta E = E_{\text{initial}} - E_{\text{final}} = -\frac{3}{10} \cdot \frac{KM^2}{R_0} - \left(-\frac{3}{10} \cdot \frac{KM^2}{R}\right);$$

$$R_0 \to \infty;$$

$$\Delta E = \frac{3}{10} \cdot \frac{KM^2}{R}.$$

Given the definition of stellar luminosity (the speed at which the energy of the star decreases), we have:

$$L = \frac{\Delta E}{t_{\text{KH}}}; \quad t_{\text{KH}} = \frac{\Delta E}{L};$$

$$t_{\text{KH}} = \frac{3}{10} \cdot \frac{KM^2}{RL};$$

$$t_{\text{KH,S}} = \frac{3}{10} \cdot \frac{KM_{\text{S}}^2}{R_{\text{S}}L_{\text{S}}} \approx 55 \cdot 10^{13}\ \text{s} \approx 1.74 \cdot 10^7\ \text{years}.$$

**f)** At the initial moment, shown in drawing (a) in Figure 14.7, when the density and radius of the stellar gas are $\rho_0$ and $R_0$, at a point $\text{D}_0$

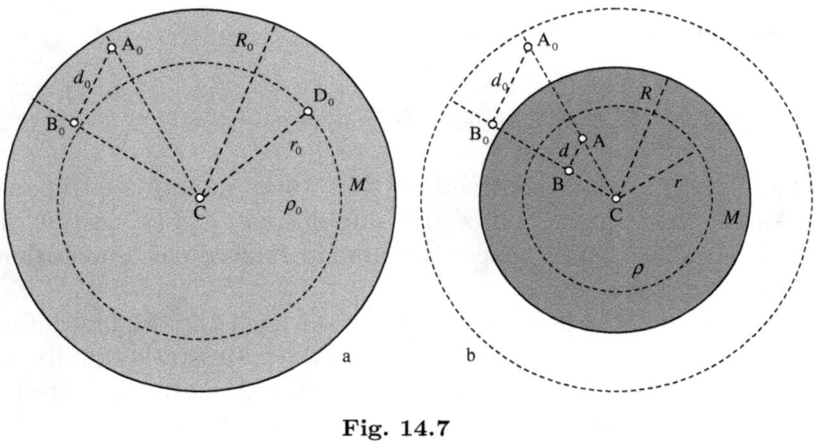


**Fig. 14.7**

at distance $r_0$ from the center of the star, the pressure of the stellar gas is

$$p(r_0) = \frac{2\pi K}{3}\rho_0^2(R_0^2 - r_0^2) = p_0.$$

At the current moment, shown in drawing (b) in Figure 14.7, when the density and radius of the stellar gas, due to the contraction of the star, are $\rho$ and $R = yR_0$, at point D at distance $r = yr_0$ from the center of the star, the pressure of the stellar gas is:

$$p(r) = \frac{2\pi K}{3}\rho^2\left(R^2 - r^2\right) = p;$$

$$r = yr_0$$

$$R = yR_0; \quad r = yr_0;$$

$$p = \frac{2\pi K}{3}\rho^2 y^2\left(R_0^2 - r_0^2\right).$$

Thus, we have:

$$\frac{p}{p_0} = \frac{\rho^2}{\rho_0^2}y^2;$$

$$\rho_0 = \frac{M}{\frac{4\pi}{3}R_0^3} = \frac{3M}{4\pi R_0^3};$$

$$\rho = \frac{M}{\frac{4\pi}{3}R^3} = \frac{3M}{4\pi R^3}; \quad R = yR_0;$$

$$\rho = \frac{3M}{4\pi y^3 R_0^3};$$

$$\frac{\rho_0}{\rho} = \frac{\frac{3M}{4\pi R_0^3}}{\frac{3M}{4\pi y^3 R_0^3}} = y^3; \quad y = \sqrt[3]{\frac{\rho_0}{\rho}} = \frac{\rho_0^{1/3}}{\rho^{1/3}};$$

$$y^2 = \frac{\rho_0^{2/3}}{\rho^{2/3}};$$

$$\frac{p}{p_0} = \frac{\rho^2}{\rho_0^2}y^2; \quad \frac{p}{p_0} = \frac{\rho^2}{\rho_0^2}\cdot\frac{\rho_0^{2/3}}{\rho^{2/3}} = \frac{\rho^{4/3}}{\rho_0^{4/3}};$$

$$\frac{p_0}{\rho_0^{4/3}} = \frac{p}{\rho^{4/3}} = \text{constant}.$$

# Problem 15

# Star Aberration

Earth's revolution around the Sun (termed the fixed inertial reference system R) can be considered as a uniform circular motion with the velocity $u = 30\,\mathrm{km/s}$. For any brief moment, the Earth can be considered an inertial reference system R$'$, in uniform linear motion with respect to the Sun, so that, as Figure 15.1 shows, the axis O$'$Y$'$ moves along OY with velocity $\vec{u}$.

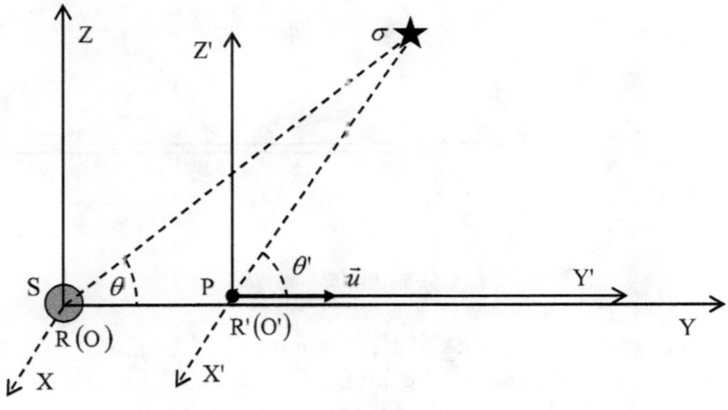


**Fig. 15.1**

For the solar observer O from the XYZ system, the direction of the star $\sigma$, in plane YOZ, is defined by the angle $\theta$, and for the terrestrial observer O', the direction of the star $\sigma$, which is in plane Y$'$O$'_{Z'}$, is defined by the angle $\theta' > \theta$.

**a)** *Establish* the relationship between $\tan\theta'$ and $\tan\theta$ as a function of $\cos\theta$ and $\beta = u/c$, where $c$ is the speed of light in vacuum $c = 3\cdot 10^5$ km/s. We know $u << c$.

**b)** *Determine* the aberration of the star $\sigma$, that is, $\Delta\theta = \theta' - \theta$, as a function of $\beta$ and $\cos\theta$.

**c)** *Express* $\sin\theta'$ as a function of $\sin\theta$ and $\beta$ and then *recompute* the aberration $\Delta\theta$.

## Solution

**a)** The components of the velocity $\vec{v}$ of the light emitted by the star $\sigma$, with respect to the inertial system R, for which $v = c$, in accordance with Figure 15.2, are as follows:

$$v_X = 0;\quad v_Y = -v\cdot\sin\theta = -c\cdot\sin\theta;\quad v_Z = -v\cdot\cos\theta = -c\cdot\cos\theta.$$

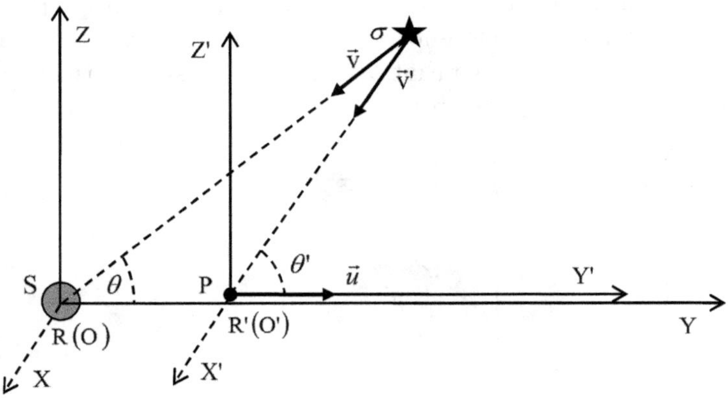


**Fig. 15.2**

As such, the components of the velocity $\vec{v}'$ of the light emitted by the star $\sigma$, with respect to the inertial system R' for which $v' = c$, in accordance with the relativistic velocity composition, are as follows:

$$v'_{X'} = 0;$$

$$v'_{Y'} = \frac{v_Y - u}{1 - \frac{v_Y u}{c^2}} = \frac{-c\cdot\sin\theta - u}{1 + \frac{c\cdot\sin\theta\cdot u}{c^2}} = -c\cdot\frac{\sin\theta + \frac{u}{c}}{1 + \sin\theta\cdot\frac{u}{c}};$$

$$\mathrm{v}'_{Y'} = -c \cdot \frac{\sin\theta + \beta}{1 + \beta \cdot \sin\theta};$$

$$\mathrm{v}'_{Z'} = \frac{\mathrm{v}_Z \cdot \sqrt{1-\beta^2}}{1 - \frac{\mathrm{v}_Y u}{c^2}} = \frac{-c \cdot \cos\theta \cdot \sqrt{1-\beta^2}}{1 + \frac{c \cdot \sin\theta \cdot u}{c^2}};$$

$$\mathrm{v}'_{Z'} = -c \cdot \sqrt{1-\beta^2} \cdot \frac{\cos\theta}{1 + \beta \cdot \sin\theta};$$

$$(\mathrm{v}')^2 = (\mathrm{v}'_{Y'})^2 + (\mathrm{v}'_{Z'})^2 = \left(-c \cdot \frac{\sin\theta + \beta}{1 + \beta \cdot \sin\theta}\right)^2$$

$$+ \left(-c \cdot \sqrt{1-\beta^2} \cdot \frac{\cos\theta}{1 + \beta \cdot \sin\theta}\right)^2 = c^2;$$

$$\mathrm{v}' = c;$$

$$\tan\theta' = \frac{-\mathrm{v}'_{Y'}}{-\mathrm{v}'_{Z'}} = \frac{c \cdot \frac{\sin\theta + \beta}{1 + \beta \cdot \sin\theta}}{c \cdot \sqrt{1-\beta^2} \cdot \frac{\cos\theta}{1 + \beta \cdot \sin\theta}} = \frac{1}{\sqrt{1-\beta^2}} \cdot \frac{\sin\theta + \beta}{\cos\theta};$$

$$\tan\theta' = \frac{1}{\sqrt{1-\beta^2}} \cdot \frac{\sin\theta + \beta}{\cos\theta};$$

$$\beta = \frac{u}{c} = \frac{30\,\mathrm{km/s}}{300000\,\mathrm{km/s}} = 10^{-4} << 1; \quad \sqrt{1-\beta^2} \approx 1;$$

$$\tan\theta' = \frac{\sin\theta + \beta}{\cos\theta} = \frac{\sin\theta}{\cos\theta} + \frac{\beta}{\cos\theta};$$

$$\tan\theta' = \tan\theta + \frac{\beta}{\cos\theta}.$$

b)

$$\Delta\theta = \theta' - \theta;$$

$$\theta' = \theta + \Delta\theta;$$

$$\tan(\theta + \Delta\theta) = \tan\theta + \frac{\beta}{\cos\theta};$$

$$\tan(\theta + \Delta\theta) - \tan\theta = \frac{\beta}{\cos\theta},$$

where $\Delta\theta$ is very small;

$$\tan(\theta+\Delta\theta)-\tan\theta=d(\tan\theta)=\frac{d\theta}{\cos^2\theta}=\frac{\Delta\theta}{\cos^2\theta};$$

$$\frac{\beta}{\cos\theta}=\frac{\Delta\theta}{\cos^2\theta};$$

$$\Delta\theta=\beta\cdot\cos\theta.$$

**c)**

$$\sin\theta'=\frac{-v'_{Y'}}{v'};$$

$$v'_{Y'}=-c\cdot\frac{\sin\theta+\beta}{1+\beta\cdot\sin\theta};\quad v'=c;$$

$$\sin\theta'=\frac{\sin\theta+\beta}{1+\beta\cdot\sin\theta};\quad \theta'=\theta+\Delta\theta;$$

$$\sin(\theta+\Delta\theta)=\frac{\sin\theta+\beta}{1+\beta\cdot\sin\theta};$$

$$\sin(\theta+\Delta\theta)=\sin\theta\cdot\cos\Delta\theta+\cos\theta\cdot\sin\Delta\theta;$$

where $\Delta\theta$ is very small;

$$\cos\Delta\theta\approx 1;\quad \sin\Delta\theta\approx\Delta\theta;$$

$$\sin(\theta+\Delta\theta)\approx\sin\theta+\Delta\theta\cdot\cos\theta;$$

$$\sin\theta+\Delta\theta\cdot\cos\theta=\frac{\sin\theta+\beta}{1+\beta\cdot\sin\theta};$$

$$\frac{1}{1+\beta\cdot\sin\theta}=(1+\beta\cdot\sin\theta)^{-1}\approx 1-\beta\cdot\sin\theta;$$

$$\sin\theta+\Delta\theta\cdot\cos\theta=(\sin\theta+\beta)\cdot(1-\beta\cdot\sin\theta);$$

$$\sin\theta+\Delta\theta\cdot\cos\theta=\sin\theta-\beta\cdot\sin^2\theta+\beta-\beta^2\cdot\sin\theta;$$

$$\Delta\theta\cdot\cos\theta=\beta\left(1-\sin^2\theta\right)-\beta^2\cdot\sin\theta;$$

$$\Delta\theta\cdot\cos\theta\approx\beta\left(1-\sin^2\theta\right);$$

$$\Delta\theta\cdot\cos\theta=\beta\cdot\cos^2\theta;$$

$$\Delta\theta=\beta\cdot\cos\theta.$$

# Problem 16

# Annual Parallax Corrections of Stars

In Figure 16.1 we show the heliocentric system of rectangular axes XYZ, with the Sun as the origin, and the axes SX and SY in the ecliptic plane – the SX axis is pointing towards the vernal point $\gamma$, the axis SY towards the summer solstice E, and the SZ axis towards the elliptical north pole $\Pi$.

In the same figure we also show the geocentric system of rectangular axes X′Y′Z′ of the Earth T, whose revolution around the Sun occurs in the ecliptic plane, and whose axes are parallel to the axes of the XYZ system.

Notation: $\vec{r}$, the position vector of the star $\sigma$ with respect to the Sun; $\vec{r}'$, the position vector of the star $\sigma$ with respect to the Earth; $\vec{a}_{\mathrm{T}}$, the position vector of the Earth with respect to the Sun; $\lambda$, the celestial heliocentric longitude of the star; $\beta$, the celestial heliocentric latitude of the star; $\lambda'$, the celestial geocentric longitude of the star; $\lambda_{\mathrm{S}}$, the elliptical longitude of the star; $\beta'$, the celestial geocentric latitude of the star.

Due to the absolute annual revolution of the Earth around the Sun, the spherical celestial geocentric coordinates of the stars, $\lambda'$ and $\beta'$, are variables.

If we compute certain corrections to these coordinates (which we call *annual parallax corrections*), we obtain the constant values of the celestial spherical heliocentric coordinates of the stars, $\lambda$ and $\beta$, which star catalogs present as having fixed values, considering the Sun to be fixed.

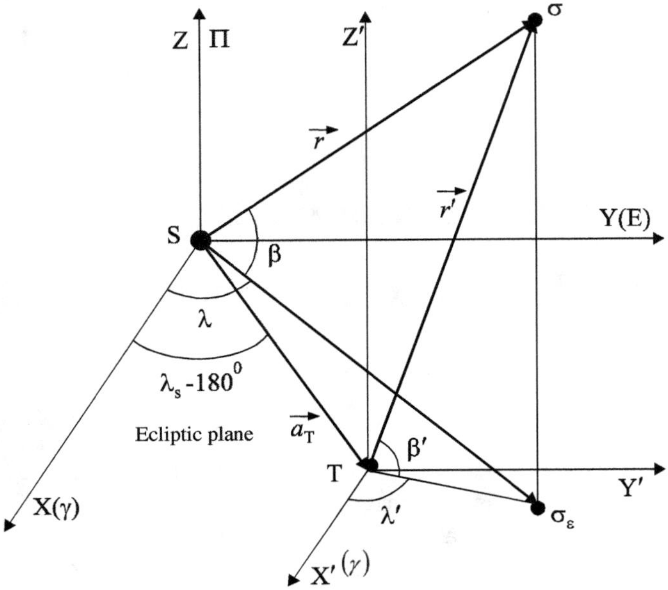


**Fig. 16.1**

*Prove* the following equations, which are the annual parallax corrections of the stars:

$$\lambda' - \lambda = p_{\text{an},\sigma} \sin(\lambda_S - \lambda) \sec\beta;$$
$$\beta' - \beta = -p_{\text{an},\sigma} \cos(\lambda_S - \lambda) \sin\beta,$$

where $p_{\text{an},\sigma}$ is the annual parallax of star $\sigma$.

## Solution

We know that, on the celestial geocentric sphere, in elliptical coordinates, the location of the Sun can be obtained with the elliptical longitude ($\lambda_\text{S}$), as measured with respect to the meridian arc of the vernal point $\gamma$, as shown in Figure 16.2 for a certain moment of the year (and for which, throughout the year, the elliptical geocentric latitude of the Sun is $\beta_\text{S} = 0$).

Knowing that the Sun–Earth distance is small compared to the interstellar distances, the directions towards the vernal point $\gamma$, from the Sun and the Earth, respectively, are very close parallels.

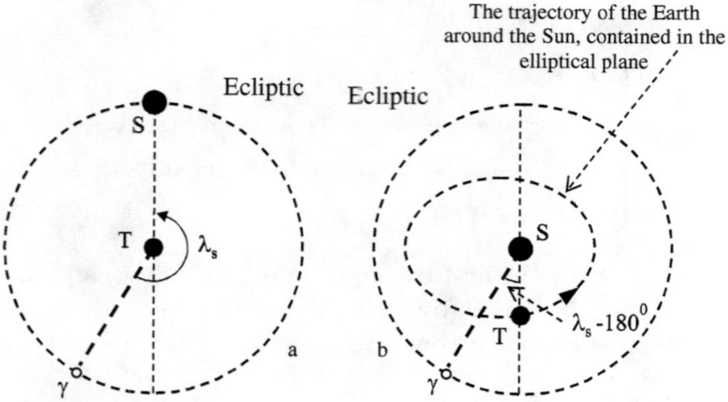


**Fig. 16.2**

Under these circumstances, if we refer to the heliocentric celestial sphere, when the trajectory of the absolute revolution of the Earth around the Sun is an ellipse contained in the elliptical plane (as Figure 16.2b shows), we have $\angle(S\gamma;\, ST) = \lambda_S - 180°$.

We know that the differences $(\lambda' - \lambda)$ and $(\beta' - \beta)$ are very small.

We can write the following equations between the Cartesian coordinates of the star $\sigma$, with respect to the two rectangular axis systems, and the elliptical coordinates with respect to the same systems:

$$\begin{cases} x = r\cos\beta\cos\lambda; \\ y = r\cos\beta\sin\lambda; \\ z = r\sin\beta; \end{cases}$$

$$\begin{cases} x' = r'\cos\beta'\cos\lambda'; \\ y' = r'\cos\beta'\sin\lambda'; \\ z' = r'\sin\beta'. \end{cases}$$

Moreover, if $a_T$ is the distance between the Earth and the Sun, and $\vec{a}_T$ is the position vector of the Earth with respect to the Sun, we have:

$$\begin{cases} x_T = a_T\cos(\lambda_S - 180°) = -a_T\sin\lambda_S; \\ y_T = a_T\sin(\lambda_S - 180°) = -a_T\sin\lambda_S; \\ z_T = 0; \end{cases}$$

$$\begin{cases} \vec{r'} = \vec{r} - -\vec{a}_{\mathrm{T}}; \\ x' = x - -x_{\mathrm{T}};\ y' = y - y_{\mathrm{T}};\ z' = z - z_{\mathrm{T}}; \\ r' \cos\beta' \cos\lambda' = r\cos\beta\cos\lambda + a_{\mathrm{T}}\cos\lambda_{\mathrm{S}}; \\ r' \cos\beta' \sin\lambda' = r\cos\beta\sin\lambda + a_{\mathrm{T}}\sin\lambda_{\mathrm{S}}; \\ r'\sin\beta' = r\sin\beta. \end{cases}$$

Then, if we multiply the first two equations by $(-\sin\lambda)$ and $\lambda$, respectively, and then by cos $\lambda$ and sin $\lambda$, respectively, adding the two resulting expressions each time, we obtain:

$$\begin{cases} r'\cos\beta'\sin(\lambda' - \lambda) = a_{\mathrm{T}}\sin(\lambda_{\mathrm{S}} - \lambda); \\ r'\cos\beta'\cos(\lambda' - \lambda) = r\cos\beta + a_{\mathrm{T}}\cos(\lambda_S - \lambda); \end{cases}$$

$$\mathrm{tg}(\lambda' - \lambda) = \frac{a_{\mathrm{T}}\sin(\lambda_{\mathrm{S}}\_\lambda)}{r\cos\beta + a_{\mathrm{T}}\cos(\lambda_{\mathrm{S}}\_\lambda)};$$

$$\mathrm{tg}(\lambda' - \lambda) = \frac{\frac{a_{\mathrm{T}}}{r}\sin(\lambda_{\mathrm{S}}\_\lambda)\sec\beta}{1 + \frac{a_{\mathrm{T}}}{r}\cos(\lambda_{\mathrm{S}}\_\lambda)\sec\beta};$$

$$a_{\mathrm{T}} << r;$$

$$\mathrm{tg}(\lambda' - \lambda) = \frac{a_{\mathrm{T}}}{r}\sin(\lambda_{\mathrm{S}}\_\lambda)\sec\beta;$$

$$\mathrm{tg}(\lambda' - \lambda) \approx \lambda' - \lambda,$$

because $(\lambda' - \lambda)$ is very small;

$$\lambda' - \lambda = \frac{a_{\mathrm{T}}}{r}\sin(\lambda_{\mathrm{S}} - \lambda)\sec\beta. \quad (1)$$

At the same time, because $(\lambda' - \lambda)$ is very small, we get:

$$\cos(\lambda' - \lambda) \approx 1;$$

$$\begin{cases} r'\cos\beta'\cos(\lambda' - \lambda) = r\cos\beta + a_{\mathrm{T}}\cos(\lambda_{\mathrm{S}} - \lambda); \\ r'\cos\beta' = r\cos\beta + a_{\mathrm{T}}\cos(\lambda_{\mathrm{S}} - \lambda); \\ r'\sin\beta' = r\sin\beta. \end{cases}$$

Then, if we multiply them by $(-\sin\beta)$ and $\cos\beta$, respectively, and then by $\cos\beta$ and $\sin\beta$, respectively, each time adding the two resulting expressions, we obtain:

$$\begin{cases} r' \sin(\beta' - \beta) = -a_{\mathrm{T}} \sin\beta \cos(\lambda_{\mathrm{S}} - \lambda); \\ r' \cos(\beta' - \beta) = r + a_{\mathrm{T}} \cos\beta \cos(\lambda_{\mathrm{S}} - \lambda); \end{cases}$$

$$\operatorname{tg}(\beta' - \beta) = \frac{-a_{\mathrm{T}} \sin\beta \cos(\lambda_{\mathrm{S}} - \lambda)}{r + a_{\mathrm{T}} \cos\beta \cos(\lambda_{\mathrm{S}} - \lambda)};$$

$$\operatorname{tg}(\beta' - \beta) = -\frac{\frac{a_{\mathrm{T}}}{r} \sin\beta \cos(\lambda_{\mathrm{S}} - \lambda)}{1 + \frac{a_{\mathrm{T}}}{r} \cos\beta \cos(\lambda_{\mathrm{S}} - \lambda)};$$

$$a_{\mathrm{T}} << r;$$

$$\operatorname{tg}(\beta' - \beta) \approx -\frac{a_{\mathrm{T}}}{r} \sin\beta \cos(\lambda_S - \lambda);$$

$$\operatorname{tg}(\beta' - \beta) \approx \beta' - \beta,$$

because $(\beta' - \beta)$ is very small;

$$\beta' - \beta = -\frac{a_{\mathrm{T}}}{r} \cos(\lambda_S - \lambda) \sin\beta. \tag{2}$$

Equations (1) and (2) are the *annual parallax corrections* of star $\sigma$, which, if they are applied to its geocentric (variable) coordinates, lead to its heliocentric (constant) coordinates, which are stored in the star data catalogs.

We call the *annual parallax* of star $\sigma$, which is outside of our solar system, the angle $p_{\mathrm{an}}$ under which we could see the medium radius of the Earth's orbit around the Sun from the center of the star at that moment of the year when the distance between the Earth and the star ($\mathrm{T}\sigma$) is perpendicular to the Earth–Sun direction (ST), as Figure 16.3 shows, so we have:

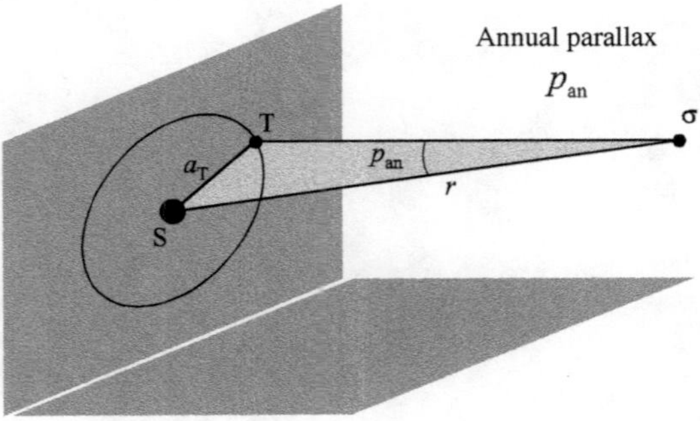


**Fig. 16.3**

$$\sin p_{\mathrm{an}} = \frac{a_{\mathrm{T}}}{r} \approx p_{\mathrm{an}},$$

because the annual parallax of a star is very small.

So, we have:

$$\lambda' - \lambda = p_{\mathrm{an},\sigma} \sin(\lambda_{\mathrm{S}} - \lambda)\sec\beta;$$

$$\beta' - \beta = -p_{\mathrm{an},\sigma} \cos(\lambda_{\mathrm{S}} - \lambda) \sin\beta.$$

# Problem 17

# Apparent and Relative Orbits

Figures 17.1 and 17.2 depict, in the plane of the sky, the apparent orbit (ellipse $E_{ap}$) of the star S in relation to the star $\Sigma$, showing the line of the nodes $N_a N_d$ and the projection $P'A'$ of the major axis PA of the relative orbit onto the plane of the sky.

*Determine the following:*

**a)** the eccentricity $e$ of the relative orbit;
**b)** the angle of inclination, $i$, between the plane of the relative orbit (ellipse) and the plane of the sky;
**c)** the argument of periapsis (periastron), that is, the angle between the line connecting the apsides and the line of the nodes, denoted by $\omega$;
**d)** the semi-axes of the relative orbit, denoted by $a$ and $b$;
**e)** the period $T$ of rotation of the star S around the star $\Sigma$;
**f)** the moment $\tau$ when the star S reaches the periastron;
**g)** the total mass, $M + m$, of the binary star system $(\Sigma; \text{S})$;
**h)** the areal velocity $\Omega_0$ of the star S;
**i)** the position of the angle $\Omega$ of the ascending node.
**j)** *Draw* the projection of the minor axis of the relative orbit from the plane $\Pi$ onto the plane of the sky, $\Pi_{sky}$.
**k)** *Draw* the ellipse E, corresponding to the orbit of the star S relative to the star $\Sigma$, in its own plane, $\Pi \neq \Pi_{sky}$, by making use of the diagram shown in Figure 17.3, which you should include in your answer sheets.

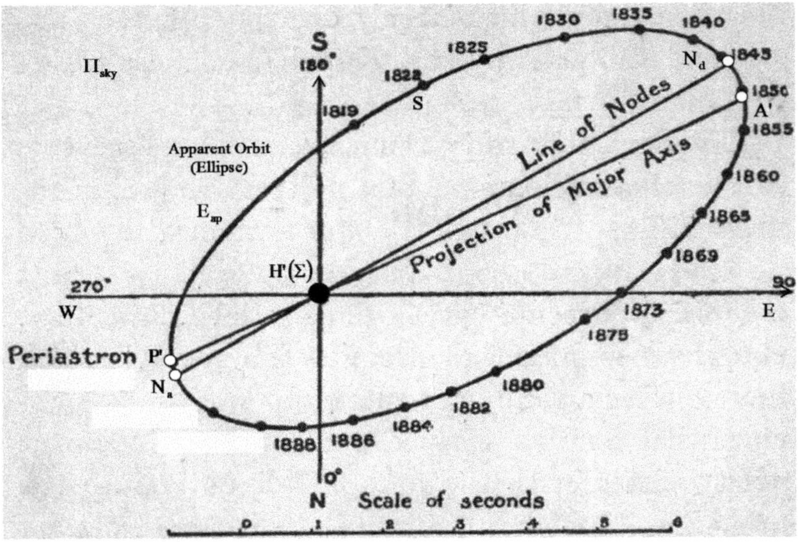


Fig. 17.1

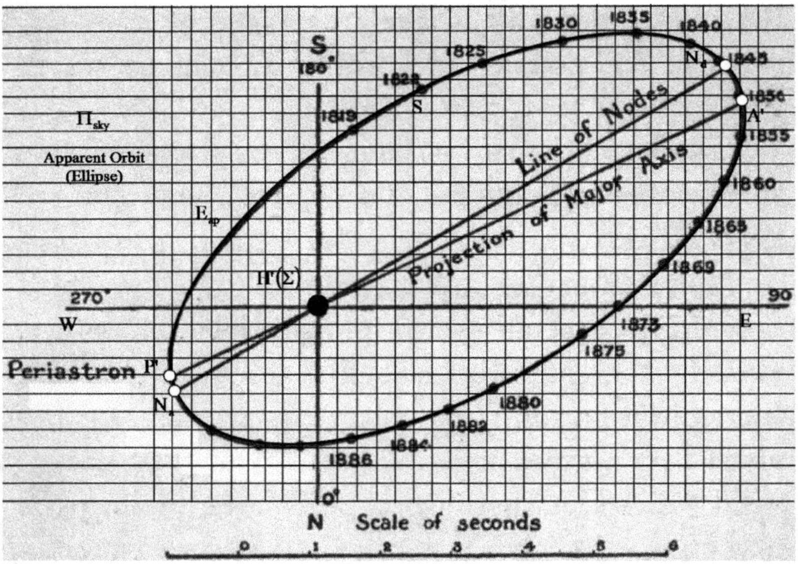


Fig. 17.2

**Answer sheet**

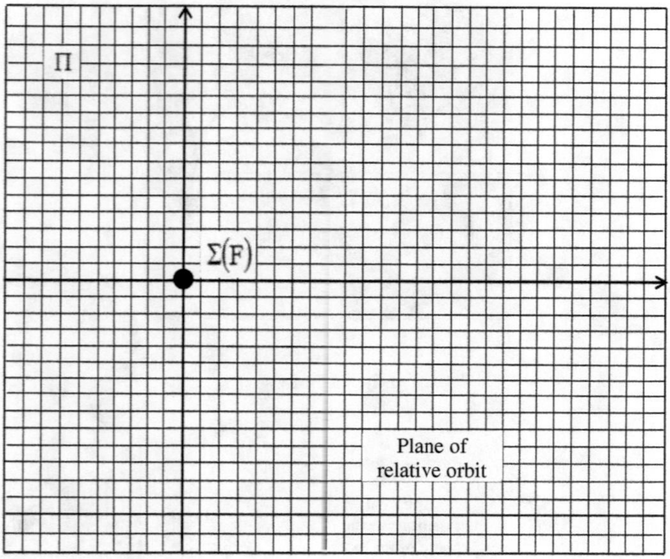


**Fig. 17.3**

*The following are given:*

The gravitational constant, $K = 6.67 \cdot 10^{-11}\,\mathrm{Nm}^2/\mathrm{kg}^2$; $1\,\mathrm{ly} = 63241\,\mathrm{AU}$; the distance from Earth to the star $\Sigma$, $\Delta = 10.5\,\mathrm{ly}$; the solar mass, $M_{Sun} = 1.9891 \cdot 10^{30}\,\mathrm{kg}$; $1\,\mathrm{AU} = 15 \cdot 10^{10}\,\mathrm{m}$.

## Solution

Figures 17.4 and 17.5 show the possible locations in the plane of the sky of the apparent positions of a star S, relative to a star $\Sigma$, both belonging to a visual binary star system. The positions are indicated using the angular coordinates $\theta$ (angular position, AP) and $\rho$ (angular separation, AS).

The drawing in the problem statement was realized using available data. It shows the ellipse $E_{ap}$, corresponding to the apparent orbit of a companion star S, relative to the main star $\Sigma$, forming a binary star system.

It is well known that any three points collinear in the plane of the relative orbit (ellipse E) remain collinear after projection onto the plane of the apparent orbit (ellipse $E_{ap}$). The projection of the

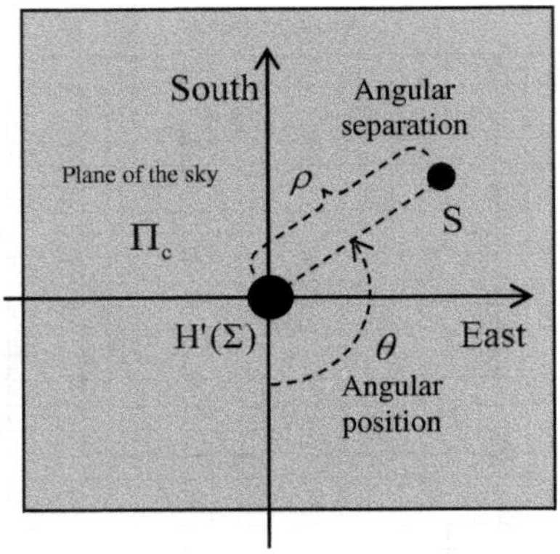


**Fig. 17.4**

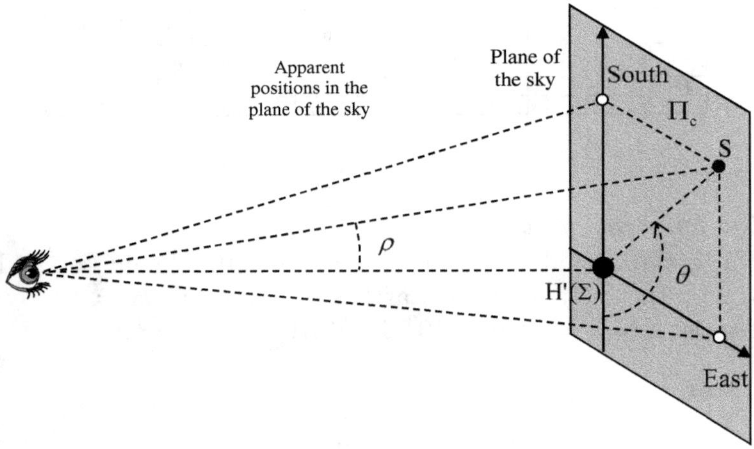


**Fig. 17.5**

major axis of the ellipse corresponding to the relative orbit (the line of the apsides $A$–$\Sigma$–P) onto the plane of the apparent orbit is denoted by the segment A′–$\Sigma$–P′, while the projection of the major axis of the relative orbit (the line of the apsides A–$\Sigma$–P) onto the line of the nodes, $N_aN_d$, corresponds to the segment $A''\Sigma P''$.

Thus, we note that in the plane of the apparent orbit, two lines intersect: the line of the nodes ($N_a\Sigma N_d$) and the line $A'\Sigma P'$ corresponding to the projection of the line of the apsides, as indicated in Figure 17.6.

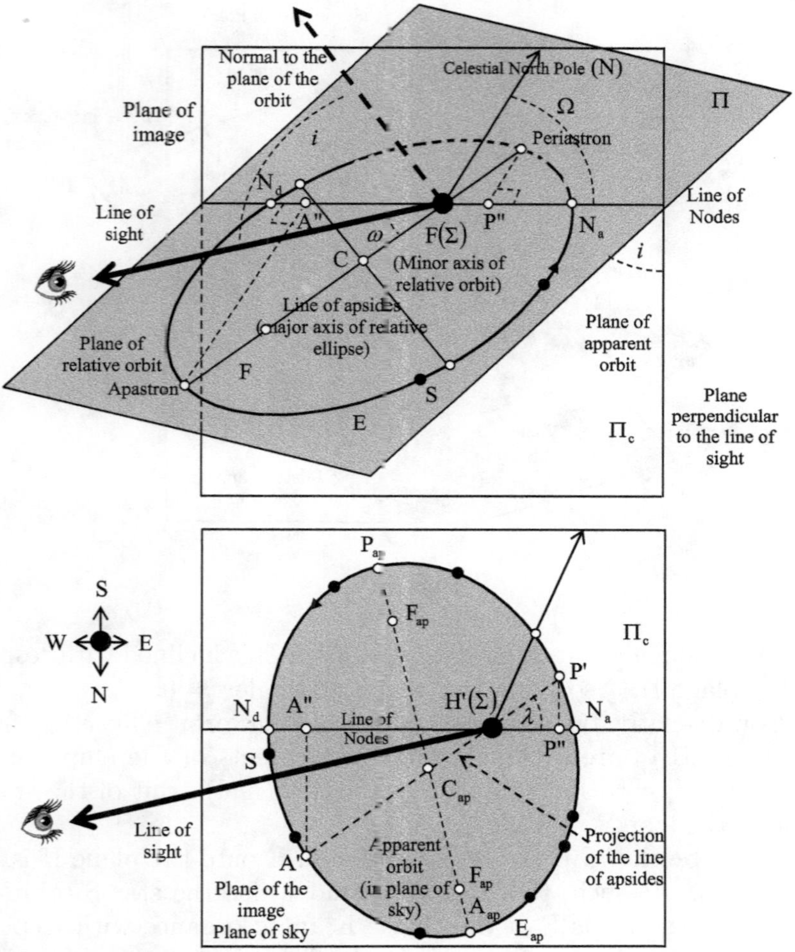


**Fig. 17.6**

Figure 17.7 shows: $\omega$ – the argument of the periastron; $\Omega$ – the angular position of the ascending node; $i$ – the inclination the relative orbit plane $\Pi$, with respect to the apparent orbit plane (the plane of the sky, $\Pi_{sky}$).

In general, in the study of the motion of a star S around another star $\Sigma$, the plane $\Pi_{sky}$ of the apparent orbit of the star S (the plane of the sky) is different from the relative orbit plane $\Pi$, which is the

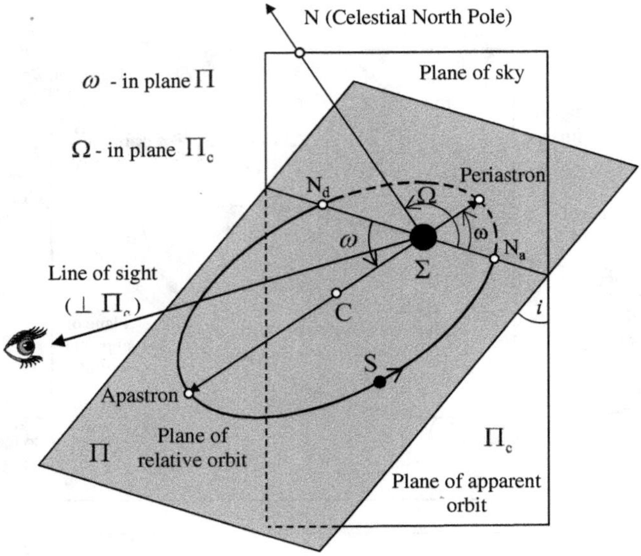


**Fig. 17.7**

plane of the real orbit. In general, the plane Π is inclined with respect to the plane $\Pi_{sky}$ so that the inclination angle $i \neq 0$.

Consequently, the elements of the apparent orbit ellipse $E_{ap}$ from the plane $\Pi_{sky}$ are different from the elements of the ellipse E, in the plane Π, corresponding to the relative (real) orbit of the star S around the star Σ.

It can be shown that the projection of E onto the plane Π is the ellipse $E_{ap}$. As such, the star Σ, around which the star S orbits, is located in the focus F of the ellipse E, in accordance with Kepler's laws. However, it is not located in the focus $F_{ap}$ of the ellipse $E_{ap}$. The point $F_{ap}$ is the apparent focus of the apparent orbit (ellipse) $E_{ap}$ in the plane of the sky $\Pi_{sky}$.

Figure 17.8 shows the apparent orbit of the companion star S with respect to the main star Σ, indicating in the corresponding plane the directions that intersect in Σ, as well as the principal axes and the foci of the ellipse. By taking measurements on this ellipse, it is possible to determine further the elements of the ellipse that correspond to the relative orbit of the star S with respect to Σ.

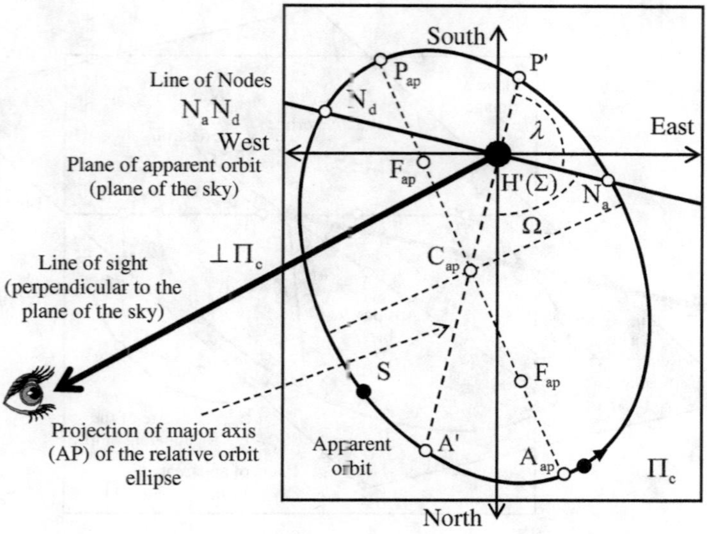


**Fig. 17.8**

Thus, by constructing the apparent orbit in the plane of the sky, it is possible to determine from its geometry the elements of the relative orbit, and hence to represent the ellipse E, which corresponds to the relative orbit of the star S in the plane Π.

Therefore, if in the relative orbit on plane Π the distance from a point Q on the relative orbit E to the line of the nodes $N_aN_d$ is $QR = x$, then the distance between the corresponding point $Q'$ on the apparent orbit $E_{ap}$ to the line of the nodes is $Q'R = x\cos i$, as indicated in Figure 17.9. The point $Q'$ is the projection of Q from the plane Π onto the plane $\Pi_{sky}$. By projecting onto the plane $\Pi_{sky}$, every segment from the plane Π that is perpendicular to the line of the nodes is reduced by the same factor of $\cos i$.

**a)** Figure 17.10 shows the following: Σ – the main star; S – the secondary star; A – the apastron (the apastron of the star S on the ellipse E with respect to the star Σ situated in the focus of the ellipse); P – the periastron (the periastron of the star S on the ellipse with respect to the star Σ); AP – the line of the apsides (the major axis of the relative orbit ellipse); AP – the projection of the line of apsides onto the plane of the sky; $N_aN_d$ – the line of the nodes;

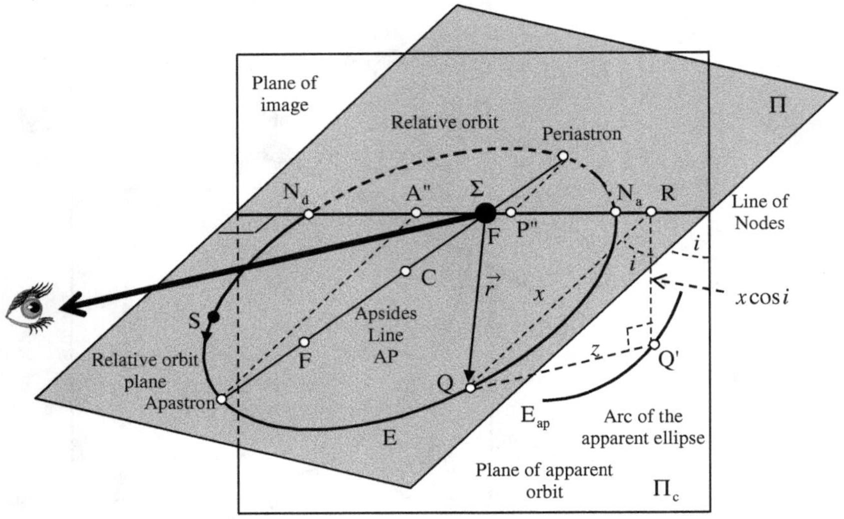


**Fig. 17.9**

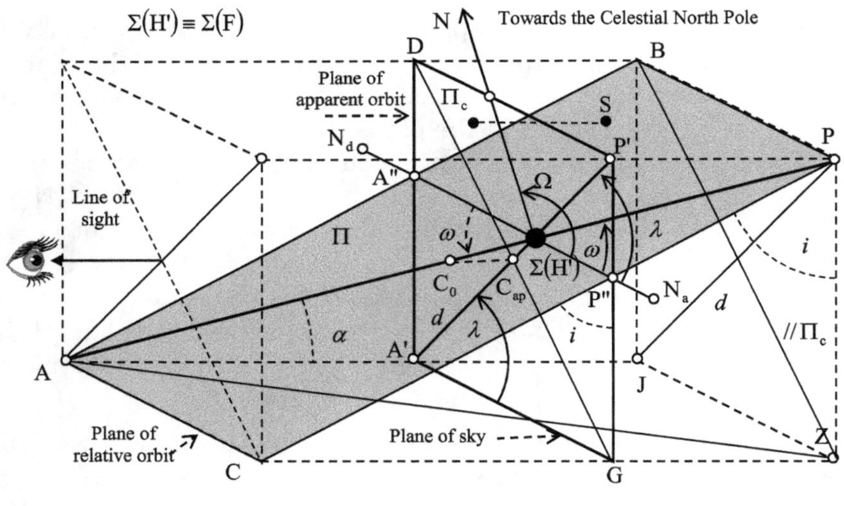


**Fig. 17.10**

$i$ – the angle between the relative orbit plane and the plane of the sky; $\omega$ – the angle between the line of the apsides and the line of the nodes; $\Pi(\text{ABPC})$ – the relative orbit plane; $\Pi_c(\text{DP}'\text{GA}')$ – the plane of the sky (the apparent orbit plane); $2a$ – the distance between the apastron and periastron (the major axis of the relative orbit ellipse);

A″P″ – the projection of the major axis of the relative orbit ellipse onto the line of the nodes.

The relative orbit of the star S with respect to the star Σ is an ellipse (E) situated in the plane Π(ABPC). The apparent orbit of the star S is the ellipse $E_{ap}$, situated in the plane of the sky $\Pi_c$(DP′GA′). The ellipse $E_{ap}$ is the projection of the ellipse E.

From Figure 17.10, the following relations result:

$$\mathrm{A\Sigma} = r_{\max} = a\,(1+e); \quad \mathrm{AA'} = r_{\max}\cos\alpha;$$

$$\mathrm{P\Sigma} = r_{\min} = a\,(1-e); \quad \mathrm{JA'} = r_{\min}\cos\alpha;$$

$$\mathrm{AA'} + \mathrm{JA'} = \mathrm{AJ} = (r_{\max} + r_{\min})\cos\alpha = 2a\cdot\cos\alpha;$$

$$\frac{A\Sigma}{P\Sigma} = \frac{r_{\max}}{r_{\min}} = \frac{A'\Sigma}{P'\Sigma} = k = \frac{1+e}{1-e};$$

$$\mathrm{A'P'} = \mathrm{A'\Sigma} + \mathrm{P'\Sigma} = d = \mathrm{JP};$$

$$\cos\alpha = \sin\omega\cdot\sin i;$$

$$d = 2a\cdot\sin\alpha;$$

$$d = 2a\cdot\sqrt{1-\sin^2\omega\cdot\sin^2 i};$$

$$\mathrm{A'\Sigma} = \mathrm{A\Sigma}\cdot\sin\alpha = \mathrm{A\Sigma}\cdot\sqrt{1-\cos^2\alpha};$$

$$\mathrm{P'\Sigma} = \mathrm{P\Sigma}\cdot\sin\alpha = \mathrm{P\Sigma}\cdot\sqrt{1-\cos^2\alpha};$$

$$\mathrm{A'P'} = (A\Sigma - P\Sigma)\sin\alpha = \mathrm{AP}\cdot\sin\alpha = \mathrm{AP}\cdot\sqrt{1-\sin^2\omega\sin^2 i};$$

$$\mathrm{A'P'} = 2a\cdot\sqrt{1-\sin^2\omega\cdot\sin^2 i} = d;$$

$$\mathrm{A'\Sigma} = \mathrm{A\Sigma}\cdot\sqrt{1-\sin^2\omega\cdot\sin^2 i} = r_{\max}\cdot\sqrt{1-\sin^2\omega\cdot\sin^2 i};$$

$$\mathrm{P'\Sigma} = \mathrm{P\Sigma}\cdot\sqrt{1-\sin^2\omega\cdot\sin^2 i} = r_{\min}\cdot\sqrt{1-\sin^2\omega\cdot\sin^2 i};$$

$$\frac{\mathrm{A'\Sigma}}{\mathrm{P'\Sigma}} = \frac{\mathrm{A\Sigma}}{\mathrm{P\Sigma}} = \frac{r_{\max}\cdot\sqrt{1-\sin^2\omega\cdot\sin^2 i}}{r_{\min}\cdot\sqrt{1-\sin^2\omega\cdot\sin^2 i}} = \frac{r_{\max}}{r_{\min}}$$

$$= \frac{a(1+e)}{a(1-e)} = \frac{1+e}{1-e} = k;$$

$$k = \frac{1+e}{1-e}; \quad e = \frac{k-1}{k+1},$$

corresponding to the numerical eccentricity of the relative orbit ellipse;

$$k = \frac{\mathrm{A'\Sigma}}{\mathrm{P'\Sigma}},$$

whose value is determined by measurements in the plane of the apparent orbit, that is, the plane of the sky;

$$(\mathrm{A'\Sigma})_{\mathrm{measured}} = 10\,\mathrm{cm}; \quad (\mathrm{P'\Sigma})_{\mathrm{measured}} = 3.5\,\mathrm{cm};$$

$$\mathrm{scale} = 10.7\,\mathrm{cm}\ \ldots\ldots\ldots\ldots\ldots\ldots\ 7\,\mathrm{arcsec};$$

$$\mathrm{A'\Sigma} = (\mathrm{A'\Sigma})_{\mathrm{measured}} \cdot \mathrm{scale}; \quad \mathrm{P'\Sigma} = (\mathrm{P'\Sigma})_{\mathrm{measured}} \cdot \mathrm{scale};$$

$$k = \frac{10\,\mathrm{cm} \cdot \mathrm{scale}}{3.5\,\mathrm{cm} \cdot \mathrm{scale}} = \frac{10}{3.5} = 2.857;$$

$$e = \frac{k-1}{k+1} = \frac{1.857}{3.857} = 0.481.$$

**b)** It can be shown, as indicated in the appendix of the problem, that

$$\cos i = \sqrt{1 - e^2},$$

its numerical value being determined by the value of $e$,

$$\cos i = \sqrt{1 - e^2} = \sqrt{1 - (0.481)^2} = 0.876.$$

**c)** From Figure 17.10, we obtain the following relations:

$$\tan \lambda = \frac{\mathrm{PZ}}{\mathrm{A''P''}} = \frac{\mathrm{CP} \cdot \cos i}{\mathrm{AP} \cdot \cos \omega} = \frac{\mathrm{AP} \cdot \sin \omega \cdot \cos i}{\mathrm{AP} \cdot \cos \omega};$$

$$\tan \lambda = \tan \omega \cdot \cos i;$$

$$\tan \omega = \frac{\tan \lambda}{\cos i}; \quad \tan^2 \omega = \frac{\tan^2 \lambda}{\cos^2 i} = \frac{\sin^2 \omega}{\cos^2 \omega} = \frac{1 - \cos^2 \omega}{\cos^2 \omega};$$

$$\cos^2 \omega = \frac{1}{1 + \tan^2 \omega}; \quad \cos \omega = \frac{1}{\sqrt{1 + \tan^2 \omega}};$$

$$\cos\omega = \frac{1}{\sqrt{1+\frac{\tan^2\lambda}{\cos^2 i}}} = \frac{\cos i}{\sqrt{\cos^2 i + \tan^2\lambda}};$$

$$\cos\omega = \frac{\cos i}{\sqrt{\cos^2 i + \tan^2\lambda}};$$

$$\cos i = 0.876;$$

$$\lambda = 5^\circ \approx 0.087\,\text{rad}; \quad \tan\lambda = 0.087;$$

$$\cos\omega = \frac{0.876}{\sqrt{(0.876)^2 + (0.087)^2}} = 0.995;$$

$$\omega = 0.099\,\text{rad} = 5.675^\circ.$$

**d)** Also from Figure 17.10, we obtain:

$$\text{AP} = 2a; \quad \text{A}''\text{P}'' = \text{AP}\cdot\cos\omega = 2a\cdot\cos\omega,$$

where $a$ is the major semi-axis of the relative orbit;

$$\text{AJ} = \text{AP}\cdot\cos\alpha = 2a\cdot\cos\alpha = \text{CZ};$$

$$\text{CP} = \text{AP}\cdot\sin\omega = 2a\cdot\sin\omega;$$

$$\text{CZ} = \text{CP}\cdot\sin i = 2a\cdot\sin\omega\cdot\sin i;$$

$$\text{AJ} = \text{CZ}; \quad 2a\cdot\cos\alpha = 2a\cdot\sin\omega\cdot\sin i;$$

$$\cos\alpha = \sin\omega\cdot\sin i;$$

$$d = \text{JP} = \text{AP}\cdot\sin\alpha = \text{A}'\text{P}'; \quad \text{AP} = 2a;$$

$$d = 2a\cdot\sin\alpha;$$

$$d = 2a\cdot\sqrt{1-\cos^2\alpha};$$

$$d = 2a\cdot\sqrt{1-\sin^2\omega\cdot\sin^2 i};$$

$$i = 0^\circ; \quad d = 2a;$$

$$i = 90^\circ; \quad d = 2a\cdot\sqrt{1-\sin^2\omega} = 2a\cdot\cos\omega;$$

$$i = 90^\circ; \quad \omega = 0; \quad d = 2a; \quad i = 0; \quad \omega = 90^\circ; \quad d = 0;$$

$$a = \frac{d}{2\cdot\sqrt{1-\sin^2\omega\cdot\sin^2 i}},$$

the value of $d$ being determined by measurements taken in the plane of the apparent orbit (the plane of the sky);

$$d_{\text{measured}} = (\text{A}'\text{P}')_{\text{measured}} = 13.5\,\text{cm};$$

$$\text{scale} = 10.7\,\text{cm} \ldots\ldots\ldots\ldots\ldots\ldots 7\,\text{arcsec};$$

$$10.7\,\text{cm} \ldots\ldots\ldots\ldots\ldots\ldots 7\,\text{arcsec};$$

$$13.5\,\text{cm} \ldots\ldots\ldots\ldots\ldots\ldots \gamma;$$

$$\gamma = 8.831\,\text{arcsec}; \quad 1\,\text{arcsec} = \frac{3.14}{180 \cdot 3600}\,\text{rad};$$

$$\gamma = 8.831 \cdot \frac{3.14}{180 \cdot 3600} \approx 0.0000427921\,\text{rad};$$

$$\Delta = 10.5\,\text{ly}.$$

Further, we use the drawing shown in Figure 17.11, where $d = \text{A}'\text{P}'$ is determined from the drawing included in the problem statement, which corresponds to the apparent orbit. Taking into account the scale factor of the drawing, it follows that:

$$d = \Delta \cdot \gamma = 10.5 \cdot 0.0000427921\,\text{ly} = 0.000449318\,\text{ly};$$

$$1\,\text{ly} = 63241\,\text{AU}; \quad d = 28.4152\,\text{AU},$$

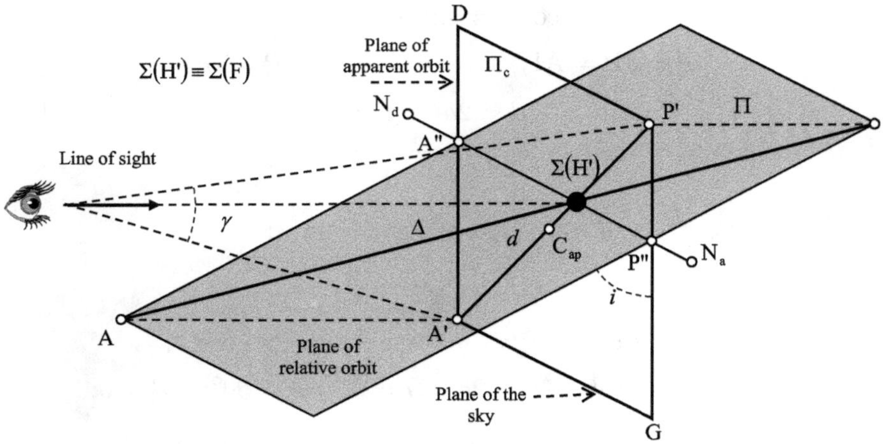


Fig. 17.11

and hence:

$$\cos\omega = 0.995; \quad \cos i = 0.876;$$

$$\sin\omega = 0.099; \quad \sin i = 0.482;$$

$$a = \frac{28.4152\,\mathrm{AU}}{2 \cdot 0.998} = 14.2360\,\mathrm{AU};$$

$$b = a\sqrt{1-e^2};$$

$$b = 14.2289\,\mathrm{AU} \cdot \sqrt{1-(0.481)^2} = 12.4747\,\mathrm{AU};$$

$$\cos i = \frac{b}{a} = \frac{12.4747\,\mathrm{AU}}{14.2289\,\mathrm{AU}} = 0.876.$$

**e)** By orthogonal projection onto the plane of the sky, all areas are reduced by the same factor cos $i$. Consequently, the radial line to the secondary star in the apparent orbit plane sweeps an equal area of space in equal amounts of time, even though the main star is not situated in the apparent focus (see Kepler's law of areas), as shown in Figure 17.12.

The apparent motion of the secondary star with respect to the main star follows an elliptic trajectory (particular cases: a circle or a segment). The main star is always situated inside the apparent ellipse, though in general not in one of the two foci. On the apparent orbit ellipse, the radial line of the secondary star, with respect to the main star, sweeps a surface whose area is directly proportional to the duration of the motion. As such, Kepler's second law (the law of areas) is still valid for the apparent orbit of the binary star system.

Using the notation from Figures 17.13 and 17.14, we obtain the following relations:

$$\frac{\Delta A_{12}}{t_2 - t_1} = \frac{\Delta A_{23}}{t_3 - t_2};$$

$$t_3 = t_1 + T;$$

$$\frac{\Delta A_{12}}{t_2 - t_1} = \frac{\Delta A_{23}}{t_1 + T - t_2}; \quad \frac{\Delta A_{12}}{t_2 - t_1} = \frac{\Delta A_{23}}{T - (t_2 - t_1)};$$

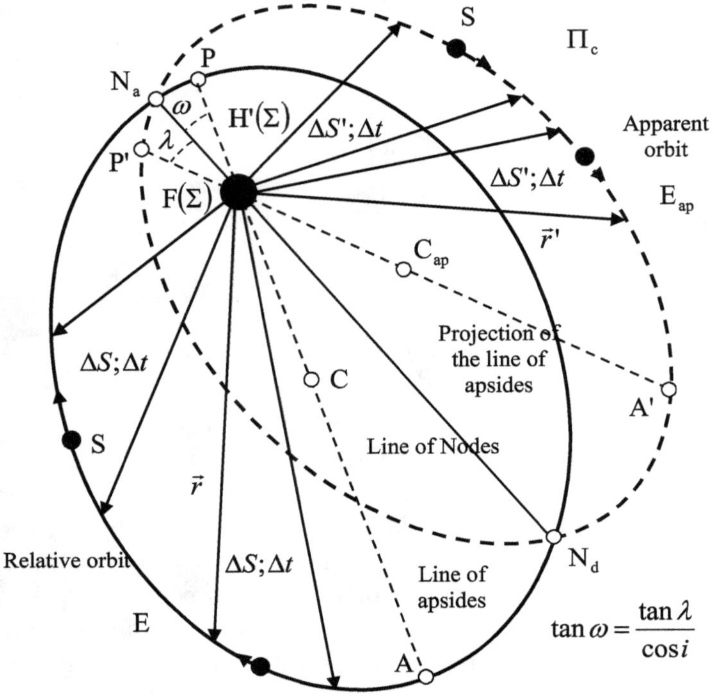


**Fig. 17.12**

$$T-(t_2-t_1)=(t_2-t_1)\,\frac{\Delta A_{23}}{\Delta A_{12}};$$

$$T=(t_2-t_1)+(t_2-t_1)\,\frac{\Delta A_{23}}{\Delta A_{12}};$$

$$T=(t_2-t_1)\left(1+\frac{\Delta A_{23}}{\Delta A_{12}}\right);$$

$$\Delta A_{12}=362\,\mathrm{u};\quad \Delta A_{23}=95\,\mathrm{u};\quad t_1=1819\,\mathrm{yrs};\quad t_2=1888\,\mathrm{yrs};$$

$$T\approx 87\,\mathrm{yrs};$$

$$t_3=t_1+T=1906\,\mathrm{yrs}.$$

This shows that the star S has come back to its original position on the apparent orbit in the year 1906.

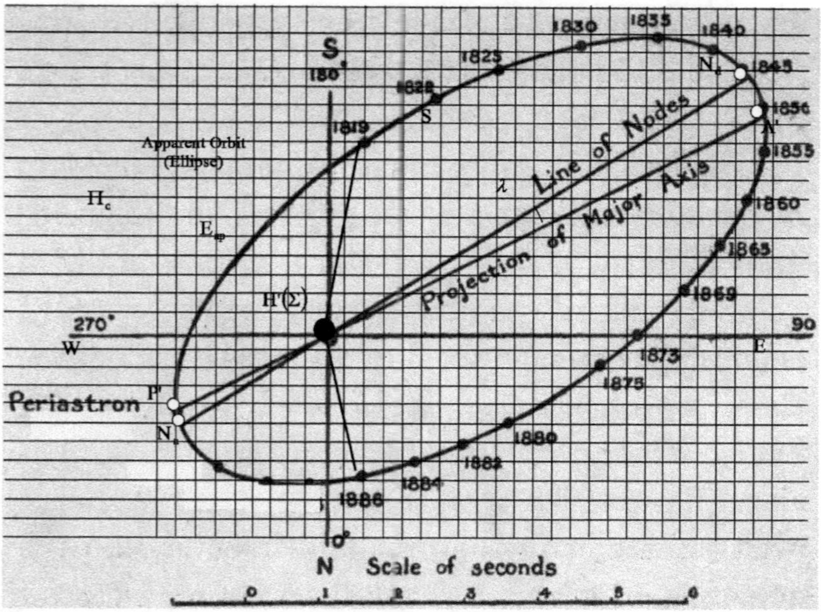


Fig. 17.13

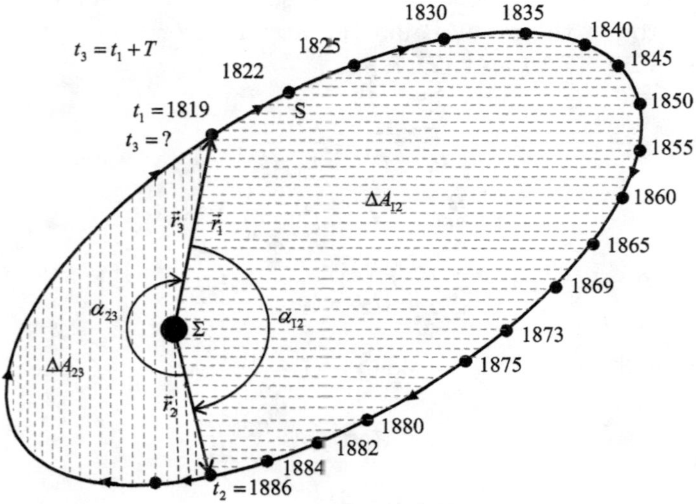


Fig. 17.14

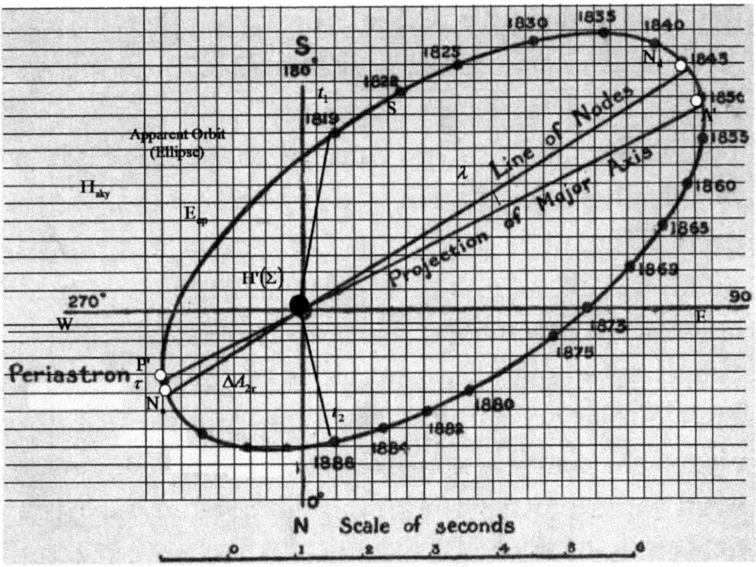


**Fig. 17.15**

**f)** The moment of time $\tau$ when the star S passes through the periastron P of the relative orbit is the same as the moment when S passes through the point P′ on the apparent orbit, as indicated in Figures 17.15, 17.16 and 17.17.

$$\frac{\Delta A_{12}}{t_2 - t_1} = \frac{\Delta A_{2\tau}}{\tau - t_2};$$

$$\tau - t_2 = (t_2 - t_1) \cdot \frac{\Delta A_{2\tau}}{\Delta A_{12}};$$

$$\tau = t_2 + (t_2 - t_1) \cdot \frac{\Delta A_{2\tau}}{\Delta A_{12}};$$

$$\Delta A_{12} = 362\,\mathrm{u}; \quad \Delta A_{2\tau} = 38\,\mathrm{u}; \quad t_1 = 1819\,\mathrm{yrs}; \quad t_2 = 1888\,\mathrm{yrs};$$

$$\tau = t_2 + (t_2 - t_1) \cdot \frac{\Delta A_{2\tau}}{\Delta A_{12}};$$

$$\tau \approx 1895,$$

which shows that the star S passes through its periastron in the year 1895.

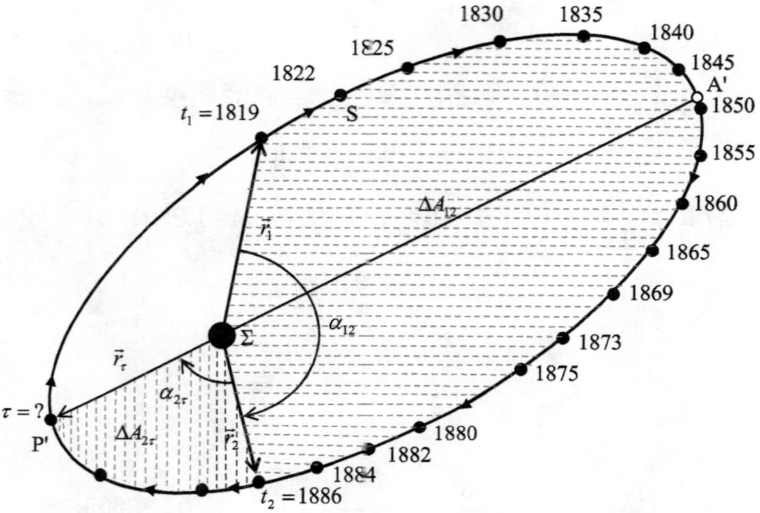


Fig. 17.16

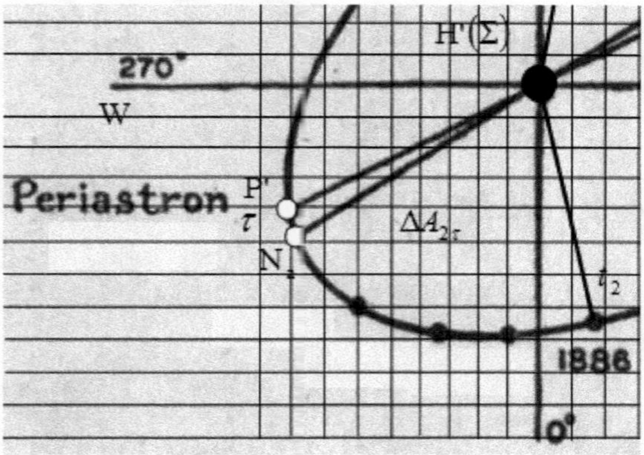


Fig. 17.17

**g)** For the computation of the mass of the star Σ, we have:

$$K = 6.67 \cdot 10^{-11}\,\mathrm{Nm^2\,kg^{-2}};$$

$$T^2 = \frac{4\pi^2}{KM}a^3;$$

$$M = \frac{4\pi^2 a^3}{KT^2}; \quad 1\,\text{AU} = 15 \cdot 10^{10}\,\text{m};$$

$$a = 14.2289\,\text{AU}; \quad T \approx 87\,\text{yrs}; \quad K = 6.67 \cdot 10^{-11}\,\text{Nm}^2/\text{kg}^2;$$

$$M = 0.763 \cdot 10^{30}\,\text{kg};$$

$$M = \frac{0.763}{1.9891} \cdot 1.9891 \cdot 10^{30}\,\text{kg} = 0.38394 \cdot 1.9891 \cdot 10^{30}\,\text{kg}$$

$$= 0.38394\,M_{Sun};$$

$$\frac{\left|T_{(\text{yrs})}\right|^2 \cdot \left|M_{(M_{Sun})}\right|}{\left|a_{(\text{AU})}\right|^3} = 1;$$

$$\left|M_{(M_{Sun})}\right| = \frac{\left|a_{(\text{AU})}\right|^3}{\left|T_{(\text{yrs})}\right|^2} = \frac{(14.2289)^3}{87^2} = 0.380605;$$

$$M = 0.380605 \cdot M_{Sun},$$

which is the mass of the star $\Sigma$;

$$M_{\text{S}} = 1.9891 \cdot 10^{30}\,\text{kg}; \quad M = 0.757 \cdot 10^{30}\,\text{kg}.$$

**h)** From the angular momentum variation theorem, we have:

$$\frac{\text{d}\vec{L}}{\text{d}t} = \vec{M} = \vec{r} \times \vec{F} = 0;$$

$$\vec{L} = \text{constant};$$

$$\vec{L} = \vec{r} \times m\vec{\text{v}} = \vec{r}_{\text{p}} \times m\vec{\text{v}}_{\text{p}} = \vec{r}_{\text{A}} \times m\vec{\text{v}}_{\text{A}};$$

$$L = rm\text{v}\sin\alpha = r_{\text{p}}m\text{v}_{\text{p}} = r_{\text{A}}m\text{v}_{\text{A}};$$

$$L = a\,(1-e)\,m\sqrt{\frac{KM\,(1+e)}{a\,(1-e)}};$$

$$p = a\left(1 - e^2\right); \quad p = b\sqrt{1-e^2};$$

$$L = m\sqrt{\frac{KMa^2(1-e)^2(1+e)}{a(1-e)}};$$

$$L = mb\sqrt{\frac{KM}{a}}.$$

From the definition of the areal speed, it follows that:

$$\vec{\Omega}_0 = \frac{\mathrm{d}\vec{A}}{\mathrm{d}t} = \frac{1}{2}\vec{r} \times \vec{v} = \frac{1}{2m}\vec{r} \times m\vec{v} = \frac{\vec{L}}{2m};$$

$$\Omega_0 = \frac{L}{2m}; \quad \Omega_0 = \frac{b}{2}\sqrt{\frac{KM}{a}};$$

$$\Omega_0 = \frac{12.4747 \cdot 15 \cdot 10^{10}\,\mathrm{m}}{2} \cdot \sqrt{\frac{6.67 \cdot 10^{-11}\,\mathrm{Nm^2}kg^{-2} \cdot 0.757 \cdot 10^{30}\,\mathrm{kg}}{14.2289 \cdot 15 \cdot 10^{10}\mathrm{m}}};$$

$$\Omega_0 = 45.506 \cdot 10^4\,\frac{\mathrm{m}^2}{\mathrm{s}}.$$

Using again the definition of the areal speed, we obtain:

$$\vec{\Omega}_0 = \frac{\mathrm{d}\vec{A}}{\mathrm{d}t} = \frac{\vec{L}}{2m}; \quad \mathrm{d}\vec{A} = \frac{\vec{L}}{2m}\mathrm{d}t;$$

$$\mathrm{d}A = \frac{L}{2m}\mathrm{d}t;$$

$$\int_0^A \mathrm{d}A = \frac{L}{2m}\int_0^T \mathrm{d}t;$$

$$A = \frac{L}{2m}T,$$

where $A$ is the area of the ellipse;

$$T = 2\pi\sqrt{\frac{a^3}{KM}};$$

$$T = 2 \cdot 3.14 \cdot \sqrt{\frac{(14.2289 \cdot 15 \cdot 10^{10})^3\,\mathrm{m}^3}{6.67 \cdot 10^{-11}\,\mathrm{Nm^2kg^{-2}} \cdot 0.757 \cdot 10^{30}\,\mathrm{kg}}};$$

$$T = 2 \cdot 3.14 \cdot \sqrt{\frac{(142.289 \cdot 15)^3}{6.67 \cdot 10^{-10} \cdot 76}} s = 27557.68086 \cdot 10^5\,\mathrm{s} =$$

$$= \frac{27557.68086 \cdot 10^5}{365 \cdot 24 \cdot 3600}\,\mathrm{yrs} = 87.384\,\mathrm{yrs}.$$

**i)** Through measurements on the drawing provided in the problem statement, the angle corresponding to the angular position of the ascending node is found to be approximately:

$$\Omega = \angle\,(\mathrm{N_a H' N}) \approx 60^\circ.$$

**j)** If $2b$ is the minor semi-axis of the relative orbit ellipse in the plane $\Pi$, we can construct its projection onto the plane of the sky, $\Pi_{sky}$.

First, on the ellipse corresponding to the apparent orbit of the secondary star in the plane of the sky, we can draw the segment ($\mathrm{C_{ap}}$, $\mathrm{H'}$, $\mathrm{P'}$), corresponding to the projection of the major axis of the relative orbit ellipse, as we already know and as shown again in Figure 17.18. This projection does not overlap with the major semi-axis of the apparent orbit ellipse. $\mathrm{C_{ap}P'}$ is not a major semi-axis in the apparent orbit. $\mathrm{P'}$ is not the periastron of the star $\Sigma$ on the apparent ellipse.

Then, on the ellipse corresponding to the apparent orbit from the plane of the sky, we draw an arbitrary chord NT, parallel to the projection of the major semi-axis of the relative ellipse, $\mathrm{C_{ap}}$ $\mathrm{H'P'}$, as indicated in Figure 17.19, where Z marks the midpoint of this chord.

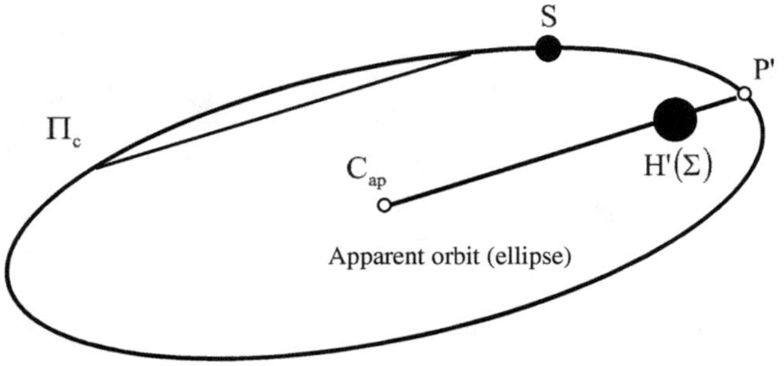


**Fig. 17.18**

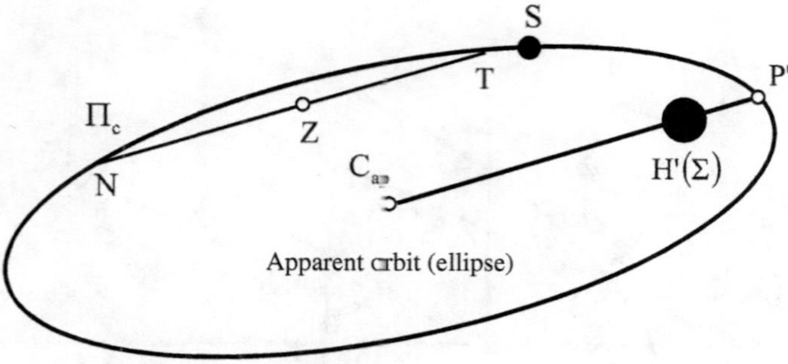


**Fig. 17.19**

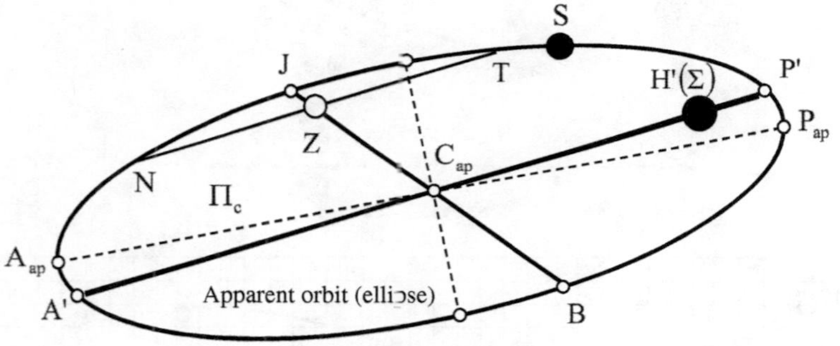


**Fig. 17.20**

We join the midpoint Z with $C_{\text{ap}}$, the center of the apparent ellipse from the plane of the sky, and then we continue this segment until it intersects the apparent ellipse. We obtain the projection in the plane of the sky of the minor axis, $2b$, of the relative orbit ellipse, as indicated in Figure 17.20. The projection onto the plane of the sky of the two axes of the relative orbit ellipse correspond to two conjugate segments.

The segment JB, from Figures 17.20 and 17.21, corresponds, in the apparent orbit plane, to the projection of the minor axis of the relative orbit from the plane Π. The segment A′P′ in the plane of the sky corresponds to the projection of the major axis of the relative orbit ellipse from the plane Π. The projections onto the plane of the sky of the axes of the relative orbit from the plane Π are not

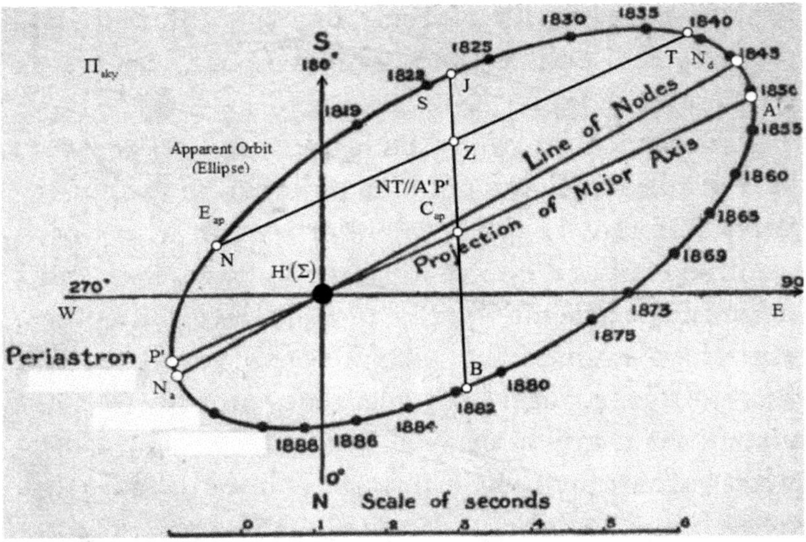


**Fig. 17.21**

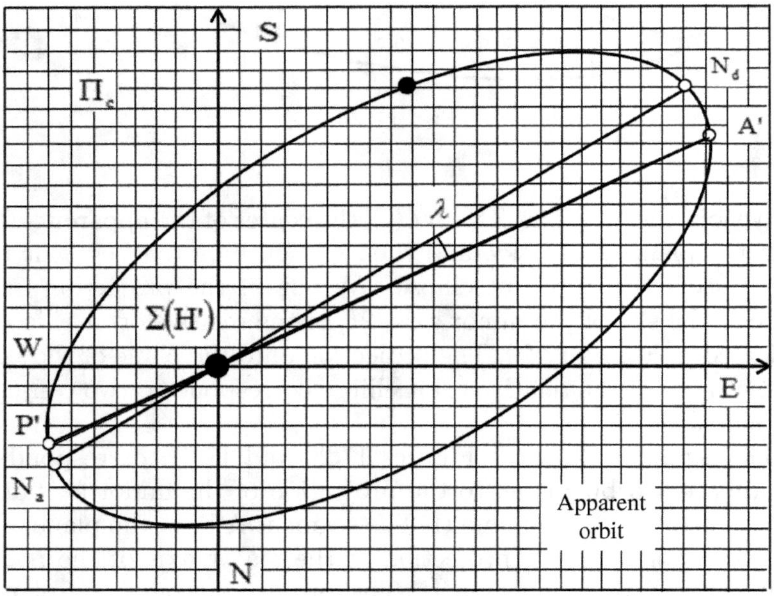


**Fig. 17.22**

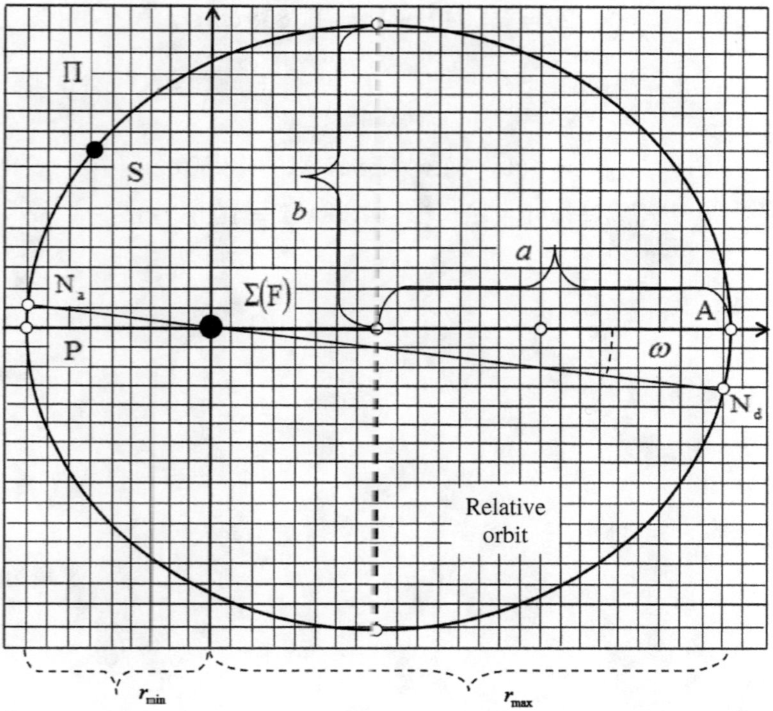


**Fig. 17.23**

perpendicular and do not overlap with the axes of the apparent orbit ellipse.

**k)** The apparent and the relative orbits are represented in their respective planes, $\Pi_{sky}$ and $\Pi$, in Figures 17.22 and 17.23, drawn using the same scale. By performing measurements and computations, we obtain the following results:

$$d = 28.4152\,\text{AU} = 13.5\,\text{cm};$$

$$a = 14.2289\,\text{AU} = 6.76\,\text{cm};$$

$$2a = 28.4578\,\text{AU} = 13.52\,\text{cm};$$

$$b = 12.4747\,\text{AU} = 5.926\,\text{cm};$$

$$2b = 24.9494\,\text{AU} = 11.858\,\text{cm};$$
$$\omega = 5.675^\circ;$$
$$e = 0.481;$$
$$r_{\text{min}} = a(1-e) = 7.3847\,\text{AU} = 3.50\,\text{cm};$$
$$r_{\text{max}} = a(1+e) = 21.0730\,\text{AU} = 10.011\,\text{cm}.$$

# Problem 18

# The Spectroscopic Binary System H.R. 8800

Figure 18.1 shows, in the plane Π, the elliptic relative orbits of the stars S and Σ, forming a binary star system whose center of mass is denoted by CM.

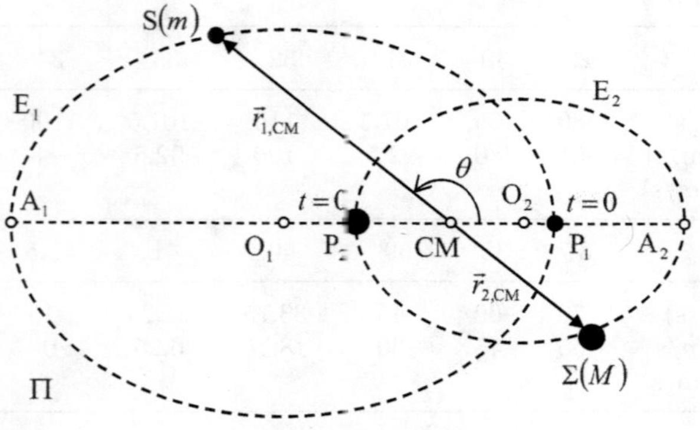


**Fig. 18.1**

The table below contains the values of the radial speed of the star S relative to an observer O, situated on Earth (or, for the sake of simplicity, on the Sun). The star S is the secondary component of the spectroscopic binary system H.R. 8800, and the data correspond to an interval of time $\Delta t = 45$ days. In the same table are included the values of the radial speed of S relative to the CM of the system, $v_{rad,S,CM}$, considered in the direction O–CM.

| $t$ (days) | 0 | 1 | 2 | 2.5 | 3 | 4 | 5 | 6 |
|---|---|---|---|---|---|---|---|---|
| $v_{rad,S,O}$ (km/s) | –90 | –80 | –65 | –60 | –55 | –40 | –27.5 | –15 |
| $v_{rad,S,CM}$ (km/s) | –75 | –65 | –50 | –45 | –40 | –25 | –12.5 | 0 |
| $v_{rad,CM,O}$ (km/s) | | | | | | | | |

| $t$ (days) | 7 | 7.5 | 8 | 9 | 10 | 11 | 12 | 13 |
|---|---|---|---|---|---|---|---|---|
| $v_{rad,S,O}$ (km/s) | –7.5 | 0 | 5 | 15 | 20 | 30.5 | 40 | 50 |
| $v_{rad,S,CM}$ (km/s) | 7.5 | 15 | 20 | 30 | 35 | 45.5 | 55 | 65 |
| $v_{rad,CM,O}$ (km/s) | | | | | | | | |

| $t$ (days) | 14 | 15 | 16 | 17 | 18.2 | 19 | 20 | 20.5 |
|---|---|---|---|---|---|---|---|---|
| $v_{rad,S,O}$ (km/s) | 55 | 60 | 62.5 | 63 | 65 | 63 | 62.5 | 60 |
| $v_{rad,S,CM}$ (km/s) | 70 | 75 | 77.5 | 78 | 80 | 78 | 77.5 | 75 |
| $v_{rad,CM,O}$ (km/s) | | | | | | | | |

| $t$ (days) | 21 | 22 | 23 | 24 | 25 | 26 | 27 | 28 |
|---|---|---|---|---|---|---|---|---|
| $v_{rad,S,O}$ (km/s) | 53 | 50 | 35 | 20 | 0 | –21.25 | –40 | –65 |
| $v_{rad,S,CM}$ (km/s) | 68 | 65 | 50 | 35 | 15 | –6.25 | –25 | –50 |
| $v_{rad,CM,O}$ (km/s) | | | | | | | | |

| $t$ (days) | 29 | 30 | 31 | 32 | 33 | 34 | 35 | 36 |
|---|---|---|---|---|---|---|---|---|
| $v_{rad,S,O}$ (km/s) | –80 | –95 | –107.5 | –115 | –107.5 | –100 | –90 | –80 |
| $v_{rad,S,CM}$ (km/s) | –65 | –80 | –92.5 | –100 | –92.5 | –85 | –75 | –65 |
| $v_{rad,CM,O}$ (km/s) | | | | | | | | |

| $t$ (days) | 37 | 38 | 39 | 40 | 41 | 41.5 | 42 |
|---|---|---|---|---|---|---|---|
| $v_{rad,S,O}$ (km/s) | –70 | –60 | –45 | –33.75 | –21.25 | –15 | –7.5 |
| $v_{rad,S,CM}$ (km/s) | –55 | –45 | –30 | –18.75 | –6.25 | 0 | 7.5 |
| $v_{rad,CM,O}$ (km/s) | | | | | | | |

| $t$ (days) | 42.5 | 43 | 44 | 45 |
|---|---|---|---|---|
| $v_{rad,S,O}$ (km/s) | 0 | 6 | 20 | 40 |
| $v_{rad,S,CM}$ (km/s) | 15 | 21 | 35 | 55 |
| $v_{rad,CM,O}$ (km/s) | | | | |

Using the notation included in Figure 18.2, which illustrates the elliptic relative orbit of the star S around the CM of the system $(S;\Sigma)$, and assuming that at $t = 0$ the secondary star S passes through the

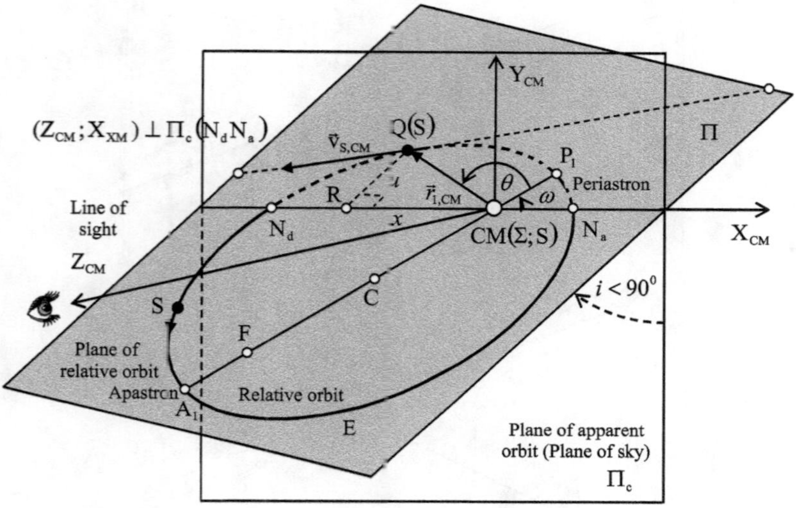


**Fig. 18.2**

periastron $P_1$ of its orbit, it can be shown, using also the drawing in Figure 18.3, that the radial speed of S relative to the CM of the system, situated in the direction of observation, is given by the following expression:

$$v_{rad,S,CM} = \frac{2\pi a_1 \sin i}{T\sqrt{1-e_1^2}}[\cos(\theta + \omega) + e_1 \cos\omega],$$

where: $a_1$ – the major semi-axis of the ellipse $E_1$, corresponding to the relative orbit of S around CM; $T$ – the period of rotation of S around CM; $e_1$ – the eccentricity of the ellipse; $i$ – the angle between the plane of the relative orbit, Π, and the plane of the apparent orbit (the plane of the sky), $\Pi_c$; $\omega$ – the argument of the periastron; $\theta$ – the true anomaly.

**a)** *Fill in the table* with the daily values of the radial speed of the CM relative to the observer O, $v_{rad,CM,O}$, and *draw*, on the same graph paper, the curves of the radial $v_{rad,S,O} = f(t)$ and $v_{rad,CM,O} = g(t)$. What conclusions can be drawn from the graph of the function $g(t)$?

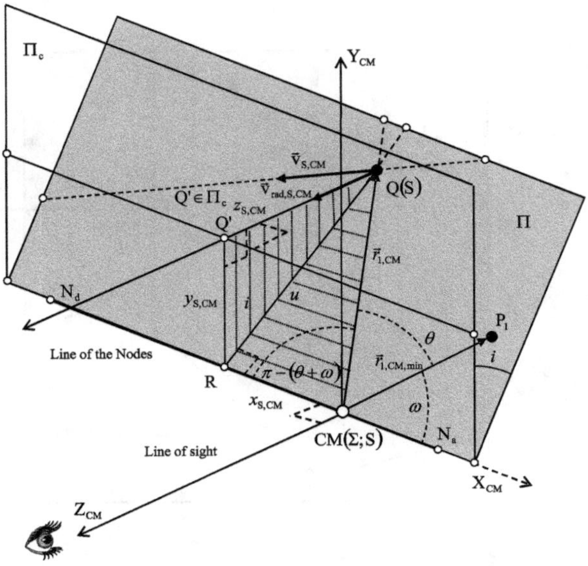


**Fig. 18.3**

*Determine the following*:

**b)** the average angular speed $\omega_{av}$ of the star S around the CM of the system;
**c)** the product $e_1 \cdot \cos\omega$;
**d)** the product $e_1 \cdot \sin\omega$;
**e)** the quantities $e_1$ and $\omega$;
**f)** the product $a_1 \cdot \sin i$;
**g)** the eccentricity $e_2$ of the elliptic orbit of the main star $\Sigma$, belonging to the system H.R. 8800.

## Solution

**a)** From Figure 18.4, we note the following relations:

$$\vec{v}_{\mathrm{rad,S,O}} = \vec{v}_{\mathrm{rad,S,CM}} + \vec{v}_{\mathrm{rad,CM,O}};$$

$$v_{\mathrm{rad,S,O}} = v_{\mathrm{rad,S,CM}} + v_{\mathrm{rad,CM,O}};$$

$$v_{\mathrm{rad,CM,O}} = v_{\mathrm{rad,S,O}} - v_{\mathrm{rad,S,CM}},$$

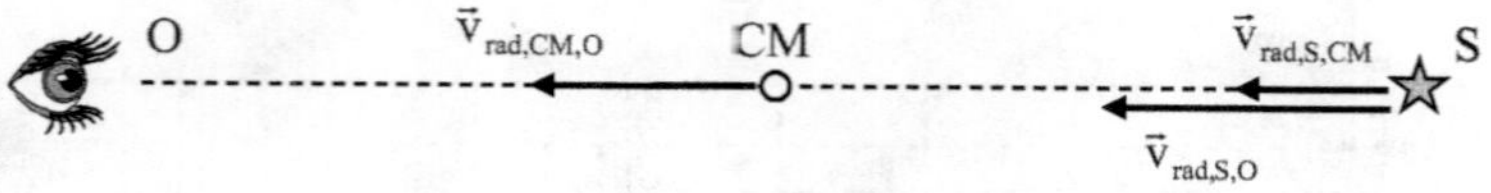


**Fig. 18.4**

whose daily values are included in the table below.

| $t$ (days) | 0 | 1 | 2 | 2.5 | 3 | 4 | 5 | 6 |
|---|---|---|---|---|---|---|---|---|
| $v_{rad,S,O}$ (km/s) | −90 | −80 | −65 | −60 | −55 | −40 | −27.5 | −15 |
| $v_{rad,S,CM}$ (km/s) | −75 | −65 | −50 | −45 | −40 | −25 | −12.5 | 0 |
| $v_{rad,CM,O}$ (km/s) | −15 | −15 | −15 | −15 | −15 | −15 | −15 | −15 |
| $t$ (days) | 7 | 7.5 | 8 | 9 | 10 | 11 | 12 | 13 |
| $v_{rad,S,O}$ (km/s) | −7.5 | 0 | 5 | 15 | 20 | 30.5 | 40 | 50 |
| $v_{rad,S,CM}$ (km/s) | 7.5 | 15 | 20 | 30 | 35 | 45.5 | 55 | 65 |
| $v_{rad,CM,O}$ (km/s) | −15 | −15 | −15 | −15 | −15 | −15 | −15 | −15 |
| $t$ (days) | 14 | 15 | 16 | 17 | 18,2 | 19 | 20 | 20.5 |
| $v_{rad,S,O}$ (km/s) | 55 | 60 | 62.5 | 63 | 65 | 63 | 62.5 | 60 |
| $v_{rad,S,CM}$ (km/s) | 70 | 75 | 77.5 | 78 | 80 | 78 | 77.5 | 75 |
| $v_{rad,CM,O}$ (km/s) | −15 | −15 | −15 | −15 | −15 | −15 | −15 | −15 |
| $t$ (days) | 21 | 22 | 23 | 24 | 25 | 26 | 27 | 28 |
| $v_{rad,S,O}$ (km/s) | 53 | 50 | 35 | 20 | 0 | −21.25 | −40 | −65 |
| $v_{rad,S,CM}$ (km/s) | 68 | 65 | 50 | 35 | 15 | −6.25 | −25 | −50 |
| $v_{rad,CM,O}$ (km/s) | −15 | −15 | −15 | −15 | −15 | −15 | −15 | −15 |
| $t$ (days) | 29 | 30 | 31 | 32 | 33 | 34 | 35 | 36 |
| $v_{rad,S,O}$ (km/s) | −80 | −95 | −107.5 | −115 | −107.5 | −100 | −90 | −80 |
| $v_{rad,S,CM}$ (km/s) | −65 | −80 | −92.5 | −100 | −92.5 | −85 | −75 | −65 |
| $v_{rad,CM,O}$ (km/s) | −15 | −15 | −15 | −15 | −15 | −15 | −15 | −15 |
| $t$ (days) | 37 | 38 | 39 | 40 | 41 | 41.5 | 42 | |
| $v_{rad,S,O}$ (km/s) | −70 | −60 | −45 | −33.75 | −21.25 | −15 | −7.5 | |
| $v_{rad,S,CM}$ (km/s) | −55 | −45 | −30 | −18.75 | −6.25 | 0 | 7.5 | |
| $v_{rad,CM,O}$ (km/s) | −15 | −15 | −15 | −15 | −15 | −15 | −15 | |
| $t$ (days) | 42.5 | 43 | 44 | 45 | | | | |
| $v_{rad,S,O}$ (km/s) | 0 | 6 | 20 | 40 | | | | |
| $v_{rad,S,CM}$ (km/s) | 15 | 21 | 35 | 55 | | | | |
| $v_{rad,CM,O}$ (km/s) | −15 | −15 | −15 | −15 | | | | |

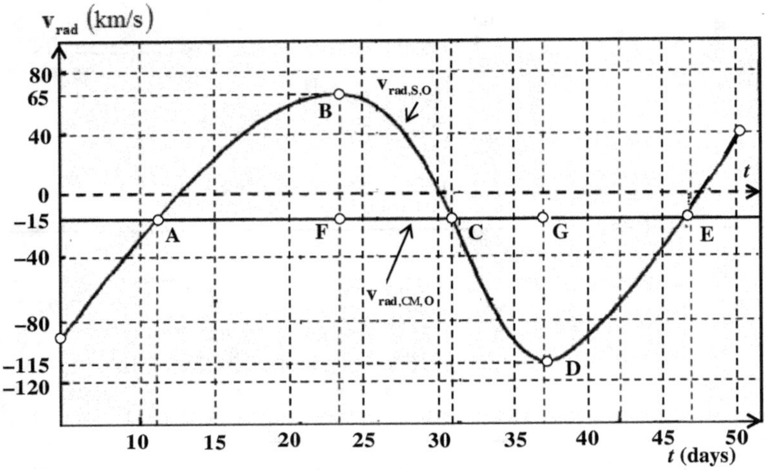


**Fig. 18.5**

Figure 18.5 shows the curves of the radial speeds $v_{rad,S,O} = f(t)$ and $v_{rad,CM,O} = g(t)$.

From the table and the graph of the function $g(t)$, it follows that the radial speed of the CM relative to the observer is constant throughout the period of observation of the binary system H.R. 8800 and has a value of $v_{rad,CM,O} = -15\,\mathrm{km/s}$, which shows that in the $\Pi$ plane the CM of the system moves in a straight line with the constant velocity $\vec{v}_{CM,O}$, relative to the observer O, as shown in Figure 18.6.

**b)** Figure 18.7 shows in the plane $\Pi$ the elliptic orbits of the components of the spectroscopic binary system $(\Sigma; S)$, relative to the CM of the system. Initially, the position of the S component corresponds to the periastron $P_1$ of its relative orbit.

Figure 18.8 shows: the radial component of the CM of the system, relative to the observer on the Earth, $\vec{v}_{rad,CM,O}$, indicating that the CM is approaching the observer; the radial components of S relative to the CM and relative to O, corresponding to four different positions $(S_1, S_2, S_3, S_4)$ of the star S relative to the CM, showing that the star S is sometimes moving towards the observer and sometimes away.

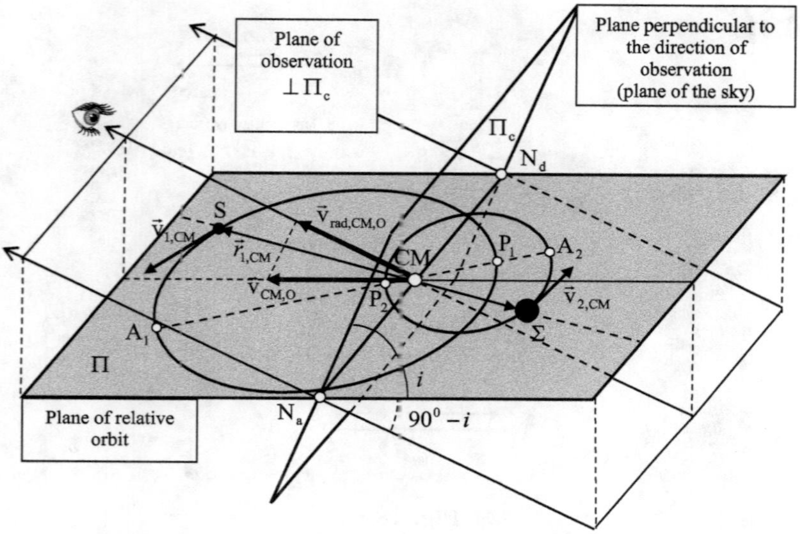


**Fig. 18.6**

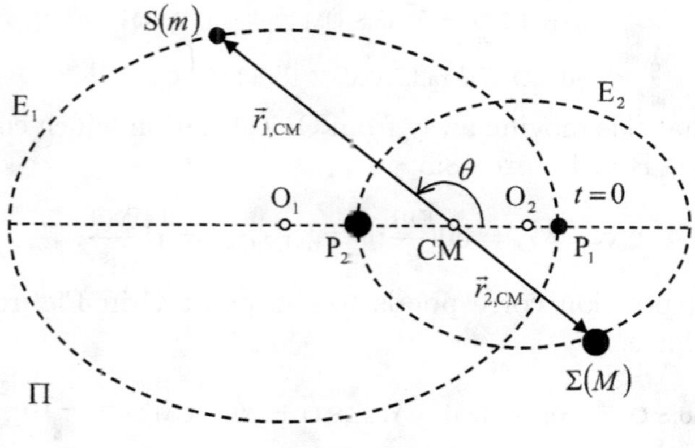


**Fig. 18.7**

In the $S_1$ position, when $\vec{v}_{rad,S,CM} = 0$, the only non-zero component is $\vec{v}_{transversal,S,CM} \neq 0$, so that for this position we have:

$$\vec{v}_{rad,S,O} = \vec{v}_{rad,CM,O}; \quad v_{rad,S,O} = v_{rad,CM,O} = -15\frac{km}{s},$$

showing that S is approaching O, a situation which corresponds to the point A in Figure 18.5.

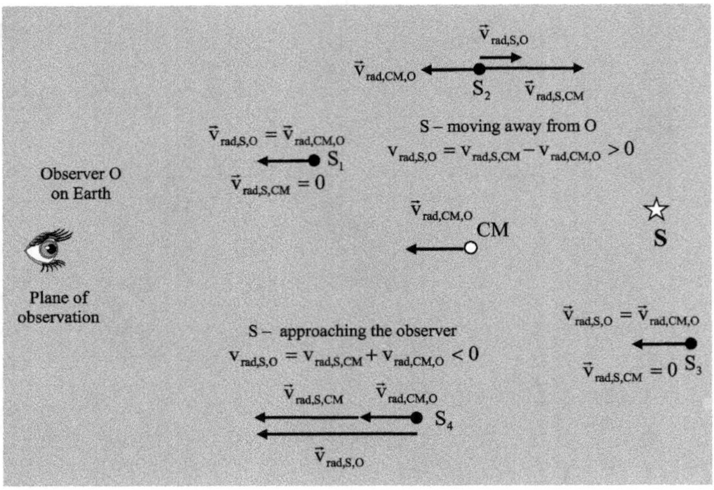


**Fig. 18.8**

In the $S_2$ position when $\vec{v}_{rad,S,CM} \neq 0$, we have:

$$\vec{v}_{rad,S,O} = \vec{v}_{rad,S,CM} + \vec{v}_{rad,CM,O};$$

$$v_{rad,S,O} = v_{rad,S,CM} - |v_{rad,CM,O}| > 0,$$

showing that S is moving away from O, a situation which corresponds to the point B in Figure 18.5;

$$v_{rad,S,O} = 60\frac{km}{s}; \quad v_{rad,S,CM} = 75\frac{km}{s}.$$

The $S_3$ position corresponds to the point C in Figure 18.5, for which we have:

$$\vec{v}_{rad,S,O} = \vec{v}_{rad,CM,O}; \quad v_{rad,S,O} = v_{rad,CM,O} = -15\frac{km}{s}.$$

In the $S_4$ position, when $\vec{v}_{rad,S,CM} \neq 0$, we obtain:

$$\vec{v}_{rad,S,O} = \vec{v}_{rad,S,CM} + \vec{v}_{rad,CM,O};$$

$$v_{rad,S,O} = v_{rad,S,CM} + v_{rad,CM,O} < 0,$$

showing that S is approaching O, a situation corresponding to the point D in Figure 18.5;

$$v_{rad,S,O} = -115\frac{km}{s}; \quad v_{rad,S,CM} = -100\frac{km}{s}.$$

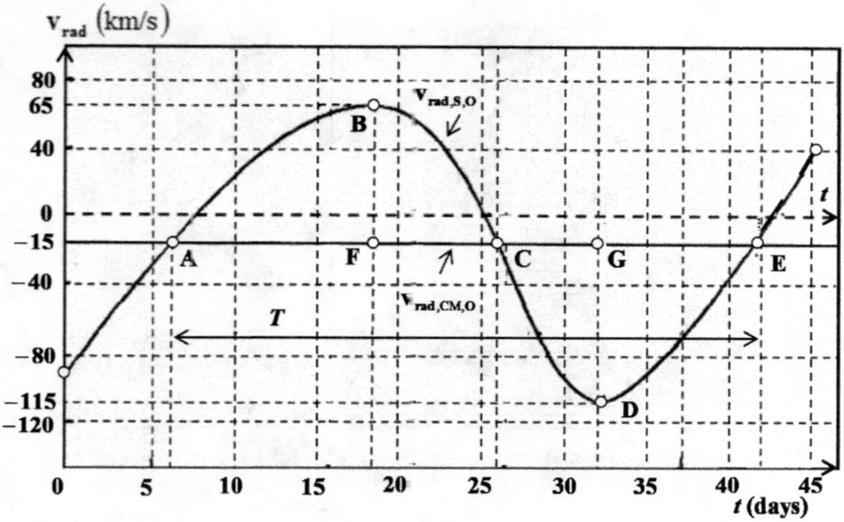


Fig. 18.9

The return of the star S to the $S_1$ position corresponds to the point E in Figure 18.5. Hence, and as shown in Figure 18.9, the period of rotation of S around the CM is given by the interval of time $\Delta t$, separating the point A and E, which is

$$T = \Delta t_{\mathrm{AE}} \approx 36.5 \text{ days},$$

such that the average angular speed of S around the CM is

$$\omega_{\mathrm{average}} = \frac{2\pi}{T} = \frac{2 \cdot 3.14}{36.5} \text{ rad/day} \approx 0.172 \text{ rad/day}.$$

**c)** Using the notation from Figure 18.10, it can be shown that the following relations hold:

$$\sin i = \frac{z_{\mathrm{S,CM}}}{u}; \quad z_{\mathrm{S,CM}} = u \cdot \sin i;$$

$$\sin[\pi - (\theta + \omega)] = \frac{u}{r} = -\cos\pi \cdot \sin(\theta + \omega) = \sin(\theta + \omega);$$

$$u = r \cdot \sin(\theta + \omega);$$

$$z_{\mathrm{S,CM}} = r \cdot \sin(\theta + \omega) \cdot \sin i.$$

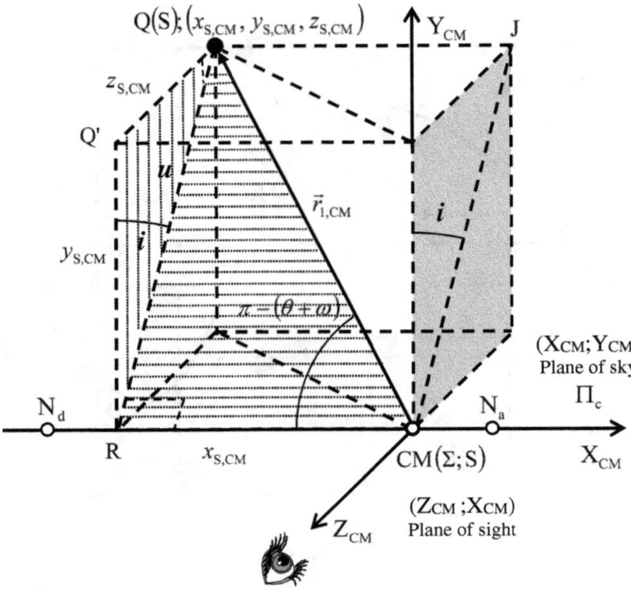


**Fig. 18.10**

Here, $z_{CM} = QQ'//CM,Z_{CM}$ is the distance from the secondary star S to the plane of the sky, $\Pi_{sky}$, since Q′ is the projection of $Q(x_{S,CM}, y_{S,CM}, z_{S,CM})$ onto the plane of the sky (i.e. the plane $\Pi_{sky} \equiv X_{CM}, CM, Y_{CM}$), which means that $z_{S,CM}$ are the coordinates of the star S corresponding to the axis $(CM; Z_{CM}) \perp \Pi_c$, and hence the radial speed of S around the CM is:

$$v_{rad,S,CM} = \frac{dz_{S,CM}}{dt} = \frac{d}{dt}[r \sin(\theta+\omega) \sin i];$$

..............................................................

$$v_{rad,S,CM} = \frac{2\pi a_1 \sin i}{T\sqrt{1-e_1^2}}[\cos(\theta+\omega) + e_1 \cos\omega].$$

From this, it follows that at any moment of time the radial speed of S with respect to the observer O on Earth (Sun) is given by the expression:

$$\vec{v}_{rad,S,O} = \vec{v}_{rad,S,CM} + \vec{v}_{rad,CM,O};$$

$$v_{rad,S,O} = v_{rad,CM,O} + \frac{2\pi a_1 \sin i}{T\sqrt{1-e_1^2}}[\cos(\theta+\omega) + e_1 \cos\omega] = f(t),$$

a function whose graph is plotted in Figure 18.7.

In particular, for the extreme points B and D on the graph of the function $f(t)$, which correspond to the positions $S_2$ and, respectively, $S_4$ of S with respect to the CM, we have:

$$(\mathrm{v}_{\mathrm{rad,S,O}})_{\mathrm{B}} = (\mathrm{v}_{\mathrm{rad,S,O}})_{\theta+\omega=0}$$
$$= \mathrm{v}_{\mathrm{rad,CM,O}} + \frac{2\pi a_1 \sin i}{T\sqrt{1-e_1^2}}(1 + e_1 \cos\omega) = 65\,\mathrm{km/s};$$

$$\mathrm{v}_{\mathrm{rad,CM,O}} + \frac{2\pi a_1 \sin i}{T\sqrt{1-e_1^2}}(1 + e_1 \cos\omega) = 65\,\mathrm{km/s};$$
$$\mathrm{v}_{\mathrm{rad,CM,O}} = -15\,\mathrm{km/s};$$
$$-15\,\mathrm{km/s} + \frac{2\pi a_1 \sin i}{T\sqrt{1-e_1^2}}(1 + e_1 \cos\omega) = 65\,\mathrm{km/s};$$
$$\alpha = \frac{2\pi a_1 \sin i}{T\sqrt{1-e_1^2}}(1 + e_1 \cos\omega) = 80\,\mathrm{km/s};$$

$$(\mathrm{v}_{\mathrm{rad,S,O}})_{\mathrm{D}} = (\mathrm{v}_{\mathrm{rad,S,O}})_{\theta+\omega=180^\circ}$$
$$= \mathrm{v}_{\mathrm{rad,CM,O}} + \frac{2\pi a_1 \sin i}{T\sqrt{1-e_1^2}}(-1 + e_1 \cos\omega) = -115\,\mathrm{km/s};$$

$$\mathrm{v}_{\mathrm{rad,CM,O}} + \frac{2\pi a_1 \sin i}{T\sqrt{1-e_1^2}}(-1 + e_1 \cos\omega) = -115\,\mathrm{km/s};$$
$$-15\,\mathrm{km/s} + \frac{2\pi a_1 \sin i}{T\sqrt{1-e_1^2}}(-1 + e_1 \cos\omega) = -115\,\mathrm{km/s};$$
$$\frac{2\pi a \sin i}{T\sqrt{1-e^2}}(-1 + e \cos\omega) = -100\,\mathrm{km/s};$$
$$-\frac{2\pi a_1 \sin i}{T\sqrt{1-e_1^2}}(1 - e_1 \cos\omega) = -100\,\mathrm{km/s};$$
$$\beta = \frac{2\pi a_1 \sin i}{T\sqrt{1-e_1^2}}(1 - e_1 \cos\omega) = 100\,\mathrm{km/s};$$
$$\frac{\alpha}{\beta} = \frac{1 + e_1 \cos\omega}{1 - e_1 \cos\omega} = \frac{80}{100} = \frac{4}{5};$$

$$e_1 \cos\omega = \frac{\alpha - \beta}{\alpha + \beta}; \quad \alpha = 80\,\text{km/s}; \quad \beta = 100\,\text{km/s};$$

$$9e_1 \cdot \cos\omega = -1; \quad e_1 \cdot \cos\omega = -\frac{1}{9} = -0,111.$$

**d)** We know that

$$\text{v}_{\text{rad,S,CM}} = \frac{dz_{\text{S,CM}}}{dt} = \frac{2\pi a_1 \sin i}{T\sqrt{1-e_1^2}}[\cos(\theta + \omega) + e_1 \cos\omega];$$

hence, for the $S_3$ position of S with respect to the CM of the system, corresponding to the point C in Figure 18.5, we obtain:

$$(\text{v}_{\text{rad,S,CM}})_{\text{S}_3} = \left(\frac{dz_{\text{S,CM}}}{dt}\right)_{\text{S}_3} = \frac{2\pi a_1 \cdot \sin i}{T\sqrt{1-e_1^2}}[\cos(\theta_{\text{S}_3} + \omega) + e_1 \cos\omega];$$

$$(\text{v}_{\text{rad,S,CM}})_{\text{C}} = \left(\frac{dz_{\text{S,CM}}}{dt}\right)_{\text{C}} = \frac{2\pi a_1 \cdot \sin i}{T\sqrt{1-e_1^2}}[\cos(\theta_{\text{C}} + \omega) + e_1 \cos\omega];$$

$$(\text{v}_{\text{rad,S,O}})_{\text{C}} = -15\text{km/s}; \quad (\text{v}_{\text{rad,CM,O}})_{\text{C}} = -15\,\text{km/s};$$

$$(\text{v}_{\text{rad,S,CM}})_{\text{C}} = 0;$$

$$\cos(\theta_{\text{C}} + \omega) = -e_1 \cdot \cos\omega;$$

$$\sin(\theta_{\text{C}} + \omega) = \sqrt{1 - \cos^2(\theta_{\text{C}} + \omega)} = \sqrt{1 - (e_1 \cdot \cos\omega)^2};$$

$$(z_{\text{S,CM}})_{\text{C}} = r_{\text{C}} \sin(\theta_{\text{C}} + \omega) \sin i;$$

$$(z_{\text{S,CM}})_{\text{C}} = r_{\text{C}} \cdot \sqrt{1 - (e_1 \cdot \cos\omega)^2} \cdot \sin i;$$

$$e_1 \cos\omega = \frac{\alpha - \beta}{\alpha + \beta}.$$

Similarly, for the point E in Figure 18.5, corresponding to the return of S to the position $S_1$, with respect to the CM of the system, it follows that:

$$(\text{v}_{\text{rad,S,CM}})_{\text{S}_1} = \left(\frac{dz_{\text{S,CM}}}{dt}\right)_{\text{S}_1} = \frac{2\pi a_1 \cdot \sin i}{T\sqrt{1-e_1^2}}[\cos(\theta_{\text{S}_1} + \omega) + e_1 \cos\omega];$$

$$(\mathrm{v}_{\mathrm{rad,S,CM}})_{\mathrm{E}} = \left(\frac{\mathrm{d}z_{\mathrm{S,CM}}}{\mathrm{d}t}\right)_{\mathrm{E}} = \frac{2\pi a_1 \cdot \sin i}{T\sqrt{1-e_1^2}}[\cos(\theta_{\mathrm{E}}+\omega) + e_1\cos\omega];$$

$$(\mathrm{v}_{\mathrm{rad,S,O}})_{\mathrm{E}} = -15\mathrm{km/s}; \quad (\mathrm{v}_{\mathrm{rad,CM,O}})_{\mathrm{E}} = -15\,\mathrm{km/s};$$

$$(\mathrm{v}_{\mathrm{rad,S,CM}})_{\mathrm{E}} = 0;$$

$$\cos(\theta_{\mathrm{E}}+\omega) = -e_1 \cdot \cos\omega;$$

$$\sin(\theta_{\mathrm{E}}+\omega) = \sqrt{1-\cos^2(\theta_{\mathrm{E}}+\omega)} = \sqrt{1-(e_1\cdot\cos\omega)^2};$$

$$(z_{\mathrm{S,CM}})_{\mathrm{E}} = r_{\mathrm{E}}\sin(\theta_{\mathrm{E}}+\omega)\sin i;$$

$$(z_{\mathrm{S,CM}})_{\mathrm{E}} = r_{\mathrm{E}}\cdot\sqrt{1-(e_1\cdot\cos\omega)^2}\cdot\sin i;$$

$$e_1\cos\omega = \frac{\alpha-\beta}{\alpha+\beta}.$$

Hence, we obtain:

$$(z_{\mathrm{S,CM}})_{\mathrm{C}} = r_{\mathrm{C}}\cdot\sqrt{1-(e_1\cdot\cos\omega)^2}\cdot\sin i;$$

$$(z_{\mathrm{S,CM}})_{\mathrm{E}} = r_{\mathrm{E}}\cdot\sqrt{1-(e_1\cdot\cos\omega)^2}\cdot\sin i;$$

$$\frac{(z_{\mathrm{S,CM}})_{\mathrm{C}}}{(z_{\mathrm{S,CM}})_{\mathrm{E}}} = \frac{r_{\mathrm{C}}}{r_{\mathrm{E}}};$$

$$r_{\mathrm{C}} = \frac{a(1-e_1^2)}{1+e_1\cdot\cos\theta_{\mathrm{C}}}; \quad r_{\mathrm{E}} = \frac{a_1(1-e_1^2)}{1+e_1\cdot\cos\theta_{\mathrm{E}}};$$

$$\frac{(z_{\mathrm{S,CM}})_{\mathrm{C}}}{(z_{\mathrm{S,CM}})_{\mathrm{E}}} = \frac{1+e_1\cdot\cos\theta_{\mathrm{E}}}{1+e_1\cdot\cos\theta_{\mathrm{C}}};$$

$$\frac{(z_{\mathrm{S,CM}})_{\mathrm{C}}}{(z_{\mathrm{S,CM}})_{\mathrm{E}}} = \frac{1+e_1\cdot\cos(\theta_{\mathrm{E}}+\omega-\omega)}{1+e_1\cdot\cos(\theta_{\mathrm{C}}+\omega-\omega)};$$

$$\frac{(z_{\mathrm{S,CM}})_{\mathrm{C}}}{(z_{\mathrm{S,CM}})_{\mathrm{E}}} = \frac{1+e_1\cdot\cos((\theta_{\mathrm{E}}+\omega)-\omega)}{1+e_1\cdot\cos((\theta_{\mathrm{C}}+\omega)-\omega)};$$

$$\frac{(z_{\mathrm{S,CM}})_{\mathrm{C}}}{(z_{\mathrm{S,CM}})_{\mathrm{E}}} = \frac{1+e_1\cdot\cos\omega\cdot\cos(\theta_{\mathrm{E}}+\omega)+e_1\cdot\sin\omega\cdot\sin(\theta_{\mathrm{E}}+\omega)}{1+e_1\cdot\cos\omega\cdot\cos(\theta_{\mathrm{C}}+\omega)+e_1\cdot\sin\omega\cdot\sin(\theta_{\mathrm{C}}+\omega)};$$

$$e_1 \cdot \cos\omega = -\frac{\alpha-\beta}{\alpha+\beta};$$

$$\cos(\theta_\mathrm{C}+\omega) = -e_1 \cdot \cos\omega = -\frac{\alpha-\beta}{\alpha+\beta};$$

$$\sin(\theta_\mathrm{C}+\omega) = \sqrt{1-\cos^2(\theta_\mathrm{C}+\omega)} = \frac{2\sqrt{\alpha\beta}}{\alpha+\beta};$$

$$\cos(\theta_\mathrm{E}+\omega) = -e_1 \cdot \cos\omega = -\frac{\alpha-\beta}{\alpha+\beta};$$

$$\sin(\theta_\mathrm{E}+\omega) = \sqrt{1-\cos^2(\theta_\mathrm{E}+\omega)} = -\frac{2\sqrt{\alpha\beta}}{\alpha+\beta};$$

$$\frac{(z_\mathrm{S,CM})_\mathrm{C}}{(z_\mathrm{S,CM})_\mathrm{E}} = \frac{1+\frac{\alpha-\beta}{\alpha+\beta}\cdot\left(-\frac{\alpha-\beta}{\alpha+\beta}\right)+e_1\cdot\sin\omega\cdot\left(-\frac{2\sqrt{\alpha\beta}}{\alpha+\beta}\right)}{1+\frac{\alpha-\beta}{\alpha+\beta}\cdot\left(-\frac{\alpha-\beta}{\alpha+\beta}\right)+e_1\cdot\sin\omega\cdot\left(\frac{2\sqrt{\alpha\beta}}{\alpha+\beta}\right)};$$

$$\frac{(z_\mathrm{S,CM})_\mathrm{C}}{(z_\mathrm{S,CM})_\mathrm{E}} = \frac{2\alpha\beta-\sqrt{\alpha\beta}\cdot(\alpha+\beta)\cdot e_1\cdot\sin\omega}{2\alpha\beta+\sqrt{\alpha\beta}\cdot(\alpha+\beta)\cdot e_1\cdot\sin\omega}.$$

Using the notation shown in Figure 18.11, we deduce

$$\int_{t_\mathrm{P}}^{t_\mathrm{Q}} z(t)\mathrm{d}t = \int_{t_\mathrm{P}}^{t_\mathrm{Q}} \mathrm{v}_\mathrm{rad,S,O}\cdot\mathrm{d}t = \int_{t_\mathrm{P}}^{t_\mathrm{Q}} \frac{\mathrm{d}z_\mathrm{S,O}}{\mathrm{d}t}\cdot\mathrm{d}t = \int_{z_\mathrm{S,O,P}}^{z_\mathrm{S,O,Q}} \mathrm{d}z_\mathrm{S,O}$$

$$= z_\mathrm{S,O,Q} - z_\mathrm{S,O,P} = A.$$

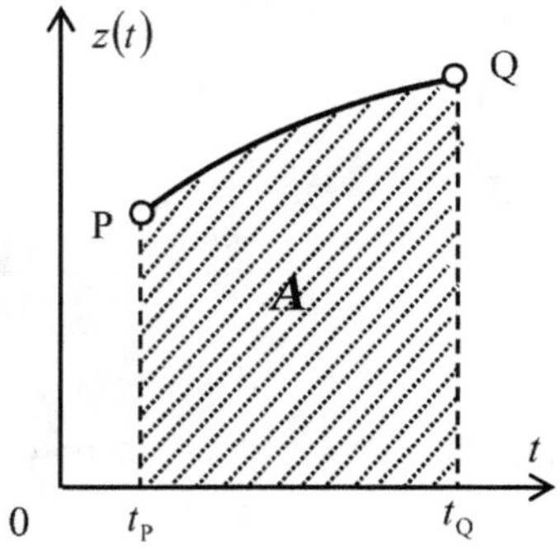


**Fig. 18.11**

Knowing that the time dependence of the radial speed of S with respect to the observer O on Earth is given by

$$\mathrm{v}_{\mathrm{rad,S,O}} = \mathrm{v}_{\mathrm{rad,CM,O}} + \frac{2\pi a_1 \sin i}{T\sqrt{1-e_1^2}}[\cos(\theta+\omega) + e_1 \cos\omega] = f(t),$$

which is plotted in Figure 18.11, the interpretations of the marked areas from Figure 18.12 are as follows:

$$A_{\mathrm{BFC}} = \int_{t_{\mathrm{B}}}^{t_{\mathrm{C}}} f(t)\cdot \mathrm{d}t = \int_{t_{\mathrm{B}}}^{t_{\mathrm{C}}} \mathrm{v}_{\mathrm{rad,S,O}}\cdot \mathrm{d}t = \int_{t_{\mathrm{B}}}^{t_{\mathrm{C}}} \frac{\mathrm{d}z_{\mathrm{S,O}}}{\mathrm{d}t}\cdot \mathrm{d}t$$

$$= \int_{(z_{\mathrm{S,O}})_{\mathrm{B}}}^{(z_{\mathrm{S,O}})_{\mathrm{C}}} \mathrm{d}z_{\mathrm{S,O}};$$

$$A_{\mathrm{BFC}} = (z_{\mathrm{S,O}})_{\mathrm{C}} - (z_{\mathrm{S,O}})_{\mathrm{B}};$$

$$(z_{\mathrm{S,O}})_{\mathrm{B}} = (z_{\mathrm{S,CM}})_{\mathrm{B}} + (z_{\mathrm{CM,O}})_{\mathrm{B}};$$

$$(z_{\mathrm{S,CM}})_{\mathrm{B}} = (r_{\mathrm{S,CM}})_{\mathrm{B}}\cdot(\sin(\theta_{\mathrm{B}}+\omega))_{\theta_{\mathrm{B}}+\omega=0}\cdot \sin i;$$

$$(\sin(\theta_{\mathrm{B}}+\omega))_{\theta_{\mathrm{B}}+\omega=0} = 0;$$

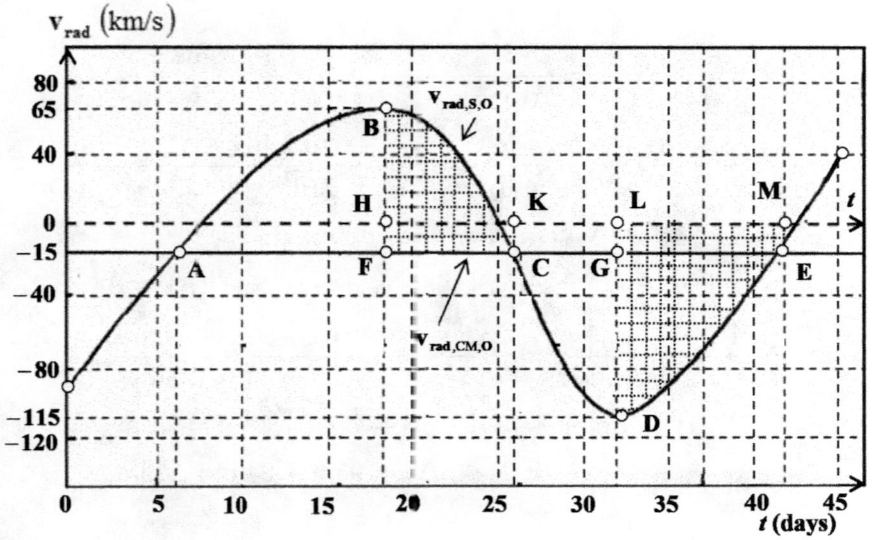


Fig. 18.12

$$(z_{\mathrm{S,CM}})_{\mathrm{B}} = 0;$$
$$(z_{\mathrm{S,O}})_{\mathrm{B}} = (z_{\mathrm{S,CM}})_{\mathrm{B}} + (z_{\mathrm{CM,O}})_{\mathrm{B}};$$
$$(z_{\mathrm{S,O}})_{\mathrm{B}} = (z_{\mathrm{CM,O}})_{\mathrm{B}};$$
$$(z_{\mathrm{S,O}})_{\mathrm{C}} = (z_{\mathrm{S,CM}})_{\mathrm{C}} + (z_{\mathrm{CM,O}})_{\mathrm{C}};$$
$$A_{\mathrm{BFC}} = (z_{\mathrm{S,O}})_{\mathrm{C}} - (z_{\mathrm{S,O}})_{\mathrm{B}};$$
$$A_{\mathrm{BFC}} = (z_{\mathrm{S,O}})_{\mathrm{C}} - (z_{\mathrm{CM,O}})_{\mathrm{B}};$$
$$A_{\mathrm{BFC}} = (z_{\mathrm{S,CM}})_{\mathrm{C}} + (z_{\mathrm{CM,O}})_{\mathrm{C}} - (z_{\mathrm{CM,O}})_{\mathrm{B}};$$
$$(z_{\mathrm{CM,O}})_{\mathrm{C}} - (z_{\mathrm{CM,O}})_{\mathrm{B}} = \mathrm{v}_{\mathrm{rad,S,CM}} \cdot (t_{\mathrm{C}} - t_{\mathrm{B}});$$
$$A_{\mathrm{BFC}} = (z_{\mathrm{S,CM}})_{\mathrm{C}} + \mathrm{v}_{\mathrm{rad,S,CM}} \cdot (t_{\mathrm{C}} - t_{\mathrm{B}});$$
$$(z_{\mathrm{S,CM}})_{\mathrm{C}} = A_{\mathrm{BFC}} - \mathrm{v}_{\mathrm{rad,S,CM}} \cdot (t_{\mathrm{C}} - t_{\mathrm{B}}).$$

Similarly, it can be shown that

$$(z_{\mathrm{S,CM}})_{\mathrm{E}} = A_{\mathrm{DGE}} - \mathrm{v}_{\mathrm{rad,S,CM}} \cdot (t_{\mathrm{E}} - t_{\mathrm{D}}).$$

With these results, we obtain:

$$\frac{(z_{\mathrm{S,CM}})_{\mathrm{C}}}{(z_{\mathrm{S,CM}})_{\mathrm{E}}} = \frac{2\alpha\beta - \sqrt{\alpha\beta} \cdot (\alpha + \beta) \cdot e_1 \cdot \sin\omega}{2\alpha\beta + \sqrt{\alpha\beta} \cdot (\alpha + \beta) \cdot e_1 \cdot \sin\omega};$$
$$\frac{A_{\mathrm{BFC}} - \mathrm{v}_{\mathrm{rad,S,CM}} \cdot (t_{\mathrm{C}} - t_{\mathrm{B}})}{A_{\mathrm{DGE}} - \mathrm{v}_{\mathrm{rad,S,CM}} \cdot (t_{\mathrm{E}} - t_{\mathrm{D}})} = \frac{2\alpha\beta - \sqrt{\alpha\beta} \cdot (\alpha + \beta) \cdot e_1 \cdot \sin\omega}{2\alpha\beta + \sqrt{\alpha\beta} \cdot (\alpha + \beta) \cdot e_1 \cdot \sin\omega};$$
$$\mathrm{v}_{\mathrm{rad,S,CM}} = -15\,\mathrm{km/s} < 0;$$
$$-\mathrm{v}_{\mathrm{rad,S,CM}}(t_{\mathrm{C}} - t_{\mathrm{B}}) = A_{\mathrm{HFCK}}; \quad -\mathrm{v}_{\mathrm{rad,S,CM}}(t_{\mathrm{E}} - t_{D}) = A_{\mathrm{GEML}};$$
$$\frac{A_{\mathrm{BFC}} + A_{\mathrm{HFCK}}}{A_{\mathrm{DGE}} + A_{\mathrm{GEML}}} = \frac{2\alpha\beta - \sqrt{\alpha\beta} \cdot (\alpha + \beta) \cdot e_1 \cdot \sin\omega}{2\alpha\beta + \sqrt{\alpha\beta} \cdot (\alpha + \beta) \cdot e_1 \cdot \sin\omega};$$
$$A_{\mathrm{BFC}} + A_{\mathrm{HFCK}} = \Delta_1; \quad \Delta_1 = 55\ \mathrm{u} + 18\ \mathrm{u} = 73\ \mathrm{u};$$
$$A_{\mathrm{DGE}} + A_{\mathrm{GEML}} = \Delta_2; \quad \Delta_2 = 95\ \mathrm{u} + 24\ \mathrm{u} = 119\ \mathrm{u};$$

$$\frac{\Delta_1}{\Delta_2} = \frac{2\alpha\beta - \sqrt{\alpha\beta}\cdot(\alpha+\beta)\cdot e_1\cdot\sin\omega}{2\alpha\beta + \sqrt{\alpha\beta}\cdot(\alpha+\beta)\cdot e_1\cdot\sin\omega};$$

$$e_1\cdot\sin\omega = \frac{2\sqrt{\alpha\beta}}{\alpha+\beta}\cdot\frac{\Delta_2-\Delta_1}{\Delta_2+\Delta_1};$$

$$\alpha = 80\,\text{km/s};\quad \beta = 100\,\text{km/s};$$

$$e_1\cdot\sin\omega = \frac{2\sqrt{\alpha\beta}}{\alpha+\beta}\cdot\frac{\Delta_2-\Delta_1}{\Delta_2+\Delta_1};$$

$$\Delta_1 = 73\text{ u};\quad \Delta_2 = 119\text{ u};$$

$$e_1\cdot\sin\omega = 0.238.$$

**e)**

$$e_1\cdot\cos\omega = -0.111;\quad e_1\cdot\sin\omega = 0.238;$$

$$e_1 = 0.262;$$

$$\tan\omega = -0.466;$$

$$\omega = 2.71\text{ rad} \approx 155^\circ.$$

**f)**

$$\alpha = \frac{2\pi a_1\sin i}{T\sqrt{1-e_1^2}}(1+e_1\cos\omega) = 80\,\text{km/s};$$

$$\beta = \frac{2\pi a_1\sin i}{T\sqrt{1-e_1^2}}(1-e_1\cos\omega) = 100\,\text{km/s};$$

$$\frac{\alpha}{\beta} = \frac{1+e_1\cos\omega}{1-e_1\cos\omega} = \frac{80}{100} = \frac{4}{5};$$

$$\alpha+\beta = \frac{2\pi a_1\sin i}{T\sqrt{1-e_1^2}}(1+e_1\cos\omega) + \frac{2\pi a_1\sin i}{T\sqrt{1-e_1^2}}(1+e_1\cos\omega);$$

$$\alpha+\beta = \frac{4\pi a\sin i}{T\sqrt{1-e^2}};$$

$$a_1 \cdot \sin i = \frac{T(\alpha+\beta)\cdot\sqrt{1-e_1^2}}{4\pi};$$

$$T = 36.5 \text{ zile} = 36.5\cdot 24\cdot 3600 \text{ s};$$

$$\alpha = 80\,\text{km/s};\quad \beta = 100\,\text{km/s};\quad e_1 = 0,12;\quad \sqrt{1-e_1^2} = 0.992;$$

$$a_1 \cdot \sin i = \frac{36.5\cdot 24\cdot 3600\cdot 180\cdot 0.992}{4\cdot 3.14}\text{ km};$$

$$a_1 \cdot \sin i = 44833345.22 \text{ km}.$$

**g)** The relative orbits of the two stars with respect to the CM correspond to the two ellipses plotted in Figure 18.13.

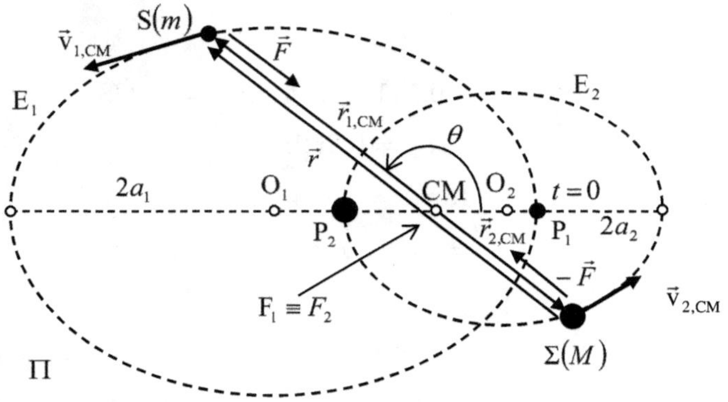


**Fig. 18.13**

In plane polar coordinates, the equations of the two elliptic orbits are:

$$r_{1,\text{CM}} = \frac{p_1}{1+e_1\cos\theta} = \frac{a_1(1-e_1^2)}{1+e_1\cos\theta};$$

$$r_{2,\text{CM}} = \frac{p_2}{1+e_2\cos\theta} = \frac{a_2(1-e_2^2)}{1+e_2\cos\theta}.$$

**The motion of two stars, S and Σ, interacting gravitationally with each other and having masses $m$ and $M$, respectively, leads to elliptic orbits with respect to the center of**

**mass. This is known in classical mechanics as the *two-body problem*.**

It can be shown that the *two-body problem* is equivalent to the *one-body problem,* corresponding to a single celestial body $S_0$, with mass

$$\mu = \frac{mM}{m+M}$$

(known as the "reduced mass" of the binary system), interacting gravitationally with a second fixed celestial body, $\Sigma_0$, with mass $(m+M)$, the distance between the two bodies, $S_0$ and $\Sigma_0$, being equal to the distance between the two original components, S and Σ, of the given binary system.

For the equivalent system, shown in Figure 18.14, we know the following:

$$F_{\text{equivalent}} = K\frac{\mu(m+M)}{r^2} = K\frac{\frac{mM}{m+M}(m+M)}{r^2} = K\frac{mM}{r^2} = F;$$

$$\mu\frac{\mathrm{d}^2\vec{r}}{\mathrm{d}t^2} = K\frac{\mu(m+M)}{r^2}\cdot \text{versor } \vec{F}_{\text{equivalent}} = -K\frac{\mu(m+M)}{r^2}\cdot \text{versor } \vec{r};$$

$$\mu\frac{\mathrm{d}^2\vec{r}}{\mathrm{d}t^2} = -K\frac{\mu(m+M)}{r^2}\cdot\frac{\vec{r}}{r} = -K\frac{\mu(m+M)}{r^3}\cdot\vec{r};$$

$$\frac{\mathrm{d}^2\vec{r}}{\mathrm{d}t^2} = -K\frac{(m+M)}{r^3}\cdot\vec{r}.$$

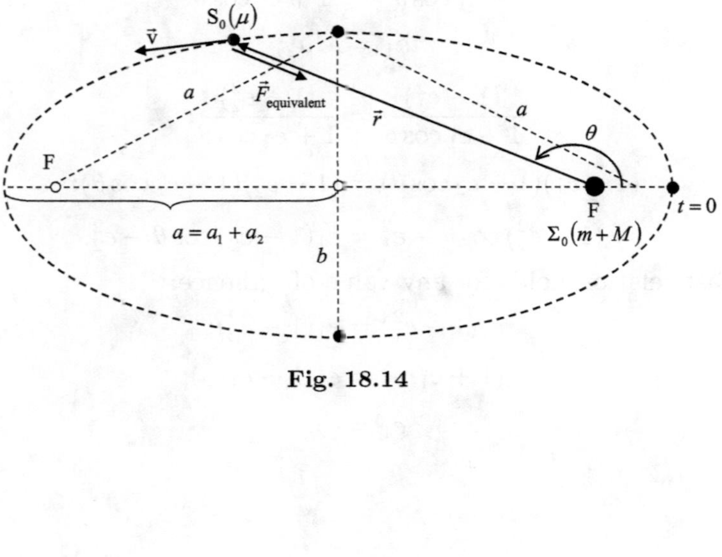


**Fig. 18.14**

After integration, this gives:

$$r = \frac{p}{1 + e\cos\theta} = \frac{a(1 - e^2)}{1 + e\cos\theta}; \quad T^2 = \frac{4\pi^2}{K(m + M)}a^3.$$

Hence, we obtain the following relations for the motion of the two components on their elliptic orbits with respect to the CM:

$$r_{1,\text{CM}} + r_{2,\text{CM}} = r;$$

$$mr_{1,\text{CM}} = Mr_{2,\text{CM}};$$

$$r_{1,\text{CM}} = \frac{M}{m + M}r; \quad r_{2,\text{CM}} = \frac{m}{m + M}r;$$

$$mr_{1,\text{CM}} = \frac{mM}{m + M}r = Mr_{2,\text{CM}};$$

$$mr_{1,\text{CM}} = \frac{mp_1}{1 + e_1\cos\theta} = \frac{ma_1(1 - e_1^2)}{1 + e_1\cos\theta} = \frac{mM}{m + M}\frac{p}{1 + e\cos\theta}$$

$$= \frac{mM}{m + M} \cdot \frac{a(1 - e^2)}{1 + e\cos\theta};$$

$$Mr_{2,\text{CM}} = \frac{Mp_2}{1 + e_2\cos\theta} = \frac{Ma_2(1 - e_2^2)}{1 + e_2\cos\theta} = \frac{mM}{m + M}\frac{p}{1 + e\cos\theta}$$

$$= \frac{mM}{m + M} \cdot \frac{a(1 - e^2)}{1 + e\cos\theta};$$

$$\frac{ma_1(1 - e_1^2)}{1 + e_1\cos\theta} = \frac{Ma_2(1 - e_2^2)}{1 + e_2\cos\theta};$$

$$ma_1 = Ma_2;$$

$$\frac{(1 - e_1^2)}{1 + e_1\cos\theta} = \frac{(1 - e_2^2)}{1 + e_2\cos\theta};$$

$$(1 - e_1^2)(1 + e_2\cos\theta) = (1 - e_2^2)(1 + e_1\cos\theta);$$

$$e_2(1 - e_1^2)\cos\theta - e_1^2 = e_1(1 - e_2^2)\cos\theta - e_2^2.$$

The last relation holds for any value of $\theta$; hence:

$$e_2(1 - e_1^2) = e_1(1 - e_2^2);$$

$$e_2(1 + e_1e_2) = e_1(1 + e_1e_2);$$

$$e_1 = e_2.$$

# Problem 19

# A Star and the Virial Theorem

The density distribution in a star with mass $M$ and radius $R$ is given by the following expression:

$$\rho(r) = \rho_c \left(1 - \frac{r}{R}\right),$$

where $\rho_c$ is the density at the center of the star, and $0 \leq r \leq R$.

**a)** Determine the relationship $\rho_c = \rho_c(M, R)$ and express the mass contained within a concentric spherical region of the star of radius $r$.

**b)** *Determine* the total gravitational potential energy link of the star $E_{pg}$.

**c)** Determine $p(r)$, the pressure of the stellar gas at inner level $r$, if at the surface of the star the pressure is $p(R) = 0$.

**d)** For the given star, verify the virial theorem: that is, $2U + E_{pg} = 0$, where $U$ is the total inner energy of the star. You will consider the star to consist of a monoatomic ideal gas.

### Solution

**a)** According to Figure 19.1:

$$\mathrm{d}V = 4\pi r^2 \mathrm{d}r; \quad \mathrm{d}m = \rho(r) \cdot \mathrm{d}V;$$

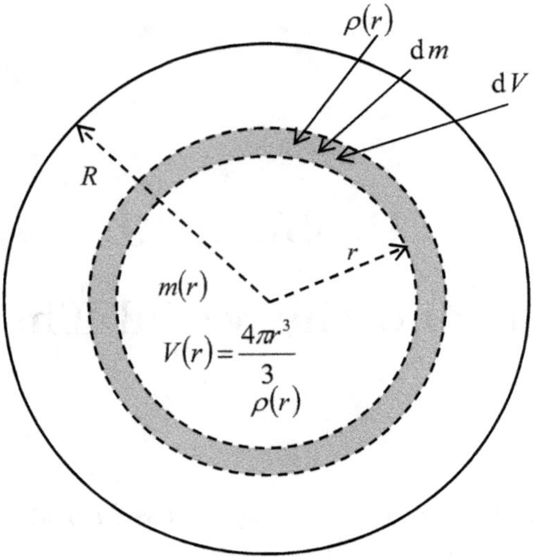


**Fig. 19.1**

$$M = \int_0^M \mathrm{d}m = \rho_\mathrm{c} 4\pi \int_0^R \left(1 - \frac{r}{R}\right) \cdot r^2 \mathrm{d}r = \frac{\pi \rho_\mathrm{c} R^3}{3};$$

$$\rho_\mathrm{c} = \frac{3M}{\pi R^3};$$

$$\rho(r) = \frac{3M}{\pi R^3} \cdot \left(1 - \frac{r}{R}\right);$$

$$m(r) = \int \rho(r) \cdot \mathrm{d}V = \frac{3M}{\pi R^3} \cdot 4\pi \int_0^r \left(1 - \frac{r}{R}\right) \cdot r^2 \mathrm{d}r;$$

$$m(r) = \frac{12M}{R^3} \cdot \int_0^r \left(1 - \frac{r}{R}\right) \cdot r^2 \mathrm{d}r;$$

$$m(r) = \frac{4M}{R^3} \cdot r^3 \left(1 - \frac{3r}{4R}\right);$$

$$m(r) = M \left(\frac{r}{R}\right)^3 \cdot \left(4 - 3\frac{r}{R}\right).$$

**b)** The gravitational potential energy of the system in Figure 19.1 is

$$\mathrm{d}E_{\mathrm{pg}} = -K\frac{m(r)\cdot \mathrm{d}m}{r}.$$

Thus, the gravitational potential link energy of the whole star is:

$$E_{\mathrm{pg}} = -K\int \frac{m(r)}{r}\cdot \mathrm{d}m;$$

$$m(r) = M\left(\frac{r}{R}\right)^3\cdot\left(4-3\frac{r}{R}\right);$$

$$\mathrm{d}m = \rho(r)\cdot \mathrm{d}V = \rho(r)\cdot 4\pi\cdot r^2\mathrm{d}r = \frac{3M}{\pi R^3}\cdot\left(1-\frac{r}{R}\right)\cdot 4\pi\cdot r^2\mathrm{d}r;$$

$$\mathrm{d}m = \frac{12M}{R^3}\cdot\left(1-\frac{r}{R}\right)\cdot r^2\mathrm{d}r;$$

$$E_{\mathrm{pg}} = -\frac{12KM^2}{R^2}\int_0^R\left(\frac{r}{R}\right)^4\cdot\left(4-3\frac{r}{R}\right)\cdot\left(1-\frac{r}{R}\right)\cdot \mathrm{d}r;$$

$$\frac{r}{R} = x;\quad \mathrm{d}r = R\cdot \mathrm{d}x;$$

$$E_{\mathrm{pg}} = -\frac{12KM^2}{R}\int_0^1 x^4\cdot(4-3x)\cdot(1-x)\cdot \mathrm{d}x;$$

$$E_{\mathrm{pg}} = -\frac{12KM^2}{R}\int_0^1 (4x^4-7x^5+3x^6)\cdot \mathrm{d}x;$$

$$E_{\mathrm{pg}} = -\frac{12KM^2}{R}\int_0^1\left(4\cdot\frac{x^5}{5}-7\cdot\frac{x^6}{6}+3\cdot\frac{x^7}{7}\right)\cdot \mathrm{d}x;$$

$$E_{\mathrm{pg}} = -\frac{26}{35}\cdot\frac{KM^2}{R}.$$

**c)** A star with a gaseous structure is in a quasi-equilibrium state. That means that every elementary layer is in hydrostatic equilibrium inside the star (see Figure 19.2) under the combined action of the

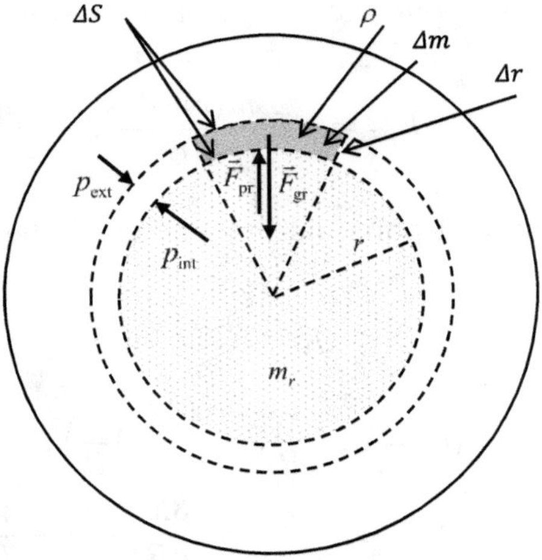


**Fig. 19.2**

gravitational attraction force and pressure forces:

$$F_{\text{gr}} = K\frac{m_r \cdot \Delta m}{r^2} = K\frac{m_r}{r^2} \cdot \rho \cdot \Delta m = K\frac{m_r}{r^2} \cdot \rho \cdot \Delta S \cdot \Delta r;$$

$$F_{\text{pr}} = (p_{\text{int}} - p_{\text{ext}}) \cdot \Delta S = \Delta p \cdot \Delta S;$$

$$\vec{F}_{\text{pr}} = -\vec{F}_{\text{gr}};$$

$$\Delta p \cdot \Delta s = -K\frac{m_r}{r^2} \cdot \rho \cdot \Delta S \cdot \Delta r;$$

$$\Delta p = -\rho\frac{Km_r}{r^2}\Delta r;$$

$$\frac{\Delta p}{\Delta r} = -\rho\frac{Km_r}{r^2};$$

$$\frac{\mathrm{d}p}{\mathrm{d}r} = -\rho\frac{Km_r}{r^2},$$

the hydrostatic equilibrium equation for the considered star;

$$\rho(r) = \frac{3M}{\pi R^3} \cdot \left(1 - \frac{r}{R}\right); \quad m(r) = M\left(\frac{r}{R}\right)^3 \cdot \left(4 - 3\frac{r}{R}\right);$$

$$\frac{\mathrm{d}p}{\mathrm{d}r} = -\frac{3KM^2}{\pi R^5} \cdot \left(\frac{r}{R}\right) \cdot \left(1 - \frac{r}{R}\right) \cdot \left(4 - 3 \cdot \frac{r}{R}\right);$$

$$\mathrm{d}p = -\frac{3KM^2}{\pi R^5} \cdot \left(\frac{r}{R}\right) \cdot \left(1 - \frac{r}{R}\right) \cdot \left(4 - 3 \cdot \frac{r}{R}\right) \cdot \mathrm{d}r;$$

$$\int_{p(r)}^{p(R)} \mathrm{d}p = -\frac{3KM^2}{\pi R^5} \cdot \int_r^R \left(\frac{r}{R}\right) \cdot \left(1 - \frac{r}{R}\right) \cdot \left(4 - 3 \cdot \frac{r}{R}\right) \cdot \mathrm{d}r;$$

$$\frac{r}{R} = x; \quad \mathrm{d}r = R \cdot \mathrm{d}x;$$

$$p(R) - p(r) = -\frac{3KM^2}{\pi R^4} \cdot \int_x^1 x \cdot (1 - x) \cdot (4 - 3 \cdot x) \cdot \mathrm{d}x;$$

$$p(R) - p(r) = -\frac{3KM^2}{\pi R^4} \cdot \int_x^1 (4x - 7x^2 + 3x^3) \cdot \mathrm{d}x;$$

$$p(R) - p(r) = -\frac{3KM^2}{\pi R^4} \left(2x^2 - \frac{7}{3}x^3 + \frac{3}{4}x^4\right)_x^1;$$

$$p(R) - p(r) = -\frac{3KM^2}{\pi R^4} \left(2 - 2x^2 - \frac{7}{3} + \frac{7}{3}x^3 + \frac{3}{4} - \frac{3}{4}x^4\right);$$

$$p(R) - p(r) = -\frac{3KM^2}{\pi R^4} \left(2 - \frac{7}{3} + \frac{3}{4} - 2x^2 + \frac{7}{3}x^3 - \frac{3}{4}x^4\right);$$

$$p(R) - p(r) = -\frac{3KM^2}{\pi R^4} \left(\frac{5}{12} + \frac{-24x^2 + 28x^3 - 9x^4}{12}\right);$$

$$p(r) = \frac{KM^2}{4\pi R^4} (5 - 24x^2 + 28x^3 - 9x^4);$$

$$p(R) = 0;$$

$$p(r) = \frac{KM^2}{4\pi R^4} (5 - 24x^2 + 28x^3 - 9x^4);$$

$$p(r) = \frac{KM^2}{4\pi R^4} \left(5 - 24\left(\frac{r}{R}\right)^2 + 28\left(\frac{r}{R}\right)^3 - 9\left(\frac{r}{R}\right)^4\right).$$

**d)** For an ideal monoatomic gas:

$$U = \frac{3}{2}vRT = \frac{3}{2}\frac{N}{N_A}RT = \frac{3}{2}\frac{R}{N_A}NT;$$

$$p = nkT = \frac{N}{V}kT; \quad NT = \frac{pV}{k};$$

$$U = \frac{3}{2}\frac{R}{N_A}\frac{pV}{k}; \quad N_A k = R;$$

$$U = \frac{3}{2}pV; \quad V = \frac{m}{\rho}; \quad U = \frac{3}{2}p\frac{m}{\rho};$$

$$u = \frac{U}{m} = \frac{3}{2}\frac{p}{\rho},$$

the internal energy per unit mass of a monoatomic ideal gas.

To calculate the internal energy of the whole star:

$$u = \frac{U}{m}; \quad U = um;$$

$$\mathrm{d}U = u\mathrm{d}m = u\rho\mathrm{d}V;$$

$$U(R) = \int_0^R u\rho\mathrm{d}V; \quad \mathrm{d}V = 4\pi r^2\mathrm{d}r;$$

$$U(R) = \int_0^R u\rho \cdot 4\pi \cdot r^2\mathrm{d}r; \quad u = \frac{3}{2}\frac{p}{\rho};$$

$$U(R) = \int_0^R \frac{3}{2}\frac{p}{\rho}\rho \cdot 4\pi \cdot r^2\mathrm{d}r; \quad U(R) = 6\pi \cdot \int_0^R p \cdot r^2\mathrm{d}r;$$

$$\frac{r}{R} = x; \quad r = xR; \quad \mathrm{d}r = R\mathrm{d}x;$$

$$p(r) = \frac{KM^2}{4\pi R^4}(5 - 24x^2 + 28x^3 - 9x^4);$$

$$U(R) = 6\pi \cdot \int_0^R \frac{KM^2}{4\pi R^4}(5 - 24x^2 + 28x^3 - 9x^4) \cdot x^2R^2 \cdot R \cdot \mathrm{d}x;$$

$$U(R) = \frac{3}{2}\frac{KM^2}{R} \cdot \int_0^1 x^2(5 - 24x^2 + 28x^3 - 9x^4) \cdot \mathrm{d}x;$$

$$U(R) = \frac{3}{2}\frac{KM^2}{R} \cdot \int_0^1 (5x^2 - 24x^4 + 28x^5 - 9x^6) \cdot \mathrm{d}x;$$

$$U(R) = \frac{3}{2}\frac{KM^2}{R} \cdot \left(\frac{5x^3}{3} - \frac{24x^5}{5} + \frac{28x^6}{6} - \frac{9x^7}{7}\right)_0^1;$$

$$U(R) = \frac{3}{2}\frac{KM^2}{R} \cdot \left(\frac{5}{3} - \frac{24}{5} + \frac{28}{6} - \frac{9}{7}\right);$$

$$U(R) = \frac{3}{2}\frac{KM^2}{R} \cdot \frac{156}{630}; \quad U(R) = \frac{3}{2}\frac{KM^2}{R} \cdot \frac{52}{210};$$

$$U(R) = \frac{13}{35}\frac{KM^2}{R}.$$

This is the total internal energy of the star, according to the virial theorem:

$$E_{\text{pg}} = -\frac{26}{35} \cdot \frac{KM^2}{R}; \quad U(R) = \frac{13}{35}\frac{KM^2}{R};$$

$$2U + E_{\text{pg}} = 0.$$

# Problem 20

# Solar Annular Eclipse

Figure 20.1 shows a magnified photograph of an annular solar eclipse, taken from a photographic plate of width $l = 17\,\text{mm}$ positioned at the focal plane of a telescope's objective lens. The telescope was fixed on the surface of the Earth during an annular eclipse of the Sun at a point on the Earth–Moon–Sun line. The focal length of the convergent lens was $f = 150\,\text{cm}$. The width of the photograph in Figure 20.1, that is, $l_{\text{photograph}}$, corresponds to the actual width of the photographic plate, $l = 17\,\text{mm}$, on which the photographic image of the annular eclipse was recorded.

*Determine:*

**a)** the distance between the center of the Sun and the center of the Earth, $\Delta_{\text{SE}}$;

**b)** the diameter of the optical (visual) projection of the Moon on the Sun disk, $D_{\text{pM}}$;

**c)** the distance between the center of the Moon and the center of the Earth, $\Delta_{\text{ME}}$;

**d)** the angular diameter of the Sun, $\delta_{\text{S}}$, the angular diameter of the Moon, $\delta_{\text{M}}$, and the angular diameter of the optical (visual) projection of the Moon on the Sun's disk, $\delta_{\text{pM}}$, when viewed by the Earth surface observatory;

**e)** the length of the shadow cone of the Moon, $L_{\text{uM}}$, specifying whether its peak does or does not reach the surface of the Earth;

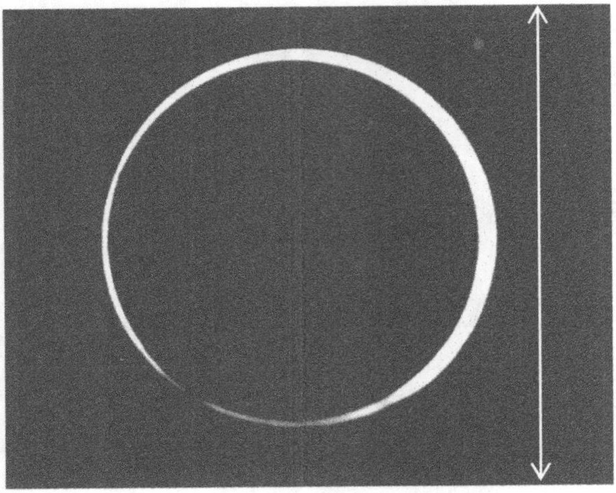


**Fig. 20.1**

**f)** the percentage of solar disk coverage, $\eta$, during the Sun's annular eclipse;
**g)** the thickness of the Sun's luminous ring, $\Delta R_{\text{S}}$, when the annular eclipse is centered;
**h)** the difference between the radius of the optical (visual) projection of the Moon on the Sun's disk and the radius of the geometric projection of the Moon on the Sun's disk, $\Delta R_{\text{M}}$.

The following are given: the diameter of the Sun, km; the diameter of the Moon, $D_{\text{M}} = 3476\,\text{km}$.

The radius of the Earth is negligible in relation to the distances between the Earth, Sun and Moon.

## Solution

**a)** For observer O on the surface of the Earth, the formation of the annular eclipse of the Sun and the Moon's shadow cone are highlighted in the drawing in Figure 20.2.

Since the distance between the Sun and Earth is $\Delta_{\text{SE}} \gg f$, the Sun's image will form in the focal plane of the lens of the telescope, as shown in drawing I of Figure 20.3, where the photographic plate is

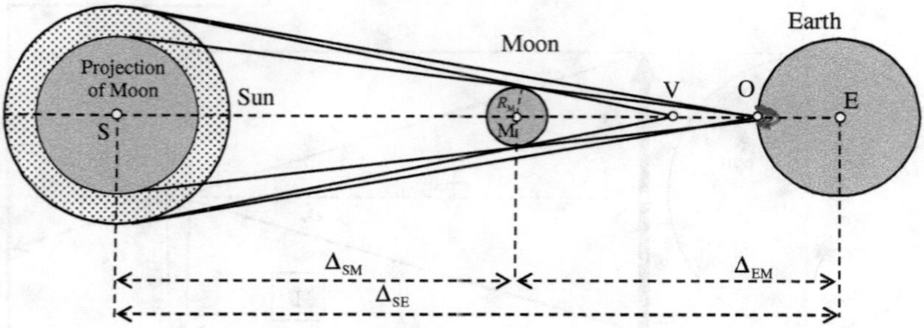


**Fig. 20.2**

located. Notation: $D_S$ – the diameter of the Sun; $f$ – the focal length of the lens; $d_S$ – the diameter of the Sun's image on the photographic plate; $\delta_S$ – the angular diameter of the Sun, seen by the observer on Earth.

Under these conditions, for the Sun's image on the photographic plate in the focal plane of the lens, it follows that:

$$\tan\frac{\delta_S}{2} = \frac{d_S/2}{f} = \frac{D_S/2}{\Delta_{SE}};$$

$$\Delta_{SE} = \frac{f}{d_S} D_S.$$

From the measurements made on the photograph in the statement of the problem, and in accordance with the notation present in the drawings of Figures 20.3 and 20.4, it follows that:

$$l_{\text{photograph}} = 65\,\text{mm} \ldots\ldots\ldots\ldots\ldots \quad l = 17\,\text{mm};$$

$$d_{S,\text{photograph}} = 52\,\text{mm} \ldots\ldots\ldots\ldots \quad d_S = ?;$$

$$d_S = \frac{d_{S,\text{photograph}} \cdot l}{l_{\text{photograph}}} = \frac{52\,\text{mm} \cdot 17\,\text{mm}}{65\,\text{mm}} = 13.6\,\text{mm};$$

$$\Delta_{SE} = \frac{f}{d_S} D_S; \quad D_S = 13.92 \cdot 10^5\,\text{km}; \quad R_S = 6.96 \cdot 10^5\,\text{km};$$

$$\Delta_{SE} = \frac{1500\,\text{mm}}{13.6\,\text{mm}} \cdot 13.92 \cdot 10^5\,\text{km} = 153\,639\,705.9\,\text{km},$$

representing the distance between the Earth and the Sun.

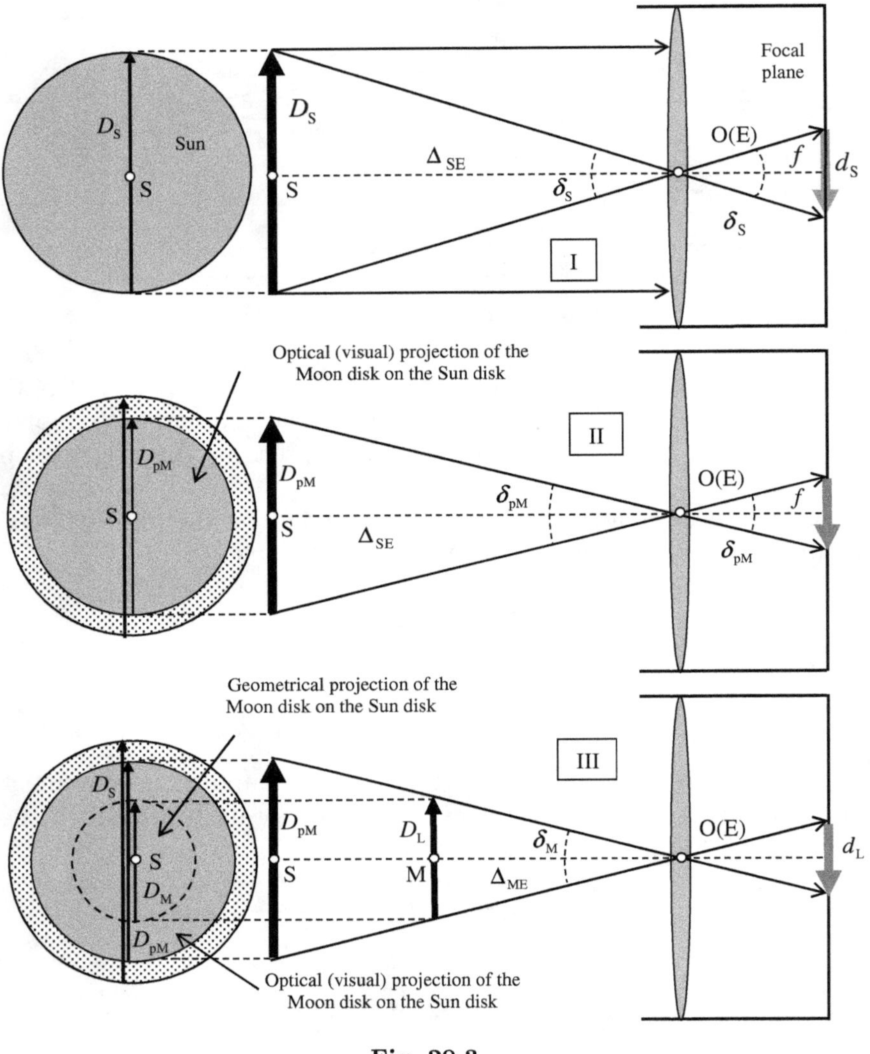


**Fig. 20.3**

**b)** Similarly, for the diameter of the visual (optical) projection of the Moon on the Sun disk, we consider drawing II of Figure 20.3, where we use the following notation: $D_{pM}$ – the diameter of the visual (optical) projection of the Moon on the Sun disk; $f$ – the focal

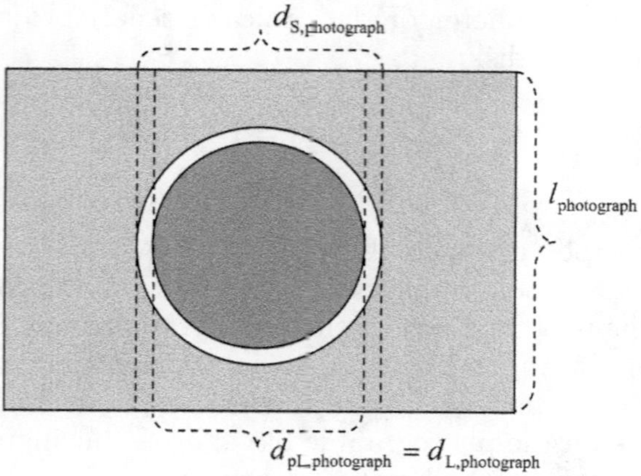


**Fig. 20.4**

length of the lens; $d_M$ – the diameter of the Moon's image on the photographic plate; $\delta_M$ – the angular diameter of the Sun, seen by the observer on Earth. This results in:

$$\tan\frac{\delta_{pM}}{2} = \frac{d_{pM}/2}{f} = \frac{D_{pM}/2}{\Delta_{SP}};$$

$$D_{pM} = \Delta_{SE}\cdot\frac{d_{pM}}{f};$$

$$l_{photograph} = 65\,\text{mm} \ldots\ldots\ldots\ldots\ldots\ldots \quad l = 17\,\text{mm};$$

$$d_{pM,photograph} = 50\,\text{mm} \ldots\ldots\ldots\ldots\ldots \quad d_{pM} = ?;$$

$$d_{pM} = \frac{d_{pM,photograph}\cdot l}{l_{photograph}} = \frac{50\,\text{mm}\cdot 17\,\text{mm}}{65\,\text{mm}};$$

$$d_{pM} = 13.07\,\text{mm};$$

$$D_{pM} = \Delta_{SE}\cdot\frac{d_{pM}}{f};$$

$$\Delta_{SE} = 153\,639\,705\;9\,\text{km}; \quad f = 1500\,\text{mm};$$

$$D_{pM} = 153\,639\,705.9\,\text{km}\cdot\frac{13.07\,\text{mm}}{1500\,\text{mm}} = 1338\,713.97\,\text{km},$$

representing the diameter of the optical (visual) projection of the Moon on the Sun's disk;

$$D_{\mathrm{S}} = 13.92 \cdot 10^5\,\mathrm{km} = 1\,392\,000\,\mathrm{km};$$

$$D_{\mathrm{pM}} < D_{\mathrm{S}}.$$

**c)** Because the distance between the Moon and Earth is $\Delta_{\mathrm{ME}} \gg f$, the Moon's image will also form in the focal plane of the lens of the telescope, where the photographic plate is located, as shown in the drawing in Figure 20.5. Notation: $D_{\mathrm{M}}$ – the diameter of the Moon; $f$ – the focal length of the lens; $d_{\mathrm{M}}$ – the diameter of the Moon's image on the photographic plate; $\delta_{\mathrm{M}}$ – the angular diameter of the Moon, seen by the Earth observer.

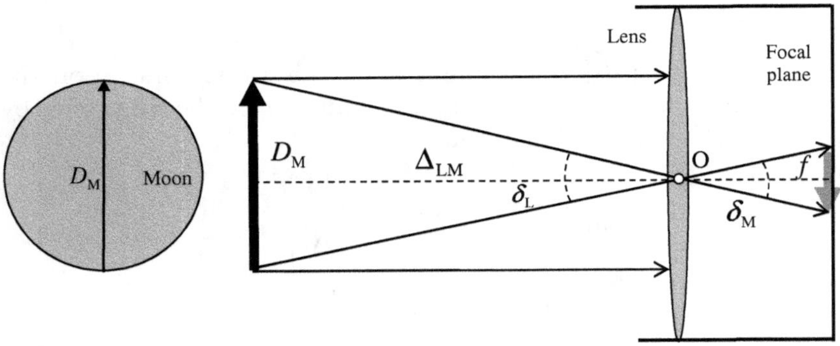


**Fig. 20.5**

In these circumstances, it follows that:

$$\tan\frac{\delta_{\mathrm{M}}}{2} = \frac{d_{\mathrm{M}}/2}{f} = \frac{D_{\mathrm{M}}/2}{\Delta_{\mathrm{SE}}};$$

$$\Delta_{\mathrm{ME}} = \frac{f}{d_{\mathrm{M}}} D_{\mathrm{M}}.$$

From the measurements made on the picture in the statement of the problem, and in accordance with the notation present in the drawings of Figures 20.4 and 20.5, it follows that:

$$l_{\mathrm{photograph}} = 65\,\mathrm{mm} \ldots\ldots\ldots\ldots\ldots\ldots \quad l = 17\,\mathrm{mm};$$

$$d_{\mathrm{M,\,photograph}} = 49\,\mathrm{mm} \ldots\ldots\ldots\ldots\ldots \quad d_{\mathrm{M}} = ?;$$

$$d_{\mathrm{M}} = \frac{d_{\mathrm{M,photograph}} \cdot l}{l_{\mathrm{photograph}}} = \frac{49\,\mathrm{mm} \cdot 17\,\mathrm{mm}}{65\,\mathrm{mm}} = 12.81\,\mathrm{mm};$$

$$\Delta_{\mathrm{ME}} = \frac{f}{d_{\mathrm{M}}} D_{\mathrm{M}}; \quad D_{\mathrm{M}} = 3476\,\mathrm{km}; \quad R_{\mathrm{M}} = 1738\,\mathrm{km};$$

$$\Delta_{\mathrm{ME}} = \frac{1500\,\mathrm{mm}}{12.81\,\mathrm{mm}} \cdot 3496\,\mathrm{km} = 409\,367.68\,\mathrm{km},$$

representing the distance between the center of the Moon and the center of the Earth.

**d)** In accordance with the notation in Figures 20.3, 20.5 and 20.6, it follows that:

$$\tan\frac{\delta_{\mathrm{S}}}{2} = \frac{D_{\mathrm{S}}/2}{\Delta_{\mathrm{SE}}} \approx \frac{\delta_{\mathrm{S}}}{2}; \quad \delta_{\mathrm{S}} = \frac{D_{\mathrm{S}}}{\Delta_{\mathrm{SE}}};$$

$$D_{\mathrm{S}} = \Delta_{\mathrm{SE}} \cdot \delta_{\mathrm{S}}; \quad D_{\mathrm{S}} = 13.92 \cdot 10^5\,\mathrm{km}; \quad \Delta_{\mathrm{SE}} = 153\,639\,705.9\,\mathrm{km};$$

$$\delta_{\mathrm{S}} = \frac{D_{\mathrm{S}}}{\Delta_{\mathrm{SE}}} = \frac{13.92 \cdot 10^5\,\mathrm{km}}{153\,639\,705.9\,\mathrm{km}} = 0.00906\,\mathrm{rad};$$

$$1\,\mathrm{rad} = 3439.4904' = 206369.4268'';$$

$$\delta_{\mathrm{S}} = 31.16',$$

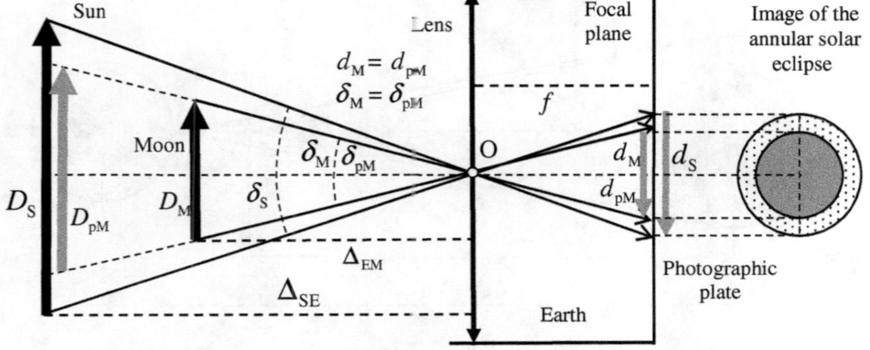


**Fig. 20.6**

representing the angular diameter of the Sun seen by the Earth observer at O;

$$\tan\frac{\delta_M}{2} = \frac{D_M/2}{\Delta_{ME}} \approx \frac{\delta_M}{2}; \quad \delta_M = \frac{D_M}{\Delta_{ME}};$$

$$D_M = \Delta_{ME}\cdot\delta_M; \quad D_M = 3476\,\text{km}; \quad \Delta_{SE} = 409\,367.68\,\text{km};$$

$$\delta_M = \frac{D_M}{\Delta_{ME}} = \frac{3476\,\text{km}}{409367.68\,\text{km}} = 0.00849\,\text{rad};$$

$$1\,\text{rad} = 3439.4904' = 206369.4268'';$$

$$\delta_M = 29.20',$$

representing the angular diameter of the Moon, seen by the Earth observer at point O.

In accordance with the notation in Figure 20.5, the relationships are obvious:

$$d_{pM} = d_M;$$
$$\delta_{pM} = \delta_M = 29.20'.$$

**e)** Knowing the meaning of the notation in Figures 20.7 and 20.8, to explain the occurrence of an annular eclipse of the Sun when the tip of the Moon's shadow cone does not touch the Earth's surface and point O, it follows that:

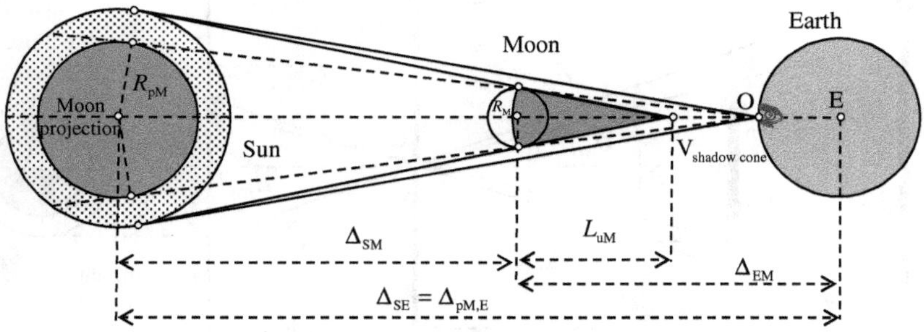


**Fig. 20.7**

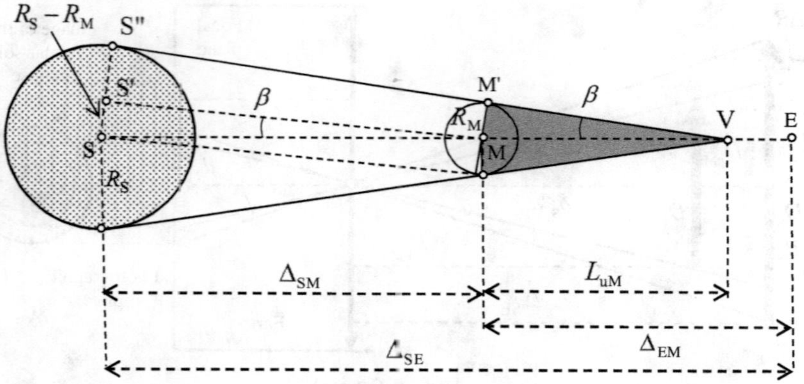


**Fig. 20.8**

$$(S'M)//(S''M');$$

$$\Delta(SS'M) \sim \Delta(MM'V);$$

$$\frac{R_M}{R_S - R_M} = \frac{L_{uM}}{\Delta_{SM}}; \quad L_{uM} = \frac{R_M}{R_S - R_M} \cdot \Delta_{SM};$$

$$\Delta_{SM} = \Delta_{SE} - \Delta_{EM};$$

$$L_{uM} = \frac{R_M}{R_S - R_M} \cdot (\Delta_{SE} - \Delta_{EM});$$

$$R_M = 1738\,\text{km}; \quad R_S = 6.96 \cdot 10^5\,\text{km};$$

$$\Delta_{SE} = 153\,639\,705.9\,\text{km}; \quad \Delta_{ME} = 409367.68\,\text{km};$$

$$L_{uM} = \frac{1738\,\text{km}}{6.96 \cdot 10^5\,\text{km} - 1738\,\text{km}} \cdot (153\,639\,705.9\,\text{km} - 409367.68\,\text{km});$$

$$L_{uM} = \frac{1738}{6.96 \cdot 10^5 - 1738} \cdot (153\,639\,705.9 - 409367.68)\,\text{km};$$

$$L_{uM} = 383593.4\,\text{km};$$

$$\Delta_{ME} = 409367.68\,\text{km};$$

$$L_{uM} < \Delta_{ME},$$

which proves that the tip of the Moon's shadow does not touch the surface of the Earth.

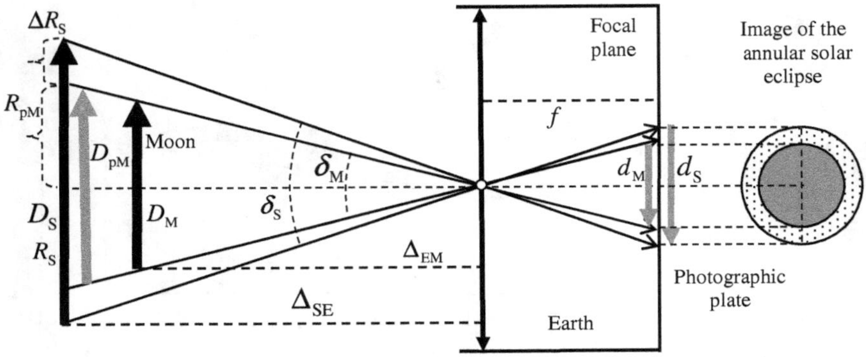


**Fig. 20.9**

**f)** The coverage percentage of the Moon's solar disk during the solar eclipse is

$$\eta = \frac{S_M}{S_S} = \frac{\frac{\pi d_M^2}{4}}{\frac{\pi d_S^2}{4}} = \left(\frac{d_M}{d_S}\right)^2 = \left(\frac{12.81\,\text{mm}}{13.6\,\text{mm}}\right)^2 \approx 0.8871 = 88.71\%.$$

**g)** In accordance with the notation in Figure 20.9, it follows that:

$$\Delta R_S = R_S - R_{pM},$$

where $R_{pM}$ is the optical (visual) projection of the Moon's radius in the direction of the Sun's radius;

$$\tan\frac{\delta_M}{2} = \frac{R_{pM}}{\Delta_{ES}} \approx \frac{\delta_M}{2}; \quad R_{pM} = \frac{\Delta_{ES}}{2}\delta_M;$$

$$\Delta_{SE} = 153\,639\,705.9\,\text{km}; \quad \delta_M = 0.00849\,\text{rad};$$

$$R_{pM} = \frac{153\,639\,705.9\,\text{km}}{2} \cdot 0.00849\,\text{rad}$$

$$D_{pM} = 153\,639\,705.9\,\text{km} \cdot \frac{13.07\,\text{mm}}{1500\,\text{mm}} = 1338\,713.97\,\text{km},$$

representing the diameter of the optical (visual) projection of the Moon on the Sun's disk;

$$D_S = 13.92 \cdot 10^5 \,\text{km} = 1\,392\,000 \,\text{km};$$

$$R_{pM} = \frac{D_{pM}}{2} = 652\,200.55 \,\text{km};$$

$$R_S = \frac{D_S}{2} = 6.96 \cdot 10^5 \,\text{km} = 696\,000 \,\text{km};$$

$$\Delta R_S = 43\,799.45 \,\text{km}.$$

h)

$$\Delta R_M = R_{pM} - R_M;$$

$$D_M = 3476 \,\text{km};$$

$$R_{pM} = \frac{D_{pM}}{2}; \quad D_{pM} = 1338\,713.97 \,\text{km};$$

$$R_{pM} = 669\,356.98 \,\text{km};$$

$$R_M = \frac{D_M}{2}; \quad D_M = 3476 \,\text{km};$$

$$R_M = 1738 \,\text{km};$$

$$\Delta R_M = R_{pM} - R_M = 666\,618.98 \,\text{km}.$$

# Problem 21

# Resonant Orbits

Several exoplanets (see the following table) have been observed in the Gliese 876 system, whose mass is $M_G = (0.33 \pm 0.03)M_{Sun}$. In the table: $M_J = M_{Jupiter} = 1.89813 \times 10^{27}$ kg; $M_E = M_{Earth} = 5.9742 \times 10^{24}$ kg.

| Gliese system | Mass | Semi-major axis (AU) |
|---|---|---|
| Gliese 876 b | 2.276 $M_J$ | 0.2083 |
| Gliese 876 c | 0.714 $M_J$ | 0.1296 |
| Gliese 876 d | 6.8 $M_E$ | 0.0208 |
| Gliese 876 e | 15 $M_E$ | 0.334 |

Assume that all these planets revolve around Gliese 876 in the same direction. Two planets are said to be in resonant orbits if the synodic period of one planet with respect to the other planet is an integer multiple of the orbital period of the second planet.

*Determine* if any of the exoplanets of the Gliese 876 system may have resonant orbits.

### Solution

In Figure 21.1 the trajectories of the exoplanets Gliese 876 c, Gliese 876 d (interior exoplanet) and Gliese 876 b (exterior exoplanet) are

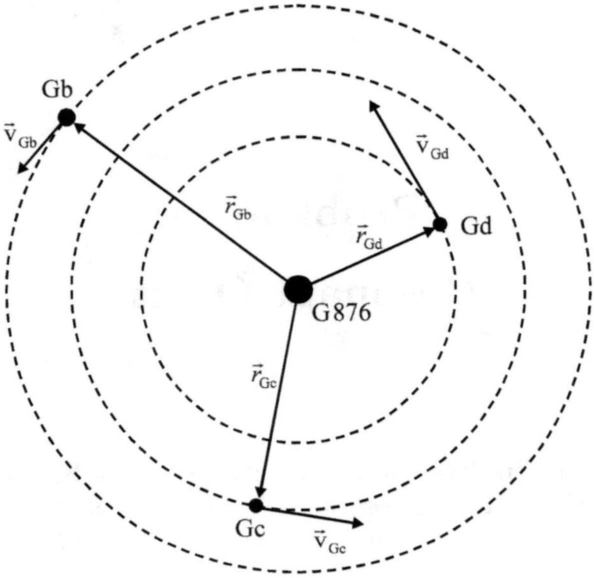


**Fig. 21.1**

represented. The trajectories are considered to be coplanar concentric circles, with the Gliese 876 system in the center.

The *sidereal rotation period* or *orbital period*, $T_{\text{sid}}$, of an exoplanet is the time interval between two successive moments when the exoplanet passes through the same position relative to the center of the Gliese 876 system, considered as stationary.

The *synodic rotation period*, $T_{\text{sin}}$, of an exoplanet is the period of time the exoplanet takes to return to the same position relative to the center of another exoplanet (the time interval between two consecutive identical configurations of the two-exoplanet system).

The relation between the sidereal periods and the synodic period for a given exoplanet and for an interior exoplanet is established using Figure 21.2. The result is:

$$\alpha_{\text{Gd}} = 2\pi + \alpha_{\text{Gc}}; \quad \alpha_{\text{Gd}} - \alpha_{\text{Gc}} = 2\pi;$$

$$(\omega_{\text{Gd}} - \omega_{\text{Gc}})T_{\text{sinodic,Gd}} = 2\pi;$$

$$\omega_{\text{Gd}} - \omega_{\text{Gc}} = \frac{2\pi}{T_{\text{sinodic,Gd}}};$$

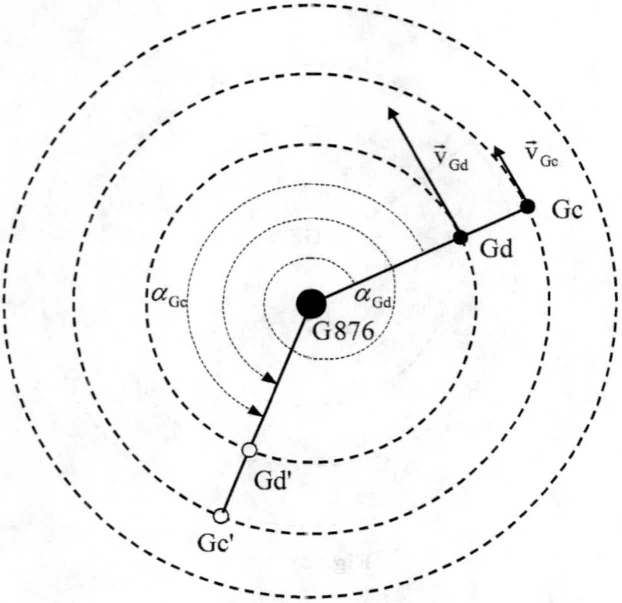


**Fig. 21.2**

$$\frac{2\pi}{T_{\text{sidereal,Gd}}} - \frac{2\pi}{T_{\text{sidereal,Gc}}} = \frac{2\pi}{T_{\text{sinodic,Gd}}};$$

$$\frac{1}{T_{\text{sinodic,Gd}}} = \frac{1}{T_{\text{sidereal,Gd}}} - \frac{1}{T_{\text{sidereal,Gc}}};$$

$$T_{\text{sinodic,Gd}} = \frac{T_{\text{sidereal,Gd}} \cdot T_{\text{sidereal,Gc}}}{T_{\text{sidereal,Gc}} - T_{\text{sidereal,Gd}}}; \quad T_{\text{sidereal,Gc}} > T_{\text{sidereal,Gd}}.$$

Generally, for two exoplanets, such as the interior Gliese and the exterior Gliese:

$$T_{\text{sinodic,interior}} = \frac{T_{\text{sidereal,interior}}\, T_{\text{sidereal,exterior}}}{T_{\text{sidereal,exterior}} - T_{\text{sidereal,interior}}};$$

$$T_{\text{sidereal,exterior}} > T_{\text{sidereal,interior}}.$$

The relation between the sidereal periods and the synodic period for a given exoplanet and for an exterior exoplanet is established

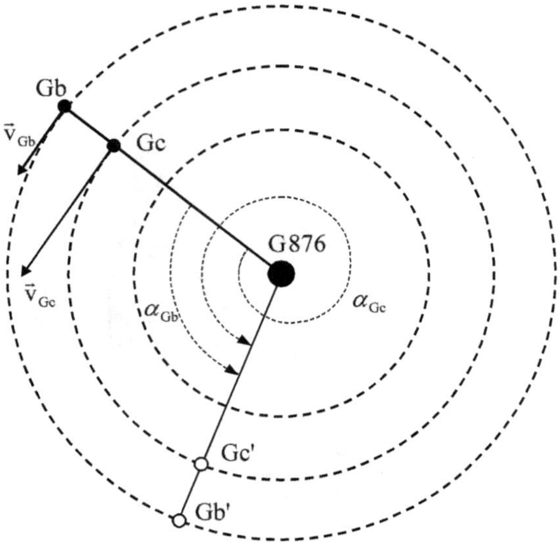


**Fig. 21.3**

using Figure 21.3. From this figure, the result is:

$$\alpha_{\mathrm{Gc}} = 2\pi + \alpha_{\mathrm{Gb}}; \quad \alpha_{\mathrm{Gc}} - \alpha_{\mathrm{Gb}} = 2\pi;$$

$$(\omega_{\mathrm{Gc}} - \omega_{\mathrm{Gb}})T_{\mathrm{sinodic,Gb}} = 2\pi; \quad \omega_{\mathrm{Gc}} - \omega_{\mathrm{Gb}} = \frac{2\pi}{T_{\mathrm{sinodic,Gb}}};$$

$$\frac{2\pi}{T_{\mathrm{sidereal,Gc}}} - \frac{2\pi}{T_{\mathrm{sidereal,Gb}}} = \frac{2\pi}{T_{\mathrm{sinodic,Gb}}};$$

$$\frac{1}{T_{\mathrm{sinodic,Gb}}} = \frac{1}{T_{\mathrm{sidereal,Gc}}} - \frac{1}{T_{\mathrm{sidereal,Gb}}}.$$

$$T_{\mathrm{sinodic,Gb}} = \frac{T_{\mathrm{sidereal,Gc}} \cdot T_{\mathrm{sidereal,Gb}}}{T_{\mathrm{sidereal,Gb}} - T_{\mathrm{sidereal,Gc}}}; \quad T_{\mathrm{sidereal,Gb}} > T_{\mathrm{sidereal,Gc}}.$$

For the same two exoplanets, the interior Gliese and the exterior Gliese:

$$T_{\mathrm{sinodic,exterior}} = \frac{T_{\mathrm{sidereal,interior}} \cdot T_{\mathrm{sidereal,exterior}}}{T_{\mathrm{sidereal,exterior}} - T_{\mathrm{sidereal,interior}}};$$

$$T_{\mathrm{sidereal,exterior}} > T_{\mathrm{sidereal,interior}}.$$

The two established relations represent the *synodic movement equations* of the planets.

For the given exoplanets, the sidereal periods are calculated, and the values found are included in the following table. They have been calculated with the formulae:

$$T = 2\pi\sqrt{\frac{a^3}{KM_G}}; \quad K = 6.67 \times 10^{-11}\ \mathrm{Nm^2/kg^2};$$

$$a_{Gd} < a_{Gc} < a_{Gb} < a_{Ge}; \quad T_{Gd} < T_{Gc} < T_{Gb} < T_{Ge};$$

$$a_{Ge} > a_{Gb} > a_{Gc} > a_{Gd}; \quad T_{Ge} > T_{Gb} > T_{Gc} > T_{Gd}.$$

| Gliese system | Mass (kg) | Semi-major axis (m) | Period (earth days) |
|---|---|---|---|
| Gliese 876 | $6.64359 \times 10$ | | |
| Gliese 876 b | $4.31938 \times 10^{27}$ | $3.1161 \times 10^{10}$ | 60.07568 |
| Gliese 876 c | $1.35564 \times 10^{27}$ | $1.9388 \times 10^{10}$ | 29.48304 |
| Gliese 876 d | $4.079 \times 10^{25}$ | $3.1116 \times 10^{9}$ | 1.8956 |
| Gliese 876 e | $8.7194 \times 10^{25}$ | $5.0011 \times 10^{10}$ | 122.1432 |

To identify the Gliese exoplanets whose orbits are resonant, we proceed as follows:

$$T_{\text{sinodic,interior}} = \frac{T_{\text{sidereal,interior}} \cdot T_{\text{sidereal,exterior}}}{T_{\text{sidereal,exterior}} - T_{\text{sidereal,interior}}};$$

$$T_{\text{sinodic,exterior}} = \frac{T_{\text{sidereal,interior}} \cdot T_{\text{sidereal,exterior}}}{T_{\text{sidereal,exterior}} - T_{\text{sidereal,interior}}};$$

$$T_{\text{sidereal,exterior}} > T_{\text{sidereal,interior}};$$

$$T_{\text{sinodic,interior}} = T_{\text{sinodic,exterior}};$$

$$T_{\text{sinodic,interior}} = T_{\text{sinodic,exterior}} = mT_{\text{sidereal,interior}};$$

$$m = \frac{T_{\text{sinodic,interior/exterior}}}{T_{\text{sidereal,interior}}} = \frac{T_{\text{sidereal,exterior}}}{T_{\text{sidereal,exterior}} - T_{\text{sidereal,interior}}}.$$

If $m$ is an integer, the orbits of the interior Gliese and of the exterior Gliese exoplanets are resonant.

The orbits of two exoplanets are resonant if their synodic period is an integer multiple of the sidereal period.

According to the exoplanets, order relative to Gliese 876, presented in Figure 21.4, the following table can be filled in, and the orbital resonance of Gliese b and c, and of Gliese b and e, will be determined.

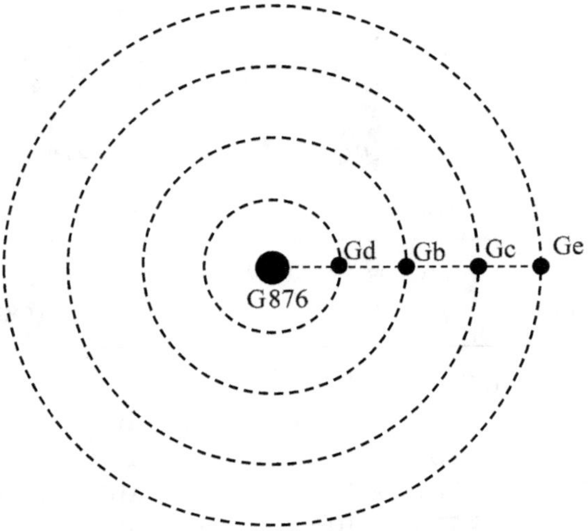


**Fig. 21.4**

| Interior exoplanet | Exterior exoplanet | $m = \dfrac{T_{\text{exterior}}}{T_{\text{exterior}} - T_{\text{interior}}}$ | Resonant orbit |
|---|---|---|---|
| Gliese d | Gliese c | $m = \dfrac{T_{\text{Gc}}}{T_{\text{Gc}} - T_{\text{Gd}}} \approx 1.06$ | – |
| Gliese d | Gliese b | $m = \dfrac{T_{\text{Gb}}}{T_{\text{Gb}} - T_{\text{Gd}}} \approx 1.03$ | – |
| Gliese d | Gliese e | $m = \dfrac{T_{\text{Ge}}}{T_{\text{Ge}} - T_{\text{Gd}}} \approx 1.01$ | – |
| Gliese c | Gliese b | $m = \dfrac{T_{\text{Gb}}}{T_{\text{Gb}} - T_{\text{Gc}}} \approx 1.96 \approx 2$ | Gb and Gc |
| Gliese c | Gliese e | $m = \dfrac{T_{\text{Ge}}}{T_{\text{Ge}} - T_{\text{Gc}}} \approx 1.31$ | – |
| Gliese b | Gliese e | $m = \dfrac{T_{\text{Ge}}}{T_{\text{Ge}} - T_{\text{Gb}}} \approx 1.96 \approx 2$ | Gb and Ge |

# Problem 22

# The Ratio Densities of Two Planets

The Moon has the orbital period $T_{\mathrm{M}} = 27\,\mathrm{d}\,7\,\mathrm{h}\,43\,\mathrm{min}$ and the semi-major axis $a_{\mathrm{M}} = 60.3\,R_{\mathrm{Earth}}$. A planet P, from our solar system, has a satellite s whose semi-major axis is $a_{\mathrm{s}} = 15.3\,R_{\mathrm{Planet}}$ and the period $T_{\mathrm{s}} = 7\,\mathrm{d}\,3\,\mathrm{h}\,43\,\mathrm{min}$. Assume that the mass of the Moon and the satellite are negligible compared to the mass of the Earth and of the planet. *Calculate* the ratio of the planet's mean density to that of the Earth.

## Solution

Notation: $M_{\mathrm{P}}$ – the planet's mass; $M_{\mathrm{E}}$ – the Earth's mass; $M_{\mathrm{S}}$ – the Sun's mass; $m_{\mathrm{M}}$ – the Moon's mass; $m_{\mathrm{s}}$ – the satellite's mass; $R_{\mathrm{P}}$ – the planet's radius; $R_{\mathrm{E}}$ – the Earth's radius; $a_{\mathrm{P}}$ – the semi-major axis of the planet's orbit (the average orbital radius of the planet); $a_{\mathrm{E}}$ – the semi-major axis of the Earth's orbit (the average orbital radius of the Earth); $a_{\mathrm{M}}$ – the semi-major axis of the Moon's orbit (the average orbital radius of the Moon); $a_{\mathrm{s}}$ – the semi-major axis of the satellite's orbit (the average orbital radius of the satellite); $T_{\mathrm{P}}$ – the period of the planet's orbital motion; $T_{\mathrm{E}}$ – the period of the Earth's orbital motion; $T_{\mathrm{M}}$ – the period of the Moon's orbital motion; $T_{\mathrm{s}}$ – the period of the satellite's orbital motion.

According to Kepler's laws, the result is:

$$K(M_{\mathrm{P}}+m_{\mathrm{s}})=4\pi^2\frac{a_{\mathrm{s}}^3}{T_{\mathrm{s}}^2};\quad m_{\mathrm{s}}\ll M_{\mathrm{P}};\quad KM_{\mathrm{P}}=4\pi^2\frac{a_{\mathrm{s}}^3}{T_{\mathrm{s}}^2};$$

$$K(M_{\mathrm{S}}+M_{\mathrm{P}})=4\pi^2\frac{a_{\mathrm{P}}^3}{T_{\mathrm{P}}^2};\quad M_{\mathrm{P}}\ll M_{\mathrm{S}};\quad KM_{\mathrm{S}}=4\pi^2\frac{a_{\mathrm{P}}^3}{T_{\mathrm{P}}^2};$$

$$\frac{M_{\mathrm{P}}}{M_{\mathrm{S}}}=\left(\frac{a_{\mathrm{s}}}{a_{\mathrm{P}}}\right)^3\left(\frac{T_{\mathrm{P}}}{T_{\mathrm{s}}}\right)^2;\quad T_{\mathrm{s}}=0.0196\text{ years};$$

$$M_{\mathrm{P}}=\left(\frac{a_{\mathrm{s}}}{a_{\mathrm{P}}}\right)^3\left(\frac{T_{\mathrm{P}}}{T_{\mathrm{s}}}\right)^2M_{\mathrm{S}}=\frac{(15.3\ R_{\mathrm{P}})^3}{(a_{\mathrm{P}})^3}\frac{(T_{\mathrm{P}})^2}{(0.0196\text{ years})^2}M_{\mathrm{S}};$$

$$K(M_{\mathrm{E}}+m_{\mathrm{M}})=4\pi^2\frac{a_{\mathrm{M}}^3}{T_{\mathrm{M}}^2};\quad m_{\mathrm{M}}\ll M_{\mathrm{E}};\quad KM_{\mathrm{E}}=4\pi^2\frac{a_{\mathrm{M}}^3}{T_{\mathrm{M}}^2};$$

$$\frac{M_{\mathrm{E}}}{M_{\mathrm{S}}}=\left(\frac{a_{\mathrm{M}}}{a_{\mathrm{E}}}\right)^3\left(\frac{T_{\mathrm{E}}}{T_{\mathrm{M}}}\right)^2;\quad T_{\mathrm{M}}=0.0749\text{ years};$$

$$M_{\mathrm{E}}=\left(\frac{a_{\mathrm{M}}}{a_{\mathrm{E}}}\right)^3\left(\frac{T_{\mathrm{E}}}{T_{\mathrm{M}}}\right)^2M_{\mathrm{S}}=\frac{(60.3\ R_{\mathrm{E}})^3}{(1\mathrm{AU})^3}\frac{(1\text{ year})^2}{(0.0749\text{ years})^2}M_{\mathrm{S}};$$

$$\frac{\rho_{\mathrm{P}}}{\rho_{\mathrm{E}}}=\frac{\frac{M_{\mathrm{P}}}{V_{\mathrm{P}}}}{\frac{M_{\mathrm{E}}}{V_{\mathrm{E}}}}=\frac{M_{\mathrm{P}}}{M_{\mathrm{E}}}\frac{V_{\mathrm{E}}}{V_{\mathrm{P}}}=\frac{M_{\mathrm{P}}}{M_{\mathrm{E}}}\left(\frac{R_{\mathrm{E}}}{R_{\mathrm{P}}}\right)^3;$$

$$\frac{\rho_{\mathrm{P}}}{\rho_{\mathrm{E}}}=\frac{(15.3\ R_{\mathrm{P}})^3}{(a_{\mathrm{P}})^3}\frac{(T_{\mathrm{P}})^2}{(0.0196\text{ y})^2}\frac{(1\text{ AU})^3}{(60.3\ R_{\mathrm{E}})^3}\frac{(0.0749\text{ y})^2}{(1\text{ y})^2}\left(\frac{R_{\mathrm{E}}}{R_{\mathrm{P}}}\right)^3;$$

$$\frac{\rho_{\mathrm{P}}}{\rho_{\mathrm{E}}}=\frac{(15.3)^3}{(a_{\mathrm{P}})^3}\frac{(T_{\mathrm{P}})^2}{(0.0196\text{ y})^2}\frac{(1\text{ AU})^3}{(60.3)^3}\frac{(0.0749\text{ y})^2}{(1\text{ y})^2};$$

$$\frac{\rho_{\mathrm{P}}}{\rho_{\mathrm{E}}}=\frac{(T_{\mathrm{P}})^2}{(a_{\mathrm{P}})^3}\frac{(15.3)^3}{(60.3)^3}\frac{(0.0749)^2}{(0.0196)^2}\frac{(1\text{ AU})^3}{(1\text{ y})^2};$$

$$K(M_{\mathrm{S}}+M_{\mathrm{P}})=4\pi^2\frac{a_{\mathrm{P}}^3}{T_{\mathrm{P}}^2};\quad M_{\mathrm{P}}\ll M_{\mathrm{S}};\quad KM_{\mathrm{S}}=4\pi^2\frac{a_{\mathrm{P}}^3}{T_{\mathrm{P}}^2};$$

$$\frac{T_{\mathrm{P}}^2}{a_{\mathrm{P}}^3}=\frac{4\pi^2}{KM_{\mathrm{S}}};$$

$$\frac{|T_{\mathrm{P(years)}}|^2(1\text{ year})^2M_{\mathrm{S}}}{|a_{\mathrm{P(AU)}}|^3(1\text{ AU})^3}=\frac{4\pi^2}{K};$$

$$\frac{|T_{\mathrm{P(years)}}|^2}{|a_{\mathrm{P(AU)}}|^3}\frac{(1\ \mathrm{year})^2 M_{\mathrm{S}}}{(1\ \mathrm{AU})^3} = \frac{4\pi^2}{K};$$

$$\frac{(1\ \mathrm{year})^2 M_{\mathrm{S}}}{(1\ \mathrm{AU})^3} = \frac{(365\cdot 24\cdot 3600)^2\ \mathrm{s}^2\cdot 1.989\cdot 10^{30}\ \mathrm{kg}}{(15\cdot 10^{10})^3\ \mathrm{m}^3}$$

$$\approx 5.86\cdot 10^{11}\ \frac{\mathrm{s}^2\mathrm{kg}}{\mathrm{m}^3};$$

$$\frac{4\pi^2}{K} = \frac{4\cdot 3.14\cdot 3.14}{6.67\cdot 10^{-11}\ \mathrm{Nm}^2\mathrm{kg}^{-2}} \approx 5.91\cdot 10^{11}\ \frac{\mathrm{s}^2\mathrm{kg}}{\mathrm{m}^3};$$

$$\frac{(1\ \mathrm{year})^2 M_{\mathrm{S}}}{(1\ \mathrm{AU})^3} \approx \frac{4\pi^2}{K}; \qquad \frac{|T_{\mathrm{P(years)}}|^2}{|a_{\mathrm{P(AU)}}|^3} = 1;$$

$$\frac{\rho_{\mathrm{P}}}{\rho_{\mathrm{E}}} = \frac{(T_{\mathrm{P}})^2}{(a_{\mathrm{P}})^3}\frac{(15.3)^3}{(60.3)^3}\frac{(0.0749)^2}{(0.0196)^2}\frac{(1\ \mathrm{AU})^3}{(1\ \mathrm{y})^2};$$

$$\frac{\rho_{\mathrm{P}}}{\rho_{\mathrm{E}}} = \frac{(1\ \mathrm{y})^2}{(1\ \mathrm{AU})^3}\frac{(15.3)^3}{(60.3)^3}\frac{(0.0749)^2}{(0.0196)^2}\frac{(1\ \mathrm{AU})^3}{(1\ \mathrm{y})^2};$$

$$\frac{\rho_{\mathrm{P}}}{\rho_{\mathrm{E}}} = \frac{(15.3)^3}{(60.3)^3}\frac{(0.0749)^2}{(0.0196)^2}; \qquad \frac{\rho_{\mathrm{P}}}{\rho_{\mathrm{E}}} = 0.265.$$

# Problem 23

# The Asteroid Julietta

On 27 May 2015 at 02:18:49, the occultation of the star HIP 89931 ($\delta$Sgr) by the asteroid 1285 Julietta was observed from Borobudur Temple, which was located at the center of the asteroid's shadow path. It lasted for only $\Delta t = 6.201\,\text{s}$. Assume that Earth's orbit is circular and the orbit of Julietta is on the ecliptic plane and revolves in same direction as Earth. At the time of the occultation, Julietta was near its aphelion, and the distances of Julietta from the Sun and the Earth were $r_J = 3.076\,\text{AU}$ and $r_{JE} = 2.156\,\text{AU}$, respectively (Figure 23.1).

*Find* the approximate diameter of asteroid Julietta, if the semi-major axis of Julietta is $a_J = 2.9914\,\text{AU}$.

### Solution

According to the details presented in Figure 23.2, the result is:

$$\text{v}_\text{E} = \frac{2\pi r_\text{E}}{T_\text{E}} = \frac{2\pi a_\text{E}}{T_\text{E}} = 29805\,\frac{\text{m}}{\text{s}};$$

$$\text{v}_\text{J} = \sqrt{KM_S\left(\frac{2}{r_J} - \frac{1}{a_J}\right)} = 16742.9\,\frac{\text{m}}{\text{s}};$$

$$r_\text{JE}^2 = r_\text{E}^2 + r_\text{J}^2 - 2r_\text{E}r_\text{J}\cos\alpha;$$

$$\cos\alpha = \frac{r_\text{E}^2 + r_\text{J}^2 - r_\text{JE}^2}{2r_\text{E}r_\text{J}} = 0.995.$$

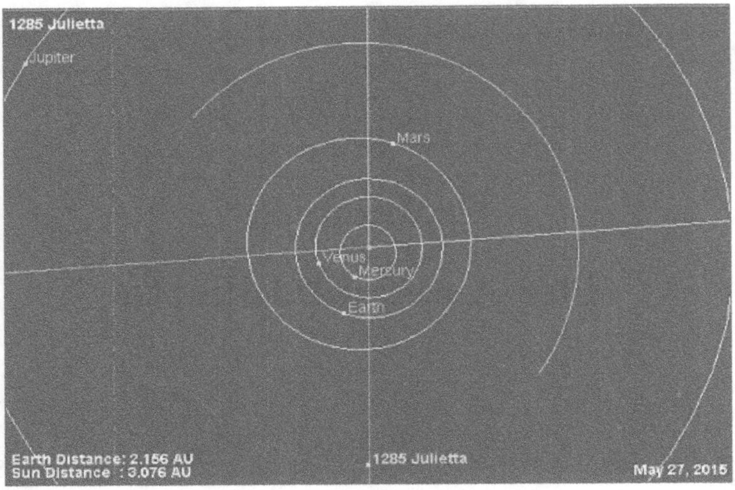


**Fig. 23.1**

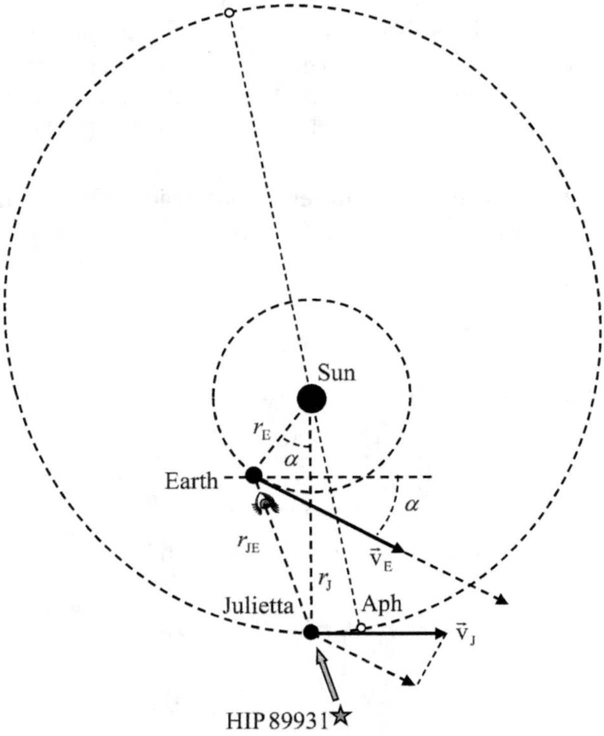


**Fig. 23.2**

The period of time for which the HIP 89931 star is occulted by the Julietta asteroid that passes between the Earth and the HIP star is determined by the component of the asteroid's relative velocity parallel to its direction $\vec{v}_E$, that is:

$$v_{J,//} = v_J \cos\alpha;$$

$$v_{J,//,E} = v_E - v_{J\,//} = v_E - v_J \cos\alpha.$$

Thus, the diameter of the Julietta asteroid is

$$d_J = (v_E - v_J \cos\alpha)\Delta t = 86701.8\,\text{m}.$$

# Problem 24

# Distance to a Black Hole

Let us assume that an observer using a hypothetical, far-infrared, Earth-sized telescope (wavelength range from $\lambda_{\text{min}} = 20\,\mu\text{m}$ to $\lambda_{\text{max}} = 640\,\mu\text{m}$) found a static and neutral supermassive black hole with a mass $M_{\text{BH}} = 2.1 \times 10^{10}\, M_{\text{S}}$. The following are considered known: $R_{\text{Schwarzschild,Sun}} = 2.95 \times 10^3$ m; $R_{\text{Earth}} = 6.3708 \times 10^6$ m.

*Determine* the maximum distance at which this black hole can be resolved by the observer.

### Solution

The angular opening of a $2R_{\text{Schwarzschild}}$ diameter black hole located at a distance $d$ from the observer is

$$\theta_{\text{BH}} = \frac{2R_{\text{Sch,BH}}}{d}.$$

The angular resolution of a telescope is known to be

$$\theta_{\text{tel}} = 1.22\frac{\lambda}{D_{\text{tel}}},$$

where $D_{\text{tel}}$ is the diameter of the telescope's mirror. Considering that the telescope's mirror is the size of the Earth, we obtain:

$$D_{\text{tel}} = 2R_{\text{Earth}}; \quad \theta_{\text{tel}} = 1.22\frac{\lambda}{2R_{\text{E}}}.$$

The conditions for the black hole to be resolved by the observer are:

$$\theta_{\text{tel}} \leq \theta_{\text{BH}};$$

$$1.22\frac{\lambda}{2R_{\text{E}}} \leq \frac{2R_{\text{Sch,BH}}}{d};$$

$$d \leq \frac{4R_{\text{Sch,BH}} \times R_{\text{E}}}{1.22 \times \lambda};$$

$$R_{\text{Sch,BH}} = \frac{2KM_{\text{BH}}}{c^2}; \quad R_{\text{Sch,Sun}} = \frac{2KM_{\text{Sun}}}{c^2};$$

$$\frac{R_{\text{Sch,BH}}}{R_{\text{Sch,Sun}}} = \frac{M_{\text{BH}}}{M_{\text{Sun}}};$$

$$d \leq \frac{4 \times M_{\text{BH}} \times R_{\text{Sch,Sun}} \times R_{\text{E}}}{1.22 \times \lambda \times M_{\text{Sun}}};$$

$$d \leq \frac{4 \times 2.1 \times 10^{10} \times M_{\text{Sun}} \times R_{\text{Sch,Sun}} \times R_{\text{E}}}{1.22 \times \lambda \times M_{\text{Sun}}};$$

$$d \leq \frac{8.2 \times 10^{10} \times R_{\text{Sch,Sun}} \times R_{\text{E}}}{1.22 \times \lambda};$$

$$d_{\text{max}} = \frac{8.2 \times 10^{10} \times R_{\text{Sch,Sun}} \times R_{\text{E}}}{1.22 \times \lambda_{\text{min}}};$$

$$R_{\text{Sch,Sun}} = 2.95 \times 10^3\ \text{m}; R_{\text{E}} = 6.3708 \times 10^6\ \text{m}; \lambda_{\text{min}} = 20 \times 10^{-6}\ \text{m};$$

$$d_{\text{max}} = 6.6 \times 10^{25}\ \text{m}.$$

# Problem 25

# The Eccentricity of a Satellite's Orbit

An observer is trying to determine an approximate value of the orbital eccentricity of a man-made satellite. When the satellite is at apogee, it is observed to have moved by $\Delta\theta_1 = 2'44''$ in a short time. When the radius vector connecting Earth and the satellite is perpendicular to the major axis (the true anomaly is equal to 90°), within the same duration of time, it is observed to have moved by $\Delta\theta_2 = 21'17''$. Assume that the observer is located at the center of the Earth.

*Find* an approximate value of the eccentricity of the satellite's orbit.

## Solution

If the satellite moves on the ellipse presented in Figure 25.1, the equation of this curve in plane polar coordinates is

$$r(\theta) = \frac{p}{1 + e\cos\theta} = \frac{a(1-e^2)}{1 + e\cos\theta},$$

resulting in:

$$r(\pi) = \frac{a(1-e^2)}{1-e} = a(1+e);$$

$$r\left(\frac{\pi}{2}\right) = a(1-e^2).$$

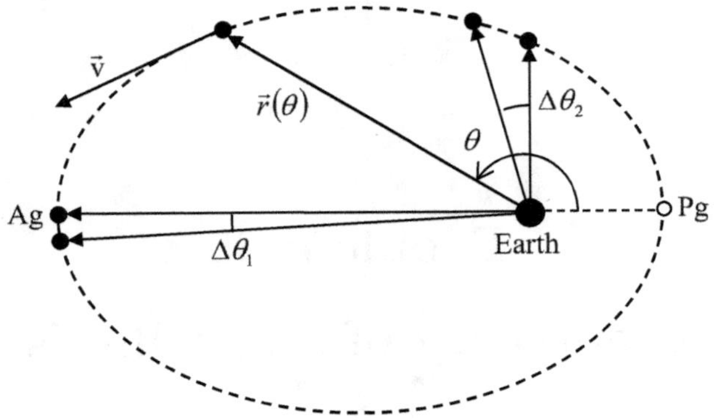


**Fig. 25.1**

The two elementary sectors of the ellipse swept by the satellite's vector radius in the very short time interval corresponding to very small center angles, $\Delta\theta_1$ and $\Delta\theta_2$, respectively, can be considered two elementary circle sectors of the following surface areas:

$$\Delta A_1 = \frac{1}{2} \times \Delta\theta_1 \times [r(\pi)]^2 = \frac{1}{2}\Delta\theta_1\, a^2(1+e)^2;$$

$$\Delta A_2 = \frac{1}{2} \times \Delta\theta_2 \times \left[r\left(\frac{\pi}{2}\right)\right]^2 = \frac{1}{2}\Delta\theta_2\, a^2(1-e^{\cdot 2})^2.$$

According to the law of equal areas (Kepler's second law), this results in:

$$\Delta A_1 = \Delta A_2;$$

$$\Delta\theta_1\, a^2(1+e)^2 = \Delta\theta_2\, a^2(1-e^{\cdot 2})^2;$$

$$\frac{\Delta\theta_1}{\Delta\theta_2} = (1-e)^2;$$

$$e = 1 - \sqrt{\frac{\Delta\theta_1}{\Delta\theta_2}} \approx 0.64.$$

# Problem 26

# Atmospheric Optical Depth

At the start of every observation, a radio telescope is pointed at a point-source calibrator that has a known flux density of $F_{\text{real}} = 21.86$ Jy, outside the Earth's atmosphere. However, on a certain date, the measured flux density of the calibrator source was $F_{\text{measured}} = 14.27$ Jy. If the calibrator was at an altitude $\varphi = 35°$, *estimate* the zenith atmospheric optical depth, $\tau_z$.

$$1 \text{ Jansky} = 1 \text{ Jy} = 10^{-26} \frac{\text{W}}{\text{m}^2\text{Hz}} = 10^{-26} \frac{J}{\text{s} \cdot \text{m}^2\text{Hz}}.$$

### Solution

When light passes through a transparent gaseous medium, the radiation flux varies and according to Beer's law. Using the notation in Figure 26.1, it results in the following:

$$F = F_0 e^{-\sigma n d},$$

where: $\sigma = \pi r^2$ is the cross-section of a gas molecule, considered to be spherical; $n = N/V$ is the gas molecules' concentration; $h$ is the gas layer thickness.

If $\sigma n h = \tau$, Beer's law yields:

$$F = F_0 e^{-\tau};$$

$$t = \frac{F}{F_0} = e^{-\tau},$$

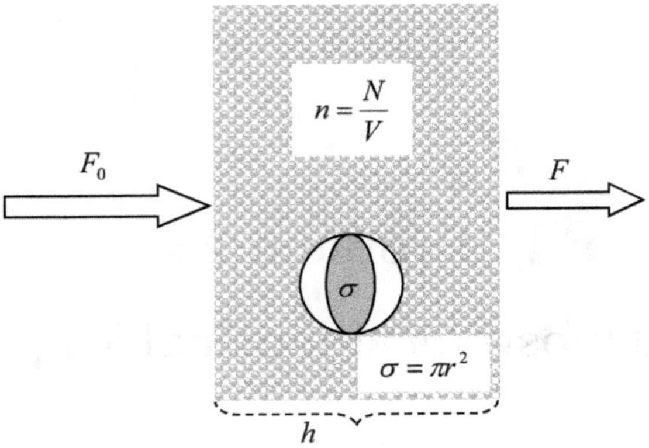


**Fig. 26.1**

where $t$ is the medium transmittance, and $\tau$ is the medium optical depth (a dimensionless unit that expresses the capacity of a medium to block light, independently of its characteristics).

Given the problem, when the calibrator star $\Sigma$ is over the horizon of the observation place at the angular altitude $\varphi$, as presented in Figure 26.2, it results in:

$$F_{\text{measured}} = F_{\text{real}}\, e^{-\tau_A},$$

where $\tau_A$ is the atmospheric optical depth;

$$\tau_A = \sigma n D;$$

$$\tau_A = -\ln \frac{F}{F_0} = -\ln \frac{F_{\text{measured}}}{F_{\text{real}}} = -\ln \frac{14.27}{21.86} = -\ln(0.65) = 0.43.$$

Corresponding to the moment when the calibrator star $\Sigma$ is at the zenith, considering the definition of the optical depth of the atmosphere, it results that:

$$\tau_Z = -\ln \frac{F_{\text{Z,measured}}}{F_{\text{real}}} = \sigma n d; \quad d = D \cos z;$$

$$d = D\cos(90^\circ - \phi) = D \sin \varphi; \quad \tau_Z = \sigma n D \sin \varphi;$$

$$\tau_Z = \tau_A \sin \varphi \approx 0.25.$$

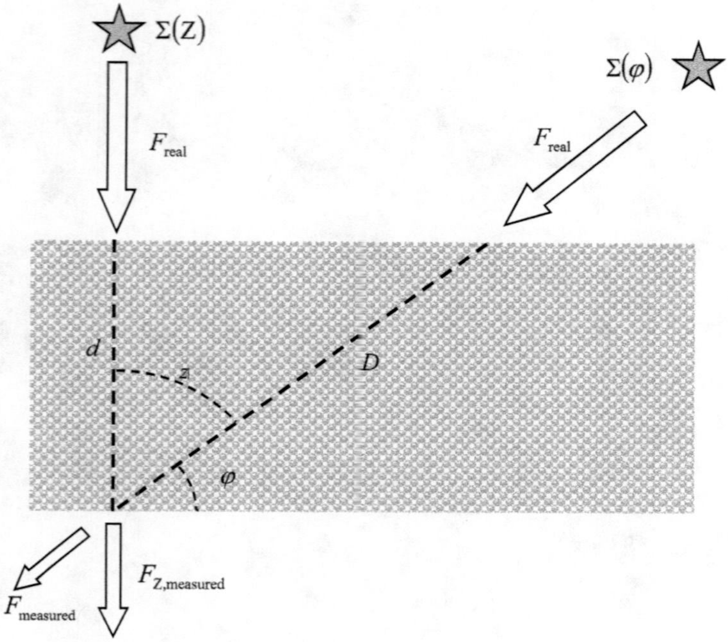


**Fig. 26.2**

# Problem 27

# Density of a Cluster

A galaxy at the boundary of a galaxy cluster of radius $R = 10$ Mpc is expected to escape from the cluster if it has an initial velocity of at least $\mathrm{v} = 700\,\mathrm{km/s}$ relative to the center of the cluster. *Calculate* the density of the cluster.

## Solution

The total energy of the system consisting of the marginal galaxy and of the cluster of galaxies it belongs to is:

$$E_{\text{total}} = E_{\text{kinetic}} + E_{\text{potential}} = \frac{m_{\text{galaxy}}\mathrm{v}^2}{2} - K\frac{m_{\text{galaxy}}M_{\text{cluster}}}{R}.$$

The marginal galaxy will be able to escape from the cluster if:

$$E_{\text{total}} = 0;$$

$$\mathrm{v}^2 = \frac{2KM_{\text{cluster}}}{R}.$$

Under these circumstances, the result is:

$$M_{\text{cluster}} = \rho_{\text{cluster}}V_{\text{cluster}} = \rho_{\text{cluster}}\frac{4\pi R^3}{3};$$

$$\mathrm{v}^2 = \frac{2K}{R}\rho_{\text{cluster}}\frac{4\pi R^3}{3}; \quad K = 6.6378 \times 10^{-11}\,\mathrm{Nm^2kg^{-2}};$$

$$\rho_{\text{cluster}} = \frac{3\mathrm{v}^2}{8\pi K R^2} \approx 9.20121 \times 10^{-27}\,\frac{\mathrm{kg}}{m^3}.$$

# Problem 28

# Radio Signal

A strong continuum radio signal from a celestial body has been observed as a burst with a very short duration $\Delta t = 700\,\mu\text{s}$. The observed flux density at a frequency $v = 1660\,\text{MHz}$ is measured to be $\Phi = 0.35\,\text{kJy}$. If the distance from the source is to be $r = 2.3\,\text{kpc}$, *estimate* the brightness temperature of this source, $T_\text{b}$.

$$1\ \text{Jansky} = 1\ \text{Jy} = 10^{-26}\,\frac{\text{W}}{\text{m}^2\text{Hz}} = 10^{-26}\,\frac{\text{J}}{\text{s}\cdot\text{m}^2\text{Hz}}.$$

## Solution

The radio waves of the domain presented in the figure below (Figure 28.1) are generated by the explosion of the celestial body. They are of frequency $v$, and the distance they travel in the time interval $\Delta t$ represents the radius $R$ of a spherical source:

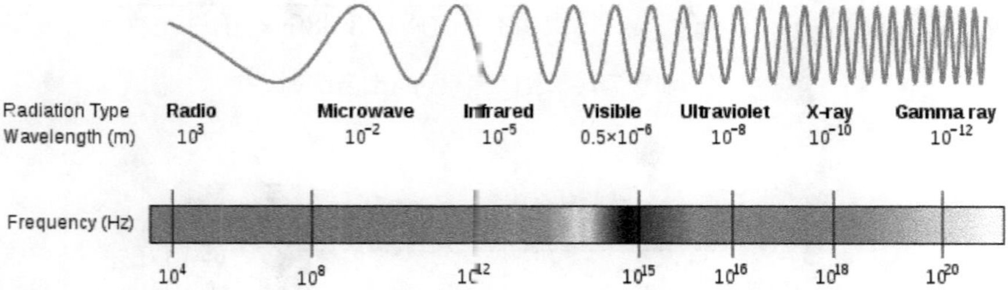


**Fig. 28.1**

$$R = c\Delta t = 3 \times 10^8 \,\frac{\text{m}}{\text{s}} \times 700 \times 10^{-6}\,\text{s} = 2.1 \times 10^5\,\text{m} = 210\,\text{km}.$$

When the radiation source is not point-like and has a spherical extension in space, the measurement unit for the radiation flux density $\Phi$ at the observer level, corresponding to a frequency $v$, is:

$$1 \text{ Jansky} = 1\,\text{Jy} = 10^{-26}\,\frac{\text{W}}{\text{m}^2\text{Hz}} = 10^{-26}\,\frac{\text{J}}{\text{s}\cdot\text{m}^2\text{Hz}},$$

so named after the American radio astronomer Karl Guthe Jansky;

$$1\,\text{J} = 10^7\,\text{erg}; \quad 1\,\text{m}^2 = 10^4\,\text{cm}^2;$$

$$1 \text{ Jansky} = 1\,\text{Jy} = 10^{-26}\,\frac{10^7\,\text{erg}}{\text{s}\cdot 10^4\,\text{cm}^2\text{Hz}} = 10^{-23}\,\frac{\text{erg}}{\text{s}\cdot\text{cm}^2\text{Hz}}.$$

Thus, for the given spherical source, the radiation flux density at the observer is:

$$\Phi = 0.35 \times 10^3\,\text{Jy} = 0.35 \times 10^3 \times 10^{-26}\,\frac{\text{W}}{\text{m}^2\text{Hz}}$$
$$= 3.5 \times 10^{-24}\,\frac{\text{J}}{\text{s}\cdot\text{m}^2\text{Hz}};$$
$$\Phi = 0.35 \times 10^3\,\text{Jy} = 0.35 \times 10^3 \times 10^{-23}\,\frac{\text{erg}}{\text{s}\cdot\text{cm}^2\text{Hz}}$$
$$= 3.5 \times 10^{-21}\,\frac{\text{erg}}{\text{s}\cdot\text{cm}^2\text{Hz}}.$$

The solid angle through which the observer watches and which contains the spherical radio wave source represented in Figure 28.2 is

$$\Omega = \frac{A}{r^2} = \frac{\pi R^2}{r^2} = 3.14\frac{(2.1 \times 10^5\,\text{m})^2}{(2.3 \times 10^3 \times 3.086 \times 10^{16}\,\text{m})^2}$$
$$\approx 2.75 \times 10^{-29}\,\text{steradian}.$$

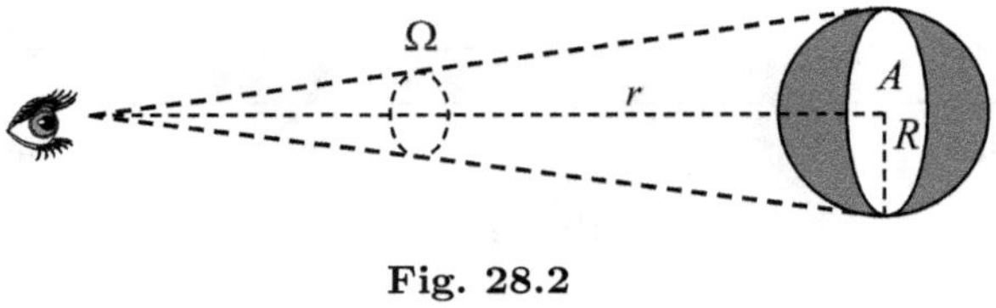


**Fig. 28.2**

The flux density (also known as the monochromatic flux) $\Phi$ of an extensive source is the integral of the spectral radiance (brightness) $B$, over the solid angle of the source:

$$\Phi = B\Omega.$$

Thus, the brightness of the given extensive source surface is:

$$B = \Phi/\Omega,$$

expressed in Jy/steradian;

$$B = \frac{3.5 \times 10^{-24}\ \frac{\mathrm{J}}{\mathrm{s \cdot m^2 Hz}}}{2.75 \times 10^{-29}\ \mathrm{sr}} = 1.27 \times 10^{5}\ \frac{J}{\mathrm{s \cdot m^2 Hz \cdot sr}}.$$

In radio astronomy, the brightness temperature ($T_\mathrm{b}$) is used as the measurement of the light intensity received by the observer. Applying Planck's law to the black body radiation, it results that:

$$I(v) = \frac{2hv^3}{c^2}\frac{1}{e^{hv/kT} - 1};$$

$$e^{hv/kT} \approx 1 + \frac{hv}{kT};$$

$$I(v) = \frac{2hv^3}{c^2}\frac{kT}{hv} = \frac{2kv^2 T}{c^2};$$

$$T = \frac{c^2 I(v)}{2kv^2};$$

$$I(v) = B; \quad T = T_b;$$

$$T_\mathrm{b} = \frac{c^2 B}{2kv^2} = \frac{\left(3 \times 10^{8}\ \frac{\mathrm{m}}{\mathrm{s}}\right)^2 (1.27 \times 10^{5}) \frac{J}{\mathrm{s \cdot m^2 Hz \cdot sr}}}{2 \times 1.381 \times 10^{-23}\ \frac{\mathrm{J}}{\mathrm{K}} \times (1660 \times 10^{6}\ \mathrm{Hz})^2};$$

$$T_\mathrm{b} = \frac{(3 \times 10^{8})^2 (1.27 \times 10^{5})}{2 \times 1.381 \times 10^{-23} \times (1660 \times 10^{6})^2}\mathrm{K} = 1.5 \times 10^{26}\ \mathrm{K}.$$

# Problem 29

# Venus – A Black Body

Assume that the Sun is a perfect black body. Venus is also assumed to be a black body, with temperature $T_V$ and in thermal equilibrium (that is, it is radiating about as much energy as it receives from the Sun) at its orbital distance $r_{SV} = 0.72\,\text{AU}$. Suppose that at its closest approach to Earth, Venus has an angular diameter $\theta = 66$ arcsec. *What is* the flux density, $\Phi$, of Venus at the closest approach to Earth as observed by a radio telescope at an observing frequency $v = 5\,\text{GHz}$? The following are considered known: the radius of Sun, $R_{\text{Sun}} = 6.96 \times 10^8\,\text{m}$; the effective temperature of the Sun, $T_{\text{Sun}} = 5780\,\text{K}$; the Stefan–Boltzmann constant, $\sigma = 5.6704 \times 10^{-8}\,\frac{\text{kg}}{\text{s}^3\text{K}^4}$; the Boltzmann constant, $k = 1.381 \times 10^{-23}\,\frac{J}{\text{K}}$.

### Solution

According to the Stefan–Boltzmann law, the radiance of the Sun (considered to be an absolute black body), that is, the total energy corresponding to all wavelengths, emitted in one time unit by one unit area of the Sun's surface, is directly proportional to the fourth power of the effective temperature of its surface, that is:

$$Q_{\text{Sun}} = \frac{E_{\text{emitted, Sun}}}{tS_{\text{Sun}}} = \sigma T_S^4,$$

where $\sigma$ is a constant;

$$\frac{E_{\text{emitted, Sun}}}{t} = P_{\text{emitted, Sun}} = L_{\text{Sun}};$$

$$\sigma T_{\text{S}}^4 = \frac{P_{\text{emitted, Sun}}}{4\pi R_{\text{S}}^2} = \frac{L_{\text{Sun}}}{4\pi R_{\text{S}}^2},$$

where $L_{\text{S}}$ is the Sun's luminosity;

$$P_{\text{emitted, Sun}} = L_{\text{Sun}} = \sigma T_{\text{S}}^4 4\pi R_{\text{S}}^2 = 4\pi\sigma R_{\text{S}}^2 T_{\text{S}}^4;$$

$$L_{\text{Sun}} = 4 \times 3.14 \times 5.6704 \times 10^{-8}\,\frac{\text{kg}}{s^3\text{K}^4}\left(6.96 \times 10^8\,\text{m}\right)^2 (5780\,\text{K})^4;$$

$$L_{\text{Sun}} = 4 \times 3.14 \times 5.6704 \times 10^{-8}\left(6.96 \times 10^8\right)^2 (5780)^4\,\frac{\text{m}^2\text{kg}}{\text{s}^3}$$

$$= 3.96 \times 10^{26}\,\frac{\text{J}}{\text{s}}.$$

If $\Sigma$ is the surface of the circumsolar sphere whose radius is $r_{\text{SV}}$, that is, the instantaneous distance between the center of the Sun and the center of Venus, as presented in Figure 29.1, then the energy of solar radiation that passes through the surface $\Sigma$ in one time unit is $L_{\text{S}}$.

The density of the Sun's energetic flux at the distance $r_{\text{Sun-Venus}} = r_{\text{SV}}$ from the Sun represents the energy of all radiation emitted by the Sun that passes through one unit surface area at normal incidence in one time unit, that is:

$$\varphi_{\text{Sun},r_{\text{SV}}} = \frac{E_{\text{emitted, Sun}}}{St} = \frac{\frac{E_{\text{emitted, Sun}}}{t}}{S} = \frac{P_{\text{emitted, Sun}}}{S} = \frac{P_{\text{emitted, Sun}}}{4\pi r_{\text{SV}}^2}$$

$$= \frac{L_{\text{Sun}}}{4\pi r_{\text{SV}}^2},$$

where $r_{\text{SV}}$ is the distance between the Sun and Venus;

$$\varphi_{\text{Sun},r_{\text{SV}}} = \frac{\sigma T_{\text{S}}^4 4\pi R_{\text{S}}^2}{4\pi r_{\text{SV}}^2}.$$

Venus's hemisphere exposed to solar radiation is equivalent to a plane disk of radius $R_{\text{V}}$ and of surface $\pi R_{\text{V}}^2$, perpendicularly oriented

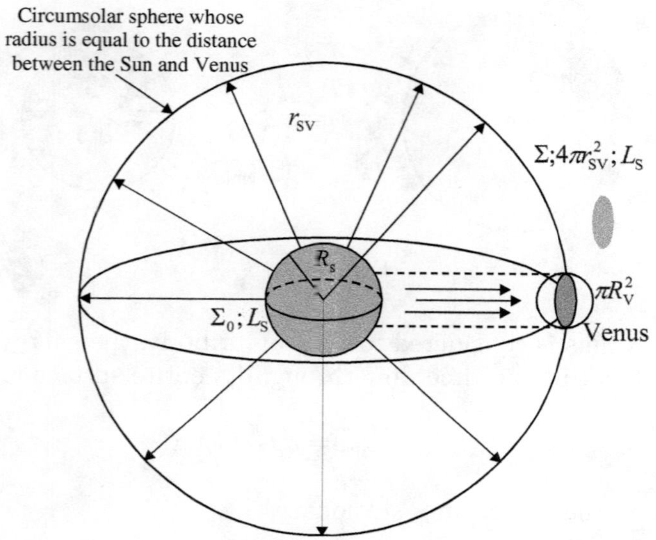


**Fig. 29.1**

in the Sun–Venus direction. The flux of incident solar radiation $F$, at the entrance to Venus's atmosphere, that is, the incident solar energy at the atmosphere level, in one time unit is:

$$F_{\text{incident}} = \varphi_{\text{Sun},r_{SV}} \cdot \pi R_V^2 = P_{\text{incident}} = P_{\text{emitted, Sun}};$$

$$F_{\text{incident}} = \frac{\sigma T_S^4 4\pi R_S^2}{4\pi r_{SV}^2} \cdot \pi R_V^2 = P_{\text{incident}}.$$

Venus's atmosphere is also a plane disk of radius $R_V$.

Considering that Venus does not reflect any of the received radiation, it means that

$$P_{\text{reflected,Venus}} = 0.$$

Consequently, according to Figure 29.2, the energetic balance of the above-mentioned process is:

$$P_{\text{incident,Venus}} = P_{\text{absorbed, Venus}};$$

$$\frac{\sigma T_S^4 4\pi R_S^2}{4\pi r_{SV}^2} \cdot \pi R_V^2 = P_{\text{absorbed, Venus}}.$$

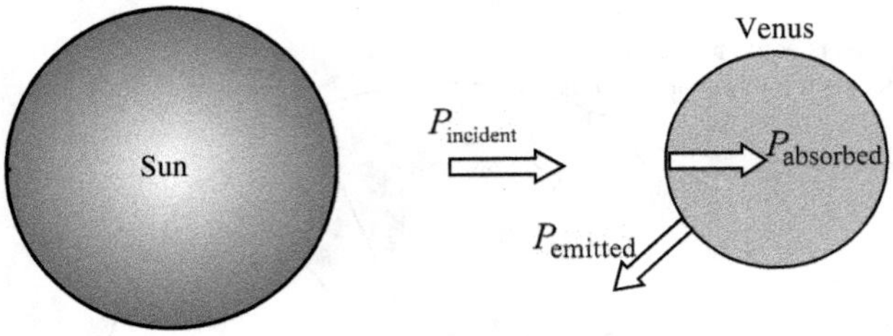


**Fig. 29.2**

Since Venus is considered to be a black body, the energy emitted by this planet in one time unit through its entire surface is

$$P_{\text{emitted, Venus}} = \sigma T_{\text{V}}^4 \cdot 4\pi R_{\text{V}}^2.$$

When the process becomes stationary,

$$P_{\text{emitted, Venus}} = P_{\text{absorbed,Venus}};$$

thus, the result is:

$$\frac{\sigma T_{\text{S}}^4 4\pi R_{\text{S}}^2}{4\pi r_{\text{SV}}^2} \cdot \pi R_{\text{V}}^2 = \sigma T_{\text{V}}^4 \cdot 4\pi R_{\text{V}}^2;$$

$$T_{\text{V}} = T_{\text{S}} \cdot \sqrt{\frac{R_{\text{S}}}{2r_{\text{SV}}}},$$

representing Venus's temperature;

$$T_{\text{V}} = 5780\,\text{K} \cdot \sqrt{\frac{6.96 \times 10^8\,\text{m}}{2 \times 0.72 \times 149.6 \times 10^{11}\,\text{m}}} \approx 328.5\,\text{K}.$$

Using the notation presented in Figure 29.3 and taking into account what was specified, as Venus is for the observer on the Earth a spherical source of radiation, the result is that at the observer's level the density of the flux emitted by Venus is:

$$\Phi = B\Omega = \frac{2kT_{\text{b,V}}v^2}{c^2}\Omega; \quad T_{\text{b,V}} = T_{\text{V}}; \quad \Omega = \frac{\pi R_{\text{V}}^2}{r_{\text{EV}}^2} = \pi\left(\frac{R_{\text{V}}}{r_{\text{EV}}}\right)^2 = \pi\theta^2;$$

$$1'' = 4.84 \times 10^{-6}\,\mathrm{rad};$$

$$\Phi = \frac{2kT_{\mathrm{b,V}}v^2}{c}\pi\cdot\theta^2$$

$$= \frac{2\times 1.381\times 10^{-23}\,\frac{\mathrm{J}}{\mathrm{K}}\times 328.5\,\mathrm{K}\times\left(5\times 10^{9}\,\mathrm{Hz}\right)^2 3.14 \times\left(66\times 4.84\times 10^{-6}\,\mathrm{rad}\right)^2}{\left(3\times 10^{8}\,\frac{\mathrm{m}}{\mathrm{s}}\right)^2};$$

$$\Phi = \frac{2\times 1.381\times 10^{-23}\times 328.5\times\left(5\times 10^{9}\right)^2 \times 3.14\times\left(66\times 4.84\times 10^{-6}\right)^2}{\left(3\times 10^{8}\right)^2}\,\frac{\mathrm{J}}{\mathrm{m}}^2;$$

$$\Phi = \frac{2\times 1.381\times 328.5\times(5)^2\times 3.14\times(66\times 4.84)^2}{(3)^2}\times 10^{-7}$$

$$\times 10^{-26}\,\frac{\mathrm{J}}{\mathrm{m}^2};$$

$$\Phi = 807541387.7\times 10^{-7}\times 10^{-26}\,\frac{\mathrm{J}}{\mathrm{m}^2} \approx 80.7\times 10^{-26}\,\frac{\mathrm{W}\cdot\mathrm{s}}{\mathrm{m}^2}$$

$$= 80.7\times 10^{-26}\,\frac{\mathrm{W}}{\mathrm{m}^2\,\frac{1}{\mathrm{s}}};$$

$$\Phi = 80.7\times 10^{-26}\,\frac{\mathrm{W}}{\mathrm{m}^2\,\mathrm{Hz}};$$

$$1\,\mathrm{Jansky} = 1\,\mathrm{Jy} = 10^{-26}\,\frac{\mathrm{W}}{\mathrm{m}^2\mathrm{Hz}};$$

$$\Phi = 80.7\,\mathrm{Jy}.$$

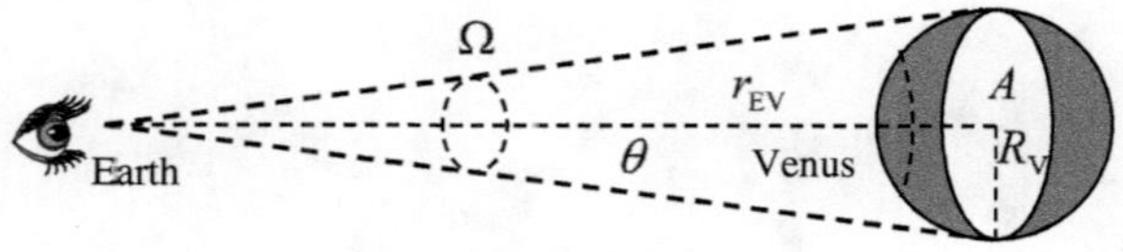


**Fig. 29.3**

# Problem 30

# Cloud of Hydrogen

A molecular hydrogen cloud is known to have a temperature $T = 115\,\text{K}$. The hydrogen atoms (assumed to be spherical) have a (covalent) radius $r_\text{H} = 0.37 \times 10^{-10}\,\text{m}$, and the separation distance between two atoms is $d_{\text{H}_2} = 0.74 \times 10^{-10}\,\text{m}$. Assume that the molecules are homogenous and in thermal equilibrium. *Estimate* the frequency at which they will radiate due to molecular rotational excitation.

## Solution

If the two hydrogen atoms in a hydrogen molecule (as presented in Figure 30.1) can be considered material points, then corresponding to the two rotation possibilities of the molecule (the molecule has two degrees of freedom $f = 2$, corresponding to rotations around the OX and OZ axis), the result is that the molecule's moment of inertia is:

$$I = 2m_\text{H}\left(\frac{d_{\text{H}_2}}{2}\right)^2 = \frac{1}{2}m_\text{H}d_{\text{H}_2}^2$$
$$= \frac{1}{2} \times 1.67 \times 10^{-27}\,\text{kg} \times (0.74 \times 10^{-10}\,\text{m})^2,$$

since the rotation of the two material points around the OY axis has no physical interpretation;

$$I = 0.46 \times 10^{-47}\,\text{kg} \cdot \text{m}^2.$$

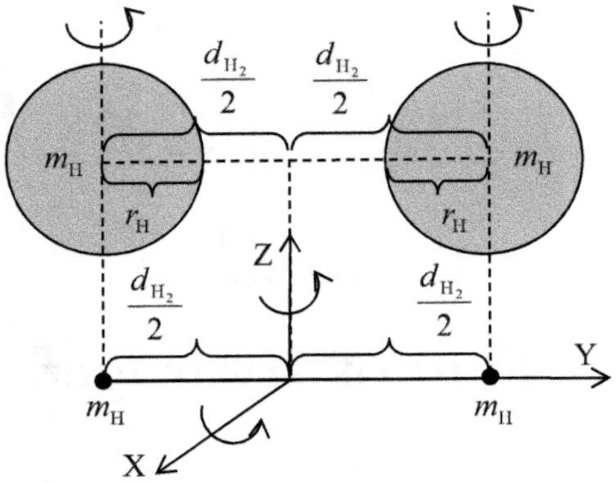


**Fig. 30.1**

Thus, in conditions of thermal equilibrium, the kinetic energy corresponding to the rotation motion of each hydrogen molecule is:

$$\frac{1}{2}I\omega^2 = 2 \times \frac{1}{2}kT = kT = \frac{1}{2}I4\pi^2 v^2 = 2\pi^2 I v^2,$$

as, according to the law of energy equipartition, the energy corresponding to each degree of freedom is $\varepsilon = kT/2$;

$$v = \sqrt{\frac{kT}{2\pi^2 I}} = \sqrt{\frac{1.381 \times 10^{-23}\,\frac{\text{J}}{\text{K}} \times 115\,\text{K}}{2 \times 3.14 \times 3.14 \times 0.46 \times 10^{-47}\,\text{kg}\cdot\text{m}^2}};$$

$$v = \sqrt{\frac{1.381 \times 115 \times 10^{-23}}{2 \times 3.14 \times 3.14 \times 0.46 \times 10^{-47}}\,\frac{1}{\text{s}}} = 4.18 \times 10^{12}\,\text{Hz}.$$

If the two hydrogen atoms cannot be considered material points, according to Steiner's theorem, the momentum of the hydrogen molecule is:

$$I = 2\left[\frac{2}{5}m_{\text{H}}r_{\text{H}}^2 + m_{\text{H}}\left(\frac{d_{\text{H}_2}}{2}\right)^2\right];$$

$$d_{\text{H}_2} = 2r_{\text{H}}; \quad I = \frac{14}{5}m_{\text{H}}r_{\text{H}}^2.$$

# Problem 31

# Mass of a Cosmic Object

The mass density of an object is inversely proportional to the radial distance from the center of the object with a factor of proportionality $\alpha = 5.0 \times 10^{13}\,\mathrm{kg/m^2}$. If the escape velocity at the surface of the object is $\mathrm{v}_0 = 1.5 \times 10^4\,\mathrm{m/s}$, *calculate* the total mass of the object, if the gravitational constant is $K = 6.6738 \times 10^{-11}\,\mathrm{Nm^2\,kg^{-2}}$.

**Solution**

A satellite of mass $m$ is able to escape from the surface of the above-mentioned cosmic object if the total energy of the system (satellite–cosmic body) at the initial moment of the escape is:

$$E_{\mathrm{total}} = \frac{1}{2}m\mathrm{v}_0^2 - G\frac{mM}{R} = 0,$$

where $M$ is the mass of the cosmic object and $R$ is the radius of the cosmic object;

$$R = \frac{2KM}{\mathrm{v}_0^2}.$$

If at a distance $r$ from the center of the cosmic object its density is $\rho(r) = \frac{\alpha}{r}$, then inside a very thin spherical layer, $\mathrm{d}r$, presented in Figure 31.1, we can consider that the density is constant, that is, $\rho(r) = \alpha r$. Consequently, the mass of the spherical layer of $\mathrm{d}r$ is:

$$\mathrm{d}m = \rho(r) \times \mathrm{d}V,$$

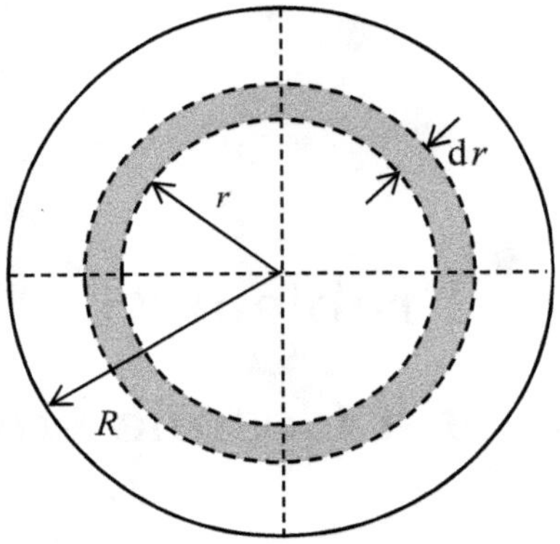


**Fig. 31.1**

where d$V$ is the volume of the spherical layer;

$$\mathrm{d}V = \frac{4\pi}{3}(r+\mathrm{d}r)^3 - \frac{4\pi}{3}r^3 \approx 4\pi r^2\mathrm{d}r;$$

$$\mathrm{d}m = \rho(r)4\pi r^2\mathrm{d}r = \frac{\alpha}{r}4\pi r^2\mathrm{d}r = 4\pi\alpha r\,\mathrm{d}r.$$

Thus, the mass of the cosmic object is:

$$M = \int_0^R \mathrm{d}m = 4\pi\alpha\int_0^R r\mathrm{d}r = 2\pi\alpha R^2;$$

$$R = \frac{2KM}{\mathrm{v}_0^2}; \quad M = 2\pi\alpha R^2 = 2\pi\alpha\frac{4K^2M^2}{\mathrm{v}_0^4};$$

$$M = \frac{\mathrm{v}_0^4}{8\pi\alpha K^2} \approx 9.1\times 10^{21}\,\mathrm{kg}.$$

# Problem 32

# Travel Time of a Proton

A proton with a kinetic energy $E_k = 1\,\text{GeV}$ propagates out from the surface of the Sun towards the Earth. Neglecting the magnetic field of the Sun, calculate the travel time of the proton as seen from the Earth.

## Solution

Since the total energy of the proton is

$$E = E_0 + E_k; \quad mc^2 = m_0c^2 + E_k,$$

the result is:

$$\frac{m_0c^2}{\sqrt{1-\frac{v^2}{c^2}}} = m_0c^2 + E_k; \quad \frac{1}{\sqrt{1-\frac{v^2}{c^2}}} = 1 + \frac{E_k}{E_0};$$

$$m_0 = m_H = 1.67 \times 10^{-27}\,\text{kg};$$

$$1\,\text{eV} = 1.607 \times 10^{-19}\,\text{J};$$

$$E_0 = 1.67 \times 10^{-27}\,\text{kg} \times 9 \times 10^{16}\,\frac{\text{m}^2}{\text{s}^2} = 15.03 \times 10^{-11}\,\text{J};$$

$$E_0 = 15.03 \times 10^{-11} \times \frac{1\,\text{eV}}{1.607 \times 10^{-19}} = 9.352 \times 10^8\,\text{eV} \approx 935\,\text{MeV};$$

$$\frac{1}{\sqrt{1-\frac{v^2}{c^2}}} = 1 + \frac{1000\,\text{Mev}}{935\,\text{MeV}} \approx 2.07;$$

$$\sqrt{1 - \frac{\mathrm{v}^2}{c^2}} \approx 0.5; \quad 1 - \frac{\mathrm{v}^2}{c^2} = 0,25; \quad \mathrm{v} \approx 0.87 \times c;$$

$$\tau = \frac{d_{\mathrm{SE}}}{\mathrm{v}} = \frac{1.5 \times 10^{11}\,\mathrm{m}}{0.87 \times 3 \times 10^8\,\frac{\mathrm{m}}{s}} = 574\,\mathrm{s} \approx 9.56\,\mathrm{min}.$$

# Problem 33

# Power of the Tide

The volcanic activity on the Io satellite, which has a synchronous orbital period, was proposed to be the result of tidal heating, mainly from Jupiter. The resultant tidal force on a body is the difference in gravitational force experienced by the near and far sides of that body due to another body. Measurements of the surface distortion of Io via satellite radar altimeter mapping indicate that the surface rises and falls by up to $d_{\text{max}} = 100\,\text{m}$ during one half-orbit. Only the surface layers will move by this amount. Interior layers within Io will move by a smaller amount, and thus we assume that on average the entire mass of Io is moved by $d = 50\,\text{m}$. Consider Io to be two hemispheres each treated as a point mass. *Calculate* the average power of the tidal heating on Io.

*Hint*: you can use the following approximation: $(1+x)^n \approx 1+nx$, for a small $x$.

The following are considered known: the mass of Io, $M_{\text{Io}} = 8.931938 \times 10^{22}\,\text{kg}$; the perijove distance, $r_{\text{Per}} = 420000\,\text{km}$; the apojove distance, $r_{\text{Apo}} = 423400\,\text{km}$; the orbital period of Io, $T_{\text{Io}} = 152853\,\text{s}$; the radius of Io, $R_{\text{Io}} = 1821.6\,\text{km}$.

### Solution

The gravitational interactions of Io with Jupiter and with the other satellites of Jupiter presented in Figure 33.1 cause strong tides.

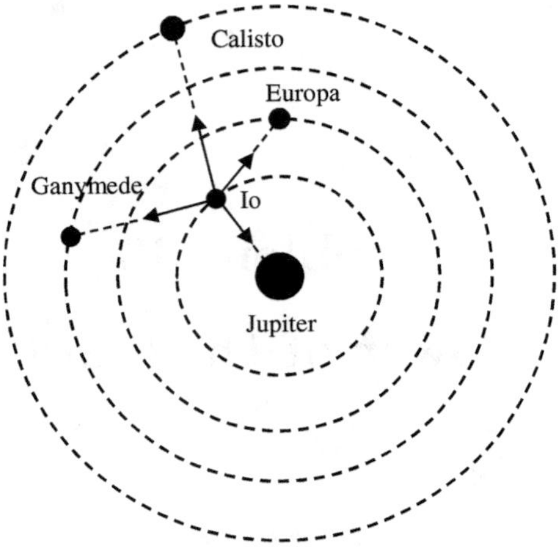


**Fig. 33.1**

These phenomena move the internal layers of Io, and thus the heat resulting from such friction melts Io's internal rocks. The melt substance maintains high volcanic activity associated with strong seismic activity.

The resonances of the satellites' orbits are presented in Figure 33.2. Ganymede moves on its orbit in resonance with the satellites Europa and Io, as follows: for each orbit traveled by Ganymede around Jupiter, Europa moves twice around Jupiter and Io orbits four times around Jupiter. As a consequence, the orbits of Jupiter's satellites are synchronous.

The problem states that the resultant tidal force, $F_{\text{tidal}}$, applied to Io, which is ultimately responsible for Io's intense volcanic activity, equals the difference between the gravitational attraction force exerted by Jupiter on Io's half facing Jupiter and the gravitational attraction force exerted by Jupiter on the half of Io opposed to Jupiter, as presented in Figure 33.3.

If $r$ is the distance between the centers of Io and Jupiter, $R_{\text{Io}}$ is the radius of Io and $x_{\text{MC}} = \frac{3}{8}R_{\text{Io}}$ is the coordinate of the mass center of Io's hemisphere (representing the point where the gravitational attraction force exert by Jupiter is applied), the result is:

$$F_{\text{tidal}} = F_{(r-x_{\text{MC}})} - F_{(r+x_{\text{MC}})} = K\frac{\frac{M_{\text{Io}}}{2}M_{\text{J}}}{(r-x_{\text{MC}})^2} - K\frac{\frac{M_{\text{Io}}}{2}M_{\text{J}}}{(r+x_{\text{MC}})^2};$$

$$F_{\text{tidal}} = K\frac{M_{\text{Io}}M_{\text{J}}}{2\left(r - x_{\text{MC}}\right)^2} - K\frac{M_{\text{Io}}M_{\text{J}}}{2\left(r + x_{\text{MC}}\right)^2};$$

$$F_{\text{tidal}} = K\frac{M_{\text{Io}}M_{\text{J}}}{2r^2}\left[\frac{1}{(1 - \frac{x_{\text{MC}}}{\text{r}})^2} - \frac{1}{(1 + \frac{x_{\text{MC}}}{r})^2}\right];$$

$$F_{\text{tidal}} = K\frac{M_{\text{Io}}M_{\text{J}}}{2r^2}\left[\left(1 - \frac{x_{\text{MC}}}{r}\right)^{-2} - \left(1 + \frac{x_{\text{MC}}}{r}\right)^{-2}\right];$$

$$F_{\text{tidal}} = K\frac{M_{\text{Io}}M_{\text{J}}}{2r^2}\left[\left(1 + 2\frac{x_{\text{MC}}}{r}\right) - \left(1 - 2\frac{x_{\text{MC}}}{r}\right)\right];$$

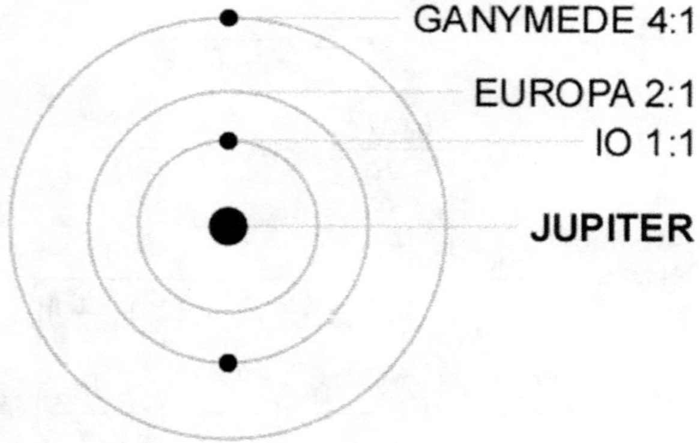


**Fig. 33.2**

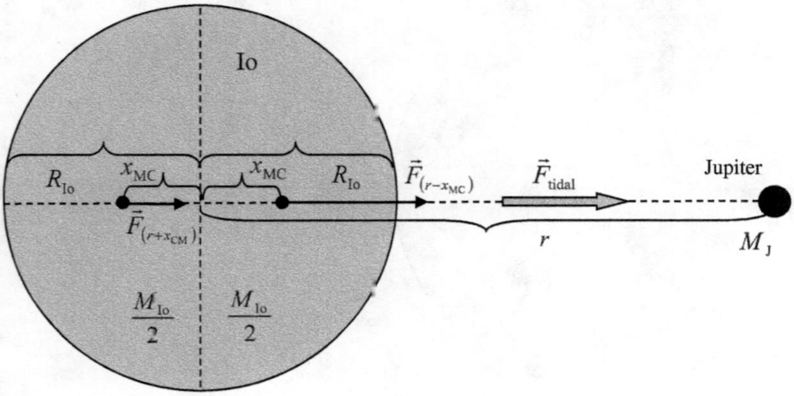


**Fig. 33.3**

$$F_{\text{tidal}} = 2K\frac{M_{\text{Io}}M_{\text{J}}}{r^3}x_{\text{MC}}; \quad x_{\text{MC}} = \frac{3}{8}R_{\text{Io}};$$

$$F_{\text{tidal}} = \frac{3}{4}K\frac{M_{\text{Io}}M_{\text{J}}}{r^3}R_{\text{Io}}.$$

Let us consider that the points where the gravitational forces exerted by Jupiter are applied on each of Io's hemispheres are located at the surface of Io. If $r$ is the distance between Io's and Jupiter's centers and $R_{\text{Io}}$ is Io's radius, as presented in Figure 33.4, the result is:

$$F_{\text{tidal}} = F_{(r-R_{\text{Io}})} - F_{(r+R_{\text{Io}})} = K\frac{\frac{M_{\text{Io}}}{2}M_{\text{J}}}{(r-R_{\text{Io}})^2} - K\frac{\frac{M_{\text{Io}}}{2}M_{\text{J}}}{(r+R_{\text{Io}})^2};$$

$$F_{\text{tidal}} = K\frac{M_{\text{Io}}M_{\text{J}}}{2(r-R_{\text{Io}})^2} - K\frac{M_{\text{Io}}M_{\text{J}}}{2\,(r+R_{\text{Io}})^2};$$

$$F_{\text{tidal}} = K\frac{M_{\text{Io}}M_{\text{J}}}{2r^2}\left[\frac{1}{\left(1-\frac{R_{\text{Io}}}{r}\right)^2} - \frac{1}{\left(1+\frac{R_{\text{Io}}}{\text{r}}\right)^2}\right];$$

$$F_{\text{tidal}} = K\frac{M_{\text{Io}}M_{\text{J}}}{2r^2}\left[\left(1-\frac{R_{\text{Io}}}{r}\right)^{-2} - \left(1+\frac{R_{\text{Io}}}{r}\right)^{-2}\right];$$

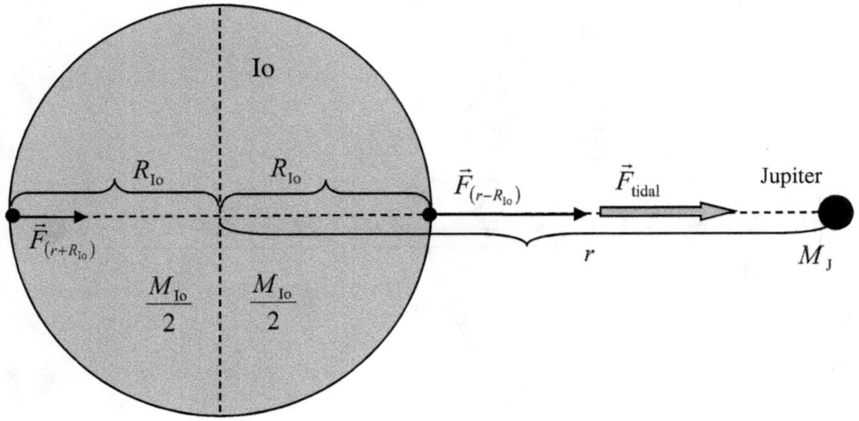


**Fig. 33.4**

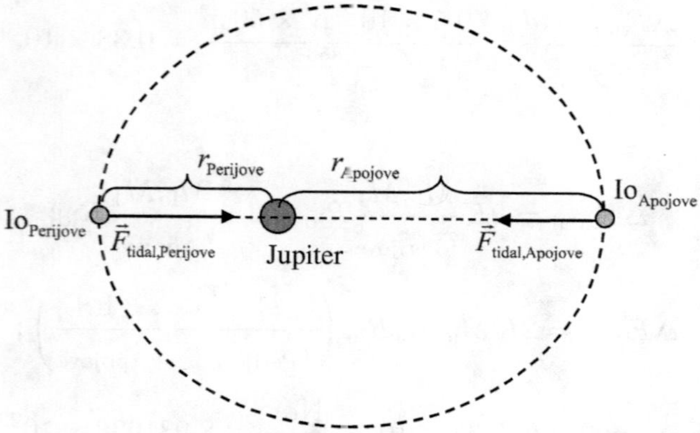


**Fig. 33.5**

$$F_{\text{tidal}} = K\frac{M_{\text{Io}}M_{\text{J}}}{2r^2}\left[\left(1+2\frac{R_{\text{Io}}}{r}\right)-\left(1-2\frac{R_{\text{Io}}}{r}\right)\right];$$

$$F_{\text{tidal}} = 2K\frac{M_{\text{Io}}M_{\text{J}}}{r^3}R_{\text{Io}}.$$

**a)** According to the values stated in the problem and using Figure 33.5, the result is:

$$\Delta F_{\text{tidal}} = F_{\text{tidal,Perijove}} - F_{\text{tidal,Apojove}};$$

$$\Delta F_{\text{tidal}} = \frac{3}{4}K\frac{M_{\text{Io}}M_{\text{J}}}{r^3_{\text{Perijove}}}R_{\text{Io}} - \frac{3}{4}K\frac{M_{\text{Io}}M_{\text{J}}}{r^3_{\text{Apojove}}}R_{\text{Io}};$$

$$\Delta F_{\text{tidal}} = \frac{3}{4}KM_{\text{Io}}M_{\text{J}}R_{\text{Io}}\left(\frac{1}{r^3_{\text{Perijove}}}-\frac{1}{r^3_{\text{Apojove}}}\right);$$

$$\Delta F_{\text{tidal}} = \frac{3}{4}\times 6.6738\times 10^{-11}\,\frac{\text{Nm}^2}{\text{kg}^2}\times 8.931938\times 10^{22}\,\text{kg}$$
$$\times 1.89813\times 10^{27}\,\text{kg}\times 1821.6\times 10^3$$
$$\times\left(\frac{1}{(42\times 10^7)^3}-\frac{1}{(42.34\times 10^7)}\right)\frac{1}{\text{m}^3} = 0.5\times 10^{19}\,\text{N};$$

$$\overline{P} = \frac{\Delta F_{\text{tidal}} \times d}{\frac{T_{\text{Io}}}{2}} = \frac{0.5 \times 10^{19} N \times 50\,\text{m}}{\frac{152853\,\text{s}}{2}} = 0.38 \times 10^{16}\,\text{W}.$$

**b)**

$$\Delta F_{\text{tidal}} = 2K\frac{M_{\text{Io}}M_{\text{J}}}{r^3_{\text{Perijove}}}R_{\text{Io}} - 2K\frac{M_{\text{Io}}M_{\text{J}}}{r^3_{\text{Apojove}}}R_{\text{Io}};$$

$$\Delta F_{\text{tidal}} = 2KM_{\text{Io}}M_{\text{J}}R_{\text{Io}}\left(\frac{1}{r^3_{\text{Perijove}}} - \frac{1}{r^3_{\text{Apojove}}}\right);$$

$$\Delta F_{\text{tidal}} = 2 \times 6.6738 \times 10^{-11}\,\frac{\text{Nm}^2}{\text{kg}^2} \times 8.931938 \times 10^{22}\,\text{kg}$$
$$\times 1.89813 \times 10^{27}\,\text{kg} \times 1821.6 \times 10^3 \times \left(\frac{1}{(42 \times 10^7)^3}\right.$$
$$\left.-\frac{1}{(42.34 \times 10^7)}\right)\frac{1}{\text{m}^3} = 1.33 \times 10^{19}\,\text{N};$$

$$\overline{P} = \frac{\Delta F_{\text{tidal}} \times d}{\frac{T_{\text{Io}}}{2}} = \frac{1.33 \times 10^{19}\text{N} \times 50\,\text{m}}{\frac{152853\,\text{s}}{2}} = 0.88 \times 10^{16}\,\text{W}.$$

# Problem 34

# Static Universe

Suppose we live in a static and infinitely large universe where the average density of stars is $n = 10^9\,\mathrm{Mpc}^{-3}$ and the average stellar radius is equal to the solar radius. Assume that standard Euclidean geometry holds true in this universe. *How far*, on average, could you see in any direction before your line of sight strikes a star? Please write your answer in Mpc.

### Solution

As presented in the problem, let's consider that the universe is full of stars whose average radius is equal to the Sun's radius $\overline{R} = R_{\mathrm{S}}$. To determine the average distance reached by a radio signal emitted by an observer on the Earth, let's consider a long cylinder. The observer's view line will be considered to be along the cylinder's axis, as presented in Figure 34.1.

If in this cylinder there is a star of radius $\overline{R}$ whose center is at a distance $d < \overline{R}$ from the cylinder's axis, then the observer's view line crosses the star's spherical surface.

For an average distance $\overline{L}$, the cylindrical volume that contains such stars is $V = \pi\overline{R}^2\overline{L}$. If the density of stars in this universe is $n$, the volume $V = \pi\overline{R}^2\overline{L}$ has to meet the condition

$$n = \frac{N}{V} = \frac{N}{\pi\overline{R}^2\overline{L}}$$

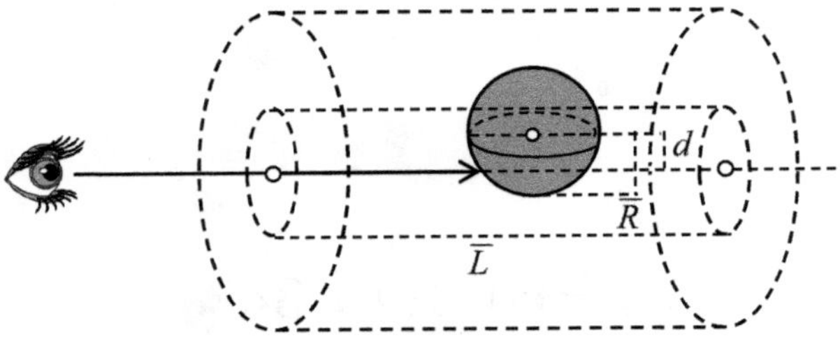


**Fig. 34.1**

in order to have a single star within it, that is,

$$N = \pi \overline{R}^2 \overline{L} n = 1.$$

Thus, the average distance is:

$$\overline{L} = \frac{1}{\pi \overline{R}^2 n};$$

$$\overline{R}_{\text{star}} = \overline{R} = R_{\text{S}} = 6.96 \times 10^8\,\text{m};$$

$$1\,\text{Mpc} = 10^6 \times 3.086 \times 10^{16}\,\text{m} = 3.086 \times 10^{22}\,\text{m};$$

$$\overline{R} = 6.96 \times 10^8\,\text{m} = 6.96 \times 10^8 \frac{1\,\text{Mpc}}{3.086 \times 10^{22}} = 2.25 \times 10^{-14}\,\text{Mpc};$$

$$\overline{L} = \frac{1}{3.14 \times (2.25 \times 10^{-14}\,\text{Mpc})^2 \times 10^9\,\text{Mpc}^{-3}} = 6.3 \times 10^{17}\,\text{Mpc}.$$

# Problem 35

# Flying from Lima to Yogyakarta

An airplane was flying from Lima, capital of Peru ($\varphi_1 = 12°2'$ S; $\lambda_1 = 77°1'$ W), to Yogyakarta in Indonesia ($\varphi_2 = 7°47'$ S; $\lambda_2 = 110°26'$ E), near the venue of the 9th IOAA (Figure 35.1). The airplane chose the shortest flight path from Lima to Yogyakarta. *Find* the latitude of the southernmost point of the flight path.

For the spherical triangle in Figure 35.2:

$$\sin a \sin B = \sin b \sin A;$$

$$\sin a \sin B = \sin b \sin A;$$

$$\cos a = \cos b \cos c + \sin b \sin c \cos A.$$

## Solution

### a) *Method 1*

On the sphere representing the Earth in Figure 35.3, the following elements are marked: the Greenwich meridian, the Equator and the Earth's rotation axis; Lima and Yogyakarta, localized by the position vectors $\vec{r}_{\rm L}$ and $\vec{r}_{\rm Y}$, respectively, and the geographic coordinates corresponding to these locations; the Cartesian axis system XYZ attached to the Earth, having its origin in the center of the Earth, O; the great circle C the plane moves along on the shortest trajectory between Lima and Yogyakarta; the flight trajectory's plane $\Pi(\mathrm{LOY})$;

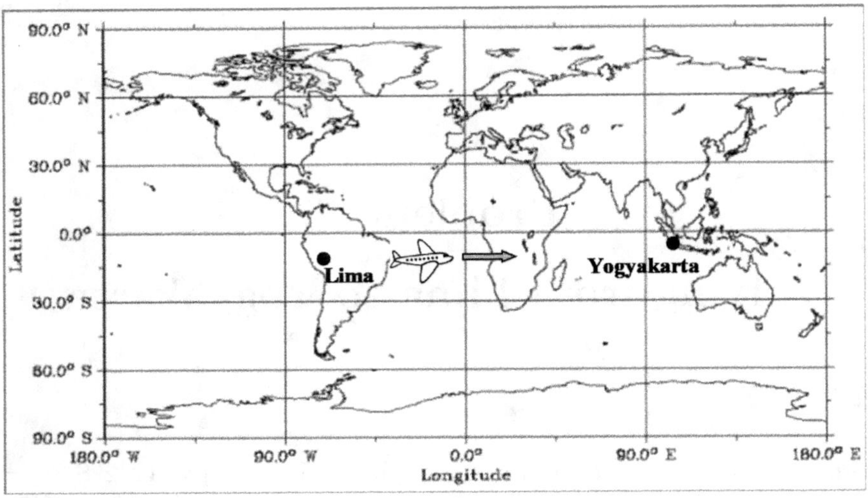


**Fig. 35.1**

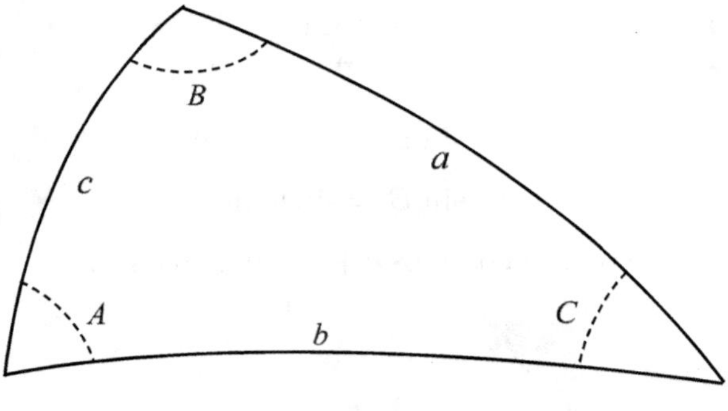


**Fig. 35.2**

the cardinal (geographic) points; the unit vector (versor) normal to the flight trajectory's plane $\vec{n}_{(\mathrm{LOY})}$.

Knowing that for the Equator $z = 0$, considering that the Earth's radius is $R_{\mathrm{E}} = 1$, and using the numeric information offered in the problem, we can determine the Cartesian coordinates of the two cities, Lima and Yogyakarta:

$$\vec{r}_{\mathrm{L}} = x_1\vec{i} + y_1\vec{j} + z_1\vec{k}; \quad r_{\mathrm{L}} = R_{\mathrm{Earth}} = 1;$$

$$\vec{r}_{\mathrm{L}} = \cos\varphi_1 \cos\lambda_1\vec{i} - \cos\varphi_1 \sin\lambda_1\vec{j} - \sin\varphi_1\vec{k};$$

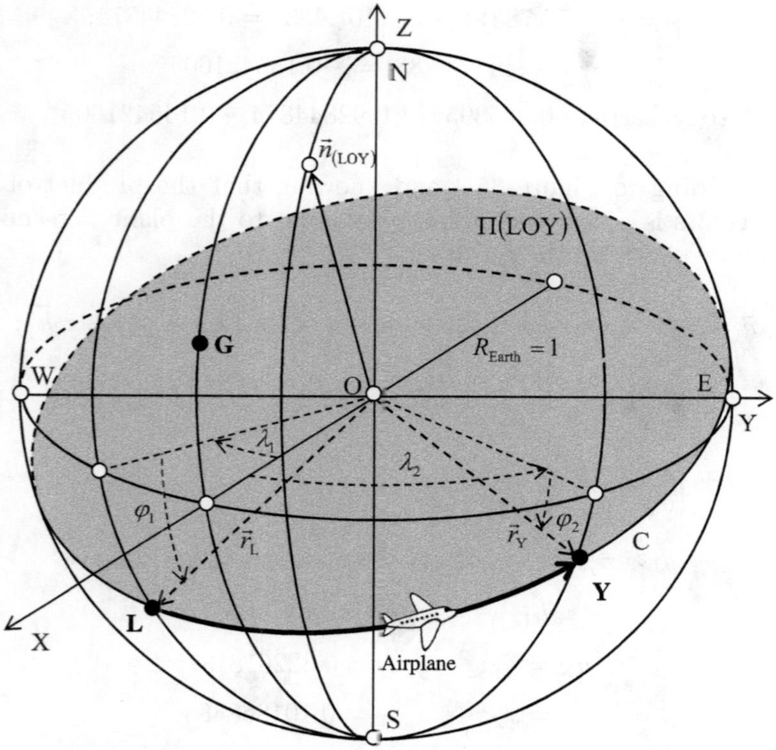


**Fig. 35.3**

$$x_1 = \cos\varphi_1 \cos\lambda_1; \quad y_1 = -\cos\varphi_1 \sin\lambda_1; \quad z_1 = -\sin\varphi_1;$$

$$x_1 = \cos(12^\circ.033) \times \cos(77^\circ.016) = 0.219742234;$$

$$y_1 = -\cos(12^\circ.033) \times \sin(77^\circ.016) = -0.953022304;$$

$$z_1 = -\sin(12^\circ.033) = -0.208475028;$$

$$\text{Lima}\,(0.219742234; -0.953022304; -0.208475028);$$

$$\vec{r}_Y = x_2\vec{i} + y_2\vec{j} + z_2\vec{k}; \; r_Y = R_{\text{Earth}} = 1;$$

$$\vec{r}_Y = \cos\varphi_2 \cos\lambda_2\vec{i} + \cos\varphi_2 \sin\lambda_2\vec{j} - \sin\varphi_2\vec{k};$$

$$x_2 = \cos\varphi_2 \cos\lambda_2; \quad y_2 = \cos\varphi_2 \sin\lambda_2; \quad z_2 = -\sin\varphi_2;$$

$$x_2 = \cos(7^\circ.783) \times \cos(110^\circ.433) = -0.345895829;$$

$$y_2 = \cos(7^\circ.783) \times \sin(110^\circ.433) = 0.92844874;$$

$$z_2 = -\sin(7^\circ.783) = -0.135421605;$$

$$\text{Yogyakarta}\,(-0.345895829; 0.92844874; -0.135421605).$$

According to Figure 35.4 and knowing that the product of the two vectors is a new vector, perpendicular to the plane determined by the two vectors, the result is:

$$\vec{n}_{(\mathrm{LOY})} = \vec{r}_{\mathrm{L}} \times \vec{r}_{\mathrm{Y}} = \left(x_1\vec{i} + y_1\vec{j} + z_1\vec{k}\right) \times \left(x_2\vec{i} + y_2\vec{j} + z_2\vec{k}\right);$$

$$r_{\mathrm{L}} = r_{\mathrm{Y}} = R_{\mathrm{E}} = 1; \quad n_{(\mathrm{POY})} = 1;$$

$$\vec{n}_{(\mathrm{LOY})} = \begin{vmatrix} \vec{i} & \vec{j} & \vec{k} \\ x_1 & y_1 & z_1 \\ x_2 & y_2 & z_2 \end{vmatrix}$$

$$= (y_1z_2 - y_2z_1)\,\vec{i} + (x_2z_1 - x_1z_2)\,\vec{j} + (x_1y_2 - x_2y_1)\,\vec{k};$$

$$\vec{n}_{(\mathrm{LOY})} = n_{\mathrm{X}}\vec{i} + n_{\mathrm{Y}}\vec{j} + n_{\mathrm{Z}}\vec{k};$$

$$n_{\mathrm{X}} = y_1z_2 - y_2z_1 = 0.322618187;$$

$$n_{\mathrm{Y}} = x_2z_1 - x_1z_2 = 0.101868488;$$

$$n_{\mathrm{Z}} = x_1y_2 - x_2y_1 = -0.125627039;$$

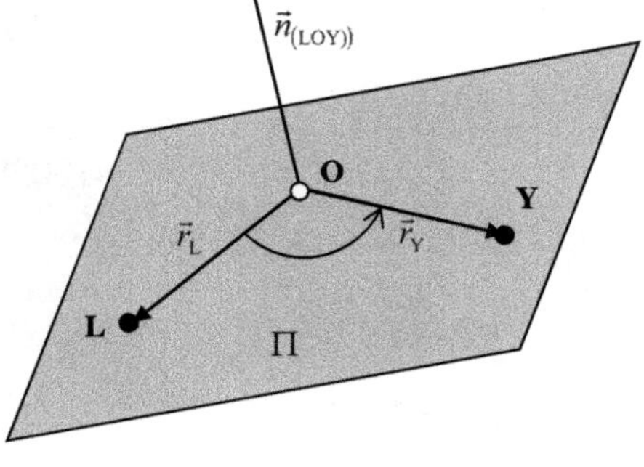


**Fig. 35.4**

The Π plane, including Lima, Yogyakarta and the Earth's center, O (also the origin of the Cartesian axis system XYZ) is perpendicular to the unit vector, that is, the vector

$$\vec{n}_{(\mathrm{LOY})} = n_{\mathrm{X}}\vec{i} + n_{\mathrm{Y}}\vec{j} + n_{\mathrm{Z}}\vec{k},$$

which satisfies the following equation:

$$n_{\mathrm{X}}x + n_{\mathrm{Y}}y + n_{\mathrm{Z}}z = 0;$$

$$y = -\frac{n_{\mathrm{X}}}{n_{\mathrm{Y}}}x - \frac{n_{\mathrm{Z}}}{n_{\mathrm{Y}}}z;$$

$$\frac{n_{\mathrm{X}}}{n_{\mathrm{Y}}} = a_0 = 3.167006729; \quad \frac{n_{\mathrm{Z}}}{n_{\mathrm{Y}}} = c_0 = -1.233227679;$$

$$y = -a_0 x - c_0 z,$$

representing the equation of the aircraft's trajectory plane, Π, in Cartesian coordinates.

The Earth's spherical surface and the aircraft's trajectory plane Π have the following equations:

$$x^2 + y^2 + z^2 = 1; \quad y = -a_0 x - c_0 z.$$

From the intersection of these curves it follows that:

$$x^2 + (-a_0 x - c_0 z)^2 + z^2 = 1;$$

$$x^2 + a_0^2 x^2 + 2a_0 c_0 xz + c_0^2 z^2 + z^2 = 1;$$

$$\left(1 + a_0^2\right) x^2 + 2a_0 c_0 xz + \left(1 + c_0^2\right) z^2 - 1 = 0,$$

representing the equation of the great circle C that contains the aircraft's trajectory flying from Lima to Yogyakarta on the shortest path.

To find the aircraft's southernmost point during the flight L → Y, let us consider a plane $z = m$ parallel to the Equator that intersects the great circle C at two points. The intersection can either take place at a single point (superior or inferior), or not take place at all.

Under these conditions, using the equation of the circle C, it results that:

$$\left(1+a_0^2\right)x^2+2a_0c_0xz+\left(1+c_0^2\right)z^2-1=0;$$

$$z=m;$$

$$\left(1+a_0^2\right)x^2+2a_0c_0mx+\left(1+c_0^2\right)m^2-1=0.$$

The roots of this equation represent the values of coordinate $x$ corresponding to the intersection points between the circle C and the plane $z=m$.

The plane $z = m$ touches the great circle C at a single point if the above equation has a double root, which happens only if the equation's discriminant is zero, that is:

$$\Delta=B^2-4AC;$$

$$\Delta=(2a_0c_0m)^2-4\left(1+a_0\right)\left[\left(1+c_0^2\right)m^2-1\right]$$
$$=4+4a_0^2-\left(4+4a_0^2+4c_0^2\right)m^2;$$

$$\Delta=0;$$

$$m^2=\frac{1+a_0^2}{1+a_0^2+c_0^2};\quad m=\pm\sqrt{\frac{1+a_0^2}{1+a_0^2+c_0^2}}=\pm 0.937456262;$$

$$z=-0.937456262;$$

$$z=-\sin\varphi_{\max};$$

$$\sin\varphi_{\max}=0.937456262;$$

$$\varphi_{\max}\approx 69^\circ 37'\,\mathrm{S},$$

representing the extreme southern latitude during the aircraft's flight from Lima to Yogyakarta, on the shortest trajectory.

**b) *Method 2***

For the LSY spherical triangle in Figure 35.5, the cosine formulas for the edges are:

$$\cos b=\cos a\cos c+\sin a\sin c\cos B;$$

$$\cos b=\cos\left(90^\circ-\varphi_1\right)\cos\left(90^\circ-\varphi_2\right)+\sin\left(90^\circ-\varphi_1\right)\sin$$
$$\times\ \left(90^\circ-\varphi\right)\cos\left(\lambda_1+\lambda_2\right);$$

$$\cos b = \sin\varphi_1 \sin\varphi_2 + \cos\varphi_1 \cos\varphi_2 \cos(\lambda_1 + \lambda_2)\,;$$

$$\cos a = \cos b \cos c + \sin b \sin c \cos A;$$

$$\cos(90^\circ - \varphi_1) = \cos b \cos(90^\circ - \varphi_2) + \sin b \sin(90^\circ - \varphi_2)\cos A;$$

$$\sin\varphi_1 = \cos b \sin\varphi_2 + \sin b \cos\varphi_2 \cos A;$$

$$\cos A = \frac{\sin\varphi_1 - \cos b \sin\varphi_2}{\sin b \cos\varphi_2};$$

$$\cos c = \cos b \cos a + \sin b \sin a \cos C;$$

$$\cos(90^\circ - \varphi_2) = \cos b \cos(90^\circ - \varphi_1) + \sin b \sin(90^\circ - \varphi_1)\cos C;$$

$$\sin\varphi_2 = \cos b \sin\varphi_1 + \sin b \cos\varphi_1 \cos C;$$

$$\cos C = \frac{\sin\varphi_2 - \cos b \sin\varphi_1}{\sin b \cos\varphi_1}.$$

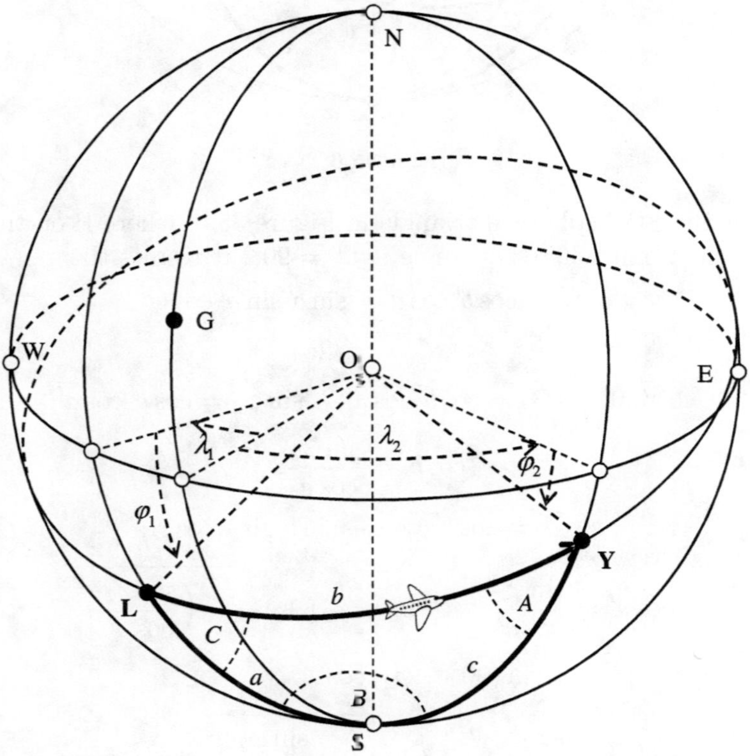


**Fig. 35.5**

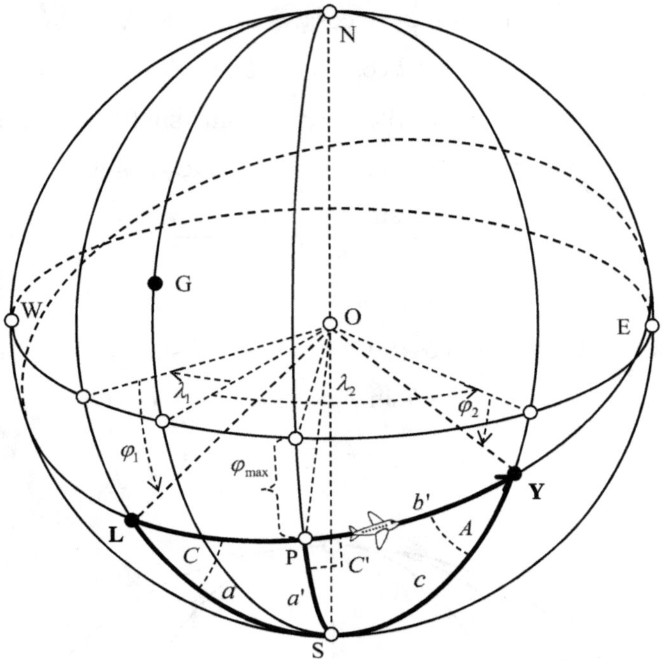


**Fig. 35.6**

For the SPY spherical triangle in Figure 35.6, where P on the LY arc is the point where the angle is $C' = 90°$, it results that:

$$\cos c = \cos b' \cos a' + \sin b' \sin a' \cos C';$$

$$C' = \pi/2;$$

$$\cos(90° - \varphi_2) = \cos b' \cos a'; \quad \sin\varphi_2 = \cos b' \cos a';$$

$$\cos b' = \frac{\sin\varphi_2}{\cos a'};$$

$$\cos a' = \cos b' \cos c + \sin b' \sin c \cos A;$$

$$\cos a' = \frac{\sin\varphi_2}{\cos a'} \cos(90° - \varphi_2) + \sqrt{1 - \left(\frac{\sin\varphi_2}{\cos a'}\right)^2}$$

$$\times \sin(90° - \varphi_2) \cos A;$$

$$\cos a' = \frac{\sin\varphi_2}{\cos a'} \sin\varphi_2 + \sqrt{1 - \left(\frac{\sin\varphi_2}{\cos a'}\right)^2} \cos\varphi_2 \cos A;$$

$$\cos a' = x;$$

$$x = \frac{\sin\varphi_2}{x}\sin\varphi_2 + \sqrt{1 - \left(\frac{\sin\varphi_2}{\cos a'}\right)^2}\cos\varphi_2\cos A;$$

$$x = \frac{\sin^2\varphi_2}{x} + \sqrt{\frac{x^2 - \sin^2\varphi_2}{x^2}}\cos\varphi_2\cos A;$$

$$x - \frac{\sin^2\varphi_2}{x} = \sqrt{\frac{x^2 - \sin^2\varphi_2}{x^2}}\cos\varphi_2\cos A;$$

$$\frac{x^2 - \sin^2\varphi_2}{x} = \sqrt{\frac{x^2 - \sin^2\varphi_2}{x^2}}\cos\varphi_2\cos A;$$

$$x^2 - \sin^2\varphi_2 = \sqrt{x^2 - \sin^2\varphi_2}\cos\varphi_2\cos A;$$

$$y = x^2 - \sin^2\varphi_2;$$

$$y = \sqrt{y}\cos\varphi_2\cos A; y^2 = y\cos\varphi_2\cos A;$$

$$y = \cos\varphi_2\cos A;$$

$$x^2 = \sin^2\varphi_2 + \cos\varphi_2\cos A;$$

$$x = \sqrt{\sin^2\varphi_2 + \cos\varphi_2\cos A} = \cos a';$$

$$\cos b = \sin\varphi_1\sin\varphi_2 + \cos\varphi_1\cos\varphi_2\cos(\lambda_1 + \lambda_2);$$

$$\cos A = \frac{\sin\varphi_1 - \cos b\sin\varphi_2}{\sin b\cos\varphi_2};$$

$$\varphi_{\max} = 90° - a' \approx 69°37'\,\mathrm{S}.$$

**c) *Method 3***

From the SPY spherical triangle, the result is:

$$\sin a'\sin C' = \sin c\sin A; \quad \sin a'\sin 90° = \sin(90° - \varphi_2)\sin A;$$

$$\sin a' = \cos\varphi_2\sin A;$$

$$\varphi_{\max} = 90° - a' \approx 69°37'\,\mathrm{S}.$$

# Problem 36

# A Planet and Its Moon

A moon is orbiting a planet such that the orbit is perpendicular to the surface of the planet where an observer is standing (Figure 36.1). After some necessary scaling, suppose the orbit satisfies the following equation:

$$9\left(\frac{x}{2}+\frac{\sqrt{3}y}{2}-4\right)^2+25\left(-\frac{\sqrt{3}x}{2}+\frac{y}{2}\right)^2=225.$$

Let $r$ be the radius of the moon. Assume that the period of rotation of the planet is much larger than the orbital period of the moon. *Determine* $\tan\frac{\theta_0}{2}$, where $\theta_0$ is the value of the elevation angle $\theta$ for the moment when the moon looks largest to the observer.

### Solution

The measurement of the angle $\varphi$ between the apsides' line (pariastron–apastron) and the OX line in the image drawn for the problem finds a value of $\varphi = 60^\circ = \pi/3$. By rotating the elliptic orbit in the XOY plane with an angle $\varphi$ around the origin O, the standard ellipse presented in Figure 36.2 is obtained. The center of the ellipse on the OX axis is at the point $h = 4$ coordinate units.

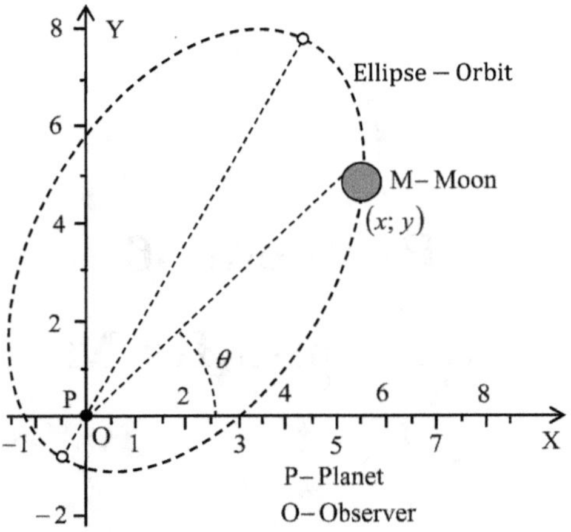


**Fig. 36.1**

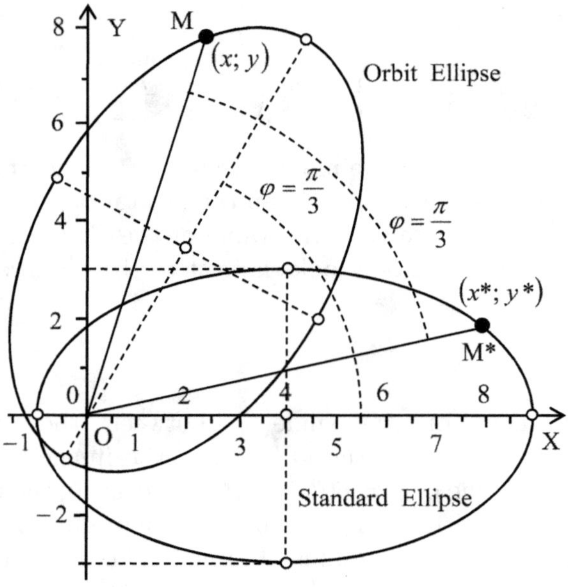


**Fig. 36.2**

Corresponding to the scale used, for the two ellipses the following results are determined:

$$a = 5\,\text{units}; \quad b = 3\,\text{units}; \quad c = \sqrt{a^2 - b^2} = 4\,\text{units};$$

$$e = \sqrt{1 - \frac{b^2}{a^2}} = 0.8.$$

Under these conditions, the $P(x; y)$ point on the elliptic orbit moves to point $P^*(x^*; y^*)$ on the standard ellipse as a consequence of the rotation of the OP segment by an angle $\varphi$ around the origin O. Thus, the standard ellipse equation becomes:

$$\frac{(x^* - h)^2}{a^2} + \frac{(y^* - 0)^2}{b^2} = 1;$$

$$\frac{(x^* - 4)^2}{5^2} + \frac{(y^*)^2}{3^2} = 1.$$

From the equation of the elliptic orbit given in the statement of the problem,

$$9\left(\frac{x}{2} + \frac{\sqrt{3}y}{2} - 4\right)^2 + 25\left(-\frac{\sqrt{3}x}{2} + \frac{y}{2}\right)^2 = 225.$$

The result is:

$$\frac{\left(\frac{x}{2} + \frac{\sqrt{3}y}{2} - 4\right)^2}{5^2} + \frac{\left(-\frac{\sqrt{3}x}{2} + \frac{y}{2}\right)^2}{3^2} = 1;$$

$$\frac{\left(\frac{x}{2} + \frac{\sqrt{3}y}{2} - 4\right)^2}{a^2} + \frac{\left(-\frac{\sqrt{3}x}{2} + \frac{y}{2}\right)^2}{b^2} = 1;$$

$$x^* = \frac{x}{2} + \frac{\sqrt{3}y}{2} \quad y^* = -\frac{\sqrt{3}x}{2} + \frac{y}{2},$$

representing the relations between the coordinates of the points P and $P^*$, respectively, on the two ellipses.

The same relations can also be obtained through the matrix method:

$$\begin{bmatrix} x^* \\ y^* \end{bmatrix} = \begin{bmatrix} \cos\varphi & \sin\varphi \\ -\sin\varphi & \cos\varphi \end{bmatrix} \cdot \begin{bmatrix} x \\ y \end{bmatrix};$$

$$\begin{bmatrix} x^* \\ y^* \end{bmatrix} = \begin{bmatrix} \frac{1}{2} & \frac{\sqrt{3}}{2} \\ -\frac{\sqrt{3}}{2} & \frac{1}{2} \end{bmatrix} \cdot \begin{bmatrix} x \\ y \end{bmatrix} = \begin{bmatrix} \frac{x}{2} + \frac{\sqrt{3}y}{2} \\ -\frac{\sqrt{3}x}{2} + \frac{y}{2} \end{bmatrix}.$$

For any point M* $(x^*;\ y^*)$ on the standard ellipse represented in Figure 36.3, let us calculate the distances corresponding to the foci $F_1\,(0;\ 0)$ and $F_2\,(8;\ 0)$:

$$d_1^2 = (x^*)^2 + (y^*)^2;$$

$$d_2^2 = (8 - x^*)^2 + (y^*)^2 = (x^* - 8)^2 + (y^*)^2;$$

$$\frac{(x^* - 4)^2}{5^2} + \frac{(y^*)^2}{3^2} = 1;$$

$$(y^*)^2 = 9 - \frac{9\,(x^* - 4)^2}{25};$$

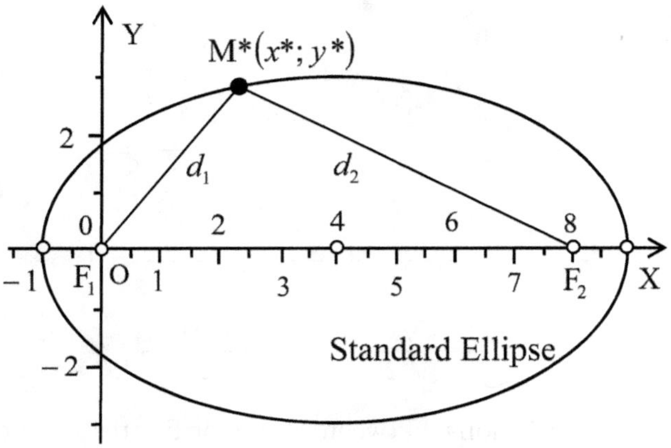


**Fig. 36.3**

$$d_1^2 = (x^*)^2 + 9 - \frac{9\,(x^* - 4)^2}{25};$$

$$d_1^2 = \frac{16\,(x^*)^2 + 72\,(x^*) + 81}{25}; \quad d_2^2 = \frac{16\,(x^*)^2 - 328\,(x^*) + 1681}{25}.$$

By observing the movement of the moon around the planet presented in Figures 36.4, 36.5 and 36.6, the result is:

$$d_{1,0}^2 = \frac{16\left(x_0^*\right)^2 + 72\left(x_0^*\right) + 81}{25}; \quad 25\,d_{1,0}^2 = 16\left(x_0^*\right)^2 + 72\left(x_0^*\right) + 81;$$

$$d_{1,0}^2 = x_0^2 + y_0^2 = x_0^2 + r^2; \quad 25\,d_{1,0}^2 = 25x_0^2 + 25r^2;$$

$$\frac{16\left(x_0^*\right)^2 + 72\left(x_0^*\right) + 81}{25} = x_0^2 + r^2;$$

$$x_0^* = \frac{x_0}{2} + \frac{\sqrt{3}y_0}{2} = \frac{x_0}{2} + \frac{r\sqrt{3}}{2};$$

$$16\left(x_0^*\right)^2 + 72\left(x_0^*\right) + 81 = 25x_0^2 + 25r^2;$$

$$16\left(\frac{x_0}{2} + \frac{r\sqrt{3}}{2}\right)^2 + 72\left(\frac{x_0}{2} + \frac{r\sqrt{3}}{2}\right) + 81 = 25\,x_0^2 + 25\,r^2;$$

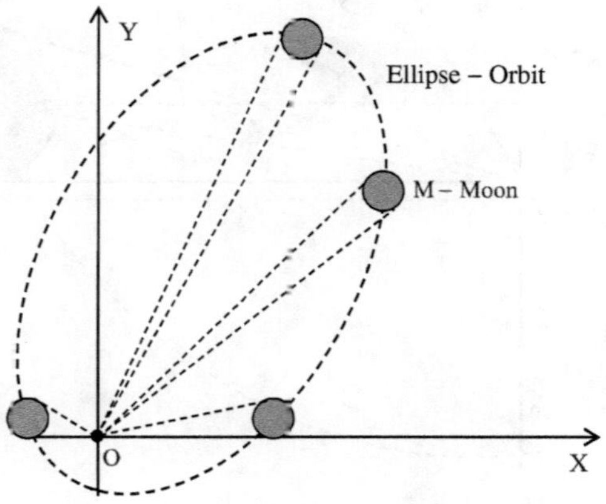


**Fig. 36.4**

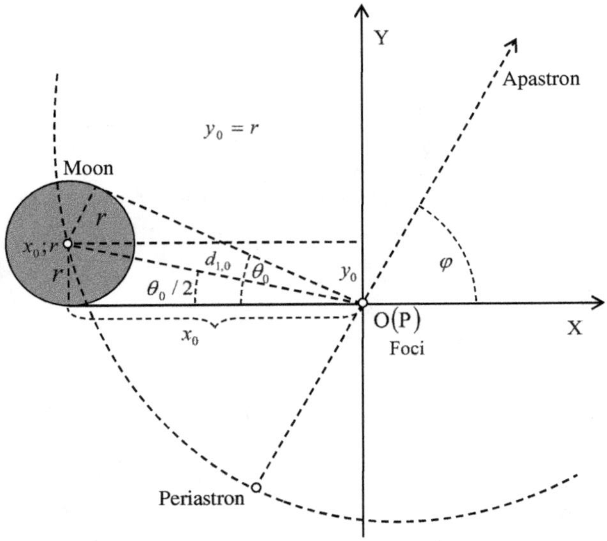


**Fig. 36.5**

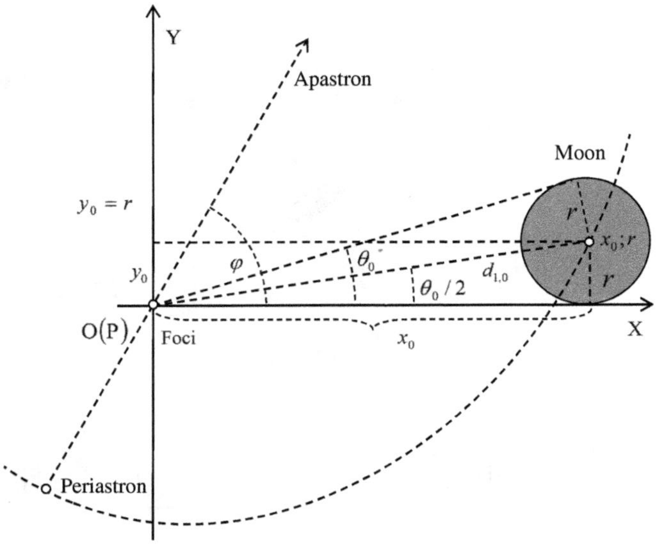


**Fig. 36.6**

$$25\,x_0^2 + 25\,r^2 = 4\,x_0^2 + \left(8r\sqrt{3} - 36\right)x_0 + \left(12r^2 + 36\sqrt{3}\,r + 81\right);$$

$$21\,x_0^2 - \left(8r\sqrt{3} + 36\right)x_0 + \left(13r^2 - 36r\sqrt{3} - 81\right) = 0;$$

$$x_0 = \frac{\left(4r\sqrt{3} + 18\right) \pm \sqrt{\left(4r\sqrt{3} + 18\right)^2 - 21\left(13r^2 - 36r\sqrt{3} - 81\right)}}{21};$$

$$x_{0,\min} = \frac{\left(4r\sqrt{3} + 18\right) - 15\sqrt{-r^2 + 4r\sqrt{3} + 9}}{21};$$

$$\tan\frac{\theta_0}{2} = \frac{r}{x_{0,\min}} = \frac{21\,r}{4r\sqrt{3} - 18 - 15\sqrt{-r^2 + 4r\sqrt{3} + 9}}.$$

# Problem 37

# Neutron Star or Black Hole?

Two massive stars A and B with mass $m_A$ and $m_B$ are separated by a distance $d$. Both stars are orbiting each other with respect to their center of gravity, and their orbits are circular. Suppose the stars lie on the X–Y plane (Figure 37.1) and are moving under gravitational force.

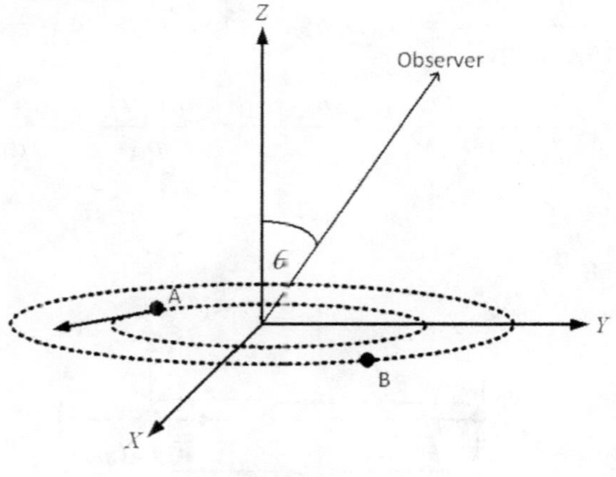


**Fig. 37.1**

**a)** *Calculate* the speed of star A and its angular velocity.

**b)** An observer lying on the Y–Z plane sees the stars from a large distance with angle $\theta$ relative to the Z axis. The observer measures that the velocity component of A to the line of his sight has the form $K\cos(\omega t + \varepsilon)$, with $K$ and $\varepsilon$ being positive.

*Express* the value $K^3/\omega G$ in terms of $m_\mathrm{A}$, $m_\mathrm{B}$ and $\theta$, where $G$ is the universal gravitational constant.

**c)** The observer can then identify that the star A has a mass equal to $30M_\mathrm{S}$, where $M_\mathrm{S}$ is the Sun's mass. On the other hand, he observes that the star B produces X-rays, so it could be a neutron star or a black hole. These situations depend on $m_\mathrm{B}$: 1) if $m_\mathrm{B} < 2M_\mathrm{S}$, then B is a neutron star; 2) if $m_\mathrm{B} > 2M_\mathrm{S}$, then B is a black hole. A measurement is taken by the observer which results in $K^3/\omega G = M_S/250$.

If the value of $\cos\theta$ has the same probability, then calculate the probability of B being a black hole. Use: $\int \sin x \mathrm{d}x = -\cos x + C$.

## Solution

**a)** According to the notation used in Figure 37.2, the result is:

$$m_\mathrm{A}\mathrm{v}_\mathrm{A} = m_\mathrm{B}\mathrm{v}_\mathrm{B}; \quad \mathrm{v}_\mathrm{A} = \omega a_\mathrm{A}; \quad \mathrm{v}_\mathrm{B} = \omega a_\mathrm{B};$$

$$m_\mathrm{A} a_\mathrm{A} = m_\mathrm{B} a_\mathrm{B};$$

$$F = G\frac{m_\mathrm{A} m_\mathrm{B}}{(a_\mathrm{A} + a_\mathrm{B})^2} = m_\mathrm{A}\omega^2 a_\mathrm{A} = m_\mathrm{B}\omega^2 a_\mathrm{B}; \quad a_\mathrm{A} + a_\mathrm{B} = d;$$

$$F = G\frac{m_\mathrm{A} m_\mathrm{B}}{(a_\mathrm{A} + a_\mathrm{B})^2} = G\frac{m_\mathrm{A} m_\mathrm{B}}{d^2} = \frac{m_\mathrm{A}\mathrm{v}_\mathrm{A}^2}{a_\mathrm{A}} = \frac{m_\mathrm{B}\mathrm{v}_\mathrm{B}^2}{a_\mathrm{B}};$$

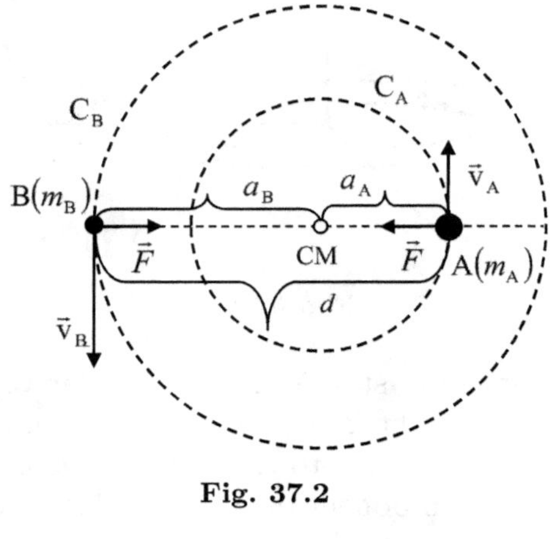


**Fig. 37.2**

$$a_A + a_B = d; \quad a_B = \frac{m_A}{m_B} a_A; \quad a_A + \frac{m_A}{m_B} a_A = d;$$

$$a_A = \frac{m_B}{m_A + m_B} d; \quad a_B = \frac{m_A}{m_A + m_B} d;$$

$$G\frac{m_A m_B}{d^2} = \frac{m_A v_A^2}{a_A} = \frac{m_B v_B^2}{a_B};$$

$$G\frac{m_A m_B}{d^2} = \frac{m_A v_A^2}{\frac{m_B d}{m_A + m_B}} = \frac{m_B v_B^2}{\frac{m_A d}{m_A + m_B}};$$

$$v_A = m_B \sqrt{\frac{G}{(m_A + m_B)\, d}}; \quad v_B = m_A \sqrt{\frac{G}{(m_A + m_B)\, d}};$$

$$\omega = \frac{v_A}{a_A} = \frac{v_B}{a_B} = \sqrt{\frac{G\,(m_A + m_B)}{d^3}}.$$

**b)** According to the notation used in Figure 37.3, the result is:

$$\vec{v}_A = v_A \left( -\sin(\theta + \varepsilon)\, \vec{i} + \cos(\theta + \varepsilon)\, \vec{j} \right);$$

$$\vec{w} = \text{unit vector of the observer} = \sin\theta\, \vec{j} + \cos\theta\, \vec{k};$$

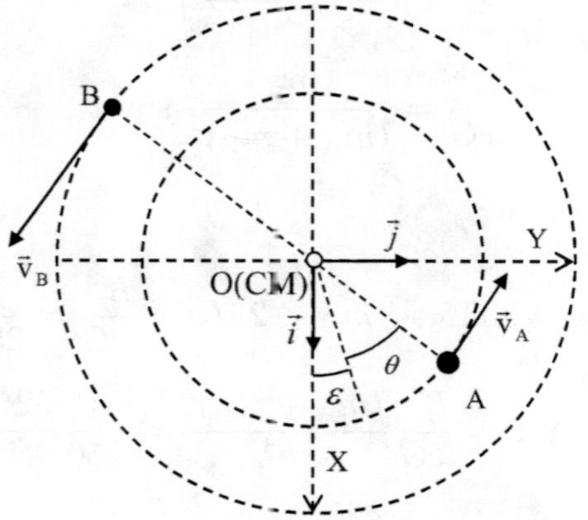


**Fig. 37.3**

$$\begin{aligned}\mathrm{v}_{\mathrm{rad,A}} &= \vec{\mathrm{v}}_{\mathrm{A}} \cdot \vec{w} \\ &= \mathrm{v}_{\mathrm{A}} \left(-\sin\left(\theta+\varepsilon\right)\vec{i} + \cos\left(\theta+\varepsilon\right)\vec{j}\right) \cdot \left(\sin\theta\,\vec{j} + \cos\theta\,\vec{k}\right);\end{aligned}$$

$$\mathrm{v}_{\mathrm{rad,A}} = \mathrm{v}_{\mathrm{A}}\ \sin\theta\ \cos\left(\theta+\varepsilon\right);$$

$$\mathrm{v}_{\mathrm{rad,A}} = \mathrm{v}_{\mathrm{A}}\ \sin\theta\ \cos\left(\omega t+\varepsilon\right);$$

$$\mathrm{v}_{\mathrm{rad,A}} = K\ \cos\left(\omega t+\varepsilon\right);$$

$$K = \mathrm{v}_{\mathrm{A}}\sin\theta; \quad K^3 = \mathrm{v}_{\mathrm{A}}^3\ \sin^3\theta;$$

$$\mathrm{v}_{\mathrm{A}} = m_{\mathrm{B}}\sqrt{\frac{G}{\left(m_{\mathrm{A}}+m_{\mathrm{B}}\right)d}}; \quad \omega = \sqrt{\frac{G\left(m_{\mathrm{A}}+m_{\mathrm{B}}\right)}{d^3}};$$

$$\frac{K^3}{\omega G} = \frac{\mathrm{v}_{\mathrm{A}}^3\ \sin^3\theta}{\omega G} = \frac{m_{\mathrm{B}}^3\left(\frac{G}{(m_{\mathrm{A}}+m_{\mathrm{B}})d}\right)^{3/2}}{G\left(\frac{G(m_{\mathrm{A}}+m_{\mathrm{B}})}{d^3}\right)^{1/2}}\ \sin^3\theta;$$

$$\frac{K^3}{\omega G} = \frac{m_{\mathrm{B}}^3\left(\frac{G^{3/2}}{(m_{\mathrm{A}}+m_{\mathrm{B}})^{3/2}d^{3/2}}\right)}{\left(\frac{G^{3/2}(m_{\mathrm{A}}+m_{\mathrm{B}})^{1/2}}{d^{3/2}}\right)}\ \sin^3\theta;$$

$$\frac{K^3}{\omega G} = \frac{m_{\mathrm{B}}^3\left(\frac{1}{(m_{\mathrm{A}}+m_{\mathrm{B}})^{3/2}}\right)}{\left(\frac{(m_{\mathrm{A}}+m_{\mathrm{B}})^{1/2}}{1}\right)}\ \sin^3\theta;$$

$$\frac{K^3}{\omega G} = \frac{m_{\mathrm{B}}^3}{\left(m_{\mathrm{A}}+m_{\mathrm{B}}\right)^2}\ \sin^3\theta.$$

**c)**

$$m_{\mathrm{A}} = 30M_{\mathrm{S}}; \quad m_{\mathrm{B}} < 2M_{\mathrm{S}}; \quad \frac{K^3}{\omega G} = \frac{1}{250};$$

$$\sin^3\theta = \frac{K^3}{\omega G}\,\frac{\left(m_{\mathrm{A}}+m_{\mathrm{B}}\right)^2}{m_{\mathrm{B}}^3} < \frac{1}{250}\,\frac{32^2}{2^3};$$

$$\sin^3\theta < \frac{64}{125}; \quad \sin^3\theta < 0.512;$$

$$\theta \in [0;\pi]; \quad \sin\theta < 0.8;$$

Under these conditions, the probability for the star B to be a black hole is equal to the probability that $\sin\theta < 0.8$ when $\theta \in [0;\pi]$.

It results that

$$P_{\mathrm{B}\to\mathrm{Black\,Hole}} = 1 - \frac{\int_{53^\circ}^{127^\circ} \sin\theta \mathrm{d}\theta}{\int_{0}^{180^\circ} \sin\theta \mathrm{d}\theta} = 1 - 0.6 = 0.4.$$

## Annex: Radial Velocity

Let us initially consider that a star S is moving on a circular orbit around a star $\Sigma$. If the observation plane is perpendicular to the sky plane (the angle between the celestial plane and the plane of the relative orbit is $i = 0$), as presented in Figure 37.4, the radial speed of the star S is constantly zero.

If the observation direction plane coincides with the orbit plane (the angle between the celestial plane and the plane of the orbit is $i = 90^\circ$), as presented in Figure 37.5, then the radial speed of star S is variable over time, as presented below:

$$\begin{aligned} \mathrm{v}_{\mathrm{rad}} &= \mathrm{v} \cdot \sin\alpha = \omega r \sin\alpha = \frac{2\pi r}{T}\sin\omega t \\ &= \mathrm{v}_{\mathrm{rad,max}} \cdot \sin\omega t = \mathrm{v}_{\mathrm{rad,max}} \cdot \sin\frac{2\pi}{T}t. \end{aligned}$$

Thus, the graph of this dependence is represented in Figure 37.6.

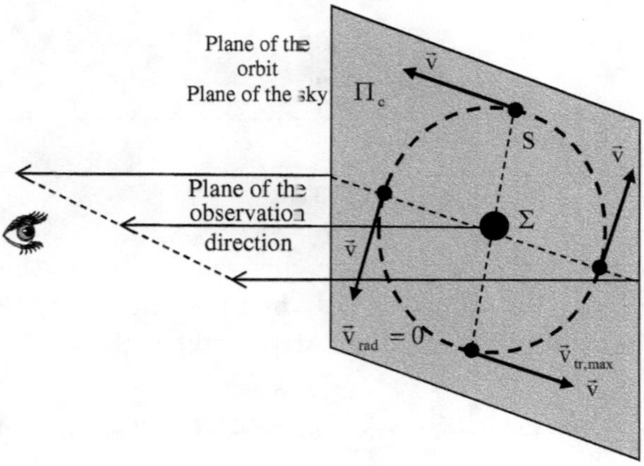


**Fig. 37.4**

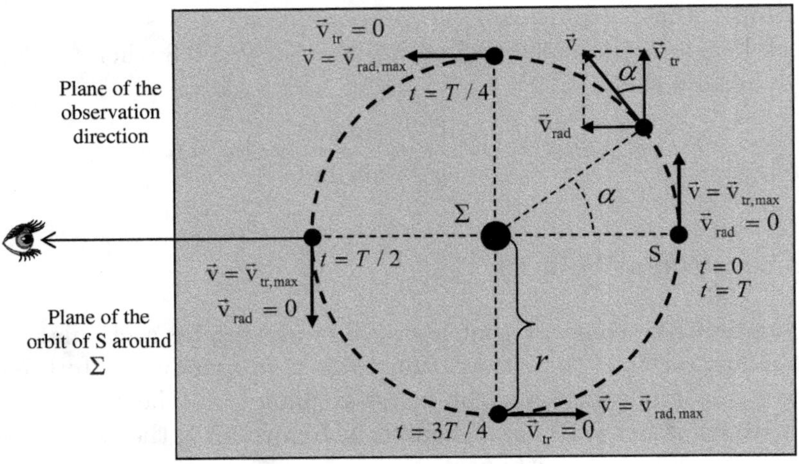


**Fig. 37.5**

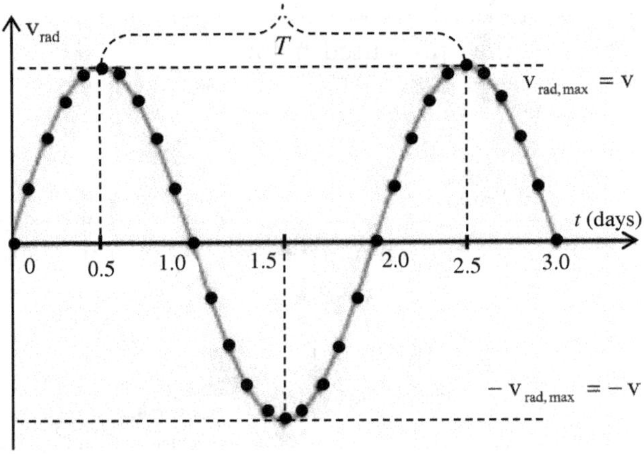


**Fig. 37.6**

If the plane of the observation direction is other than the orbit plane, as indicated in Figure 37.7, when the angle between the celestial plane and the plane of the relative orbit is $0 < i < 90°$, then:

$$\mathrm{v}_{\mathrm{rad}} = \mathrm{v} \cdot \sin i \cdot \sin \alpha = \mathrm{v}_{\mathrm{rad,max}} \cdot \sin \omega t = \mathrm{v}_{\mathrm{rad,max}} \cdot \sin \frac{2\pi}{T} t;$$

$$\mathrm{v}_{\mathrm{rad,max}} = \mathrm{v} \cdot \sin i.$$

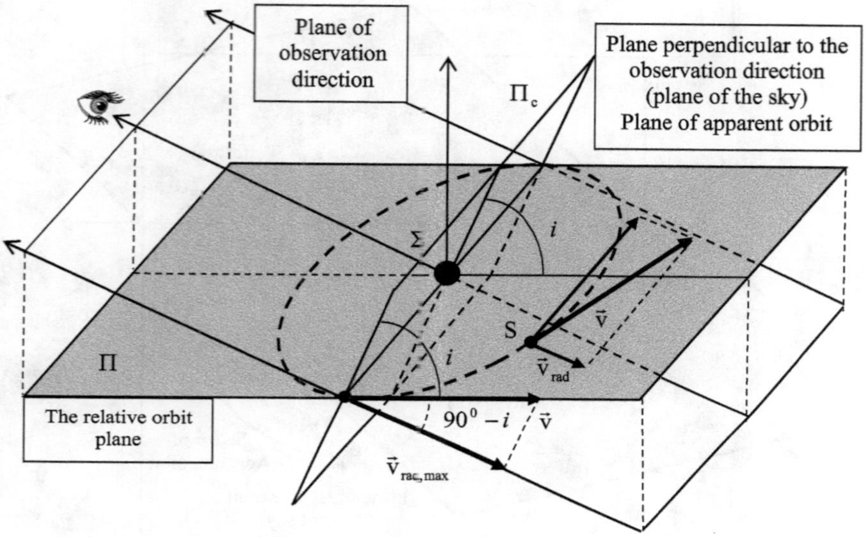


**Fig. 37.7**

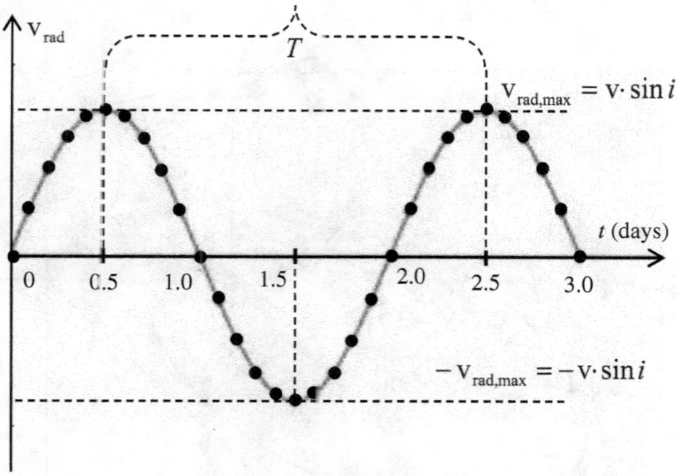


**Fig. 37.8**

The dependence graph $v_{rad}(t)$ is presented in Figure 37.8.

Let us admit then that the orbit of the star S, relative to star $\Sigma$ in the $\Pi$ plane, is an ellipse, as presented in Figures 37.9 and 37.10. In both images, the plane of the apparent orbit is the celestial plane

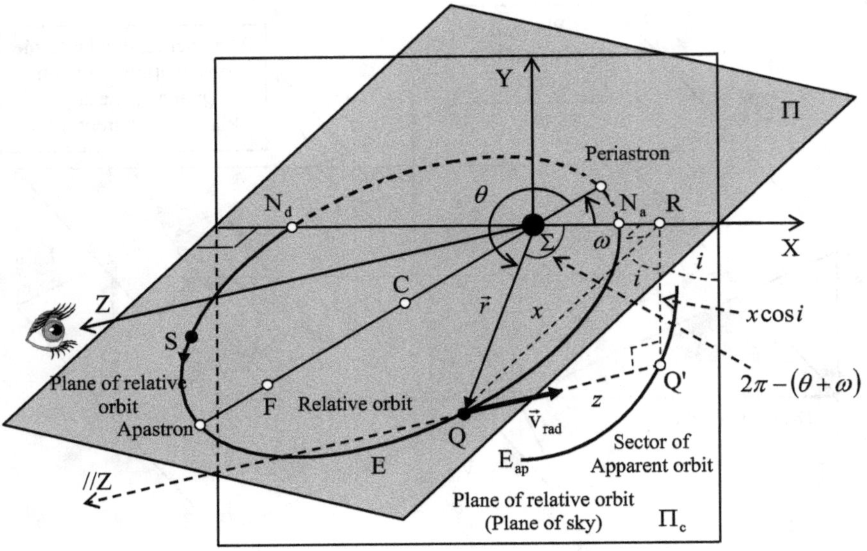


Fig. 37.9

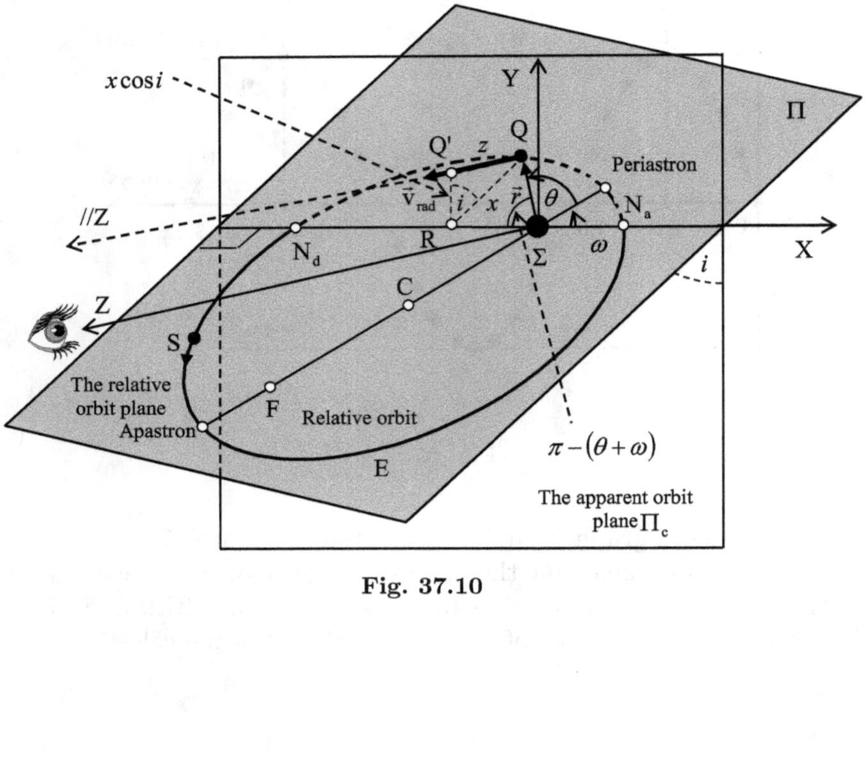


Fig. 37.10

$\Pi_c$, and the direction of the observation line is the direction of axis Z, perpendicular to the celestial plane. The X and Y axes are included in the celestial plane.

At any moment, the radial speed of the star S is the velocity component $\vec{v}_{rad}$ perpendicular to the celestial plane (parallel with the line of view direction, along the Z axis). Figures 37.9 and 37.10 illustrate the positions of the star S relative to the line of nodes at the points marked with Q, either at the apastron or at the periastron. In both images the instantaneous position coordinate of the star S relative to the Z axis is $z$.

Under these conditions, the result is:

$$\mathrm{v}_{\mathrm{rad}} = \frac{\mathrm{d}z}{\mathrm{d}t} = \frac{\mathrm{d}}{\mathrm{d}t}\left[r \sin(\theta + \omega) \sin i\right]; \quad \theta = \theta(t); r = r(t);$$

$$i = \text{constant}; \quad \omega = \text{constant};$$

$$\mathrm{v}_{\mathrm{rad}} = r\frac{\mathrm{d}}{\mathrm{d}t}\left[\sin(\theta + \omega) \sin i\right] + \sin(\theta + \omega) \sin i \frac{\mathrm{d}r}{\mathrm{d}t};$$

$$\mathrm{v}_{\mathrm{rad}} = r \sin(\theta + \omega) \frac{\mathrm{d}}{\mathrm{d}t}(\sin i) + r \sin i \frac{\mathrm{d}}{\mathrm{d}t}\left[\sin(\theta + \omega)\right]$$
$$+ \sin(\theta + \omega) \sin i \frac{\mathrm{d}r}{\mathrm{d}t};$$

$$\mathrm{v}_{\mathrm{rad}} = r \sin i \cos(\theta + \omega) \frac{\mathrm{d}}{\mathrm{d}t}(\theta + \omega) + \sin(\theta + \omega) \sin i \frac{\mathrm{d}r}{\mathrm{d}t};$$

$$\mathrm{v}_{\mathrm{rad}} = r \sin i \cos(\theta + \omega) \frac{\mathrm{d}\theta}{\mathrm{d}t} + \sin(\theta + \omega) \sin i \frac{\mathrm{d}r}{\mathrm{d}t};$$

$$\mathrm{v}_{\mathrm{rad}} = r \sin i \cos(\theta + \omega)\, \dot{\theta} + \sin(\theta + \omega) \sin i\, \dot{r};$$

$$\mathrm{v}_{\mathrm{rad}} = \left[r\, \dot{\theta} \cos(\theta + \omega) + \dot{r} \sin(\theta + \omega)\right] \sin i;$$

$$r = \frac{p}{1 + e \cos\theta} = \frac{a(1 - e^2)}{1 + e \cos\theta};$$

$$\dot{r} = \frac{\mathrm{d}r}{\mathrm{d}t} = \frac{\mathrm{d}}{\mathrm{d}t}\left[\frac{a(1 - e^2)}{1 + e \cos\theta}\right];$$

$$\dot{r} = \frac{\mathrm{d}r}{\mathrm{d}t} = \frac{(1 + e \cos\theta) \frac{\mathrm{d}}{\mathrm{d}t}\left[a(1 - e^2)\right] - a(1 - e^2) \frac{\mathrm{d}}{\mathrm{d}t}(1 + e \cos\theta)}{(1 + e \cos\theta)^2};$$

$$\dot{r} = \frac{\mathrm{d}r}{\mathrm{d}t} = \frac{a\,(1-e^2)\;e\,\sin\theta\,\frac{\mathrm{d}\theta}{\mathrm{d}t}}{(1+e\,\cos\theta)^2};$$

$$\dot{r} = \frac{\mathrm{d}r}{\mathrm{d}t} = \frac{a\,(1-e^2)}{1+e\,\cos\theta}\,\frac{e\,\frac{\mathrm{d}\theta}{\mathrm{d}t}\,\sin\theta}{1+e\,\cos\theta};$$

$$r = \frac{p}{1+e\,\cos\theta} = \frac{a\,(1-e^2)}{1+e\,\cos\theta};$$

$$\dot{r} = \frac{r\,e\,\dot{\theta}\,\sin\theta}{1+e\,\cos\theta};$$

$$\frac{\mathrm{d}A}{\mathrm{d}t} = \frac{1}{2}\,r^2\dot{\theta};$$

$$\frac{A}{T} = \frac{1}{2}\,r^2\dot{\theta};$$

$$A = \pi ab; \quad b = a\sqrt{1-e^2};$$

$$A = \pi a^2\sqrt{1-e^2};$$

$$\frac{\pi a^2\sqrt{1-e^2}}{T} = \frac{1}{2}\,r^2\dot{\theta};$$

$$r\,\dot{\theta} = \frac{2\pi a^2\sqrt{1-e^2}}{rT}; \quad r\,\dot{\theta} = \frac{1}{r}\,\frac{2\pi a^2\sqrt{1-e^2}}{T};$$

$$r\,\dot{\theta} = \frac{1+e\,\cos\theta}{a\,(1-e^2)}\,\frac{2\pi a^2\sqrt{1-e^2}}{T};$$

$$r\,\dot{\theta} = \frac{2\pi a\,(1+e\,\cos\theta)}{T\sqrt{1-e^2}};$$

$$\dot{r} = \frac{r\,e\,\dot{\theta}\,\sin\theta}{1+e\,\cos\theta} = r\dot{\theta}\,\frac{e\,\sin\theta}{1+e\,\cos\theta};$$

$$\dot{r} = \frac{2\pi a\,(1+e\,\cos\theta)}{T\sqrt{1-e^2}}\,\frac{e\,\sin\theta}{1+e\,\cos\theta};$$

$$\dot{r} = \frac{2\pi\,a\,e\,\sin\theta}{T\sqrt{1-e^2}};$$

$$\mathrm{v_{rad}} = \Big[r\,\dot{\theta}\,\cos(\theta+\omega) + \dot{r}\,\sin(\theta+\omega)\Big]\,\sin i;$$

$$\mathrm{v_{rad}} = \left[\frac{2\pi a\,(1+e\cos\theta)}{T\sqrt{1-e^2}}\cos(\theta-\omega) + \frac{2\pi ae\sin\theta}{T\sqrt{1-e^2}}\sin(\theta+\omega)\right]\sin i;$$

$$\mathrm{v_{rad}} = \frac{2\pi a\sin i}{T\sqrt{1-e^2}}\left[(1+e\cos\theta)\cos(\theta+\omega) + e\sin\theta\sin(\theta+\omega)\right];$$

$$\mathrm{v_{rad}} = \frac{2\pi a\sin i}{T\sqrt{1-e^2}}[\cos(\theta+\omega) + e\cos\theta\cos(\theta+\omega) + e\sin\theta\sin(\theta+\omega)];$$

$$\cos(\theta+\omega) = \cos\theta\cos\omega - \sin\theta\sin\omega;$$

$$\sin(\theta+\omega) = \sin\theta\cos\omega + \cos\theta\sin\omega;$$

$$[\cos(\theta+\omega) + e\cos\theta\cos(\theta+\omega) + e\sin\theta\sin(\theta+\omega)]$$
$$= \cos\theta\cos\omega - \sin\theta\sin\omega + e\cos\omega = \cos(\theta+\omega) + e\cos\omega;$$

$$\mathrm{v_{rad}} = \frac{2\pi\, a\,\sin i}{T\sqrt{1-e^2}}\left[\cos(\theta+\omega) + e\cos\omega\right],$$

representing the general form of star S's radial velocity.

# Problem 38

# Star of Neutral Particles

Suppose a static spherical star, with radius $R$, consists of $N$ neutral particles (Figure 38.1), with $0 \leq \theta \leq \pi$ and $0 \leq \varphi \leq 2\pi$, satisfying the following equation of states:

$$pV = Nk\frac{T_R - T_0}{\ln(T_R/T_0)},$$

where: $p$ – the pressure inside the star; $V$ – the volume of the star; $k$ – the Boltzmann constant; $T_R$ – the temperature at the surface of the star, $r = R$; $T_0$ – the temperature at the center of the star, $r = 0$. Assume that $T_R \leq T_0$.

**a)** *Simplify* the stellar equation of states if $\Delta T = T_R - T_0 \approx 0$ (this is called the *ideal star*). Use:

$$\ln(1 + x) \approx x, \quad \text{for a small } x.$$

**b)** Suppose the star undergoes a quasi-static process, in which it may slightly contract or expand, such that the above stellar equation of states still holds.

*Find* the work of the star when it expands from $V_1$ to $V_2$ in an isothermal process where $T_R$ and $T_0$ are constants.

**c)** The star satisfies the first law of thermodynamics:

$$Q = c^2\Delta M + W,$$

where: Q – heat; $M$ – the mass of the star; $W$ – work; $c$ – the speed of light in vacuum; $\Delta M = M_{\text{final}} - M_{\text{initial}}$. In the following, we assume $T_0$ to be constant, while $T_R \equiv T$ varies.

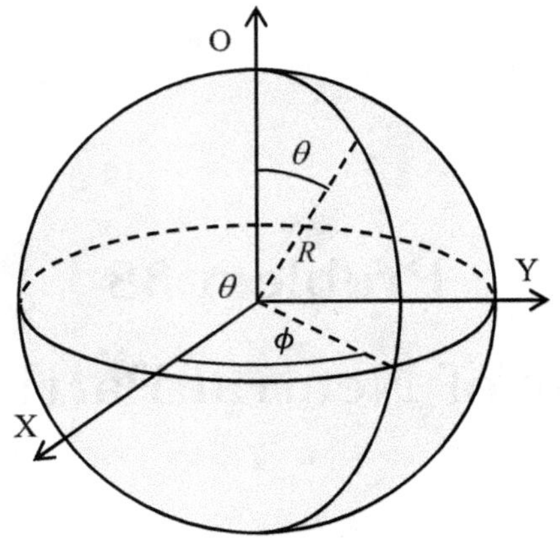


**Fig. 38.1**

*Find* the heat capacity of the star at a constant volume, $C_{\mathrm{v}}$, in terms of $M$ at a constant pressure, $C_{\mathrm{p}}$, expressed in $C_{\mathrm{v}}$ and $T$. Use the approximation $(1+x)^n \approx 1+nx$ for a small $x$.

**d)** Assume that $C_{\mathrm{v}}$ is constant and the gas undergoes an isobaric process so the star produces heat and radiates it out into space. *Find* the heat produced by this isobaric process if the initial temperature and the final temperature are $T_{\mathrm{i}}$ and $T_{\mathrm{f}}$, respectively.

**e)** Suppose there is an observer far away from the star. Relative to point (d), *estimate* the distance of the observer if the observer has a 0.1 % error in measuring the effective temperature around the star.

**f)** If sunlight were monochromatic with a frequency $5 \times 10^{14}$ Hz, *estimate* the number of photons radiated by the Sun per second.

**g)** *Calculate* the heat capacity $C_{\mathrm{v}}$ of the Sun, assuming its surface temperature runs from 5500 K to 6000 K in this period.

## Solution

**a)**

$$pV = Nk\frac{T_R - T_0}{\ln(T_R/T_0)} = Nk\frac{\Delta T}{\ln\frac{T_R}{T_0}} = Nk\frac{\Delta T}{\ln\frac{T_0+\Delta T}{T_0}} = Nk\frac{\Delta T}{\ln\left(1+\frac{\Delta T}{T_0}\right)};$$

$$\frac{\Delta T}{T_0} \ll 1; \quad \ln\left(1 + \frac{\Delta T}{T_0}\right) \approx \frac{\Delta T}{T_0};$$

$$pV = NkT_0.$$

**b)** If the gas undergoes an isothermal process where $T_R$ and $T_0$ are constant, then the work has the form

$$W = \int_{V_1}^{V_2} p\mathrm{d}V = Nk\frac{T_R - T_0}{\ln\frac{T_R}{T_0}} \int_{V_1}^{V_2} \frac{\mathrm{d}V}{V} = Nk\frac{T_R - T_0}{\ln\frac{T_R}{T_0}} \ln\frac{V_2}{V_1}.$$

**c)** The internal energy of the star is $U = Mc^2$, where $U(T) = M(T)c^2$ for an ideal star. Thus, the constant volume heat capacity of the star has the form

$$C_{\mathrm{v}} = \left(\frac{\Delta Q}{\Delta T}\right)_V = \left(\frac{\Delta M}{\Delta T}\right)_V c^2,$$

for a small $\Delta T$. Then, using the first law of thermodynamics, the constant pressure heat capacity of the star is

$$C_{\mathrm{p}} = \left(\frac{\Delta Q}{\Delta T}\right)_p = \left(\frac{\Delta M}{\Delta T}\right)_p c^2 + p\frac{\Delta V}{\Delta T} = C_{\mathrm{v}} + p\frac{\Delta V}{\Delta T},$$

for a small $\Delta T$. If $\Delta T = T_2 - T_1$ then:

$$p\Delta V = Nk\left(\frac{T_2 - T_0}{\ln\frac{T_2}{T_0}}\right) - Nk\left(\frac{T_1 - T_0}{\ln\frac{T_1}{T_0}}\right); \quad T_2 = T_1 + \Delta T;$$

$$p\Delta V = Nk\left(\frac{T_1 + \Delta T - T_0}{\ln\frac{T_1+\Delta T}{T_0}}\right) - Nk\left(\frac{T_1 - T_0}{\ln\frac{T_1}{T_0}}\right);$$

$$\ln\frac{T_1 + \Delta T}{T_0} = \ln\left(\frac{T_1}{T_0} + \frac{\Delta T}{T_0}\right) = \ln\left[\frac{T_1}{T_0}\left(1 + \frac{\Delta T}{T_0}\frac{T_0}{T_1}\right)\right]$$

$$= \ln\left[\frac{T_1}{T_0}\left(1 + \frac{\Delta T}{T_1}\right)\right];$$

$$\ln\frac{T_1+\Delta T}{T_0}=\ln\frac{T_1}{T_0}+\ln\left(1+\frac{\Delta T}{T_1}\right);$$

$$\Delta T \ll T_1; \quad \ln\left(1+\frac{\Delta T}{T_1}\right)\approx\frac{\Delta T}{T_1};$$

$$\ln\frac{T_1+\Delta T}{T_0}=\ln\frac{T_1}{T_0}+\frac{\Delta T}{T_1};$$

$$\frac{1}{\ln\frac{T_1+\Delta T}{T_0}}=\frac{1}{\ln\frac{T_1}{T_0}+\frac{\Delta T}{T_1}}=\frac{1}{\left(1+\frac{\Delta T}{T_1\ln\frac{T_1}{T_0}}\right)\cdot\ln\frac{T_1}{T_0}}$$

$$=\frac{1}{\ln\frac{T_1}{T_0}}\left(1+\frac{\Delta T}{T_1\ln\frac{T_1}{T_0}}\right)^{-1};$$

$$\left(1+\frac{\Delta T}{T_1\ln\frac{T_1}{T_0}}\right)^{-1}\approx 1-\frac{\Delta T}{T_1\ln\frac{T_1}{T_0}};$$

$$\frac{1}{\ln\frac{T_1+\Delta T}{T_0}}=\frac{1}{\ln\frac{T_1}{T_0}}\left(1-\frac{\Delta T}{T_1\ln\frac{T_1}{T_0}}\right);$$

$$p\Delta V=Nk\left[\frac{T_1+\Delta T-T_0}{\ln\frac{T_1}{T_0}}\left(1-\frac{\Delta T}{T_1\ln\frac{T_1}{T_0}}\right)-\frac{T_1-T_0}{\ln\frac{T_1}{T_0}}\right];$$

$$p\Delta V=Nk\left[\left(\frac{T_1-T_0}{\ln\frac{T_1}{T_0}}+\frac{\Delta T}{\ln\frac{T_1}{T_0}}\right)\cdot\left(1-\frac{\Delta T}{T_1\ln\frac{T_1}{T_0}}\right)-\frac{T_1-T_0}{\ln\frac{T_1}{T_0}}\right];$$

$$p\Delta V=Nk\left[\frac{T_1-T_0}{\ln\frac{T_1}{T_0}}-\frac{(T_1-T_0)\Delta T}{T_1\left(\ln\frac{T_1}{T_0}\right)^2}+\frac{\Delta T}{\ln\frac{T_1}{T_0}}\right.$$

$$\left.+\frac{(\Delta T)^2}{T_1\left(\ln\frac{T_1}{T_0}\right)^2}-\frac{T_1-T_0}{\ln\frac{T_1}{T_0}}\right];$$

$$\frac{(\Delta T)^2}{T_1\left(\ln\frac{T_1}{T_0}\right)^2} \to 0;$$

$$p\Delta V = Nk\left[-\frac{(T_1 - T_0)\Delta T}{T_1\left(\ln\frac{T_1}{T_0}\right)^2} + \frac{\Delta T}{\ln\frac{T_1}{T_0}}\right];$$

$$p\Delta V = \frac{Nk}{\ln\frac{T_1}{T_0}}\left(1 - \frac{T_1 - T_0}{T_1\ln\frac{T_1}{T_0}}\right)\cdot\Delta T;$$

$$T_1 \equiv T;$$

$$p\Delta V = \frac{Nk}{\ln\frac{T}{T_0}}\left(1 - \frac{T - T_0}{T\ln\frac{T}{T_0}}\right)\cdot\Delta T;$$

$$C_\mathrm{p} = C_\mathrm{v} + p\frac{\Delta V}{\Delta T};$$

$$C_\mathrm{p} = C_\mathrm{v} + \frac{Nk}{\ln\frac{T}{T_0}}\left(1 - \frac{T - T_0}{T\ln\frac{T}{T_0}}\right).$$

**d)**

$$Q_\mathrm{p} = C_\mathrm{p}(T_\mathrm{f} - T_\mathrm{i}) = \left(C_\mathrm{v} + p\frac{\Delta V}{\Delta T}\right)(T_\mathrm{f} - T_\mathrm{i});$$

$$Q_\mathrm{p} = C_\mathrm{v}(T_\mathrm{f} - T_\mathrm{i}) + p\frac{\Delta V}{\Delta T}(T_\mathrm{f} - T_\mathrm{i});$$

$$Q_\mathrm{p} = C_\mathrm{v}(T_\mathrm{f} - T_\mathrm{i}) + p\frac{\Delta V}{\Delta T}\Delta T; \quad Q_\mathrm{p} = C_\mathrm{v}(T_\mathrm{f} - T_\mathrm{i}) + p\Delta V;$$

$$pV = Nk\frac{T_R - T_0}{\ln(T_R/T_0)};$$

$$p\Delta V = Nk\left(\frac{T_\mathrm{f} - T_0}{\ln\frac{T_\mathrm{f}}{T_0}} - \frac{T_\mathrm{i} - T_0}{\ln\frac{T_\mathrm{i}}{T_0}}\right);$$

$$Q_\mathrm{p} = C_\mathrm{v}(T_\mathrm{f} - T_\mathrm{i}) + Nk\left(\frac{T_\mathrm{f} - T_0}{\ln\frac{T_\mathrm{f}}{T_0}} - \frac{T_\mathrm{i} - T_0}{\ln\frac{T_\mathrm{i}}{T_0}}\right).$$

**e)**

$$\varepsilon = \frac{T_{\mathrm{f}} - T_{\mathrm{effective}}}{T_{\mathrm{f}}} = 0.1\% = \frac{0.1}{100} = \frac{1}{1000};$$

$$T_{\mathrm{effective}} = \frac{999}{1000} T_{\mathrm{f}},$$

which, according to Stefan's law for blackbody radiation, results in

$$\frac{Q_{\mathrm{p}}}{4\pi r_0^2} = \sigma T_{\mathrm{effective}}^4 = \sigma \left(\frac{999}{1000}\right)^4 T_{\mathrm{f}}^4,$$

where $r_0$ is the observer's distance, which is given by

$$r_0 = \left(\frac{1000}{999}\right)^2 T_{\mathrm{f}}^{-2} \sqrt{\frac{Q_{\mathrm{p}}}{4\pi\sigma}}.$$

**f)** The luminosity of the Sun (the radiation energy emitted by the Sun per unit of time) is

$$L_{\mathrm{Sun}} = Nhv,$$

where $N$ is the number of photons emitted by the Sun per unit of time. The result is:

$$N = \frac{L_{\mathrm{Sun}}}{hv} = \frac{3.96 \times 10^{26}\,\mathrm{J/s}}{6.6261 \times 10^{-34}\,\mathrm{Js} \times 5 \times 10^{14}\,\mathrm{s}^{-1}}$$

$$= 1.195 \times 10^{45}\,\frac{\mathrm{photons}}{\mathrm{s}}.$$

**g)**

$$U_{\mathrm{Sun}} = M_{\mathrm{Sun}} c^2;$$

$$L_{\mathrm{Sun}} = \frac{\Delta U_{\mathrm{Sun}}}{\Delta t} = \frac{\Delta M_{\mathrm{Sun}}}{\Delta t} c^2;$$

$$C_{\mathrm{Sun}} = \frac{\Delta U_{\mathrm{Sun}}}{\Delta T} = \frac{L_{\mathrm{Sun}} \Delta t}{\Delta T} = \frac{3.96 \times 10^{26}\,\frac{\mathrm{J}}{\mathrm{s}} \times 1\mathrm{s}}{500\,\mathrm{K}} = 7.92 \times 10^{23}\,\frac{\mathrm{J}}{\mathrm{K}}.$$

# Problem 39

# The Star Cepheid HV2257

Photometry and radial velocity data for the Cepheid type star HV2257 are given in Tables 39.1–39.3, based on observations by Gieren (MNRAS vol. 265, 1993). The pulsation period of the star is $P = 39.294$ days. A reference graph for the temperature–color relation and the bolometric correction tables are given in Figure 39.1 (based on Houdashelt *et al.*, 2000) and Table 39.4 (http://xoner.virgillio.it/hrtrace/Straizys.htm). The solar luminosity is $L_{\text{Sun}} = 3.96 \times 10^{26}\ \text{Js}^{-1}$ and its bolometric magnitude is $M_{\text{Sun,bol}} = 4.72$.

**a)** *Plot* the light curve based on Table 39.1, between phases 0.6 and 1.
**b)** *Plot* the color in Table 39.2, between phases 0.6 and 1.
**c)** *Plot* the radial velocity curve from Table 39.3, between phases 0.6 and 1.
**d)** *Calculate* the average radial velocity of the star.
**e)** *Calculate* the distance to this pulsating star using the observed data and supplementary data given in Table 39.4 and Figure 39.1. Assume that there is no extinction in this direction.

**Table 39.1**

| Phase | V mag | Phase | V mag |
|---|---|---|---|
| 0.11 | 12.81 | 0.64 | 13.62 |
| 0.13 | 12.84 | 0.72 | 13.68 |
| 0.14 | 12.87 | 0.74 | 13.61 |
| 0.16 | 12.88 | 0.77 | 13.45 |
| 0.19 | 12.90 | 0.79 | 13.18 |
| 0.19 | 12.94 | 0.80 | 13.12 |
| 0.24 | 12.99 | 0.80 | 13.07 |
| 0.43 | 13.32 | 0.82 | 12.80 |
| 0.46 | 13.31 | 0.82 | 12.78 |
| 0.46 | 13.32 | 0.82 | 12.73 |
| 0.51 | 13.36 | 0.84 | 12.57 |
| 0.54 | 13.41 | 0.85 | 12.54 |
| 0.54 | 13.45 | 0.85 | 12.53 |
| 0.56 | 13.46 | 0.87 | 12.48 |
| 0.59 | 13.53 | 0.87 | 12.47 |
| 0.59 | 13.52 | 0.89 | 12.49 |
| 0.61 | 13.55 | 0.90 | 12.51 |
| 0.64 | 13.60 | 0.92 | 12.51 |

**Table 39.2**

| Phase | V − R | Phase | V − R |
|---|---|---|---|
| 0.22 | 0.71 | 0.69 | 0.90 |
| 0.24 | 0.73 | 0.76 | 0.88 |
| 0.25 | 0.74 | 0.78 | 0.82 |
| 0.27 | 0.75 | 0.80 | 0.79 |
| 0.29 | 0.75 | 0.82 | 0.70 |
| 0.29 | 0.75 | 0.82 | 0.70 |
| 0.34 | 0.77 | 0.82 | 0.68 |
| 0.51 | 0.87 | 0.84 | 0.60 |
| 0.53 | 0.85 | 0.84 | 0.59 |
| 0.53 | 0.87 | 0.84 | 0.58 |
| 0.57 | 0.85 | 0.86 | 0.53 |
| 0.60 | 0.87 | 0.86 | 0.51 |
| 0.60 | 0.88 | 0.87 | 0.52 |
| 0.62 | 0.87 | 0.88 | 0.51 |
| 0.64 | 0.90 | 0.89 | 0.51 |
| 0.64 | 0.90 | 0.90 | 0.55 |
| 0.66 | 0.88 | 0.91 | 0.53 |
| 0.68 | 0.91 | 0.93 | 0.56 |

**Table 39.3**

| Phase | RadVel (km/s) | Phase | RadVel (km/s) |
|---|---|---|---|
| 0.03 | 232 | 0.59 | 274 |
| 0.05 | 234 | 0.61 | 273 |
| 0.08 | 234 | 0.62 | 274 |
| 0.08 | 237 | 0.64 | 274 |
| 0.13 | 242 | 0.67 | 276 |
| 0.13 | 246 | 0.67 | 274 |
| 0.18 | 243 | 0.69 | 274 |
| 0.20 | 249 | 0.71 | 274 |
| 0.23 | 250 | 0.72 | 276 |
| 0.28 | 254 | 0.74 | 278 |
| 0.33 | 259 | 0.77 | 271 |
| 0.35 | 261 | 0.77 | 264 |
| 0.36 | 260 | 0.79 | 253 |
| 0.38 | 266 | 0.80 | 259 |
| 0.40 | 265 | 0.82 | 242 |
| 0.44 | 266 | 0.85 | 230 |
| 0.46 | 272 | 0.87 | 228 |
| 0.46 | 265 | 0.90 | 224 |
| 0.49 | 270 | 0.92 | 224 |
| 0.51 | 270 | 0.92 | 225 |
| 0.54 | 272 | 0.95 | 228 |
| 0.54 | 273 | 0.96 | 228 |
| 0.56 | 274 | | |

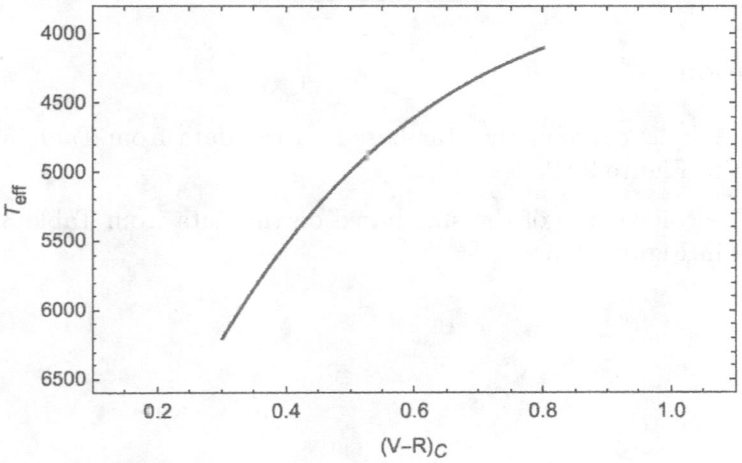


**Fig. 39.1**

**Table 39.4** Bolometric correction.

| $T_{eff}$,K | BC, mag |
|---|---|
| 9600 | −0.25 |
| 9400 | −0.16 |
| 9150 | −0.10 |
| 8900 | −0.03 |
| 8400 | 0.05 |
| 8000 | 0.09 |
| 7300 | 0.13 |
| 7100 | 0.11 |
| 6500 | 0.08 |
| 6150 | 0.03 |
| 5950 | 0.00 |
| 5800 | −0.05 |
| 5500 | −0.13 |
| 5250 | −0.22 |
| 5050 | −0.29 |
| 4950 | −0.35 |
| 4850 | −0.42 |
| 4700 | −0.57 |
| 4600 | −0.75 |
| 4400 | −1.17 |
| 3900 | −1.25 |
| 3750 | −1.40 |
| 3550 | −1.60 |
| 3400 | −2.00 |

## Solution

**a)** The light curve of the star based on the data from Table 39.1 is given in Figure 39.2.

**b)** The color curve of the star based on the data from Table 39.2 is given in Figure 39.3.

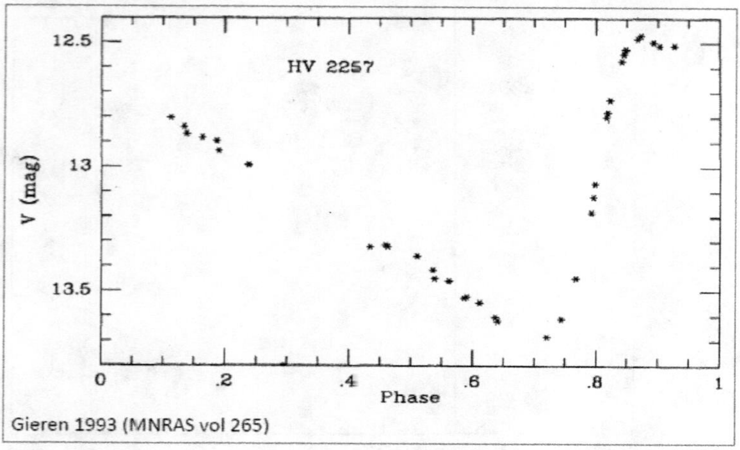


**Fig. 39.2**

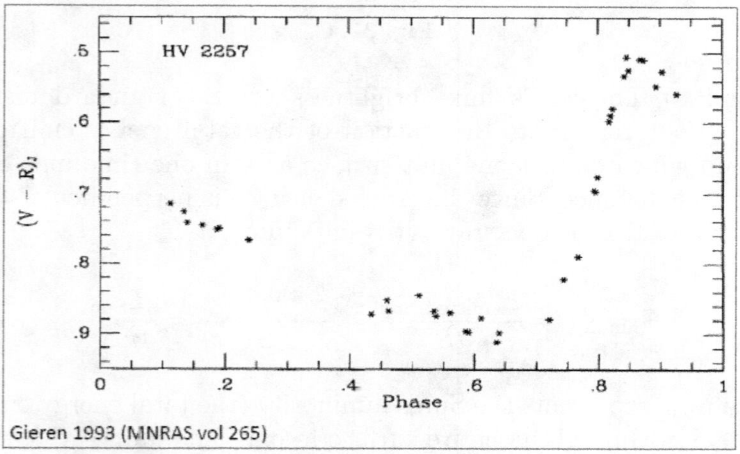


**Fig. 39.3**

**c)** The radial velocity curve of the star based on the data from Table 39.3 is given in Figure 39.4.

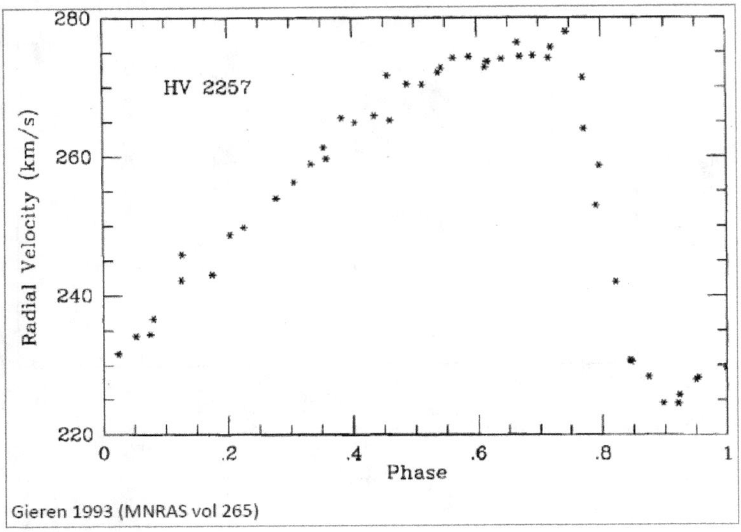


**Fig. 39.4**

**d)** and **e)** The Sun's flux (brightness) at the standard distance $\Delta_{\text{st}} = 10\,\text{pc}$ represents the fraction of the total energy emitted by the Sun which crosses one unit surface area in one time unit at the respective distance. Since the crossed surface is perpendicular to the direction of the incident rays, it results in:

$$F_{\text{Sun},\Delta_{\text{st}}} = \frac{E_{\text{emitted Sun}}}{tS} = \frac{\frac{E_{\text{emitted Sun}}}{t}}{S} = \frac{L_{\text{Sun}}}{4\pi\Delta_{\text{st}}^2},$$

where $L_{\text{Sun}}$ represents the Sun's luminosity (the total energy emitted by the Sun through its entire surface in one time unit);

$$F_{\text{Sun},\Delta_{\text{st}}} = \frac{3.96 \times 10^{26}\,\text{Js}^{-1}}{4 \times 3.14 \times (10 \times 3.086 \times 10^{16}\,\text{m})^2}$$
$$= 3.31 \times 10^{-10}\,\text{Wm}^{-2}.$$

The Sun's flux (brightness), $F_{\text{Sun}}$, depends on the distance from the Sun's center.

The flux (brightness) at the surface of the Sun, $R_{\text{Sun}}$, represents the fraction of the total energy emitted by the Sun which crosses one unit of the Sun's surface in one time unit, that is,

$$F_{\text{Sun},R_{\text{Sun}}} = \frac{L_{\text{Sun}}}{4\pi R_{\text{Sun}}^2} = \frac{3.96 \times 10^{26}\,\text{Js}^{-1}}{4 \times 3.14 \times (6.96 \times 10^8\,\text{m})^2}$$

$$\approx 1386\,\frac{\text{J}}{\text{sm}^2} = k_{\text{Sun}},$$

representing the solar constant.

On the other hand, according to the Stefan–Boltzmann law, the flux (brightness) at the surface of the Sun is given by

$$F_{\text{Sun},R_{\text{Sun}}} = \sigma T^4_{\text{effective Sun}}.$$

Thus,

$$L_{\text{Sun}} = 4\pi R^2_{\text{Sun}}\sigma T^4_{\text{effective Sun}}.$$

The Sun's flux (brightness) for an observer on the Earth, located at a distance $D$ from the center of the Sun, is:

$$F_{\text{Sun},D} = \frac{L_{\text{Sun}}}{4\pi D^2};$$

$$F_{\text{Sun},D} = \frac{\sigma R^2_{\text{Sun}} T^4_{\text{effective Sun}}}{D^2}.$$

Similarly, for any star, the following equations hold:

$$F_{\text{star},d} = \frac{E_{\text{emitted star}}}{tS} = \frac{\frac{E_{\text{emitted star}}}{t}}{S} = \frac{L_{\text{star}}}{4\pi d^2},$$

representing the star's flux (brightness) for the observer on the Earth, located at a distance $d$ from the center of the star (where $L_{\text{star}}$ represents the star's luminosity);

$$F_{\text{star},R_{\text{star}}} = \frac{L_{\text{star}}}{4\pi R^2_{\text{star}}}; \quad F_{\text{star},R_{\text{star}}} = \sigma T^4_{\text{effective star}};$$

$$L_{\text{star}} = 4\pi R^2_{\text{star}}\sigma T^4_{\text{effective star}};$$

$$F_{\text{star},d} = \frac{\sigma R^2_{\text{star}} T^4_{\text{effective star}}}{d^2}.$$

Using Pogson's formula for the observer on the Earth relative to the Sun and to a star, it results that:

$$m_{\text{star}} - m_{\text{Sun}} = -2.5 \times \log \frac{F_{\text{star},d}}{F_{\text{Sun},D}},$$

$$\log \frac{F_{\text{star},d}}{F_{\text{Sun},D}} = -0.4(m_{\text{star}} - m_{\text{Sun}}),$$

where $m_{\text{star}}$ and $m_{\text{Sun}}$ are the apparent magnitudes of the star and of the Sun, respectively, and $F_{\text{star},d}$ and $F_{\text{Sun},D}$ are the flux (brightness) of the star and of the Sun at the observer level, respectively;

$$m_{\text{star}} - m_{\text{Sun}} = -2.5 \times \log \left(\frac{R_{\text{star}}}{R_{\text{Sun}}}\right)^2 \left(\frac{T_{\text{effective star}}}{T_{\text{effective Sun}}}\right)^4 \left(\frac{D}{d}\right)^2;$$

$$\log \left(\frac{R_{\text{star}}}{R_{\text{Sun}}}\right)^2 \left(\frac{T_{\text{effective star}}}{T_{\text{effective Sun}}}\right)^4 \left(\frac{D}{d}\right)^2 = -0.4(m_{\text{star}} - m_{\text{Sun}}).$$

If the star and the Sun are at standard distances $\Delta_{\text{st}} = 10\,\text{pc}$ from the observer on the Earth, or if the star is observed from a planet located at a distance of $\Delta_{\text{st}} = 10\,\text{pc}$ from the considered star or from our Sun, then for these observers the apparent magnitudes of the star, $m_{\text{star}}$, and of the Sun, $m_{\text{Sun}}$, become their absolute magnitudes, $M_{\text{star}}$ and $M_{\text{Sun}}$, respectively. Thus:

$$F_{\text{star},d} = \frac{\sigma R_{\text{star}}^2 T_{\text{effective star}}^4}{d^2}; \quad F_{\text{star},\Delta_{\text{st}}} = \frac{\sigma R_{\text{star}}^2 T_{\text{effective star}}^4}{\Delta_{\text{st}}^2};$$

$$\log \frac{F_{\text{star},d}}{F_{\text{star},\Delta_{\text{st}}}} = -0.4(m_{\text{star}} - M_{\text{star}});$$

$$\log \frac{\frac{\sigma R_{\text{star}}^2 T_{\text{effective star}}^4}{d^2}}{\frac{\sigma R_{\text{star}}^2 T_{\text{effective star}}^4}{\Delta_{\text{st}}^2}} = -0.4(m_{\text{star}} - M_{\text{star}});$$

$$\log \left(\frac{\Delta_{\text{st}}}{d}\right)^2 = -0.4(m_{\text{star}} - M_{\text{star}});$$

$$\log \left(\frac{\Delta_{\text{st(pc)}}}{d_{\text{(pc)}}}\right)^2 = -0.4(m_{\text{star}} - M_{\text{star}});$$

$$\frac{\Delta_{\text{st}}}{d} = \frac{\Delta_{\text{st(pc)}}}{d_{\text{(pc)}}} = \frac{|\Delta_{\text{st(pc)}}| \times \text{pc}}{|d_{\text{(pc)}}| \times \text{pc}} = \frac{|\Delta_{\text{st(pc)}}|}{|d_{\text{pc}}|};$$

$$2\log|\Delta_{\text{st(pc)}}| - 2\log|d_{\text{(pc)}}| = -0.4(m_{\text{star}} - M_{\text{star}});$$

$$5\log|\Delta_{\text{st(pc)}}| - 5\log|d_{\text{(pc)}}| = -(m_{\text{star}} - M_{\text{star}});$$

$$M_{\text{star}} = m_{\text{star}} + 5^{\text{m}}\log|\Delta_{\text{st(pc)}}| - 5^{\text{m}}\log|d_{\text{(pc)}}|;$$

$$\Delta_{\text{st}} = 10\,\text{pc}; \quad |\Delta_{\text{st(pc)}}| = 10; \quad \log|\Delta_{\text{st(pc)}}| = 1;$$

$$M_{\text{star}} = m_{\text{star}} + 5^{\text{m}} - 5^{\text{m}}\log|d_{\text{(pc)}}|,$$

representing the absolute magnitude of the star as a function of its apparent magnitude;

$$F_{\text{Sun},D} = \frac{\sigma R^2_{\text{Sun}} T^4_{\text{effective Sun}}}{D^2}; \quad F_{\text{Sun},\Delta_{\text{st}}} = \frac{\sigma R^2_{\text{Sun}} T^4_{\text{effective Sun}}}{\Delta^2_{\text{st}}};$$

$$\log\frac{F_{\text{Sun},D}}{F_{\text{Sun},\Delta_{\text{st}}}} = -0.4(m_{\text{Sun}} - M_{\text{Sun}});$$

$$\log\frac{\frac{\sigma R^2_{\text{Sun}} T^4_{\text{effective Sun}}}{D^2}}{\frac{\sigma R^2_{\text{Sun}} T^4_{\text{effective Sun}}}{\Delta^2_{\text{st}}}} = -0.4(m_{\text{Sun}} - M_{\text{Sun}});$$

$$\log\left(\frac{\Delta_{\text{st}}}{D}\right)^2 = -0.4(m_{\text{Sun}} - M_{\text{Sun}});$$

$$\log\left(\frac{\Delta_{\text{st(pc)}}}{D_{\text{(pc)}}}\right)^2 = -0.4(m_{\text{Sun}} - M_{\text{Sun}});$$

$$\frac{\Delta_{\text{st}}}{D} = \frac{\Delta_{\text{st(pc)}}}{D_{\text{(pc)}}} = \frac{|\Delta_{\text{st(pc)}}| \times \text{pc}}{|D_{\text{(pc)}}| \times \text{pc}} = \frac{|\Delta_{\text{st(pc)}}|}{|D_{\text{pc}}|};$$

$$2\log|\Delta_{\text{st(pc)}}| - 2\log|D_{\text{(pc)}}| = -0.4(m_{\text{Sun}} - M_{\text{Sun}});$$

$$5\log|\Delta_{\text{st(pc)}}| - 5\log|D_{\text{(pc)}}| = -(m_{\text{Sun}} - M_{\text{Sun}});$$

$$M_{\text{Sun}} = m_{\text{Sun}} + 5^{\text{m}}\log|\Delta_{\text{st(pc)}}| - 5^{\text{m}}\log|D_{\text{(pc)}}|;$$

$$\Delta_{\text{st}} = 10\,\text{pc}; \quad |\Delta_{\text{st(pc)}}| = 10; \quad \log|\Delta_{\text{st(pc)}}| = 1;$$

$$M_{\text{Sun}} = m_{\text{Sun}} + 5^{\text{m}} - 5^{\text{m}}\log|D_{\text{(pc)}}|,$$

representing the absolute magnitude of the Sun as a function of its apparent magnitude;

$$F_{\text{star},\,\Delta_{\text{st}}} = \frac{E_{\text{emitted star}}}{tS} = \frac{\frac{E_{\text{emitted star}}}{t}}{S} = \frac{L_{\text{star}}}{4\pi\Delta^2_{\text{st}}};$$

$$F_{\text{Sun},\,\Delta_{\text{st}}} = \frac{E_{\text{emitted Sun}}}{tS} = \frac{\frac{E_{\text{emitted Sun}}}{t}}{S} = \frac{L_{\text{Sun}}}{4\pi\Delta_{\text{st}}^2};$$

$$F_{\text{Sun},\,\Delta_{\text{st}}} = \frac{3.96 \times 10^{26}\,\text{Js}^{-1}}{4 \times 3.14 \times (10 \times 3.086 \times 10^{16}\,\text{m})^2}$$
$$= 3.31 \times 10^{-10}\,\text{Wm}^{-2};$$

$$\log \frac{F_{\text{star},\,\Delta_{\text{st}}}}{F_{\text{Sun},\,\Delta_{\text{st}}}} = \log \frac{\frac{L_{\text{star}}}{4\pi\Delta_{\text{st}}^2}}{\frac{L_{\text{Sun}}}{4\pi\Delta_{\text{st}}^2}} = \log \frac{L_{\text{star}}}{L_{\text{Sun}}}$$

$$= -0.4(M_{\text{bol, star}} - M_{\text{bol, Sun}});$$

$$\log \frac{F_{\text{star},\,\Delta_{\text{st}}}}{F_{\text{Sun},\Delta_{\text{st}}}} = -0.4(M_{\text{bol, star}} - M_{\text{bol, Sun}});$$

$$F_{\text{star},\,\Delta_{\text{st}}} = F_{\text{Sun},\Delta_{\text{st}}} \times 10^{-0.4(M_{\text{bol, star}} - M_{\text{bol, Sun}})};$$
$$F_{\text{Sun},\,\Delta_{\text{st}}} = 3.31 \times 10^{-10}\,\text{Wm}^{-2}.$$

*Remark*: Any absolute magnitude is a particular apparent magnitude!

If the star's parallax (the angle from which the radius of the Earth's orbit around the Sun is viewed) at a distance $d$ from the observer on the Earth is $p$, as presented in Figure 39.5, it results in:

$$\tan p \approx p_{(\text{rad})} = \frac{1\,\text{AU}}{d_{(\text{pc})}} = \frac{\frac{1}{206265}\,\text{pc}}{d_{(\text{pc})}} = \frac{\frac{1}{206265}\,\text{pc}}{|d_{(\text{pc})}|\,\text{pc}}$$
$$= \frac{1}{206265 \times |d_{(\text{pc})}|}\,\text{rad};$$

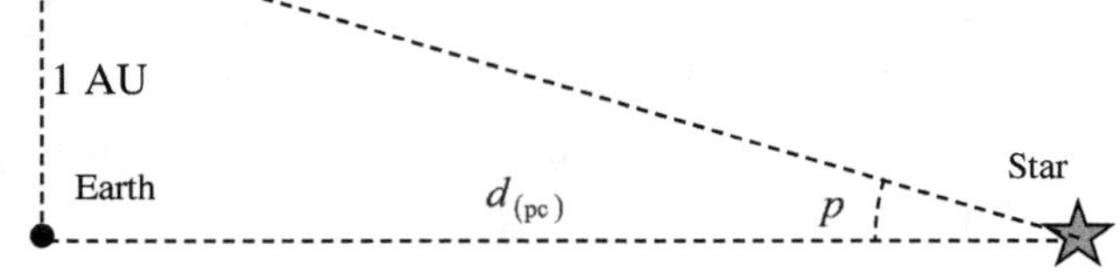


**Fig. 39.5**

$$1\,\mathrm{rad} = 206265\,\mathrm{arcsec};$$

$$p_{(\mathrm{rad})} = \frac{1}{206265 \times |d_{(\mathrm{pc})}|}\,\mathrm{rad};$$

$$p_{(\mathrm{arcs})} = \frac{1}{206265 \times |d_{(\mathrm{pc})}|} \times 206265\,\mathrm{arcs} = \frac{1}{|d_{(\mathrm{pc})}|}\,\mathrm{arcsec};$$

$$p_{(\mathrm{arcs})} = |p_{(\mathrm{arcs})}|\,\mathrm{arcs} = \frac{1}{|d_{(\mathrm{pc})}|}\,\mathrm{arcsec}; \quad |p_{(\mathrm{arcs})}| = \frac{1}{|d_{(\mathrm{pc})}|};$$

$$|d_{(\mathrm{pc})}| = \frac{1}{|p_{(\mathrm{arcsec})}|};$$

$$M_{\mathrm{star}} = m_{\mathrm{star}} + 5^{\mathrm{m}} - 5^{\mathrm{m}} \log |d_{(\mathrm{pc})}|;$$

$$M_{\mathrm{star}} = m_{\mathrm{star}} + 5^{\mathrm{m}} - 5^{\mathrm{m}} \log \frac{1}{|p_{(\mathrm{arcsec})}|};$$

$$M_{\mathrm{star}} = m_{\mathrm{star}} + 5^{\mathrm{m}} + 5^{\mathrm{m}} \log |p_{(\mathrm{arcsec})}|,$$

representing the absolute magnitude of a star as a function of its apparent magnitude and the star's parallax.

Similarly, for the Sun's absolute magnitude as function of its apparent magnitude, we obtain:

$$M_{\mathrm{Sun}} = m_{\mathrm{Sun}} + 5^{\mathrm{m}} - 5^{\mathrm{m}} \log |D_{(\mathrm{pc})}|;$$

$$D = 1\,\mathrm{AU} = \frac{1}{206265}\,\mathrm{pc}; \quad |D_{(\mathrm{pc})}| = \frac{1}{206265};$$

$$m_{\mathrm{Sun}} = -26^{\mathrm{m}}.84; \quad M_{\mathrm{Sun}} = 4^{\mathrm{m}}.71.$$

Under these conditions, from Pogson's formula for the star and for the Sun relative to the observer on the Earth, we obtain:

$$\log \frac{F_{\mathrm{star},d}}{F_{\mathrm{Sun},D}} = -0.4(m_{\mathrm{star}} - m_{\mathrm{Sun}});$$

$$m_{\mathrm{star}} = M_{\mathrm{star}} - 5^{\mathrm{m}} + 5^{\mathrm{m}} \log |d_{(\mathrm{pc})}|;$$

$$m_{\mathrm{Sun}} = M_{\mathrm{Sun}} - 5^{\mathrm{m}} + 5^{\mathrm{m}} \log |D_{(\mathrm{pc})}|;$$

$$m_{\mathrm{star}} - m_{\mathrm{Sun}} = (M_{\mathrm{star}} - M_{\mathrm{Sun}}) + 5^{\mathrm{m}} \log \frac{|d_{(\mathrm{pc})}|}{|D_{(\mathrm{pc})}|};$$

$$\log \frac{F_{\text{star},d}}{F_{\text{Sun},D}} = -0.4(M_{\text{star}} - M_{\text{Sun}}) - 2 \times \log \frac{|d_{(\text{pc})}|}{|D_{(\text{pc})}|};$$

$$\log \left(\frac{R_{\text{star}}}{R_{\text{Sun}}}\right)^2 \left(\frac{T_{\text{effective star}}}{T_{\text{effective Sun}}}\right)^4 \left(\frac{D}{d}\right)^2 = -0.4(m_{\text{star}} - m_{\text{Sun}});$$

$$\log \left(\frac{R_{\text{star}}}{R_{\text{Sun}}}\right)^2 \left(\frac{T_{\text{effective star}}}{T_{\text{effective Sun}}}\right)^4 + 2\log \frac{|D_{(\text{pc})}|}{|d_{(\text{pc})}|}$$

$$= -0.4(M_{\text{star}} - M_{\text{Sun}}) - 2\log \frac{|d_{(\text{pc})}|}{|D_{(\text{pc})}|};$$

$$\log \left(\frac{R_{\text{star}}}{R_{\text{Sun}}}\right)^2 \left(\frac{T_{\text{effective star}}}{T_{\text{effective Sun}}}\right)^4 = -0.4(M_{\text{star}} - M_{\text{Sun}});$$

$$\log \frac{R^2_{\text{star}} T^4_{\text{effective star}}}{R^2_{\text{Sun}} T^4_{\text{effective Sun}}} = -0.4(M_{\text{star}} - M_{\text{Sun}});$$

$$\log \frac{4\pi R^2_{\text{star}} \sigma T^4_{\text{effective star}}}{4\pi R^2_{\text{Sun}} \sigma T^4_{\text{effective Sun}}} = -0.4(M_{\text{star}} - M_{\text{Sun}});$$

$$L_{\text{star}} = 4\pi R^2_{\text{star}} \sigma T^4_{\text{effective star}}; \quad L_{\text{Sun}} = 4\pi R^2_{\text{Sun}} \sigma T^4_{\text{effective Sun}};$$

$$\log \frac{L_{\text{star}}}{L_{\text{Sun}}} = -0.4(M_{\text{star}} - M_{\text{Sun}});$$

$$\log \frac{F_{\text{star},d}}{F_{\text{Sun},D}} = -0.4(m_{\text{star}} - m_{\text{Sun}}).$$

The luminosity of a star represents the total energy emitted by the star's radiation on the entire electromagnetic spectrum through the star's surface, in one time unit, $L_{\text{star}} = E_{\text{total}}/t$.

For the Cepheid star and for the Sun in particular, if $F_{\text{star},d} = F_{\text{HV},d}$, Pogson's formula for an observer on the Earth is:

$$\log \frac{F_{\text{star},d}}{F_{\text{Sun},D}} = -0.4(m_{\text{star}} - m_{\text{Sun}});$$

$$\log \frac{F_{\text{HV},d}}{F_{\text{Sun},D}} = -0.4(m_{\text{HV}} - m_{\text{Sun}}),$$

where $m_{\text{HV}}$ is the apparent magnitude of the Cepheid HV2257 star.

If the Cepheid HV2257 star and the Sun were at the standard distance $\Delta_{st} = 10\,\text{pc}$, their respective apparent magnitudes, $m_{HV}$ and $m_{Sun}$, would become their absolute magnitudes $M_{HV}$ and $M_{Sun}$, respectively. Thus:

$$F_{\text{star},\,d} = \frac{\sigma R^2_{\text{star}} T^4_{\text{effective star}}}{d^2}; \quad F_{\text{Sun},\,D} = \frac{\sigma R^2_{\text{Sun}} T^4_{\text{effective Sun}}}{D^2};$$

$$F_{\text{HV},d} = \frac{\sigma R^2_{\text{HV}} T^4_{\text{effective HV}}}{d^2}; \quad F_{\text{HV},\Delta_{\text{st}}} = \frac{\sigma R^2_{\text{HV}} T^4_{\text{effective HV}}}{\Delta^2_{\text{st}}};$$

$$F_{\text{Sun},D} = \frac{\sigma R^2_{\text{Sun}} T^4_{\text{effective Sun}}}{D^2}; \quad F_{\text{Sun},\Delta_{\text{st}}} = \frac{\sigma R^2_{\text{Sun}} T^4_{\text{effective Sun}}}{\Delta^2_{\text{st}}};$$

$$M_{\text{HV}} = m_{\text{HV}} + 5^{\text{m}} - 5^{\text{m}} \log |d_{(\text{pc})}|;$$

$$M_{\text{Sun}} = m_{\text{Sun}} + 5^{\text{m}} - 5^{\text{m}} \log |D_{(\text{pc})}|.$$

Pogson's formula will become:

$$\log \frac{F_{\text{HV},d}}{F_{\text{Sun},D}} = -0.4(m_{\text{HV}} - m_{\text{Sun}});$$

$$\log \frac{L_{\text{HV}}}{L_{\text{Sun}}} = -0.4(M_{\text{HV}} - M_{\text{Sun}});$$

$$\log \frac{L_{\text{HV}}}{L_{\text{Sun}}} = -0.4(M_{\text{HV}} - M_{\text{Sun}});$$

$$\log \frac{F_{\text{HV},d}}{F_{\text{Sun},D}} = -0.4(m_{\text{HV}} - m_{\text{Sun}}).$$

Corresponding to the moments $t_1$ and $t_2$, respectively, the characteristics given in the problem statement for the variable Cepheid type HV2257 star, which is located at a distance $d$ from the observer on the Earth, are:

$$(R_1,\, T_1,\, \text{m}_1) \quad \text{and} \quad (R_2,\, T_2,\, \text{m}_2),$$

where: $R_1$ and $R_2$ are the radii of the star at the respective moments in time; $T_1$ and $T_2$ are the effective temperatures of the star at the respective moments in time; $m_1$ and $m_2$ are the apparent magnitudes of the HV2257 star at the respective moments in time. Considering this information, the fluxes for each of the two stars received by the observer are, respectively,

$$F_1 = \frac{\sigma R_1^2 T_1^4}{d^2} \quad \text{and} \quad F_2 = \frac{\sigma R_2^2 T_2^4}{d^2}.$$

Thus, using Pogson's formula for the observer on the Earth, corresponding to the HV2257 star at the moments $t_1$ and $t_2$ the result is:

$$m_1 - m_2 = -2.5 \times \log \frac{F_1}{F_2};$$

$$\log \frac{F_1}{F_2} = \log 10^{-0.4(m_1 - m_2)};$$

$$\frac{F_1}{F_2} = 10^{-0.4(m_1 - m_2)};$$

$$\frac{F_1}{F_2} = \left(\frac{T_1}{T_2}\right)^4 \left(\frac{R_1}{R_2}\right)^2;$$

$$R_2 = R_1 + \Delta R; \quad \frac{R_2}{R_1} = 1 + \frac{\Delta R_{12}}{R_1},$$

where, according to Figures 39.6 and 39.8, $\Delta R_{12}$ is:

$$\Delta R_{12} = \frac{\mathrm{v}_{\mathrm{rad},1} + \mathrm{v}_{\mathrm{rad},2}}{2} \times \Delta t_{12} = \frac{\mathrm{v}_{\mathrm{rad},1} + \mathrm{v}_{\mathrm{rad},2}}{2}(t_2 - t_1);$$

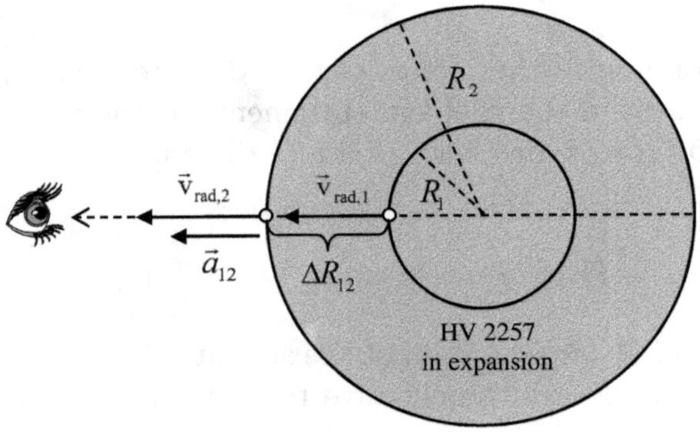


**Fig. 39.6**

$$\frac{F_1}{F_2} = \left(\frac{T_1}{T_2}\right)^4 \left(\frac{R_1}{R_1 + \Delta R_{12}}\right)^2 = \left(\frac{T_1}{T_2}\right)^4 \left(\frac{1}{1 + \frac{\Delta R_{12}}{R_1}}\right)^2;$$

$$\frac{F_1}{F_2} = \left(\frac{T_1}{T_2}\right)^4 \frac{1}{\left(1 + \frac{\Delta R_{12}}{R_1}\right)^2}; \quad \frac{F_1}{F_2} = 10^{-0.4(m_1 - m_2)};$$

$$\left(\frac{T_1}{T_2}\right)^4 \frac{1}{\left(1 + \frac{\Delta R_{12}}{R_1}\right)^2} = 10^{-0.4(m_1 - m_2)};$$

$$R_1 = \frac{\Delta R_{12}}{\left(\frac{T_1}{T_2}\right)^2 \times 10^{-0.2(m_2 - m_1)} - 1}.$$

At the moment $t_1$ for the HV2257 star located at a distance $d$ from the observer on the Earth, and for the Sun considered to be at the standard distance from the same observer, Pogson's formula for the bolometric flux is:

$$\log \frac{F_{\text{bol, star}, d}}{F_{\text{bol, Sun}, \Delta_{\text{st}}}} = -0.4(m_{\text{bol, star}} - M_{\text{bol, Sun}});$$

$$F_{\text{bol, star}, d} = F_{\text{bol, HV}, d, t_1} = F_1; \quad m_{\text{bol, star}} = m_{\text{bol}, 1};$$

$$F_{\text{bol, Sun}, \Delta_{\text{st}}} = F_{\text{Sun}, \Delta_{\text{st}}};$$

$$F_{\text{Sun}, \Delta_{\text{st}}} = 3.31 \times 10^{-10}\ \text{Wm}^{-2};$$

$$F_1 = F_{\text{Sun}, \Delta_{\text{st}}} \times 10^{-0.4(m_{\text{bol}, 1} - M_{\text{bol,Sun}})}.$$

Thus, for the distance corresponding to the Cepheid HV2257 star relative to the observer on the Earth, the following will be obtained:

$$F_1 = \frac{\sigma R_1^2 T_1^4}{d^2};$$

$$d = \sqrt{\frac{\sigma R_1^2 T_1^4}{F_1}}.$$

Identifying the linear variation of the radial velocity of the Cepheid type HV2257 star on the AB sector in the graph (Figure 39.7) between the moments $t_1$ and $t_2$, we observe that in the star's expansion the acceleration of a point on its surface is constant.

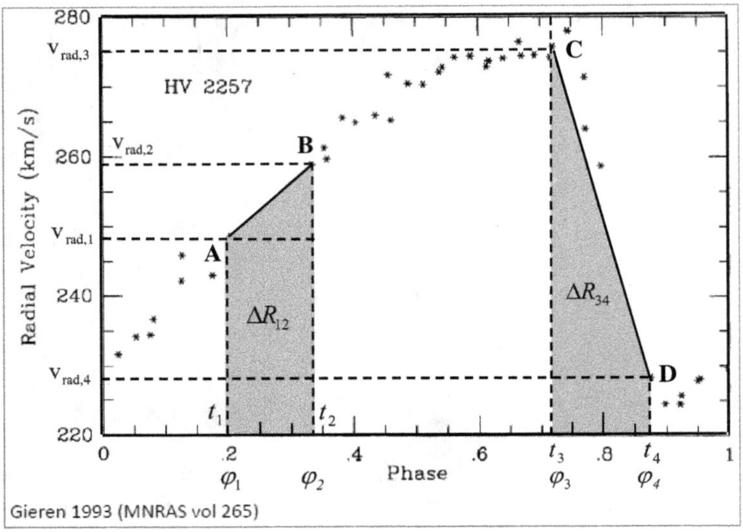


**Fig. 39.7**

The characteristics of the variable Cepheid type HV2257 star given in the problem, at a distance $d$ from the observer, corresponding to the moments $t_3$ and $t_4$, respectively, are:

$$(R_3,\, T_3,\, m_3) \quad \text{and} \quad (R_3,\, T_3,\, m_3),$$

where, corresponding to the considered moments $t_3$ and $t_4$: $R_3$ and $R_4$ are the respective radii of the star; $T_3$ and $T_4$ are the effective temperatures of the star; $m_3$ and $m_4$ are the respective apparent magnitudes of the star. It results that the flux of the two stars at the observer's level are

$$F_3 = \frac{\sigma R_3^2 T_3^4}{d^2} \quad \text{and} \quad F_4 = \frac{\sigma R_4^2 T_4^4}{d^2}.$$

Thus, using Pogson's formula, the result is:

$$m_3 - m_4 = -2.5 \times \log \frac{F_3}{F_4};$$

$$\log \frac{F_3}{F_4} = \log 10^{-0.4(m_3 - m_4)};$$

$$\frac{F_3}{F_4} = 10^{-0.4(m_3 - m_4)};$$

$$\frac{F_3}{F_4} = \left(\frac{T_3}{T_4}\right)^4 \left(\frac{R_3}{R_4}\right)^2;$$

$$R_4 = R_3 - \Delta R_{34}: \quad \frac{R_4}{R_3} = 1 - \frac{\Delta R_{34}}{R_3},$$

where, according to Figures 39.6 and 39.8, $\Delta R_{34}$ is:

$$\Delta R_{34} = \frac{v_{rad,3} + v_{rad,4}}{2} \times \Delta t_{34} = \frac{v_{rad,3} + v_{rad,4}}{2}(t_4 - t_3);$$

$$\frac{F_3}{F_4} = \left(\frac{T_3}{T_4}\right)^4 \left(\frac{R_3}{R_3 - \Delta R_{34}}\right)^2 = \left(\frac{T_3}{T_4}\right)^4 \left(\frac{1}{1 - \frac{\Delta R_{34}}{R_3}}\right)^2;$$

$$\frac{F_3}{F_4} = \left(\frac{T_3}{T_4}\right)^4 \frac{1}{\left(1 - \frac{\Delta R_{34}}{R_3}\right)^2}; \quad \frac{F_3}{F_4} = 10^{-0.4(m_3 - m_4)};$$

$$\left(\frac{T_3}{T_4}\right)^4 \frac{1}{\left(1 - \frac{\Delta R_{34}}{R_3}\right)^2} = 10^{-0.4(m_3 - m_4)};$$

$$R_3 = \frac{\Delta R_{34}}{1 - \left(\frac{T_3}{T_4}\right)^2 \times 10^{-0.2(m_4 - m_3)}}.$$

For the HV2257 star located at a distance $d$ from the observer on the Earth at the moment $t_3$ and for the Sun considered to be at the standard distance from the same observer, Pogson's formula for

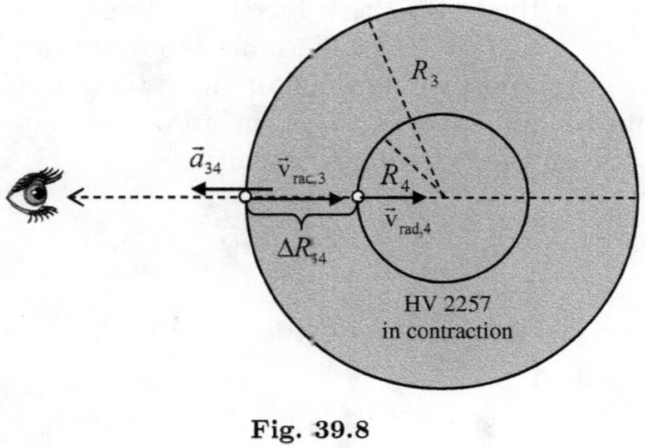


**Fig. 39.8**

bolometric flux is:

$$\log \frac{F_{\text{bol, star}, d}}{F_{\text{bol, Sun}, \Delta_{\text{st}}}} = -0.4(m_{\text{bol, star}} - M_{\text{bol, Sun}});$$

$$F_{\text{bol, star}, d} = F_{\text{bol, HV}, d, t_1} = F_3; \quad m_{\text{bol, star}} = m_{\text{bol}, 3};$$

$$F_{\text{bol, Sun}, \Delta_{\text{st}}} = F_{\text{Sun}, \Delta_{\text{st}}};$$

$$F_{\text{Sun}, \Delta_{\text{st}}} = 3.31 \times 10^{-10}\,\text{Wm}^{-2};$$

$$F_3 = F_{\text{Sun}, \Delta_{\text{st}}} \times 10^{-0.4(m_{\text{bol}, 3} - M_{\text{bol,Sun}})}.$$

Thus, at the distance where the Cepheid HV2257 star is located relative to the observer on the Earth, we obtain the following result:

$$F_3 = \frac{\sigma R_3^2 T_3^4}{d^2};$$

$$d = \sqrt{\frac{\sigma R_3^2 T_3^4}{F_3}}.$$

Identifying the linear variation of the radial velocity on the CD sector in the graph (Figure 39.7) between the moments $t_3$ and $t_4$, we observe that contrary to the star, the acceleration of a point on its surface is constant.

## Annex: Magnitudes

If Pogson's formula is applied for the star and for the Sun, considering the ratio of their respective flux (brightness) received by the observer on the Earth, we can determine the difference in apparent magnitudes. With Pogson's formula for the ratio of luminosities, we can determine the difference between the absolute magnitudes or the difference between the bolometric magnitudes:

$$\log \frac{F_{\text{star},d}}{F_{\text{Sun},D}} = -0.4(m_{\text{star}} - m_{\text{Sun}});$$

$$\log \frac{L_{\text{star}}}{L_{\text{Sun}}} = -0.4(M_{\text{star}} - M_{\text{Sun}});$$

$$\log \frac{L_{\text{star}}}{L_{\text{Sun}}} = -0.4(M_{\text{bol, star}} - M_{\text{bol, Sun}}).$$

The apparent magnitude $m_{\text{star}}$ of a star is a measure of its total energy corresponding to radiation in the visible part of the electromagnetic spectrum, received from the star by an observer located on the Earth. It is visually estimated and it depends on the distance between the star and the observer.

The difference between the apparent magnitudes of two stars is given by the ratio of the energetic flux corresponding to the visible radiation of those two stars at the observer's level on the Earth:

$$\log \frac{F_{\text{star 1}}}{F_{\text{star 2}}} = -0.4(m_{\text{star 1}} - m_{\text{star2}}).$$

The apparent bolometric magnitude $m_{\text{bol, star}}$ of a star is a measurement of its total energy corresponding to all wavelengths in the entire electromagnetic spectrum received by an observer on the Earth. The apparent bolometric magnitude is determined with a device named a bolometer and it depends on the distance between the star and the observer.

The difference between the apparent bolometric magnitudes of two stars is determined by the ratio of bolometric energetic flux corresponding to all radiation of the two stars at the level of the observer on the Earth:

$$\log \frac{F_{\text{total, star 1}}}{F_{\text{total, star 2}}} = -0.4(m_{\text{bol, star 1}} - m_{\text{bol, star 2}}).$$

If the observer is at the same standard distance $\Delta_{\text{st}} = 10\,\text{pc}$ from the star or from the Sun, each of their two apparent magnitudes ($m_{\text{star}}, m_{\text{Sun}}, m_{\text{bol, star}}, m_{\text{bol, Sun}}$) becomes their absolute magnitudes ($M_{\text{star}}, M_{\text{Sun}}, M_{\text{bol, star}}, M_{\text{bol, Sun}}$).

The differences between the absolute magnitudes of the two stars, as well as the difference between the absolute bolometric magnitudes of the two stars, are determined by the ratio of the two stars' luminosities:

$$\log \frac{L_{\text{star 1}}}{L_{\text{star 2}}} = -0.4(M_{\text{star 1}} - M_{\text{star 2}})$$
$$= -0.4(M_{\text{bol, star 1}} - M_{\text{bol, star 2}}).$$

Pogson's formula can be written for the flux ratio corresponding to any two celestial bodies, for instance for a star located at a distance $d$ from the observer and for the Sun located at the standard distance $\Delta_{\text{st}}$. Thus, it results in

$$\log \frac{F_{\text{star}, d}}{F_{\text{Sun}, \Delta_{\text{st}}}} = -0.4(m_{\text{star}} - M_{\text{Sun}}),$$

or, for the bolometric flux,

$$\log \frac{F_{\text{bol, star}, d}}{F_{\text{bol, Sun}, \Delta_{\text{st}}}} = -0.4(m_{\text{bol, star}} - M_{\text{bol, Sun}}).$$

The color index of a star represents the difference between the apparent magnitudes for two colors:

$$B - V = m_B - m_V = -2.5 \log \frac{F_B}{F_V}.$$

# Problem 40

# Artificial Satellites

Two artificial satellites, $S_1$ and $S_2$, move around the Earth on a circular orbit of a radius twice as big as the Earth's radius. At a certain moment, the two satellites must separate from one another. Satellite $S_1$ will travel towards another planet, and $S_2$ will orbit around the Earth on an elliptic trajectory, tangent to the Earth's surface at a point opposed to the location where the two satellites have separated.

*Determine* the ratio of the two satellites' masses, $m_1/m_2$, that will allow the two satellites to move on the previously mentioned trajectories after their separation. *Analyze* all possible variants.

## Solution

**a)** In Figure 40.1, the following notation is used: $\vec{v}$ – the $(S_1; S_2)$ system's velocity relative to the center of the Earth before the two satellites' separation; $\vec{v}_1$ – the velocity of the $S_1$ satellite (the one that becomes an interplanetary station) relative to the center of the Earth, after the separation; $\vec{v}_2$ – the velocity of the $S_2$ satellite (which continues to orbit around the Earth) relative to the center of the Earth, after the separation.

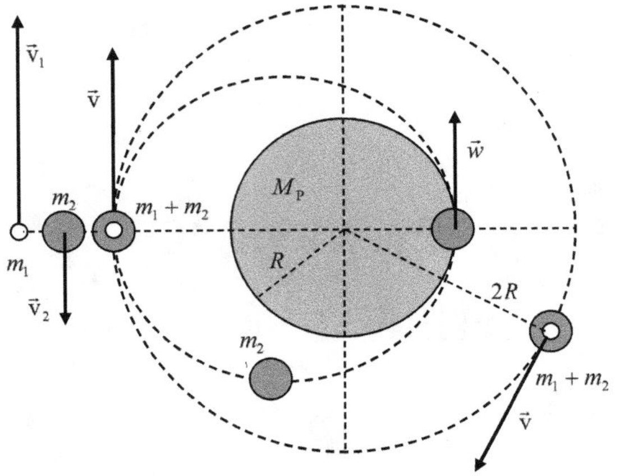


**Fig. 40.1**

The law of conservation of momentum yields this result:

$$(m_1 + m_2)\vec{v} = m_1\vec{v}_1 + m_2\vec{v}_2; \quad (m_1 + m_2)v = m_1 v_1 - m_2 v_2;$$

$$m_1(v_1 - v) = m_2(v + v_2); \quad \frac{m_1}{m_2} = \frac{v_2 + v}{v_1 - v},$$

where

$$v\sqrt{K\frac{M_P}{2R}}.$$

After the separation, the $S_1$ satellite must travel on a parabolic orbit with the Earth in its focus in order to move towards another planet, as presented in Figure 40.2.

The separation of the $S_1$ satellite takes place at the vertex of the parabola, with a velocity of $v_1$, at the distance $2R$ from the center of the Earth. Knowing that the total mechanical energy of the $S_1$ satellite–Earth system is zero at any moment, the result is:

$$W = \frac{m_1 v_1^2}{2} - K\frac{m_1 M_P}{2R} = 0; \quad v_1 = \sqrt{K\frac{M_P}{R}} = \sqrt{2\frac{K M_P}{2R}}.$$

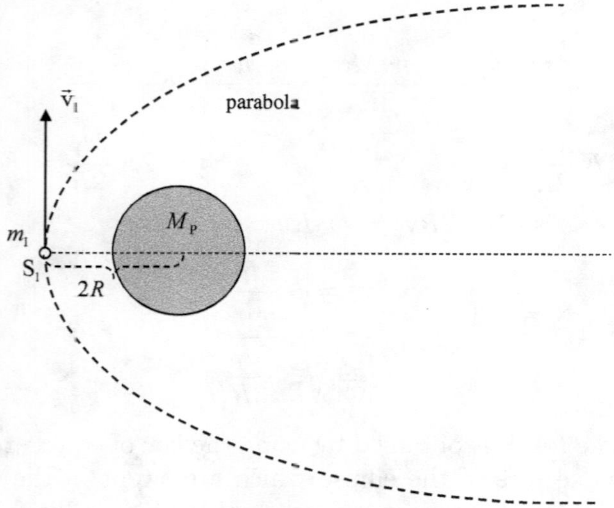


**Fig. 40.2**

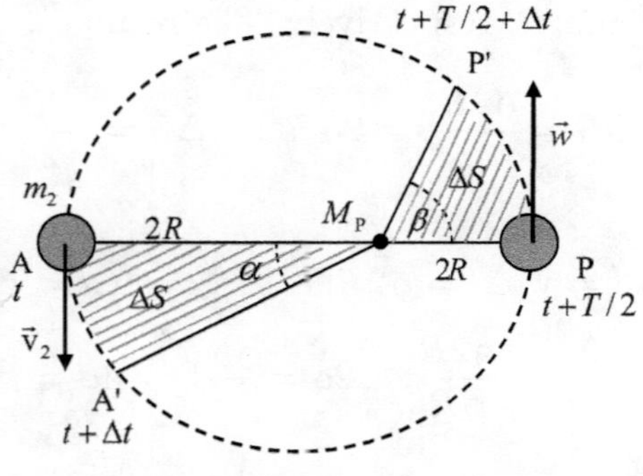


**Fig. 40.3**

To calculate the velocity ($v_2$) of the $S_2$ satellite just after the separation, we use Kepler's second law (the law of equal areas, or the momentum conservation law) and the law of energy conservation. In Figure 40.3, the areas swept by the vector radius of satellite $S_2$, after the separation of the $S_1$ satellite in the same very small time interval, $\Delta t$, close to the apogee and to the perigee, respectively, are shaded.

The results are:

$$\frac{m_2 \mathrm{v}_2^2}{2} - K\frac{m_2 M_\mathrm{P}}{2R} = \frac{m_2 w^2}{2} - K\frac{m_2 M_\mathrm{P}}{R};$$

$$\frac{\mathrm{v}_2^2}{2} - K\frac{M_\mathrm{P}}{2R} = \frac{w^2}{2} - K\frac{M_\mathrm{P}}{R}; \quad w^2 - \mathrm{v}_2^2 = 2K\frac{M_\mathrm{P}}{2R} = K\frac{M_\mathrm{P}}{R};$$

$$m_2 2R\mathrm{v}_2 = m_2 R w; \quad w = 2\mathrm{v}_2;$$

$$3\mathrm{v}_2^2 = K\frac{M_\mathrm{P}}{R};$$

$$\mathrm{v}_2 = \sqrt{K\frac{M_\mathrm{P}}{3R}}.$$

The same result is obtained by using the law of equal areas for the two shaded sectors of the ellipse which are swept in the same very brief time interval by the vector radius of the $S_2$ satellite close to the apogee and to the perigee, respectively. Under these conditions, the AA$'$ and PP$'$ sectors of the ellipse can be considered circular arcs of equal radius $2R$ and $R$, respectively. The result is:

$$\Delta S = \frac{\alpha 4R^2}{2} = 2\alpha R^2; \quad \Delta S = \frac{\beta R^2}{2};$$

$$4\alpha = \beta;$$

$$\mathrm{AA}' = \mathrm{v}_2 \Delta t = \alpha 2R; \quad \mathrm{PP}' = w\Delta t = \beta R;$$

$$\frac{\mathrm{v}_2 \Delta t}{w\Delta t} = \frac{\alpha 2R}{\beta R}; \quad 2\alpha = \frac{\mathrm{v}_2}{w}\beta; \quad 4\alpha = \beta;$$

$$w = 2\mathrm{v}_2; \quad w^2 - \mathrm{v}_2^2 = K\frac{M_\mathrm{P}}{R};$$

$$\mathrm{v}_2 = \sqrt{K\frac{M_\mathrm{P}}{3R}};$$

$$\frac{m_1}{m_2} = \frac{\mathrm{v}_2 + \mathrm{v}}{\mathrm{v}_1 - \mathrm{v}};$$

$$\frac{m_1}{m_2} = \frac{\sqrt{K\frac{M_\mathrm{P}}{3R}} + \sqrt{K\frac{M_\mathrm{P}}{2R}}}{\sqrt{K\frac{M_\mathrm{P}}{R}} - \sqrt{K\frac{M_\mathrm{P}}{2R}}} = \frac{\sqrt{2} + \sqrt{3}}{\sqrt{3}(\sqrt{2} - 1)} \approx 4.387; \quad m_1 > m_2.$$

**b)** If, after the separation of the $S_1$ satellite, the velocities of the system's elements have the orientation presented in Figure 40.4, the result is:

$$(m_1 + m_2)\vec{v} = m_1\vec{v}_1 + m_2\vec{v}_2; \quad (m_1 + m_2)v = m_1 v_1 + m_2 v_2;$$

$$m_1(v_1 - v) = m_2(v - v_2);$$

$$\frac{m_1}{m_2} = \frac{v - v_2}{v_1 - v};$$

$$v = \sqrt{K\frac{M_P}{2R}}; \quad v_1 = \sqrt{K\frac{M_P}{R}}; \quad v_2 = \sqrt{K\frac{M_P}{3R}};$$

$$\frac{m_1}{m_2} = \frac{\sqrt{K\frac{M_P}{2R}} - \sqrt{K\frac{M_P}{3R}}}{\sqrt{K\frac{M_P}{R}} - \sqrt{K\frac{M_P}{2R}}};$$

$$\frac{m_1}{m_2} = \frac{(\sqrt{3} - \sqrt{2})}{\sqrt{3}(\sqrt{2} - 1)} \approx 0.443; \quad m_1 \ll m_2.$$

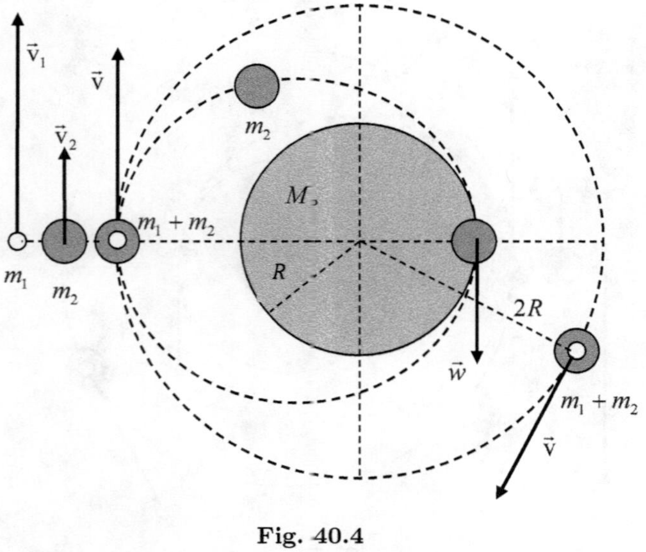


**Fig. 40.4**

**c)** If, after the separation of the $S_1$ satellite, the velocities of the system's elements have the orientation presented in Figure 40.5, the results is:

$$(m_1 + m_2)\vec{v} = m_1\vec{v}_1 + m_2\vec{v}_2; \quad (m_1 + m_2)v = -m_1 v_1 + m_2 v_2;$$

$$m_1(v_1 + v) = m_2(v_2 - v);$$

$$\frac{m_1}{m_2} = \frac{v_2 - v}{v_1 + v};$$

$$v = \sqrt{K\frac{M_P}{2R}}; \quad v_1 = \sqrt{K\frac{M_P}{R}}; \quad v_2 = \sqrt{K\frac{M_P}{3R}};$$

$$\frac{m_1}{m_2} = \frac{\sqrt{K\frac{M_P}{3R}} - \sqrt{K\frac{M_P}{2R}}}{\sqrt{K\frac{M_P}{R}} + \sqrt{K\frac{M_P}{2R}}};$$

$$\frac{m_1}{m_2} = \frac{\left(\sqrt{2} - \sqrt{3}\right)}{\sqrt{3}\left(\sqrt{2} + 1\right)} < 0,$$

which is an impossible situation. That is, in this case, after the separation, the two satellites cannot have the specified trajectories!

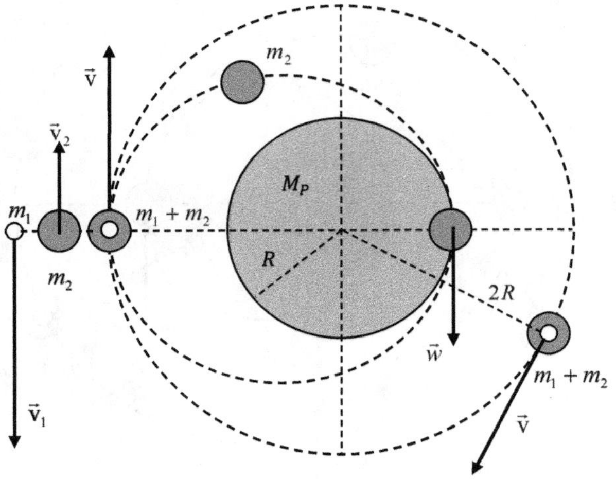


**Fig. 40.5**

**d)** If the orientations of the system's element velocities after the interplanetary station is launched are those presented in Figure 40.6, the result is:

$$(m_1 + m_2)\vec{v} = m_1\vec{v}_1 + m_2\vec{v}_2; \quad (m_1 + m_2)v = -m_1 v_1 - m_2 v_2;$$

$$m_1(v + v_1) = -m_2(v + v_2);$$

$$\frac{m_1}{m_2} = -\frac{v + v_2}{v + v_1} < 0,$$

which also represents an impossible situation.

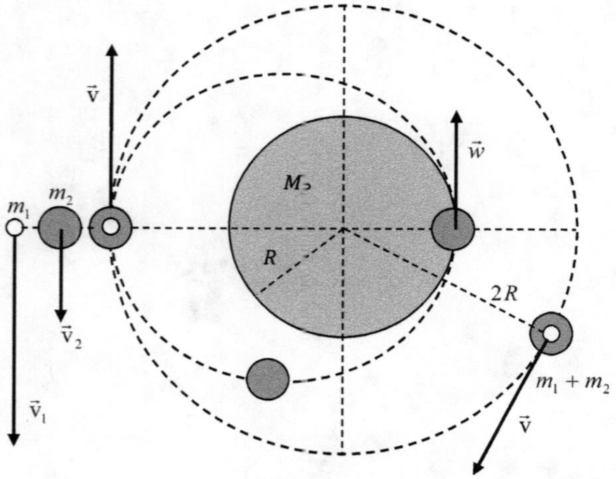


**Fig. 40.6**

# Problem 41

# A Launched Satellite

A special satellite S is moving in the equatorial plane of the Earth, on an ellipse of eccentricity $e$ with the Earth in one of its foci. When the satellite is at perigee and the distance between the satellite and the center of the Earth is $2R$, a special mini-satellite, $S_0$, is launched from the satellite. The $S_0$ mini-satellite has an interplanetary destination. $R$ is the radius of the Earth.

*Determine* the values for the ratio of the two satellites' masses, $m/M$, if after the $S_0$ satellite is launched, S continues orbiting around the Earth on a circular trajectory.

## Solution

When the special satellite S is at the minimum distance from the center of the Earth, as presented in Figure 41.1, its velocity is:

$$u = \mathrm{v}_{\max} = \sqrt{KM_{\mathrm{P}}\left(\frac{2}{r_{\min}} - \frac{1}{a}\right)};$$

$$r_{\min} = \frac{p}{1+e} = \frac{a(1-e^2)}{1+e} = a(1-e);$$

$$r_{\min} = 2R; \quad 2R = a(1-e);$$

$$a = \frac{2R}{1-e};$$

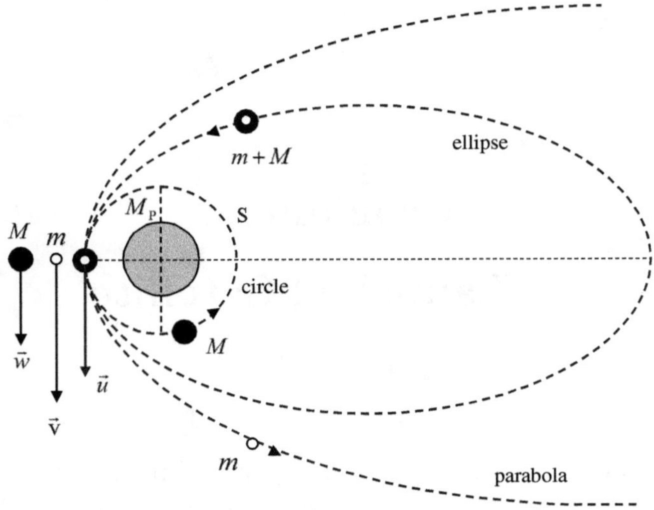


**Fig. 41.1**

$$u = \mathrm{v}_{\max} = \sqrt{KM_{\mathrm{P}}\left(\frac{2}{2R} - \frac{1-e}{2R}\right)} = \sqrt{\frac{KM_{\mathrm{P}}}{2R}(1+e)};$$

$$u = \sqrt{\frac{KM_{\mathrm{P}}}{2R}(1+e)}.$$

After launching the mini-satellite with an interplanetary destination, $\mathrm{S}_0$ travels on a parabolic trajectory. If its velocity at the launching moment is

$$\mathrm{v} = \sqrt{2\frac{KM_{\mathrm{P}}}{r_{\min}}} = \sqrt{2\frac{KM_{\mathrm{P}}}{2R}} = \sqrt{\frac{KM_{\mathrm{P}}}{R}},$$

and the velocity of satellite S, which continues to move on a circular trajectory, must be

$$w = \sqrt{\frac{KM}{r_{\min}}} = \sqrt{\frac{KM}{2R}}.$$

Using the momentum conservation law, it results in:

$$(m+M)\vec{u} = m\vec{\mathrm{v}} + M\vec{w};$$

$$(m+M)u = m\mathrm{v} + Mw;$$

$$\frac{m}{M} = \frac{u-w}{\mathrm{v}-u};$$

$$\frac{m}{M} = \frac{\sqrt{\frac{KM_{\mathrm{P}}}{2R}(1+e)} - \sqrt{\frac{KM_{\mathrm{P}}}{2R}}}{\sqrt{2\frac{KM_{\mathrm{P}}}{2R}} - \sqrt{\frac{KM_{\mathrm{P}}}{2R}(1+e)}} = \frac{\sqrt{1+e}-1}{\sqrt{2}-\sqrt{1+e}}.$$

# Problem 42

# A Space Station Reunites With a Satellite

A space station moves together with a satellite on a circular orbit of radius $1.25R$ around the Earth, where $R$ is the Earth's radius. At a certain moment, the satellite is catapulted from the space station on the tangent to the circular trajectory, in the direction of the movement. After that, the satellite will continue its movement on an elliptic orbit, with the apogee at a distance of $10R$ from the center of the Earth. The space station and the satellite are considered to be material points.

If $m$ is the mass of the satellite, and $M$ is the space station mass, *determine* the $m/M$ ratio for which the satellite will meet with the space station again after one rotation of the satellite around the Earth. The following values are known: $10^{2/3} = 4.64; 11^{2/3} = 4.94$.

## Solution

Figure 42.1 shows the circular trajectory of the system before the two bodies have separated, as well as the elliptical trajectories of the system's elements after the separation: 1 – the trajectory of the satellite with mass $m$; 2 – the trajectory of the space station of mass $M$.

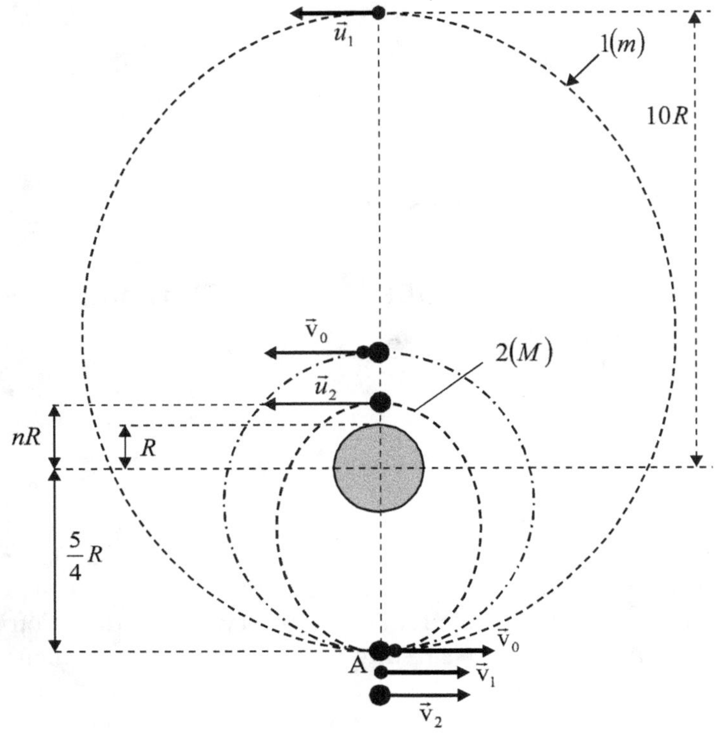


**Fig. 42.1**

Considering $T_1$ and $T_2$ to be the rotation periods of the satellite and of the shuttle, respectively, then the two bodies can meet again at point A after one rotation of the satellite, if

$$\frac{T_1}{T_2} = k > 1,$$

where $k$ must be an integer.

The semi-axes of the two ellipses are:

$$a_1 = \frac{1}{2}\left(\frac{5}{4}R + 10R\right) = \frac{45}{8}R; \quad a_2 = \frac{1}{2}\left(\frac{5}{4}R + nR\right) = \frac{5+4n}{8}R.$$

According to Kepler's third law, the result is:

$$\frac{T_1^2}{T_2^2} = \frac{a_1^3}{a_2^3}; \quad \frac{T_1}{T_2} = \left(\frac{45}{5+4n}\right)^{\frac{3}{2}} = k.$$

The two elements of the system separate by respecting the law of conservation of momentum:

$$(M+m)\vec{v}_0 = m\vec{v}_1 + M\vec{v}_2; \quad (M+m)v_0 = mv_1 + Mv_2.$$

Here, $v_0$ is the velocity of the two joined bodies on the circular trajectory:

$$v_0 = 2\sqrt{\frac{g_0 R}{5}}; \quad g_0 = K\frac{M_E}{R^2}; \quad M_E \text{ – the Earth's mass.}$$

The movement of the two elements after separation complies with the conservation laws for energy and angular momentum.

We know that, at a certain point, the gravitational potential energies of the satellite–Earth and shuttle–Earth systems are:

$$E_{p_1} = -mg_0\frac{R^2}{r_1}; \quad E_{p_2} = -Mg_0\frac{R^2}{r_2};$$

$$\frac{mv_1^2}{2} - mg_0\frac{R^2}{\frac{5}{4}R} = \frac{mu_1^2}{2} - mg_0\frac{R^2}{10R};$$

$$\frac{Mv_2^2}{2} - Mg_0\frac{R^2}{\frac{5}{4}R} = \frac{Mu_2^2}{2} - Mg_0\frac{R^2}{nR};$$

$$\frac{5}{4}v_1 = 10u_1; \quad \frac{5}{4}v_2 = nu_2; \quad v_1 = \frac{4v_0}{3}; \quad v_2 = 2v_0\sqrt{\frac{2n}{4n+5}};$$

$$n = 5\left(1-\frac{m}{3M}\right)^2 : 4\left(2-\left(1-\frac{m}{3M}\right)^2\right).$$

Imposing a condition that prevents the shuttle from falling on the Earth ($n < 1$), we obtain:

$$\frac{m}{M} < 3 - 2\sqrt{2};$$

$$\frac{m}{M} = 3 - \sqrt{2(9-k^{2/3})}; \quad k < 5^{3/2} = 11.2;$$

$$\frac{m}{M} > 0; \quad k > 9.5;$$

$$9.5 < k < 11.2.$$

Since $k$ must be an integer, the possible values are: $k_1 = 10$, $k_2 = 11$.

This results in:

$$\left(\frac{m}{M}\right)_1 = 3 - \sqrt{2(9 - 10^{2/3})} = 0.047;$$

$$\left(\frac{m}{M}\right)_2 = 3 - \sqrt{2(9 - 11^{2/3})} = 0.150.$$

# Other Books by Mihail Sandu

1. **PROBLEME DE FIZICĂ PENTRU GIMNAZIU**, *Editura Didactică şi Pedagogică*, Bucharest, 1977, 327 p.
2. **FIZICĂ, MANUAL PENTRU CLASA a VI-a**, coauthor Emanuel Nichita, *Editura Didactică şi Pedagogică*, Bucharest, 1978, 160 p.
3. **PROBLEME DE FIZICĂ PENTRU GIMNAZIU**, coauthors Emanuel Nichita and Tudorel Ştefan, *Editura Didactică şi Pedagogică*, Bucharest, 1982, 223 p.
4. **CAIET METODIC CU PROBLEME DE FIZICĂ PENTRU GIMNAZIU**, *Casa Personalului Didactic*, Rm. Vâlcea, 1983, 181 p.
5. **GHIDUL PROFESORULUI ŞI AL ELEVULUI PENTRU CERCURILE DE FIZICĂ, VOL. I**, *Casa de Cultură a Ştiinţei şi Tehnicii pentru tineret*, Rm. Vâlcea, 1984, 498 p.
6. **GHIDUL PROFESORULUI ŞI AL ELEVULUI PENTRU CERCURILE DE FIZICĂ, VOL. II**, *Casa de Cultură a Ştiinţei şi Tehnicii pentru tineret*, Rm. Vâlcea, 1984, 405 p.
7. **CULEGERE DE PROBLEME DE FIZICĂ, VOL. I**, *Societatea de Ştiinţe Fizice şi Chimice din România*, Bucharest, 1986, 338 p.

8. **CULEGERE DE PROBLEME DE FIZICĂ, VOL. II**, *Societatea de Ştiinţe Fizice şi Chimice din România*, Bucharest, 1986, 118 p.

9. **PROBLEME DE FIZICĂ**, *Editura Scrisul Românesc*, Craiova, 1988, 277 p.

10. **GHID PENTRU CERCURILE DE FIZICĂ**, *Editura Academiei Române*, Bucharest, 1991, 325 p.

11. **PROBLEME DE FIZICĂ PENTRU GIMNAZIU**, *Editura Didactică şi Pedagogică*, Bucharest, 1991, 208 p.

12. **500 PROBLEME DE FIZICĂ**, *Editura Tehnică*, Bucharest, 1991, 283 p.

13. **PROBLEME DE PERFORMANŢĂ ÎN FIZICĂ**, *Editura Tehnică*, Bucharest, 1992, 340 p.

14. **PROBLEME DE FIZICĂ PENTRU GIMNAZIU**, *Editura Lumina*, Chişinău, Republic of Moldova, 1993, 272 p.

15. **CAIET METODIC CU PROBLEME DE FIZICĂ PENTRU GIMNAZIU**, *Editura Lumina*, Chişinău, Republic of Moldova, 1993, 179 p.

16. **TEME ŞI PROBLEME PENTRU CERCURILE DE FIZICĂ**, *Editura Hyperion XXI*, Bucharest, 1993, 254 p.

17. **PROBLEME DE FIZICĂ DIN REVISTA "KVANT", VOL. I**, *Editura Didactică şi Pedagogică*, Bucharest, 1993, 182 p.

18. **PROBLEME DE FIZICĂ PENTRU LICEU**, *Editura Ex Libris*, Rm. Vâlcea, 1993, 378 p.

19. **PROBLEME DE FIZICĂ DIN REVISTA "KVANT", VOL. II**, *Editura Didactică şi Pedagogică*, Bucharest, 1994, 194 p.

20. **CULEGERE DE PROBLEME DE FIZICĂ, VOL. I**, *Editura TipCim*, Chişinău, Republic of Moldova, 1995, 338 p.

21. **CULEGERE DE PROBLEME DE FIZICĂ, VOL. II**, *Editura TipCim*, Chişinău, Republic of Moldova, 1995, 117 p.

22. **GHIDUL PROFESORULUI ŞI AL ELEVULUI PENTRU CERCURILE DE FIZICĂ, VOL. I**, *Editura TipCim, Chişinău*, Republic of Moldova, 1995, 498 p.

23. **PROBLEME DE FIZICĂ PENTRU GIMNAZIU**, *Editura Didactică şi Pedagogică*, Bucharest, 1995, 202 p.

24. **GHIDUL PROFESORULUI ŞI AL ELEVULUI PENTRU CERCURILE DE FIZICĂ, VOL. II**, *Editura TipCim, Chişinău*, Republic of Moldova, 1996, 400 p.

25. **PROBLEME DE FIZICĂ PENTRU GIMNAZIU**, *Editura ALL*, Bucharest, 1996, 1st Edition, 503 p.

26. **PROBLEME DE FIZICĂ DIN REVISTA "KVANT", VOL. III**, *Editura Didactică şi Pedagogică*, Bucharest, 1996, 208 p.

27. **PROBLEME DE FIZICĂ DIN REVISTA "KVANT", VOL. IV**, *Editura Didactică şi Pedagogică*, Bucharest, 1996, 229 p.

28. **PROBLEME DE FIZICĂ PENTRU GIMNAZIU**, *Editura ALL*, Bucharest, 1997, 2nd Edition, 503 p.

29. **PROBLEME DE FIZICĂ – CONCURSURI ŞI OLIMPIADE**, *Editura Petrion*, Bucharest, 1998, 335 p.

30. **PROBLEME DE FIZICĂ PENTRU GIMNAZIU**, *Editura ALL*, Bucharest, 1998, 3rd Edition, 503 p.

31. **MECANICĂ FIZICĂ** (university course), *Editura Didactică şi Pedagogică*, Bucharest, 2002, 462 p.

32. **MECANICĂ TEORETICĂ** (university course), *Editura Didactică şi Pedagogică*, Bucharest, 2002, 476 p.

33. **ASTRONOMIE** (university course), *Editura Didactică şi Pedagogică*, Bucharest, 2003, 400 p.

34. **FIZICĂ. ÎNVĂŢĂMÂNTUL LICEAL ŞI CERCETAREA ŞTIINŢIFICĂ. MONOGRAFIA JUDEŢULUI VÂLCEA**, *Editura Conphys*, Rm. Vâlcea, 2004, 406 p.

35. **IN MEMORIAM – PROFESORUL LIVIU TĂTAR**, *Editura Conphys*, Rm. Vâlcea, 2004.

36. **PROBLEME DE FIZICĂ PENTRU GIMNAZIU**, *Editura ALL*, Bucharest, 2005, 4th Edition, 416 p.

37. **TEORIA RELATIVITĂŢII** (university course), *Editura Didactică şi Pedagogică*, Bucharest, 2005, 341 p.

38. **EVRIKA! PROBLEME DE FIZICĂ**, *Editura Didactică şi Pedagogică*, Bucharest, 2005, 600 p.

39. **CONCURSUL DE SELECŢIE PENTRU OLIMPIADA INTERNAŢIONALĂ DE FIZICĂ – 2005**, coauthor, *Editura Conphys*, Rm. Vâlcea, 2006, 262 p.

40. **PROBLEME DE FIZICĂ PENTRU GIMNAZIU**, *Editura ALL*, Bucharest, 2007, 5th Edition, 416 p.

41. **ACTIVITĂŢI OLIMPICE LA C.P.P.P. CĂLIMĂNEŞTI-CĂCIULATA, 2004 – 2005 – 2006, ASTRONOMIE ŞI ŞTIINŢE**, *Editura Conphys*, Rm. Vâlcea, 2007, 611 p.

42. **ACTIVITĂŢI OLIMPICE LA C.P.P.P. CĂLIMĂNEŞTI-CĂCIULATA, 2004 – 2005 – 2006, FIZICĂ**, *Editura Conphys*, Rm. Vâlcea, 2007, 530 p.

43. **TOP-FIZ, PROBLEME DE FIZICĂ**, *Editura Didactică şi Pedagogică*, Bucharest, 2009, 833 p.

44. **LUCRĂRI EXPERIMENTALE DE FIZICĂ**, *Editura Conphys*, Rm. Vâlcea, 2009, 156 p.

45. **ŞTIINŢE PENTRU JUNIORI. CHIMIE – FIZICĂ – BIOLOGIE**, coauthor, *Editura MISTRAL*, Bucharest, 2009, 358 p.

46. **CONCURSUL INTERJUDEŢEAN DE FIZICĂ "LIVIU TĂTAR"**, coauthor, *Editura Universitaria*, Craiova, 2011, 236 p.

47. **ŞTIINŢE PENTRU JUNIORI. CHIMIE – FIZICĂ – BIOLOGIE**, coauthor, *Editura MISTRAL*, 2nd Edition, Bucharest, 2011, 358 p.

48. **PROBLEME ŞI EXPERIMENTE DE FIZICĂ**, *Editura Didactică şi Pedagogică*, Bucharest, 2012, 820 p.

49. **INTERNATIONAL OLYMPIAD ON ASTRONOMY AND ASTROPHYSICS, PROBLEMS, 2007–2013, SOLUTIONS, COMMENTS, DETAILS, EXTENSIONS**, *Editura CYGNUS*, Suceava, 2014, 600 p.

50. **OLIMPIADA INTERNAŢIONALĂ DE ASTRONOMIE Ş ASTROFIZICĂ, PROBLEME, VOL. 1**, *Editura CYGNUS*, Suceava, 2015, 400 p.

51. **OLIMPIADA INTERNAŢIONALĂ DE ASTRONOMIE ŞI ASTROFIZICĂ, PROBLEME, VOL. 2**, *Editura CYGNUS*, Suceava, 2015, 460 p.

52. **CONCURSUL INTERJUDEŢEAN DE FIZICĂ "LIVIU TĂTAR"**, coauthor, *Editura else*, Craiova, 2016, 280 p.

53. **INTERNATIONAL OLYMPIAD ON ASTRONOMY AND ASTROPHYSICS, PROBLEMS, VOL. I**, *Trisula Adisakti*, Jakarta, Indonesia; Amazon, USA, 2016, 500 p.

54. **INTERNATIONAL OLYMPIAD ON ASTRONOMY AND ASTROPHYSICS, PROBLEMS, VOL. II**, *Trisula Adisakti*, Jakarta, Indonesia; Amazon, USA, 450 p.

55. **ASTRONOMIE Ş ASTROFIZICĂ – EVENIMENTE OLIMPICE – 1996–2010, PROBLEME**, *Editura Didactică şi Pedagogică*, Bucharest, 2018, 972 p.

**56.** **EXPERIMENTE DE FIZICĂ**, *Editura Didactică şi Pedagogică*, Bucharest, 2018, 476 p.

**57.** **ASTRONOMIE ŞI ASTROFIZICĂ. TEME ŞI PROBLEME PENTRU OLIMPIADE Ę CONCURSURI**, *Editura Didactică şi Pedagogică*, Bucharest, 2019.

**58.** **ASTRONOMY AND ASTROPHYSICS. THEMES AND PROBLEMS FOR OLYMPIADS AND COMPETITIONS**, *Editura Didactică şi Pedagogică*, Bucharest, 2019.

**59.** **ASTRONOMIE ŞI ASTROFIZICĂ – EVENIMENTE OLIMPICE – 2011–2013, PROBLEME, VOL. II**, *Editura Didactică şi Pedagogică*, Bucharest, 2020, 500 p.

**60.** **ASTRONOMIE ŞI ASTROFIZICĂ – EVENIMENTE OLIMPICE – 2013–2015, PROBLEME, VOL. III**, *Editura Didactică şi Pedagogică*, Bucharest, 2020, 500 p.

**61.** **ASTRONOMIE ŞI ASTROFIZICĂ – EVENIMENTE OLIMPICE – 2016–2017, PROBLEME, VOL. IV**, *Editura Didactică şi Pedagogică*, Bucharest, 2020, 500 p.

**62.** **ASTRONOMIE ŞI ASTROFIZICĂ – EVENIMENTE OLIMPICE – 2017–2018, PROBLEME, VOL. V**, *Editura Didactică şi Pedagogică*, Bucharest, 2020, 500 p.

**63.** **ASTRONOMIE ŞI ASTROFIZICĂ – EVENIMENTE OLIMPICE – 2019, PROBLEME, VOL. VI**, *Editura Didactică şi Pedagogică*, Bucharest, 2020, 548 p.

**64.** **INTERNATIONAL ASTRONOMY OLYMPIAD, VOL. I**, *Editura CYGNUS,* Suceava, 2021, 464 p.

**65.** **INTERNATIONAL ASTRONOMY OLYMPIAD, VOL. II,** *Editura CYGNUS,* Suceava, Romania, 2021, 484 p.

**66.** **INTERNATIONAL OLYMPIAD ON ASTRONOMY AND ASTROPHYSICS, VOL. III,** *Editura CYGNUS,* Suceava, Romania, 2021, 589 p.

**67.** **ASTRONOMY AND ASTROPHYSICS. ALL MY PROBLEMS FOR INTERNATIONAL OLYMPIADS, VOL. I,** *Editura CYGNUS,* Suceava, Romania, 2021, 344 p.

68. **ASTRONOMY AND ASTROPHYSICS. ALL MY PROBLEMS for INTERNATIONAL OLYMPIADS, VOL. II,** *Editura CYGNUS,* Suceava, Romania, 2021, 314 p.

69. **SUB CERUL BUCOVINEI, VOL. I, CONCURSUL INTERJUDEŢEAN DE FIZICĂ CYGNUS, CONCURSUL NAŢIONAL DE FIZICĂ MARIN DACIAN BICA, Clasele VI–IX, 2015–2019**, *Editura CYGNUS,* Suceava, 2021, 300 p.

70. **SUB CERUL BUCOVINEI, Vol. II, CONCURSUL INTERJUDEŢEAN DE FIZICĂ CYGNUS, CONCURSUL NAŢIONAL DE FIZICĂ MARIN DACIAN BICA, CLASELE X–XII, 2015–2019,** *Editura CYGNUS,* Suceava, 2021, 326 p.

71. **SUB CERUL BUCOVINEI, VOL. III, CONCURSUL NAŢIONAL DE ASTRONOMIE ŞI ASTROFIZICĂ MARIN DACIAN BICA FIZICĂ, 2015–2019, CONCURSUL INTERDISCIPLINAR ŞTIINŢELE PĂMÂNTULUI, OLIMPIADA NAŢIONALĂ DE ASTRONOMIE ŞI ASTROFIZICĂ,** *Editura CYGNUS,* Suceava, 2021, 388 p.

72. **PROBLEME DE FIZICĂ, VOL. I, EVENIMENTE OLIMPICE, SELECŢII PENTRU IPhO 1995–2009**, *Editura Didactică şi Pedagogică*, Bucharest, 2021, 340 p.

73. **PROBLEME DE FIZICĂ, VOL. II, EVENIMENTE OLIMPICE, SELECŢII PENTRU IPhO 2010–2021**, *Editura Didactică şi Pedagogică*, Bucharest, 2021, 340 p.

74. **ASTRONOMIE ŞI ASTROFIZICĂ, EVENIMENTE OLIMPICE, 2020–2021, PROBLEME, VOL. VII,** *Editura Didactică şi Pedagogică,* Bucharest, 2022, 600 p.

75. **PROBLEME DE PERFORMANŢĂ ÎN FIZICĂ, VOL. I**, *Editura Didactică şi Pedagogică*, Bucureşti, 2023, 664 p.

76. **ASTRONOMIE ŞI ASTROFIZICĂ, EVENIMENTE OLIMPICE, 2020–2022, PROBLEME, VOL. VIII,** *Editura Didactică şi Pedagogică,* Bucharest, 2023, 595 p.

**77. ASTRONOMY AND ASTROPHYSICS – MY NEW PROBLEMS, VOL. I** (for IOAA 2023, Edition XVI, Poland), *Editura Didactică şi Pedagogică*, Bucureşti, 2023, 395 p.

**78. ASTRONOMY AND ASTROPHYSICS – MY NEW PROBLEMS, VOL. II** (for IOAA 2023, Edition XVI, Poland), *Editura Didactică şi Pedagogică*, Bucureşti, 2023, 460 p.

**79. ASTRONOMY AND ASTROPHYSICS – MY NEW PROBLEMS, SECOND ED., VOL. I** (for IOAA Juniors 2023, Edition II, Greece), *Editura Didactică şi Pedagogică*, Bucharest, 2023, 395 p.

**80. ASTRONOMY AND ASTROPHYSICS – MY NEW PROBLEMS, SECOND ED.,VOL. II** (for IOAA Juniors 2023, Edition II, Greece), *Editura Didactică şi Pedagogică*, Bucharest, 2023, 460 p.

**81. ASTRONOMY AND ASTROPHYSICS – MY NEW PROBLEMS, THIRD ED., VOL. I** (for IAO 2023, Edition XXVII, China), *Editura Didactică şi Pedagogică*, Bucharest, 2023, 460 p.

**82. ASTRONOMY AND ASTROPHYSICS – MY NEW PROBLEMS, THIRD ED., VOL. II** (for IAO 2023, Edition XXVII, China), *Editura Didactică şi Pedagogică*, Bucharest, 2023, 460 p.

**83. PROBLEME DE PERFORMANŢĂ ÎN FIZICĂ, VOL. II,** *Editura Didactică şi Pedagogică,* Bucharest, 2023, 500 p.

**84. PROBLEME DE PERFORMANŢĂ ÎN FIZICĂ, VOL. III,** *Editura Didactică şi Pedagogică,* Bucharest, 2024, 500 p.

**85. INTERNATIONAL PRE-OLYMPIC CONTEST OF PHYSICS, ROMANIA, HUNGARY, MOLDOVA,** *Editura Didactică şi Pedagogică*, Bucharest, 2024, 350 p.

**86. ŞTIINŢE PENTRU JUNIORI ÎN ROMÂNIA 2004–2023, PROBLEMELE MELE DE FIZICĂ,** *Editura Didactică şi Pedagogică*, Bucharest, 2024, 480 p.

**87. SCIENCE FOR JUNIORS IN ROMANIA 2004–2023, MY PROBLEMS OF PHYSICS,** *Editura Didactică şi Pedagogică*, Bucharest, 2024, 480 p.

**88. ŞTIINŢE PENTRU JUNIORI ÎN ROMÂNIA, 2024, PROBLEMELE MELE DE FIZICĂ,** *Editura Didactică şi Pedagogică*, Bucharest, 2024, 200 p.

**89. SCIENCE FOR JUNIORS IN ROMANIA, 2024, MY PROBLEMS OF PHYSICS,** *Editura Didactică şi Pedagogică*, Bucharest, 2024, 200 p.

**90. CONCURSUL NAŢIONAL DE FIZICĂ ŞI CHIMIE IMPULS PERPETUUM! AL ELEVILOR DE GIMNAZIU DIN MEDIUL RURAL, PROBLEMELE MELE DE FIZICĂ, 2011, 2013–2020**, *Editura CONPHYS*, Rm. Vâlcea, 2025, 200 p.

**91. PROBLEMELE MELE DE FIZICĂ PENTRU EVENIMENTE OLIMPICE, VOL. I, 2022–2023**, *Editura Didactică şi Pedagogică*, Bucharest, 2025, 300 p.

**92. PROBLEMELE MELE DE FIZICĂ PENTRU EVENIMENTE OLIMPICE, VOL. II, 2023–2024**, *Editura Didactică şi Pedagogică*, Bucharest, 2025, 350 p.

**93. ASTRONOMIE ŞI ASTROFIZICĂ, PENTRU ELEVI OLIMPICI, STUDENŢI ŞI PROFESORI**, *Editura Didactică şi Pedagogică*, Bucharest, 2025, 450 p.

**94. ASTRONOMY AND ASTROPHYSICS OLYMPIAD: TOPICS, PROBLEMS AND SOLUTIONS, VOL. I**, *World Scientific*, London, 2025, 596 p.

**95. ASTRONOMY AND ASTROPHYSICS OLYMPIAD: PROBLEMS AND SOLUTIONS, VOL. II**, *World Scientific,* London, 2025, 432 p.

**96. ASTRONOMY AND ASTROPHYSICS: PROBLEMS AND SOLUTIONS, VOL. III**, *World Scientific,* London, 2025, 456 p.

**97. PHYSICS OLYMPIAD: PROBLEMS AND SOLUTIONS**, *World Scientific,* London, 2025, 396 p.